W9-AFT-708

THE BIOLOGICAL PERSPECTIVE
INTRODUCTORY READINGS

The Biological Perspective

Introductory Readings

selected by **Watson M. Laetsch**, *comp.*

University of California, Berkeley

BRIAR CLIFF COLLEGE
LIBRARY
SIOUX CITY, IOWA

Little, Brown and Company • Boston

COPYRIGHT © 1969 BY LITTLE, BROWN AND COMPANY
(INC.)

ALL RIGHTS RESERVED. NO PART OF THIS BOOK MAY BE
REPRODUCED IN ANY FORM OR BY ANY ELECTRONIC OR
MECHANICAL MEANS INCLUDING INFORMATION STOR-
AGE AND RETRIEVAL SYSTEMS WITHOUT PERMISSION
IN WRITING FROM THE PUBLISHER, EXCEPT BY A RE-
VIEWER WHO MAY QUOTE BRIEF PASSAGES IN A REVIEW.

LIBRARY OF CONGRESS CATALOG CARD NO. 68-20752

FIRST PRINTING

PUBLISHED SIMULTANEOUSLY IN CANADA
BY LITTLE, BROWN & COMPANY (CANADA) LIMITED

PRINTED IN THE UNITED STATES OF AMERICA

QH
302
.L3

Preface

Biology is unique among the sciences in that its basic concepts are few in number and can readily be understood by the beginning student. This means that the basic literature of this science can be read in an introductory course. The opportunity to analyze the sources of current dogma and to criticize the main ideas of biology meaningfully at this introductory level is one which biologists have too often ignored. One of the reasons for this omission is the lack of a collection of papers which adequately reflect the current state of biological knowledge. The newer basic biology texts are increasingly concerned with the experimental background for present facts, and most of the experiments they discuss have been performed in the last twenty years. Most of the papers in this book fall within this period, and many are what might be called "modern classics." The overriding concern in the selection of these papers has been to present students with something they can read and understand. There are some obvious "classics" which are excluded because they fail to meet this requirement.

The papers are arranged in three sections following the "horizontal" division of biology, and each of these is in turn subdivided. A short introduction precedes each main section and attempts to place the papers within a general context. It is not expected that all students will be able to understand every paper, but it is felt that all students will be able to grasp some of the papers in each section. Redundancy in certain sections is intentional for this reason. Most of the papers are taken from original research publications, and with a few exceptions they are unabridged. A student may not read all of each paper, but

69843

the complete paper is important so he can have an idea of how a scientist struggles with a problem. In a few cases, I have selected short reviews because of the difficulty in finding concise, readable papers on particular subjects.

The selection of papers in this volume is, of course, arbitrary and reflects my own interest and bias. Space problems preclude the inclusion of papers in all areas of biology. Instead, the focus is on a number of basic areas from which I have tried to select readable and significant papers.

I wish to thank the publishers and authors for permission to reprint the papers. A long list of friends and colleagues offered valuable suggestions and I am indebted to them.

Watson M. Laetsch
Berkeley, California
July, 1968

Contents

x   Contents

Hints on Reading Scientific Papers

To the uninitiated, scientific papers usually appear formidable. Therefore, the following advice is offered to help you overcome your initial resistance to this form of literature.

A frontal attack on a paper covering unfamiliar material can overwhelm you. (This is as true for the professional biologist as it is for the novice.) It is far better to awaken the appetite for a subject by nibbling around the edges, and the format of scientific papers encourages this plan of attack. Papers can be broken down into various components: Introduction, Materials and Methods, Results, and Discussion. In addition, most papers have a Summary either at the beginning or at the end. The professional biologist must keep abreast of a tremendous amount of new information, and the Summaries enable him rapidly to select those papers he wants to read in detail. The Summary, therefore, is a good place to start because it tells you what the author thinks is important about his paper. You cannot, however, depend on the Summary alone since the author's claims might not be justified, and you can only find this out by reading the body of the paper.

It is still not necessary to rush into a full-scale attack on the paper. Flip through the pages and glance at the pictures or other illustrations and read their captions. Read the last few sentences of the Discussion. This may sound a bit like the summary, but here the author is likely to speculate on how he thinks his work fits into the general scientific picture.

You should now be ready for the Introduction. This is where the background of the problem is discussed, and where the author presents the question he attempts to answer in the rest of the paper — you might say it establishes the tone of the paper. Skip over the Materials and Methods and read through the Results. This part comprises the heartland of the paper because it contains the facts upon which the conclusions are based. You may stumble here, so go slowly and do not be afraid to retrace your steps. The test for a well written scientific paper is whether it presents results in a concise and unambiguous fashion.

After you have a general idea about the paper, you should go back to the Materials and Methods. This part contains technical details about procedures, and it often has discussions of experimental design. This section is of great importance to the specialist because the validity of the results depends on the way the observations are made. It is impossible to understand fully the author's interpretation of his results unless you know exactly what methods he used. The information presented in Materials and Methods should enable you to repeat the author's experiments exactly. The basis of the scientific method is that statements of fact can be tested by repeated observations. A scientist establishes his "credit rating" in the Methods section of his papers.

Now that you have sampled the paper here and there, you should go back to the beginning and read it through. Keep the following queries in mind: What is the basic question the author is asking? What answer has he provided for this question? Does a critical examination of the procedures and results substantiate his claims?

These hints are not presented as rules for reading scientific papers. If you can devise your own procedure, so much the better. The main concern is introducing you to what many consider to be a rewarding form of literature.

Prologue

Darwin, Charles. 1872. Summary of Chapter IV of *The Origin of Species by Means of Natural Selection, or the Preservation of Favoured Races in the Struggle for Life.* 6th ed. John Murray, London.

from
The Origin of Species

Charles Darwin

SUMMARY OF CHAPTER IV

If under changing conditions of life organic beings present individual differences in almost every part of their structure, and this cannot be disputed; if there be, owing to their geometrical rate of increase, a severe struggle for life at some age, season, or year, and this certainly cannot be disputed; then, considering the infinite complexity of the relations of all organic beings to each other and to their conditions of life, causing an infinite diversity in structure, constitution, and habits, to be advantageous to them, it would be a most extraordinary fact if no variations had ever occurred useful to each being's own welfare, in the same manner as so many variations have occurred useful to man. But if variations useful to any organic being ever do occur, assuredly individuals thus characterised will have the best chance of being preserved in the struggle for life; and from the strong principle of inheritance, these will tend to produce offspring similarly characterised. This principle of preservation, or the survival of the fittest, I have called Natural Selection. It leads to the improvement of each creature in relation to its organic and inorganic conditions of life; and consequently, in most cases, to what must be regarded as an advance in organisation. Nevertheless, low and simple forms will long endure if well fitted for their simple conditions of life.

Natural selection, on the principle of qualities being inherited at corresponding ages, can modify the egg, seed, or young, as easily as the adult. Amongst many animals, sexual selection will have given its aid to ordinary selection, by assuring to the most vigorous and best adapted males the greatest number of offspring. Sexual selection will also give characters useful to the males alone, in their struggles or rivalry with other males; and these characters will be transmitted to one sex or to both sexes, according to the form of inheritance which prevails.

Whether natural selection has really thus acted in adapting the various forms of life to their several conditions and stations, must be judged by the general tenor and balance of evidence given in the following chapters. But we have already seen how it entails extinction; and how largely extinction has acted in the world's history, geology plainly declares. Natural selection, also leads to divergence of character; for the more organic beings diverge in structure, habits, and constitution, by so much the more can a large number be supported on the area — of which we see proof by looking to the inhabitants of any small spot, and to the productions naturalised in foreign lands. Therefore, during the modification of the descendants of any one species, and during the incessant struggle of all species to increase in numbers, the more diversified the descendants become, the better will be their chance of success in the battle for life. Thus the small differences distinguishing varieties of the same species steadily tend to increase, till they equal the greater differences between species of the same genus, or even of distinct genera.

We have seen that it is the common, the widely-diffused and widely-ranging species, belonging to the larger genera within each class, which vary most; and these tend to transmit to their modified offspring that superiority which now makes them dominant in their own countries. Natural selection, as has just been remarked, leads to divergence of character and to much extinction of the less improved and intermediate forms of life. On these principles, the nature of the affinities, and the generally well-defined distinctions between the innumerable organic beings in each class throughout the world may be explained. It is a truly wonderful fact — the wonder of which we are apt to overlook from familiarity — that all animals and all plants throughout all time and space should be related to each other in groups, subordinate to groups, in the manner which we everywhere behold — namely, varieties of the same species most closely related, species of the same genus less closely and unequally related, forming sections and sub-genera, species of distinct genera much less closely related, and genera related in different degrees, forming sub-families, families, orders, sub-classes and classes. The several subordinate groups in any class cannot be ranked in a single file, but seem clustered round points, and these round other points, and so on in almost endless cycles. If species had been independently created, no explanation would have been possible of this kind of classification; but it is explained through inheritance and the complex action of natural selection, entailing extinction and divergence of character. . . .

The affinities of all the beings of the same class have sometimes been represented by a great tree. I believe this simile largely speaks the truth. The green and budding twigs may represent existing species; and those produced during former years may represent the long succession of extinct species. At each period of growth all the growing twigs have tried to branch out on all sides, and to overtop and kill the surrounding twigs and branches, in the same manner as species and groups of species have at all times overmastered other species in the great battle for life. The limbs divided into great branches, and these into lesser and lesser branches, were themselves once, when the tree was young, budding twigs, and this connection of the former and present buds by ramifying branches may well represent the classification of all extinct and living species in groups subordinate to groups. Of the many twigs which flourished when the tree was a mere bush, only two or three, now grown into great branches, yet survive and bear the other branches; so with the species which lived during long-past geological periods, very few have left living and modified descendants. From the first growth of the tree, many a limb and branch has decayed and dropped off; and these fallen branches of various sizes may represent those whole orders, families, and genera which have now no living representatives, and which are known to us only in a fossil state. As we here and there see a thin straggling branch springing from a fork low down in a tree, and which by some chance has been favoured and is still alive on its summit, so we occasionally see an animal like the Ornithorhynchus or Lepidosiren, which in some small degree connects by its affinities two large branches of life, and which has apparently been saved from fatal competition by having inhabited a protected station. As buds give rise by growth to fresh buds, and these, if vigorous, branch out and overtop on all sides many a feebler branch, so by generation I believe it has been with the great Tree of Life, which fills with its dead and broken branches the crust of the earth, and covers the surface with its ever-branching and beautiful ramifications.

SECTION ONE The Cell

Charles Darwin's theories on the evolution of organisms and the role played by natural selection in this process provide the intellectual glue holding together the facts and ideas of modern biology. The concept that all organisms share a common origin and are related through time provides a base line for all types of biological investigation. Every biologist — whether biochemist, morphologist or population geneticist — is, in the last analysis, seeking to unravel the origin and interrelatedness of living things. All the papers in this volume, therefore, reflect some facet of this common purpose. The Prologue (an excerpt from Darwin) sets the theme, and the Epilogue (by Michael Lerner) provides an essay summarizing our current views of evolution in light of the kinds of evidence reported in the papers in this text.

The papers in this first section concern the origin of life and the structure and function of contemporary cells. Our best estimates at the moment put the age of the earth at around five billion years. The paper by J. William Schopf *et al.** suggests that life has been on the earth for somewhat less than half this time. These time spans are impossible for the mind to grasp fully, so the considerable margins of error likely in these estimates are relatively unimportant in terms of overall time. It should be realized, however, that it is difficult to date accurately such ancient

* An asterisk indicates that the paper is included in this section.

7

fossils as the ones mentioned in this paper. The general trend has been to err on the side of youth, and revised estimates of the age of the earth and of the first organisms generally push events farther and farther back in time. This is illustrated by the fact that Schopf and other workers have recently described fossil algae over three billion years old. These algae are relatively complex cells, so life must have originated at a much earlier period than the above estimate. Darwin placed emphasis upon the fact that the earth was probably much older than realized in his time and that new discoveries in this area would provide greater support for his theory. The kind of work presented in the first paper widens our dimensions by increasing the time scale for organic evolution.

We are increasing our knowledge of *when* life began, so the question of *how* life began becomes especially pertinent. This is a question which has always bothered man. A vigorous debate raged well into the 19th century over the question of spontaneous generation. Those who believed it was a recurring and even frequent event were pitted against those who believed life arose from preexisting life. This question was resolved in the middle of the last century by Louis Pasteur. He showed that microorganisms would not appear in boiled broth unless the broth was exposed to air which contained spores. His experiments provided a triumph for mechanistic interpretations of life, but they left unanswered the problem of the origin of life. For many years biologists lived with a paradox stating that living things do not arise at present from inorganic matter, but that life was spontaneously generated sometime in the past.

It remained for the Russian biologist A. I. Oparin to focus on the necessary prerequisites for life on the primitive earth. His views on the composition of the primitive atmosphere were particularly important. A good hypothesis in biology is readily tested, and Stanley L. Miller* and Harold C. Urey tested Oparin's. Their experiment consisted of a closed system simulating the hypothesized primitive atmosphere. The continuous exposure of water vapor, methane, hydrogen and ammonia to an electric discharge resulted in the production of a variety of more complex organic compounds. The most important of these were amino acids, because amino acids are the building blocks for proteins. Their experiment provided some of the first definite clues to how we might reconstruct the events leading to the first living things.

The influence of Miller and Urey's experiment was great because it removed the mental blinkers surrounding discussions of the origin of life and stimulated people to think about the problem. Many complex organic compounds peculiar to living organisms have been synthesized in what are now called primitive earth conditions. One such compound that must be accounted for in any scheme concerning the origin of life is adenosine triphosphate, or ATP. This compound is the primary energy broker in cells — a point which will be made clear in various papers. It was very interesting, therefore, when Cyril Ponnamperuma *et al.** demonstrated that ATP could also be synthesized under primitive earth conditions. Other workers have synthesized sugars, nucleic acids, and even protein-like compounds in similar experiments, so the cast of molecular characters found in cells is essentially complete. Future work in this field could tell us how these isolated compounds arranged themselves into the intricate relationships characteristic of living cells.

Now that we have some idea how spontaneous generation occurred at one point in time, we must ignore Pasteur's experiments for the moment and ask if it is possible for life to originate in a similar fashion today. We may never have an absolutely certain answer to this question, but all evidence indicates that such an event is unlikely. Organisms have become extremely diverse in the several billion years available for their evolution, and most of the available habitats have been exploited. Any significant accumulation of organic material is quickly utilized as a food source, and if some assemblage of macromolecules did cross the threshhold into the living world, it would not find the free and open spaces available to its remote predecessors. It would instead find a multitude of highly specialized predators to which it would fall an easy prey. The first organisms are thought to have been heterotrophes, or "other feeders" — these were organisms which fed upon the organic soup from which they were initially derived. They were also anaerobic organisms and were therefore limited in their evolutionary potential, because anaerobic respiration is a very inefficient way to obtain energy. As the organic soup was depleted, there was a positive selection for those organisms which could synthesize complex compounds from simple precursors. The ultimate expression of this trend was an organism which could use the carbon from carbon dioxide to synthesize organic compounds. This type of synthesis required substantial amounts of energy, and this was made available when organisms developed a pigment to absorb and convert solar energy to chemical energy. The autotrophic way of life was then available, and the evolution of photosynthetic organisms resulted in both a surplus of energy and an oxygen-containing atmosphere. The availability of these new commodities opened new evolutionary vistas.

The two papers on photosynthesis in this volume represent the two main lines of investigation into this process. The overall photosynthetic reaction can be divided into two parts. The incorporation of carbon from carbon dioxide into carbohydrate is called the dark reaction because it can go to completion independent of light. The evolution of oxygen and the accumulation of chemical energy in the form of ATP is called the light reaction because it can only take place when chlorophyll is absorbing visible light. The paper by M. Calvin and A. A. Benson* is one of a series concerned with the dark reaction of photosynthesis. Calvin received the Nobel Prize for this work because it solved many parts of the dark-reaction puzzle. Two techniques were essential to the success of this research: A radioactive isotope of carbon was used to make carbon dioxide, and this permitted the investigator to keep track of the specific carbon atoms as they were passed along from one compound to another during the synthesis of sugar; paper chromatography was the means of identifying the intermediate products containing radioactive carbon.

The events taking place during the light reaction are the subject of the paper by Daniel I. Arnon *et al.** The manner in which ATP is formed is the point of interest for these workers. This generation of chemical energy is the unique aspect of photosynthesis, and the research conducted in Arnon's laboratory represents a milestone in our efforts to understand this process. Our understanding of photosynthesis has increased greatly in recent years; and we can now say certain main features of this process are well understood. All the mysteries, however, have not been removed, and the biggest one concerns the production of oxygen. The oxygen comes from water, but we have almost no idea how this happens. An answer to this problem will provide us with the next major breakthrough in understanding photosynthesis.

A continuing problem of cell biology is to identify the biochemical role played by specific morphological entities, or organelles, within cells. Many years of investigation went by before it was firmly established that photosynthesis takes place in discrete green bodies called chloroplasts. Even today we are still not completely certain about all the things which chloroplasts can do, and many researchers are currently investigating this problem. We now take it for granted that mitochondria are cell organelles where oxidative respiration takes place, but only within the last twenty-five years has this definitely been established. Mitochondria had been observed in cells many years earlier, but their specific function was unknown. It was only possible to determine their function after methods for cell fractionation and high resolution microscopy had been developed. Mitochondria are very small (about 0.2–5.0 microns) and their structural details cannot be observed with the light microscope. The electron microscope permitted biologists to correlate a specific morphological unit with a cell fraction which carried on specific chemical reactions. The papers by George H. Hogeboom *et al.** and D. E. Green and Y. Hatefi* provide insights into the research on form and function in mitochondria. This organelle is of fundamental importance to cells because the final "burning" of food sources, such as glucose, takes place within its boundaries. The involvement of oxygen in respiration results in a highly efficient machine for energy conversion.

The chloroplast and the mitochondrion are both concerned with energy transfer, so they share a number of similar features. At every level of biological complexity a similar function results in similar form. The colorless organelles in plant meristems and in dark-grown leaves, which develop into chloroplasts, are often similar to mitochondria, and there has been much discussion about possible common origins of chloroplasts and mitochondria. Both of these organelles perpetuate themselves from one cell generation to the next, and it is now known that they possess their own nucleic acids and protein-synthesizing systems. The existence of autonomous genetic systems in these organelles has induced speculation that they were at one time free-living bacteria-like organisms, and their present inclusion within cells resulted from initial symbiotic relationships. Many cell biologists hope for the day when they can culture these organelles independently of the cell. This would provide the opportunity for greater insights into the nature of these subunits than has heretofore been possible.

Our knowledge of the cell has increased in proportion to our technical ability to divide the cell into its component parts and to study these parts in isolation. The mitotic spindle is one such subunit about which very little was known before Daniel Mazia and Katsuma Dan* succeeded in isolating it. Unlike many organelles, it is transient in nature and was available for study only during periods of cell division. Its isolation and characterization is a triumph of the cell biologist's art and has contributed immeasurably to our understanding of how cells manage to divide. We must understand this process if we are to fathom the problem of how organisms develop.

There is a legitimate argument for the statement that we now know more about muscle fibrils than about any other cell subunit. This information has been possible only since the advent of the electron microscope. Jean Hanson and Hugh Huxley* were pioneers in the research devoted to explaining muscle in molecular terms, and their paper is one of the first in which electron microscopy was applied to muscle structure; this and succeeding papers helped to establish the mode for this type of research. An army of investigators are presently conducting research in this area, and the discovery of an explanation for the mechanism of muscle action cannot be far away.

A catalogue of cell organelles has by no means been completed. The electron microscope continues to expose new subunits within cells. Many of these await assignment to a specific functional role. The explosion of knowledge in cell structure and function within the last twenty-five years has been so immense it almost seems as if we knew nothing about cells before that time. It will be interesting to see if the same can be said twenty-five years from now.

The most significant development in biology in this generation has been the identification of the genetic material and the breaking of the genetic code. The triumphs of molecular biology and biochemical genetics have influenced the focus of research in every discipline because at this time we know a great deal about how genes work. These recent triumphs, however, represent the culmination of vast efforts originating with the work of Gregor Mendel. Mendel established that the units of inheritance were particulate, and it was shown in the early part of this century that the units of inheritance, or genes, were located on the chromosomes. With the advantage of hindsight, we can see that the next obvious step was to determine the composition of the chromosome and to determine which component satisfied the requirements for genetic material. The solution to this problem was published by O. T. Avery, C. M. MacLeod, and M. McCarty* in 1944. It had been shown previously that pneumococcal bacteria of one genotype could be changed or transformed by pneumococcal bacteria of another type — in other words, one strain of bacteria could impose its genotype upon another strain. Avery *et al.* demonstrated that the transforming principle was a class of macromolecules called nucleic acid. The specific nucleic acid was deoxyribonucleic acid or DNA. The genes could now be discussed in chemical terms.

A replicating system such as a dividing cell must have some way of transferring information. The knowledge that the genetic material was DNA did not provide the answer to the problem of how information was transferred from one cell generation to the next. The explanation is presented in the paper by J. D. Watson and F. H. C. Crick* in which they describe a model for the replication of DNA. This model continues to account for the evidence, and there is every reason to believe that it is a satisfactory explanation for the transfer of genetic information from one cell to the next. Watson and Crick were awarded the Nobel Prize for this work.

How is the information in the genes translated into the phenotype of cells and organisms? Phenotypic expression is a function of the kinds of proteins which are synthesized, so gene action must result in the production of particular proteins. George Beadle and Edward Tatum were awarded the Nobel Prize for their work in the 1940's which showed that genes were responsible for the production of particular proteins. The next major breakthrough in biochemical genetics was the deciphering of the code used by the cell in synthesizing specific proteins from a nucleic acid template. The development of our understanding of the relationships between DNA, RNA, and protein synthesis is described in the paper by J. D. Watson.*

Many people feel that the primary problems in biochemical genetics are well on their way to solution and that the next questions to be answered lie in the field of developmental biology. The papers in Section II are devoted to this topic.

SUGGESTIONS FOR FURTHER READING

Adelberg, E. A. 1966. *Papers on Bacterial Genetics.* 2nd ed. Little, Brown, Boston.

Anfinsen, C. B. 1963. *The Molecular Basis of Evolution.* John Wiley & Sons, New York.

Bassham, J. A., and M. Calvin. 1957. *The Path of Carbon in Photosynthesis.* Prentice-Hall, Englewood Cliffs, N.J.

Branton, Daniel, and Roderic B. Park. 1968. *Papers on Biological Membrane Structure.* Little, Brown, Boston.

Blum, H. F. *Time's Arrow and Evolution.* 1962. 2nd ed. Harper & Row, New York.

Case, J. 1966. *Sensory Mechanisms.* Macmillan, New York.

Herskowitz, I. H. 1967. *Basic Principles of Molecular Genetics.* Little, Brown, Boston.

Jensen, W. A., and R. B. Park. 1967. *Cell Ultrastructure.* Wadsworth Publishing Co., Belmont, Calif.

Keosian, J. 1964. *The Origin of Life.* Reinhold Publishing Corp., New York.

Loewy, A. G., and P. Siekevitz. 1963. *Cell Structure and Function.* Holt, Rinehart & Winston, New York.

Oparin, A. I. 1964. *Life: Its Nature, Origin, and Development.* Academic Press, New York.

Stent, G. S. 1965. *Papers on Bacterial Viruses.* 2nd ed. Little, Brown, Boston.

Sturtevant, A. H. 1965. *A History of Genetics.* Harper & Row, New York.

Watson, J. D. 1965. *Molecular Biology of the Gene.* W. A. Benjamin, New York.

A Origin of life

Schopf, J. William, Elso S. Barghoorn, Morton D. Maser, and Robert O. Gordon. 1965. Electron microscopy of fossil bacteria two billion years old. *Science* **149**, 1365–1367.

Miller, Stanley L. 1953. A production of amino acids under possible primitive earth conditions. *Science* **117**, 528–29.

Ponnamperuma, Cyril, Carl Sagan, and Ruth Mariner. 1963. Synthesis of adenosine triphosphate under possible primitive earth conditions. *Nature* **199**, 222–26.

Electron Microscopy of Fossil Bacteria Two Billion Years Old

J. William Schopf*
Elso S. Barghoorn*
Morton D. Maser
Robert O. Gordon

Department of Biology,
Harvard University

The Gunflint chert, a sediment in southern Ontario aged about 2×10^9 years, contains the oldest known structurally preserved evidence of life (1). The diversity and complexity of this Precambrian microfossil assemblage and the occurrence of possible biogenic remnants in older sediments (2) leave little doubt that biological systems must have originated long before Gunflint time. It might be hypothesized, on the basis of speculation concerning the nature of the primitive environment, that anaerobic heterotrophic bacteria were among the earliest forms of living organisms. This hypothesis would be consistent with the morphology and metabolism exhibited by living bacteria. Moreover, it has been suggested that chlorophyll a, the dominant photosynthetic pigment of algae and higher plants, may be the evolutionary derivative of bacteriochlorophyll, a photosynthetic pigment present in purple and brown bacteria (Thiorhodaceae, Athiorhodaceae) (3). Thus the beginnings of life, the origin of the photosynthetic mechanism, and the effects of these events on the history of the earth may be intimately related to the origin and evolution of the bacteria. We now report the occurrence of ancient fossil bacteria in the Gunflint chert.

Fossil bacteria have been reported in fecal pellets, coprolites, petrified bones,

Reprinted from *Science,* 149, 1365–1367 (September 17, 1965), by permission of James William Schopf and *Science.* Copyright 1965 by the American Association for the Advancement of Science.

silicified and calcified plant tissue, salt deposits, oil shales, coal, limestones, cherts, and iron ores (4). The rod-shaped and coccoid bacteria present in the Gunflint chert lie stratigraphically below, and are hence older than, the oldest previously reported generally accepted fossil bacteria, filamentous forms from the Precambrian of northern Minnesota (5).

Mineralogists and metallurgists have used electron microscopy to great advantage in studying alloys and crystallization phenomena, but very few fossils and fossiliferous rocks have been investigated (6). Recently, remarkably well-preserved imprints of iron bacteria in pyrite 300 million years old were reported by Schopf, Ehlers, and others (7); our application of electron microscopy to the study of Precambrian life was stimulated by their demonstration of its important paleontological potentials (8).

Three techniques were used in studying the Gunflint chert. Surface replicas were prepared in the following manner. A hand-sized specimen of Gunflint chert from the Schreiber locality (9), known by study of thin sections to contain a variety of microfossils, was cut to obtain seven 1-cm cubes of dense black chert. The cubes were mounted in Bakelite, ground with Carborundum grit and finally polished with 0.05-μ γ-alumina on a nylon lap. Six of the polished samples were either etched by immersion, polished-face up, in a 4.91-percent solution of hydrofluoric acid (reagent grade) in distilled water, or fume etched by suspension, polished-face down, over the same warmed solution.

Five of the seven samples contained bacteria; the surfaces of these five samples were prepared as follows: sample 1, not etched; samples 2, 5, and 6, etched by immersion for 60, 90, and 180 seconds, respectively; sample 7, fume etched for 30 seconds over the same solution held at 60°C.

In a vacuum evaporator, the surfaces of the samples were then shadowed with platinum at about a 2:1 angle and replicated with a film of evaporated carbon. The surfaces were then scored to 0.5-cm squares; the platinum-carbon replicas were floated off in a dilute hydrofluoric acid solution and picked up on microscope grids. Micrographs were taken with an RCA-EMU-3F electron microscope.

In addition to surface replicas, hydrofluoric acid macerations and ultrathin sections of the Gunflint specimen were studied by electron microscopy. The acid-resistant residue from hydrofluoric acid maceration was prepared for study by placing drops of the macerated suspension on coated grids, blotting off the excess liquid, and shadowing the grids with platinum. Numerous septate filaments (*Gunflintia* spp.) and reticulate spheroidal bodies (*Huroniospora* spp.) were observed in these preparations (10). This method of preparation has the advantage of concentrating the organic material for rapid examination. This advantage is more than offset, however, by the destruction of microstructure resulting from the dissociation of the organic residues from the mineral matrix, which destruction accompanied even very slow maceration in dilute acid.

Ultrathin sections (0.05μ to 0.15μ thick) of the specimen were cut with a diamond knife on a Sorvall MT-2 ultramicrotome, for which purpose a thin slice of the specimen was embedded in Epon 812. Although it is possible to cut sections in this manner, microconchoidal fracturing of the chalcedonic matrix and the low concentration of organic material in a section of such thinness make examination difficult and relatively unrewarding.

A variety of microfossils has been observed in the Gunflint chert in each of the three types of preparation described. Of particular interest are rod-shaped (Figs. 1–4) and coccoid (Figs. 5 and 6) bacterial remains which are best studied by the replica method. The photographs presented are negative prints of micrographs of surface replicas. The electron density of both bacterial forms shown indicates that the organic particles have been pulled from the inorganic matrix during replication, and that we are observing in most cases the organic material itself and not a replica of it. In some instances (Fig. 2) the bacterial cells have separated slightly from the replica, producing electron-transparent edges; these electron-transparent areas should not be confused with the more-electron-dense shadowed structures.

Rod-shaped bacterial cells occur in the five samples listed. Measurements of 20 of these elongate bacteria, oriented parallel to the plane of the replica, show that they are approximately 1.1μ long and 0.55μ wide. Orientations of the many other rod-shaped cells present, passing through the plane of the replica, make meaningful measurement difficult (see Figs. 2–4). In size and shape the cells closely resemble certain modern rod-shaped bacteria. The fossil microorganisms sometimes occur as apparently isolated cells (Fig. 1), but more frequently are clumped in groups of six or eight (Fig. 2) or are in chains up to seven cells long (Figs. 3 and 4). Amorphous organic material, which may be the remnant of an encompassing (possibly) mucilaginous sheath, often surrounds and connects the cells (Figs. 3 and 4).

False branching appears to be present in at least one chain (Fig. 4). Rod-shaped bacterial cells enclosed in a sheath and showing occasional false branching are the typical growth habit of the modern iron bacterium *Sphaerotilus natans (11)*. A possible relation between the fossil bacteria and this extant form is questionable, however, because of the considerably smaller size of the Gunflint organism.

Coccoid bacteria-like objects occur in samples 2 and 6. These nearly spherical, rough-surfaced bodies are approximately 0.35μ in diameter (Figs. 5 and 6). The cell walls are sometimes broken and may show surficial folding (Fig. 6). The thickness of the cell wall, up to 0.15μ in some instances, may result from concentration of various minerals, such as iron compounds, either by metabolic activity or by diagenetic alteration. These fossils resemble in size and morphology certain iron

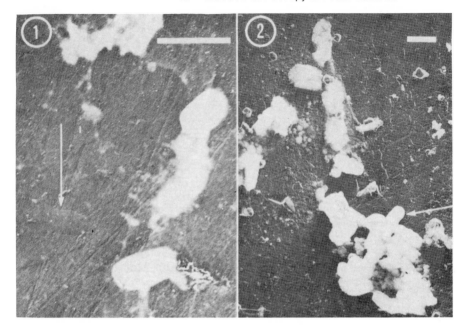

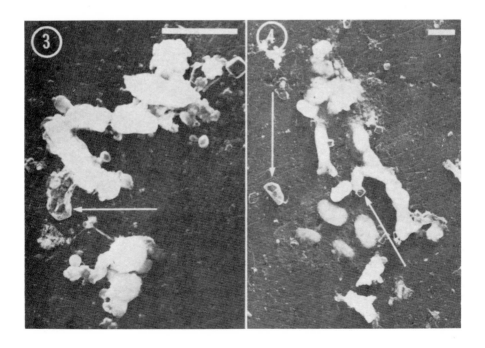

FIGURES 1–6. Bacteria in Gunflint chert: line in each figure represents 1μ.

FIGURE 1. Well-preserved, rod-shaped, apparently isolated bacteria in surface replica of sample 1. Arrow points to bacillary imprint in rock surface. Subparallel lineations oriented approximately vertically are polishing scratches (about × 19,500). FIGURE 2. Clumped and isolated rod-shaped bacteria in surface replica of sample 2. Arrow points to electron-transparent edges (dark in micrograph) where organic material (light in micrograph) has separated from carbon-platinum replica (about × 7800). FIGURE 3. Sample 2: Surface replica showing poorly preserved rod-shaped bacteria arranged in a filament. Note organic continuity between cells and the encompassing sheath-like residue; arrow points to cellular remnant in which only this surrounding amorphous material is present (about × 19,700). FIGURE 4. Sample 2: Rod-shaped bacteria both isolated and apparently arranged in a branched (false branching) filament. Arrows point to organic material interpreted as bacteria seen in transverse section; several similar rod-shaped cells, apparently passing through the plane of the replica, appear in Figure 2 (about × 7100). FIGURE 5. Sample 6: Large group of coccoid bacteria composed of more than 100 individual cells. The cells, approximately 0.35μ in diameter, appear to be randomly distributed with respect to one another. Chalcedony grain boundaries (irregular white lines) are clearly visible in this replica of a deeply etched surface (about × 10,600). FIGURE 6. Sample 6: Surface replica showing chalcedony grain boundaries and numerous coccoid bacteria. Note the pronounced thickness and irregular surface of the cell walls; arrow points to a ruptured bacterial cell (about × 30,100).

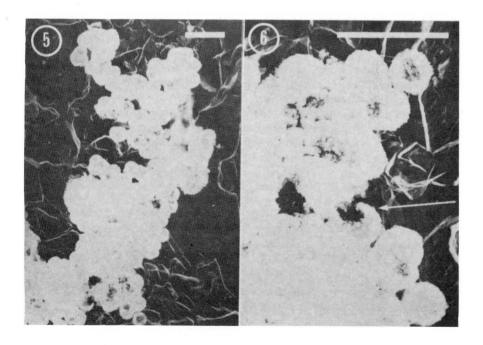

bacteria of the genera *Siderocapsa* and *Siderococcus* (*12*), members of which metabolically concentrate iron compounds; this similarity suggests that the pronounced thickness of the cell walls is metabolic rather than diagenetic. Thimann (*13*) has brought to our attention the additional similarity in size, morphology, and general organization of these fossil coccoids to Winogradsky's "microcolonies in soil" (*14*).

That these minute fossils are both organically preserved and relatively undistorted is not surprising when one considers that many other members of the Gunflint assemblage are preserved in this manner and that complex organic molecules are present within the rock (*1, 15*). That these bacteria are indigenous to the rock rather than being laboratory contaminants is supported by the following three considerations: (i) the forms occur in the replicas both as organically preserved structures, and as imprints in the rock surface (Fig. 1); (ii) they are oriented in various positions not only parallel with but passing into the prepared rock surface; and (iii) the forms are consistently present in several samples prepared by different methods.

There seems little doubt that the forms we describe and portray are bacteria; their morphology, size, complexity of structure, and association with more-complex organisms are consistent with this interpretation. Rod-shaped and coccoid forms are widely distributed throughout the bacteria and occur in anaerobic and aerobic and heterotrophic and autotrophic types. Morphology offers, therefore, limited aid in the assignment of taxonomic position to fossil bacteria. A more satisfactory assignment should be based upon physiological processes in addition to morphology. In the absence of sufficient biochemical information on these bacteria, the conferring of taxonomic status by giving them generic and specific names seems unwarranted.

The electron microscope in conjunction with optical microscopy and other traditional methods of micropaleontology provides a powerful tool for morphological investigation of ancient life. Organic and inorganic geochemistry offer means for the investigation of ancient physiological processes. The occurrence of porphyrin derivatives of chlorophyll in Precambrian sediments, as demonstrated by organic geochemical analysis (*16*), may permit determination of the time of origin of the photosynthetic mechanism. Metabolic concentration of sulfur, iron, and other elements in bacterial and other fossils may be detectable by electron probe-X-ray microanalysis. Coordinated application of these and other techniques to the investigation of ancient sediments promises elucidation of diverse aspects of the morphology and physiology of Precambrian life.

July 14, 1965

ABSTRACT

Occurence of well-preserved rod-shaped and coccoid bacteria in the Precambrian Gunflint chert (1.9×10^9 years old) has been demonstrated by electron microscopy. This appears to be the oldest definite occurrence of bacteria in the fossil record. The organisms are morphologically comparable with certain modern iron bacteria.

REFERENCES AND NOTES

* And Botanical Museum.

1. S. A. Tyler and E. S. Barghoorn, *Science* 119, 606 (1954); E. S. Barghoorn and S. A. Tyler, *Ann. N.Y. Acad. Sci.* 108, 451 (1963); *Science* 147, 563 (1965); P. E. Cloud, Jr., *ibid.* 148, 27 (1965).

2. A. M. Macgregor, *Geol. Soc. So. Africa Trans.* 43, 9 (1941); T. Belsky *et al., Nature* 206, 446 (1965); P. E. Cloud, Jr., J. W. Gruner, H. Hagen, *Science* 148, 1713 (1965); W. G. Meinschein, *Science,* in press.

3. E. I. Rabinowitch, *Photosynthesis and Related Processes. Vol. I, Chemistry of Photosynthesis, Chemosynthesis and Related Processes in vitro and in vivo* (Interscience, New York, 1945), chap. 5, pp. 99–107, 445–46.

4. C. E. ZoBell, in "Treatise on marine ecology and paleoecology, 2," *Geol. Soc. Amer. Mem.* 67, p. 693 (1957); S. I. Kuznetsov, M. V. Ivanov, N. N. Lyalikova, *Introduction to Geological Microbiology,* C. H. Oppenheimer, Ed., transl. by P. T. Broneer (McGraw-Hill, New York, 1963), pp. 40–50.

5. J. W. Gruner, *Econ. Geol.* 17, 415 (1922).

6. H. M. Barton and D. J. Jones, *Science* 108, 745 (1948); see articles and references in *Handbook of Paleontological Techniques,* B. Kummel and D. Raup, Eds. (Freeman, San Francisco, 1965).

7. J. M. Schopf, E. G. Ehlers, D. V. Stiles, J. D. Birle, *Proc. Amer. Phil. Soc.,* in press; E. G. Ehlers, D. V. Stiles, J. D. Birle, *Science* 148, 1719 (1965).

8. We thank J. M. Schopf, USGS, for his interest and suggestions.

9. See (*1*) for description of Schreiber locality.

10. Similar results are reported by P. E. Cloud, Jr., and H. Hagen, *Proc. Nat. Acad. Sci. U.S.* 54, 1 (1965).

11. E. G. Pringsheim, *Trans. Roy. Soc. London B* 233, 453 (1949); K. V. Thimann, *The Life of Bacteria* (Macmillan, New York, ed. 2, 1963), pp. 709–11.

12. P. Dorff, "Die eisenorganismen, systematik und morphologie," in *Pflanzenforschung 16,* R. Kolkwitz, Ed. (1934), pp. 6–12.

13. K. V. Thimann, private communication, July 14, 1965.

14. S. Winogradsky, *Ann. Inst. Pasteur* 39, 299 (1925).

15. J. Oro, D. W. Nooner, A. Zlatkis, S. A. Wikstrom, E. S. Barghoorn, *Science* 148, 77 (1965).

16. W. G. Meinschein, E. S. Barghoorn, J. W. Schopf, *ibid.* 145, 262 (1964); E. S. Barghoorn, W. G. Meinschein, J. W. Schopf, *ibid.* 148, 461 (1965).

17. We thank Roger Branson, Harvard University, for assistance. Work supported by NSF grants GP-2794 and G-19727 and by PHS grants CA-06018 and GM-06637; one of us (J. W. S.) is a NSF graduate fellow.

A Production of Amino Acids Under Possible Primitive Earth Conditions

Stanley L. Miller[*]

G. H. Jones Chemical Laboratory,
University of Chicago

The idea that the organic compounds that serve as the basis of life were formed when the earth had an atmosphere of methane, ammonia, water, and hydrogen instead of carbon dioxide, nitrogen, oxygen, and water was suggested by Oparin (1) and has been given emphasis recently by Urey (2) and Bernal (3).

In order to test this hypothesis, an apparatus was built to circulate CH_4, NH_3, H_2O, and H_2 past an electric discharge. The resulting mixture has been tested for amino acids by paper chromatography. Electrical discharge was used to form free radicals instead of ultraviolet light, because quartz absorbs wavelengths short enough to cause photo-dissociation of the gases. Electrical discharge may have played a significant role in the formation of compounds in the primitive atmosphere.

The apparatus used is shown in Figure 1. Water is boiled in the flask, mixes with the gases in the 5-1 flask, circulates past the electrodes, condenses and empties back into the boiling flask. The U-tube prevents circulation in the opposite direction. The acids and amino acids formed in the discharge, not being volatile, accumulate in the water phase. The circulation of the gases is quite slow, but this seems to be an asset, because production was less in a different apparatus with an aspirator arrangement to promote circulation. The discharge, a small corona, was provided by an induction coil designed for detection of leaks in vacuum apparatus.

Reprinted from *Science* 117, 528–29 (May 15, 1953), by permission of the author and *Science*.

FIGURE 1.

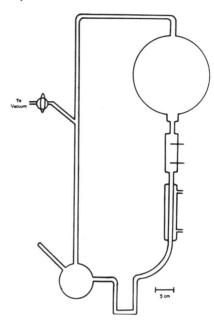

The experimental procedure was to seal off the opening in the boiling flask after adding 200 ml of water, evacuate the air, add 10 cm pressure of H_2, 20 cm of CH_4, and 20 cm of NH_3. The water in the flask was boiled, and the discharge was run continuously for a week.

During the run the water in the flask became noticeably pink after the first day, and by the end of the week the solution was deep red and turbid. Most of the turbidity was due to colloidal silica from the glass. The red color is due to organic compounds adsorbed on the silica. Also present are yellow organic compounds, of which only a small fraction can be extracted with ether, and which form a continuous streak tapering off at the bottom on a one-dimensional chromatogram run in butanol-acetic acid. These substances are being investigated further.

At the end of the run the solution in the boiling flask was removed and 1 ml of saturated $HgCl_2$ was added to prevent the growth of living organisms. The ampholytes were separated from the rest of the constituents by adding $Ba(OH)_2$ and evaporating *in vacuo* to remove amines, adding H_2SO_4 and evaporating to remove the acids, neutralizing with $Ba(OH)_2$, filtering and concentrating *in vacuo*.

The amino acids are not due to living organisms because their growth would be prevented by the boiling water during the run, and by the $HgCl_2$, $Ba(OH)_2$, H_2SO_4 during the analysis.

In Figure 2 is shown a paper chromatogram run in *n*-butanol-acetic acid-water mixture followed by water-saturated phenol, and spraying

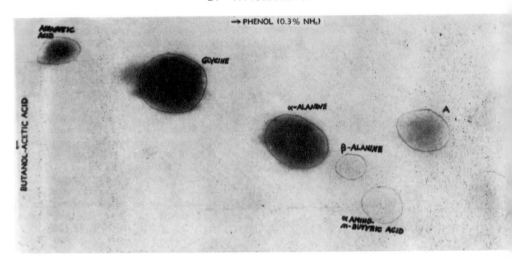

FIGURE 2.

with ninhydrin. Identification of an amino acid was made when the R_f value (the ratio of the distance traveled by the amino acid to the distance traveled by the solvent front), the shape, and the color of the spot were the same on a known, unknown, and mixture of the known and unknown; and when consistent results were obtained with chromatograms using phenol and 77% ethanol.

On this basis glycine, α-alanine and β-alanine are identified. The identification of the aspartic acid and α-amino-n-butyric acid is less certain because the spots are quite weak. The spots marked A and B are unidentified as yet, but may be beta and gamma amino acids. These are the main amino acids present, and others are undoubtedly present but in smaller amounts. It is estimated that the total yield of amino acids was in the milligram range.

In this apparatus an attempt was made to duplicate a primitive atmosphere of the earth, and not to obtain the optimum conditions for the formation of amino acids. Although in this case the total yield was small for the energy expended, it is possible that, with more efficient apparatus (such as mixing of the free radicals in a flow system, use of higher hydrocarbons from natural gas or petroleum, carbon dioxide, etc., and optimum ratios of gases), this type of process would be a way of commercially producing amino acids.

A more complete analysis of the amino acids and other products of the discharge is now being performed and will be reported in detail shortly.

Manuscript received February 13, 1953

REFERENCES AND NOTES

* National Science Foundation Fellow, 1952–53.

Thanks are due Harold C. Urey for many helpful suggestions and guidance in the course of this investigation.

1. A. I. Oparin, *The Origin of Life* (Macmillan, New York, 1938).
2. H. C. Urey, *Proc. Nat. Acad. Sci. U.S.* **38**, 351 (1952); *The Planets* (Yale Univ. Press, New Haven, 1952), chap. 4.
3. J. D. Bernal, *Proc. Phys. Soc. (London)* **62A**, 537 (1949); **62B**, 597 (1949); *Physical Basis of Life* (Routledge and Kegan Paul, London, 1951).

Synthesis of Adenosine Triphosphate Under Possible Primitive Earth Conditions

Cyril Ponnamperuma*
Carl Sagan†
Ruth Mariner

Department of Genetics,
Stanford University
School of Medicine‡

It has been suggested that the prebiological synthesis of nucleoside phosphates on the primitive Earth was a consequence of the absorption of ultraviolet light by purines and pyrimidines in an appropriate aqueous medium (1, 2). The basis for this suggestion is as follows:

Even the simplest living organisms are statistically unlikely aggregations of organic molecules. The improbability of contemporary organisms is extracted from the field of possibilities through natural selection. But before the advent of self-replicating systems, natural selection as we understand it today could have played no such part. The origin and subsequent replication of life must therefore have involved molecules preferentially produced in the primitive environment. Such a view is implicit in the early works of Haldane (3) and Oparin (4). While it is possible that the fundamental molecular basis of living systems has itself evolved, the simplest working hypothesis holds that the molecules that are fundamental now were fundamental at the time of the origin of life. The production of amino acids, purines, pyrimidines and pentose sugars under simulated primitive conditions during the past decade lends support to this hypothesis.

There are, however, still several molecular species the involvement of which in the origin of life remains to be demonstrated. Chief among these are the nucleoside

Reprinted from *Nature* 199, 222–26 (1963), by permission of the authors and the editors of *Nature*, Macmillan (Journals) Limited.

phosphates. Adenosine triphosphate (ATP) is the "universal" energy intermediary of contemporary terrestrial organisms, and one of the major products of plant photosynthesis. The need for its production in primitive times was first emphasized by Blum (5). Guanosine triphosphate has recently been implicated as the energy source for peptide linkage (6). The deoxynucleoside triphosphates are the precursors for contemporary DNA biosynthesis (7). To the extent that the origin of DNA plays a fundamental part in the origin of life, the abiogenic synthesis of deoxynucleoside triphosphates seems indicated (2). Several fundamental coenzymes of intermediate metabolism and plant photosynthesis (CoA, DPN, TPN, FAD) are nucleoside phosphates. All these molecules contain purines or pyrimidines which have strong ultraviolet absorption maxima near 2600 Å. The possibility then arises that the absorption of ultraviolet photons by purines and pyrimidines provided the bond energy for the synthesis of nucleoside phosphates in primitive times; and it is therefore of some interest to investigate the ultraviolet transparency of the early terrestrial atmosphere.

There is evidence from astronomy (8, 9) that the Earth's atmosphere was reducing at the time life first arose. Laboratory experiments have shown that it is far easier to synthesize organic matter under reducing than under oxidizing conditions (10–12). The molecules O_2 and O_3 are thermodynamically unstable in an excess of hydrogen, and the principal sources of the ultraviolet opacity of the present terrestrial atmosphere cannot have then been present. The ultraviolet absorption which did exist arose from intermediate oxidation state molecules, principally aldehydes and ketones. In experiments in which electrical discharges were passed through simulated primitive atmospheres, the only aldehyde or ketone produced in high yield was formaldehyde (13). Nevertheless, the production of some acetaldehyde (14) and acetone can be expected. Formaldehyde absorption extends longwards of about 2900 Å. Acetaldehyde and acetone absorb throughout the 2400–2900 Å region. Ammonia, acetylene, and other molecules absorb shortwards of 2400 Å.

Therefore, the question of the transparency of the primitive terrestrial atmosphere near 2600 Å turns mainly on the unknown early abundance of CH_3CHO and CH_3COCH_3. Because of the relatively low acetaldehyde and acetone yields in simulation experiments, and because of possible independent biological indications of high ultraviolet fluxes in primitive times (2), it seems likely that the early reducing atmosphere was at least slightly transparent between 2400 and 2900 Å. From models of the evolution of the Sun, and an integration of the Planck function, the ultraviolet flux of wavelength $2900Å \geqslant \lambda \geqslant 2400$ Å incident on the Earth's atmosphere 4×10^9 years ago is computed to be about 7×10^{14} photons $cm^{-2} sec^{-1}$ (15). Even with substantial atmospheric absorption, ultraviolet radiation in this window will greatly exceed other energy sources for organic synthesis (16).

The synthesis of purines and pyrimidines which absorb in this wavelength region has recently been accomplished in a variety of primitive

Earth simulation experiments. Adenine has been produced by thermal polymerization of 1.5 molar hydrocyanic acid in an aqueous ammonia solution (17); by 5-MeV electron irradiation of methane, ammonia, water and hydrogen (18); and by ultraviolet irradiation of a 10^{-4} molar solution of hydrocyanic acid (19). Guanine also appears to be formed in the last experiment. Another guanine synthesis occurs in the thermal copolymerization of amino acids (20). Uracil has been produced by heating urea and malic acid (21).

The yields of purines and pyrimidines are sometimes quite high. In the electron beam irradiation of primitive atmospheres by Ponnamperuma, Lemmon, Mariner and Calvin (18), autoradiography indicates that the substance produced in highest yield is adenine. Thus it appears possible that ultraviolet light passing the 2400–2900 Å partial window in the primitive terrestrial atmosphere was strongly absorbed by purines and pyrimidines in the early oceans.

The production rates of organic molecules from reducing atmospheres suggest that the primitive oceans were about a 1 percent solution of organic matter (2, 9). In addition to purines and pyrimidines the pentose sugars, ribose and 2-deoxyribose can be expected to be present. The laboratory production of 2-deoxyribose has been achieved through the condensation of formaldehyde and acetaldehyde, or of acetaldehyde and glyceraldehyde in aqueous salt solutions (22). (Indeed, this is an example of a mechanism which keeps the atmospheric aldehyde concentration low.) Both ribose and 2-deoxyribose have been synthesized by either ultraviolet or γ-irradiation of dilute formaldehyde solutions (23). Phosphates and other phosphorus compounds can be expected in the primitive oceans, even at very early times (24).

It therefore seems of some interest to attempt synthesis of nucleoside phosphates by ultraviolet irradiation of dilute solutions of purine or pyrimidine bases, pentose sugars, and phosphorus compounds, both because of our expectation that such syntheses were easily performed in primitive times, and because ultraviolet irradiation of dilute solutions of adenine and ribose has already produced the nucleoside adenosine (25).

MATERIALS AND EXPERIMENTAL TECHNIQUES

Adenine-8-^{14}C of specific activity 23.4 μc./mg, adenosine-8-^{14}C of specific activity 7.2 μc./mg, and adenylic acid-8-^{14}C of specific activity 3.1 μc/mg were supplied by Schwarz Bioresearch, Orangeburg, New York. The nonradioactive AMP, ADP and ATP used as carriers were supplied by C. F. Boehringer, Mannheim, Germany. The adenosine tetraphosphate was a gift of Dr. John Moffat of Syntex, Ltd., Palo Alto, California.

The ethyl metaphosphate used in the experiment was prepared by dissolving 150 gm of phosphorus pentoxide in 300 ml of ethyl ether and refluxing the solution for several hours with chloroform (26). The excess solvent was removed by evaporation under vacuum, leaving a syrupy residue of ethyl metaphosphate.

The method of irradiation and analysis has already been described (25). Quantities of the labelled adenine, adenosine and adenylic acid, varying from 1.5×10^{-6} to 1.5×10^{-5} moles in various experiments, were sealed in aqueous solution in "Vycor" tubes with approximately stoichiometric quantities of ribose, phosphoric acid or polyphosphate ester, as shown in Table 1. The final concentration of base nucleoside and nucleotide in each solution did not exceed 10^{-3} moles/l. The solutions were irradiated by four General Electric ultraviolet germicidal lamps, type 782H-10, which emit 95 percent of their light in the mercury resonance line at 2537 Å. The "Vycor" glass of which the tubes were made transmitted 80 percent of light of this wavelength. During a 1-hr. irradiation, the sample absorbed a total of $\sim 10^8$ ergs. During the irradiation the ambient temperature of the samples was $40° \pm 2°C$.

The reaction products were first analysed by paper chromatography, autoradiography and ultraviolet absorption studies. An aliquot of the reaction products was spotted on a Whatman No. 4 paper and the chromatogram run in two solvents, butanol–propionic acid–water (27) and isobutyric-acid-ammonia (28). The positions of the carriers adenosine, AMP, ADP, ATP and A4P were detected by shadowgrams (29). Coincidence both in position and in shape between the carriers on the shadowgrams and the radioactivity on the autoradiograph was the chromatographic basis for the identifications. The formation of adenosine has already been reported (25). A further aliquot was chromatographed in two other solvent systems, trichloroacetic acid–acetone (30) and butanol–formic acid–water (31). Once again there was coincidence between the carrier as outlined in the shadowgram and the radioactivity on the film.

Separations effected using thin-layer chromatography, and ion-exchange chromatography confirmed the result obtained from paper chromatography.

RESULTS

The results of the investigation are summarized in Table 1 and in Figures 1–4. Four different categories of experiments were performed. In the first the starting material was adenine, in the second adenosine, in the third adenosine monophosphate, and in the fourth adenosine diphosphate. The conversion of adenine to adenosine, adenosine to adenosine monophosphate, adenosine monophosphate to adenosine diphosphate, and adenosine diphosphate to adenosine triphosphate has been established. Experiments using adenine as the starting material have produced adenosine, AMP, ADP and ATP.

The previously reported experiment showed that adenosine is not produced in detectable amounts in the absence of a phosphorus compound (25). While adenosine is produced in the presence of both phos-

TABLE 1

Exp.	Adenosine	AMP	ADP	ATP	A4P
(1)					
(i) Adenine-14C + ribose					
(ii) Adenine-14C + ribose + phosphoric acid	+ (0.01%)	−	−	−	−
(iii) Adenine-14C + ribose and ethyl metaphosphate	+ (0.01%)	+ (0.08%)	+ (0.06%)	+ (0.05%)	+ (0.04%)
(2)					
(i) Adenosine-14C + phosphoric acid		−	−	−	−
(ii) Adenosine-14C + ethyl metaphosphate		+ (0.5%)	+ (0.2%)	+ (0.1%)	+
(3)					
(i) Adenosine monophosphate-14C + phosphoric acid			−	−	−
(ii) Adenosine monophosphate-14C + ethyl metaphosphate			+ (3%)	+ (0.3%)	+ (0.1%)
(4)					
(i) Adenosine diphosphate + phosphoric acid				−	−
(ii) Adenosine diphosphate + ethyl metaphosphate				+	+

Figures in brackets show conversion as percentage of starting material.

With the techniques used in this experiment the lower limit of detectability was 0.001 percent.

In Exp. 4 no quantitative estimates were performed as unlabelled ADP was used. The ATP in this case was located by shadowgrams.

phoric acid and ethyl metaphosphate, the nucleoside phosphates were detected only with the use of ethyl metaphosphate. Phosphoric acid was chosen first in the attempt to synthesize the nucleoside phosphates. Ethylmetaphosphate was selected as a possible reagent because of a recent report (26) that it activates carbonyl, hydroxyl and amino groups in organic synthesis. Other phosphorus compounds may also be effective in this synthesis, but they have not yet been investigated.

The yields are given in Table 1 and are further discussed below.

Controls. Two general categories of control experiments were performed to assess two possible modes of biogenic contamination of the reaction products. To test the possibility that the relatively high temperatures (40° ± 2°C) attained by the "Vycor" tubes during ultraviolet irradiation stimulated the metabolic activities of microorganisms in the reactants, we placed control tubes at these same temperatures for comparable periods, but without ultraviolet irradiation. In all other respects

FIGURE 1. Autoradiogram illustrating the formation of AMP from adenine, ribose and ethyl metaphosphate by the action of ultraviolet light.

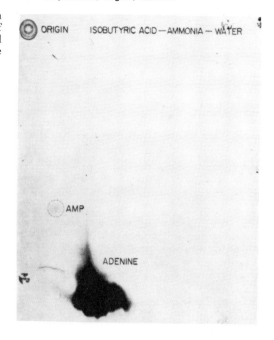

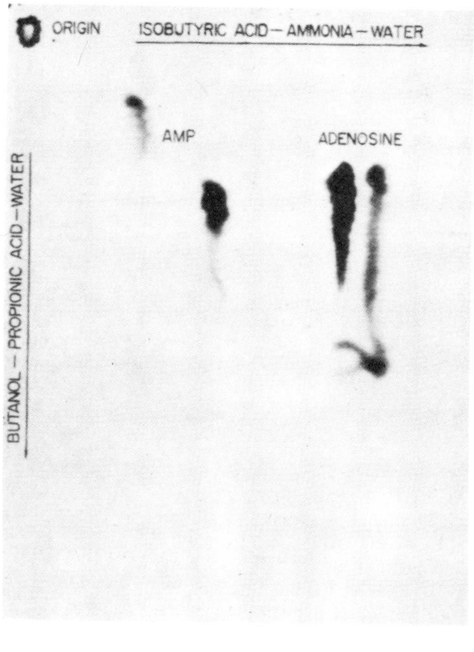

FIGURE 2. Autoradiogram illustrating the formation of AMP from adenosine, and ethyl metaphosphate by the action of ultraviolet light. The long feature to the right of the teardrop-shaped adenosine spot is adenine, produced from adenosine photolysis. The dark central feature between AMP and adenosine is at present unidentified.

FIGURE 3. Autoradiogram illustrating formation of ADP, ATP and A4P from AMP and ethyl metaphosphate by the action of ultraviolet light.

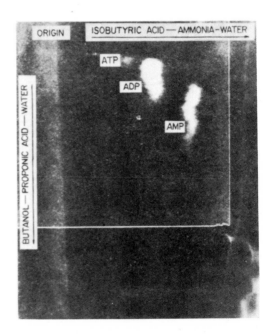

FIGURE 4. Shadowgram illustrating the formation of ATP from ADP and ethyl metaphosphate by the action of ultraviolet light. The AMP is a photolytic product.

they were handled and analysed similarly to the irradiated samples. In no case was any yield detected.

An alternative hypothetical source of contamination is the presence in the labelled reactants of microorganisms which, under ultraviolet irradiation, are photolysed, introducing their metabolic products into the medium. To test this possibility, we introduced into "Vycor" tubes which had been autoclaved for 45 min. at 120°C reactants that had been passed through an autoclaved Seitz filter. These sterile samples were then irradiated with ultraviolet light and analysed. No change in yield was observed. We conclude that the microbiological contribution to the observed yields was negligible.

DISCUSSION

The abiogenic non-enzymatic production of nucleoside phosphates and related molecules under simulated primitive Earth conditions is relevant to the problem of the origin of life. The expected availability of ATP in primitive times suggests that energy was then available in convenient form for endergonic synthetic reactions of large molecules. The question arises why adenosine triphosphate, rather than, for example, the triphosphates of guanosine, cytidine, uridine, or thymidine, were not produced in primitive times and utilized today as the primary biological energy currency. There are several possible responses. In primitive Earth simulation experiments under reducing conditions with low hydrogen content, adenine is produced in far greater yield than are other purines and pyrimidines (17–19). Secondly, no biological purine or pyrimidine has a larger absorption cross section between 2400 and 2900 Å. Thirdly, adenine is among the most stable of such molecules under ultraviolet irradiation. Finally, the ultraviolet excitation energy is readily transferred, especially by π electrons, along the conjugated double bonds of the molecule; the excited states are very long-lived, and thereby serve to provide bond energies for higher synthetic reaction. All but the first of these properties of adenine derive from the fact that it has the greatest resonance energy of all the biochemical purines and pyrimidines (32, 33). It thus appears that molecules ideally suited for the origin of life were preferentially produced in primitive times.

The yields achieved in these experiments, as shown in Table 1, are relatively quite high. In contrast, quite elaborate methods are ordinarily required for the laboratory synthesis of nucleoside phosphates (34). For the production of adenosine from adenine, ribose and a phosphorus source, the quantum yield for a 1-hr. irradiation is $\phi \sim 10^{-5}$. For production of AMP, ADP and ATP by the use of ethyl metaphosphate, the quantum yields are almost an order of magnitude greater.

It is not now known to what extent the experiments here reported accurately reproduce the environmental conditions in the primitive terrestrial oceans. It can be expected that ethyl metaphosphate was probably not the most abundant phosphorus source; but we do not know how well other, possibly more abundant, phosphate salts may efficiently substitute for ethyl metaphosphate. The irradiation period in these experiments was 1 hr. Continued irradiation, with no removal of products, must, by the second law of thermodynamics, ultimately result in lower overall quantum yields. The influence of inorganic anions on the course and rate of these reactions is largely unknown. Nevertheless, it is of some heuristic interest to compute the production rate of adenosine triphosphate in the primitive terrestrial oceans, where the conditions there were similar to those in the present experiments.

The production rate of ATP in the primitive reducing atmosphere will then be:

$$\frac{d\sigma}{dt} \simeq \frac{Q\phi\mu}{4N_A} \text{ g cm}^{-2} \text{ sec}^{-1}$$

where Q is the ultraviolet photon flux for 2400 Å $\leqslant \lambda \leqslant$ 2900 Å, ϕ is the quantum yield, μ is the molecular weight of ATP, and N_A is Avogadro's number (15). Taking $Q \sim 7 \times 10^{14}$ photons cm^{-2} sec^{-1}, (15) $\phi \sim 3 \times 10^{-5}$, and $\mu \sim 550$, we derive:

$$\frac{d\sigma}{dt} \simeq 5 \times 10^{-12} \text{ g cm}^{-2} \text{ sec}^{-1}$$

A feeling for the magnitude of this figure can be obtained by computing the steady-state population of microorganisms over the entire globe that could be maintained by this quantity of abiologically produced adenosine triphosphate. That is, we assume that the primitive Earth is populated by obligate heterotrophs that obtain all their energy from abiologically synthesized ATP. We will obtain a minimum population if we assume that the number of ATP molecules required for each replication and the doubling time per cell have values characteristic of typical contemporary organisms. Taking values for *Eschericia coli* of 10^9 ATP molecules per cell for each doubling, and a doubling time of 1 hr., we find the required ATP production rate to maintain one cell must be 2.5×10^{-16} g sec^{-1} cell^{-1}. The steady-state population of microorganisms that can be maintained over the entire globe by the abiological synthesis of ATP is then 2×10^4 cells/cm^2 column of ocean. This estimate is, of course, extremely approximate. The assumptions that all the ultraviolet light is transmitted by the atmosphere, that it is all absorbed by adenine in the ocean and that the quantum yields used in the ethyl metaphosphate experiments are applicable to the primitive environment probably increase the derived steady-state cell population; while the assumptions that the ATP requirement and doubling time for organisms are the same as for *E. coli* probably decrease the derived steady-state cell population over the true value. Nevertheless, this calculation does suggest that abiogenic ATP production by ultraviolet light in primitive times may have supported quite sizable populations of microorganisms on the primitive Earth.

Such abiogenic production of ATP is, in effect, photosynthesis without life. One striking conclusion that has emerged from recent work on the mechanism of terrestrial plant photosynthesis is that the production of ATP is the primary, and most primitive, function of the photosynthetic apparatus (35, 36). The experimental results of the present article permit us to understand why this might be so. With rather efficient abiogenic synthesis of so ideal an energy currency as ATP in the primitive environment, the transition from a reducing to an oxidizing atmosphere must have had profound results.

The transition was at least partially initiated by the ultraviolet photodissociation of water vapour in the high atmosphere, and the selective escape of hydrogen to space (8, 37). The ozone concentration of a planetary atmosphere depends approximately logarithmically on the oxygen concentration, down to a certain lower limit of the oxygen concentration (38, 39); thus the steady-state production of even 10^{-4} or 10^{-5} of the present oxygen concentration would have produced enough ozone to diminish the ultraviolet flux in the 2400–2900 Å partial window, and make the rate of ultraviolet synthesis of ATP decline. A premium was then placed on organisms with the ability to utilize visible light for ATP synthesis. One can imagine the metabolism of the primitive organisms to be so keyed to the availability of ATP that the first visible photosynthetic apparatus evolved would be adopted by all subsequent life forms.

The precise mechanism of synthesis has not yet been investigated. Ultraviolet excitation of adenine accounts for the adenosine synthesis, but the participation of phosphorus compounds in the reaction is obscure. Synthesis of nucleoside phosphates must be more indirect, since it is difficult to imagine the excitation energy being transferred across the ribose molecule, which has no conjugated double bonds. Alternative possibilities, such as the production of activated adenine or ribose phosphates, remain to be investigated.

Further investigation of so far unidentified chromatographic features should both help clarify the mechanisms of synthesis and cast light on other possible prebiological organic reactions. Ultraviolet irradiation of solutions of deoxyribose purines or pyrimidines, and phosphate compounds may have some relevance for the problem of polynucleotide origins.

Bio-assay. To establish whether the ATP synthesized by us was biochemically active, a luminescence assay was performed using dehydrated firefly tails (39). The method described by Strehler and Trotter was used. (Firefly tails were supplied by Schwarz Bioresearch, Inc., Mount Vernon, New York.) The intensity of luminescence was measured by a Turner fluorometer. The decay curve of the luminescence was identical with that of an authentic sample of ATP. The concentration of ATP in the solution used, as determined by this method, corresponded within the limits of experimental error to the value obtained by spectrophotometric measurements.

One of us (C. S.) thanks Drs. Joshua Lederberg, Matthew Meselson and Jerome Schiff for helpful discussions, and the partial support of his work by the National Aeronautics and Space Administration. We also thank Dr. John Moffatt for the gift of a sample of adenosine tetraphosphate.

REFERENCES AND NOTES

* National Aeronautics and Space Administration postdoctoral resident research associate.

† Permanent address: Department of Astronomy, Harvard University, and Smithsonian Astrophysical Observatory, Cambridge, Massachusetts.

‡ And Exobiology Division, National Aeronautics and Space Administration, Ames Research Center, Moffet Field, California.

1. C. Sagan, *Evolution* 11, 40 (1957).

2. _____, *Rad. Res.* 15, 174 (1961).

3. J. B. S. Haldane, *Rationalist Ann.* 148 (1929).

4. A. I. Oparin, *The Origin of Life* (Macmillan, New York, 1938).

5. H. F. Blum, *Time's Arrow and Evolution* (Princeton Univ. Press, Princeton, 1951), p. 168.

6. See, for example, R. Schweet and J. Bishop in *Molecular Genetics,* J. H. Taylor, Ed. (Academic Press, New York, 1963).

7. A. Kornberg, *Harvey Lectures,* Ser. 53, 83 (1959).

8. G. P. Kuiper, in *The Atmosphere of the Earth and Planets,* G. P. Kuiper, Ed. (Univ. of Chicago Press, Chicago, 2 ed., 1952).

9. H. C. Urey, *The Planets* (Yale Univ. Press, New Haven, 1952).

10. W. M. Garrison, D. C. Morrison, J. G. Hamilton, A. A. Benson, M. Calvin, Science 114, 416 (1951).

11. S. L. Miller, *Biochim. et Biophys. Acta* 23, 480 (1957).

12. P. H. Abelson, *Science* 124, 935 (1956).

13. C. Sagan and S. L. Miller, *Astro. J.* 65, 499 (1960).

14. See, for example, J. Oro, *Ann. N.Y. Acad. Sci.,* in press.

15. C. Sagan, *Nat. Acad. Sci.–Nat. Res. Counc., Pub.* 757 (1961).

16. S. L. Miller and H. C. Urey, *Science* 130, 245 (1959).

17. J. Oro and A. P. Kimball, *Arch. Biochem. Biophys.* 94, 217 (1961).

18. C. Ponnamperuma, R. M. Lemmon, R. Mariner, M. Calvin, *Proc. Nat. Acad. Sci. U.S.* 49, 737 (1963).

19. _____, and R. Mariner, *Nineteenth Intern. Cong. Pure and App. Chem.,* London (July 1963).

20. _____, R. S. Young, E. Munoz, *Fed. Proc.* 22, 479 (1963).

21. S. W. Fox and K. Harada, *Science* 133, 1923 (1961).

22. J. Oro and A. C. Cox, *Fed. Proc.* 25, 80 (1962).

23. C. Ponnamperuma and R. Mariner, *Rad. Res.* 19, 183 (1963).

24. W. W. Rubey, *Bull. Geol. Soc. Amer.* 62, 1111 (1951).

25. C. Ponnamperuma, R. Mariner, C. Sagan, *Nature* 198, 1199 (1963).

26. G. Schramm *et al., Angewandte Chemie,* Intern. ed. 1, 1 (1962).

27. J. A. Bassham and M. Calvin, *The Path of Carbon in Photosynthesis* (Academic Press, New York, 1957), p. 19.

28. H. A. Krebs and R. Hems, *Biochim. et Biophys. Acta* **12**, 172 (1953).

29. C. Ponnamperuma, *Univ. Calif. Rad. Lab. Rep.* 10053, 36 (1952).

30. S. Burroughs, F. S. M. Grylls, J. S. Harrison, *Nature* **170**, 800 (1952).

31. J. D. Smith and R. Markham, *Biochim.* **46**, 509 (1950).

32. B. Pullman and A. Pullman, *Comparative Effects of Radiation* (John Wiley & Sons, New York, 1960), p. 111.

33. _____ and _____, *Nature* **196**, 1137 (1962).

34. J. Baddiley, *The Nucleic Acids*, E. Chargaff and J. N. Davidson, Eds. (Academic Press, New York, 1955), I, 137.

35. D. I. Arnon, in *Light and Life*, W. D. McElroy and B. Glass, Eds. (The Johns Hopkins Press, Baltimore, 1961), p. 489.

36. M. Calvin, *Perspectives in Biology and Medicine* **5**, 147 (1962).

37. H. C. Urey, *Handbuch der Physik*, S. Flugge, Ed. (Springer, Berlin, 1959), 52, 363.

38. F. F. Marmo and P. Warneck, in *Geophys. Corp. Amer. Tech. Rep.*, 61–20–N (1961).

39. H. Paetzold, *Proc. Eleventh Intern. Astrophys. Colloq., Liège*, in press.

40. B. L. Strehler and J. R. Totter, *Arch. Biochem. Biophys.* **40**, 28 (1952).

B Structure and function of cell subunits

Calvin, M., and A. A. Benson. 1949. The path of carbon in photosynthesis. IV: The identity and sequence of the intermediates in sucrose synthesis. *Science* **109**, 140–42.

Arnon, Daniel I., F. R. Whatley, and M. B. Allen. 1958. Assimilatory power in photosynthesis. *Science* **127**, 1026–1034.

Hogeboom, George H., Walter C. Schneider, and George E. Palade. 1947. The isolation of morphologically intact mitochondria from rat liver. *Proc. Soc. Exper. Biol. and Med.* **65**, 320–21.

Green, D. E., and Y. Hatefi. 1961. The mitochondrion and biochemical machines. *Science* **133**, 13–19.

Mazia, Daniel, and Katsuma Dan. 1952. The isolation and biochemical characterization of the mitotic apparatus of dividing cells. *Proc. Nat. Acad. Sci. U.S.* **38**, 826–38.

Hanson, Jean, and Hugh E. Huxley. 1953. Structural basis of the cross-striations in muscle. Nature **172**, 530–32.

The Path of Carbon in Photosynthesis. IV. The Identity and Sequence of the Intermediates in Sucrose Synthesis[1]

M. Calvin
A. A. Benson

Department of Chemistry,
University of California,
Berkeley*

The ideal design of an experiment to determine the chemical path of carbon from carbon dioxide to the variety of plant constituents is relatively simple and straightforward. It would consist of feeding a photosynthesizing organism radioactive carbon dioxide for various lengths of time and stopping the reaction by killing the plant. By determining those compounds into which the radioactive carbon has been incorporated for each period of illumination and, further, by determining the distribution of radioactivity within each compound, these data could then be used to construct a family of curves depicting the increase in radioactivity in each compound (and in each carbon as it flows into the plant in the form of carbon dioxide and distributes itself among all the plant constituents.

A few such experiments have already been reported (1–4, 6). The present paper reports some further experiments toward this end with specific reference to the synthesis of sucrose.

The data are in the form of radioautographs of paper chromatograms made from the extracts of algae which have been photosynthesizing for several different periods of time, as well as one showing the dark fixation after a preliminary period of illumination in the absence of carbon dioxide.

Reprinted from *Science* 109, 140–42 (February 11, 1949), by permission of M. Calvin and *Science*.

Exposure of algae to $C^{14}O_2$. One-day-old *Chlorella pyrenoidosa* cells were grown under continuous culture conditions (3) and harvested immediately before use. A suspension of 1 cc of packed cells in 70 ml of water containing fumarate buffer (3.5 mg fumaric acid plus .032 meq sodium hydroxide) was allowed to photosynthesize for 30 minutes with 4% carbon dioxide in air. This gas mixture was then displaced by rapid flushing with air during 5 minutes. A solution of 40 μc of $NaHC^{14}O_3$ (.0143 mmol) in 0.20 ml was rapidly injected into the suspension. The vessel was shaken vigorously in the light beams (2 × 17,000 lux) until

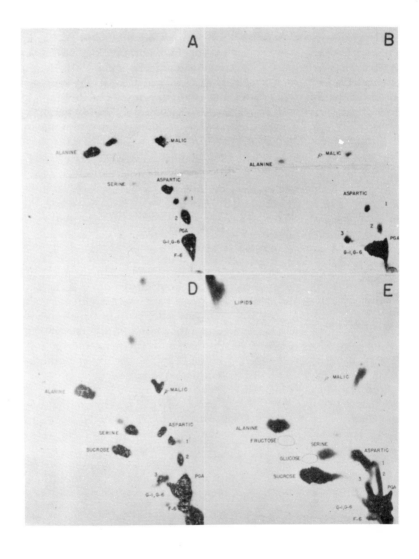

the algae were killed by opening an 8-mm stopcock and allowing the solution to flow into a beaker containing 500 ml of boiling absolute ethanol. The alcohol suspension was filtered with celite and evaporated at room temperature to a volume of 2 cc for convenient application on the filter paper sheet.

Preparation of chromatograms. Fumarate buffer in distilled water was chosen for this work, since inorganic salts, especially phosphates, interfere with movement of compounds on the paper. Alcohol extract of as much as 100 mm³ of algae may be applied to the filter paper (What-

FIGURE 1. C¹⁴ Radiograms of 80% Ethanol Extracts of Algae.[1,2] A: 15-sec. dark fixation by *Chlorella* which had been preilluminated for 15 min. in helium. B: 5-sec. photosynthetic fixation by *Chlorella*. C: 30-sec. photosynthetic fixation by *Chlorella*. D: 90-sec. photosynthetic fixation by *Chlorella* (10% of the activity fixed is insoluble in 80% ethanol). E: 5-min. photosynthetic fixation by *Chlorella*[3] (60% of the activity fixed is insoluble in 80% ethanol). F: 5-sec. photosynthetic fixation by *Scenedesmus*.[4]

[1]The term "radiogram" is used here to denote the radioautograph of a two-dimensional paper chromatogram.

[2]The abbreviations used in labeling the radiograms indicate the following compounds: PGA, phosphoglyceric acid; G-1, glucose-1-phosphate; G-6, glucose-6-phosphate; F-6, fructose-6-phosphate; p-MALIC, malic acid (position dependent on pH).

[3]Dotted circles indicate the positions of fructose and glucose which are not radioactive.

[4]Aspartic acid, encircled in the radiogram, was identified by ninhydrin spraying and has a small amount of radioactivity.

man No. 1). Development in water-saturated phenol was followed by thorough drying at room temperature. The second solvent was freshly prepared before use from equal volumes of the following solutions:

(A) 1,246 cc n-butanol—84 cc water
(B) 620 cc propionic acid—790 cc water[2]

In order to choose a suitable exposure time for the X-ray film (Eastman No-Screen, 14″ × 17″) the activity of the original spot is determined on the paper. With the number of compounds appearing in a 90-second photosynthesis, an activity of 30,000 cpm is sufficient to expose the film in 48 hours.

Although the radioactive fixation products which have been separated in the chromatogram may be eluted and their activity determined accurately, the radiogram serves as a semiquantitative record of the activity fixed in each compound. The relative amounts of each active product may be compared visually in the radioautograph.[3]

An examination of the radiograms reveals that in the very short photosynthetic experiments (30 seconds and 90 seconds) by far the major portion of the newly reduced carbon dioxide is found in the phosphoglyceric acids, triose phosphates and the hexose phosphates. This may be taken as additional confirmatory evidence of our previously proposed (4) scheme by which the six-carbon hexose skeleton is synthesized through the usual glycolytic intermediates. The details of the path by which the phosphoglyceric acid is formed and the relative rates of the several reactions involved in its conversion to hexose phosphate will be treated in subsequent publications.

What we would like to point out here is the fact that the first free carbohydrate which appears in these plants is sucrose. The positions taken on the chromatogram by free glucose and free fructose are known and they do not contain radioactivity. The nonappearance of radioactivity in a given compound does not necessarily preclude the possibility of its playing a part as an intermediate in a given sequence. For example, the reservoir of this compound in the sequence may be extremely small, or the compound may never exist as a free compound in solution but rather only as an enzyme-substrate complex, so that the amount of radioactivity present in that particular compound may be so small as to be missed. Conversely, the appearance of radioactivity in a particular compound does not necessarily prove its part as an intermediate in a direct sequence. It can be, and often is, the result of a side reaction.

It does not seem likely that, if free glucose or free fructose were intermediates in the synthesis of sucrose, they would fail to appear radioactive either prior to the appearance of radioactive sucrose or simultaneously with it, as is the case in the present experiments. We are, therefore, led to suggest that the immediate precursors to sucrose are two hexose phosphates. That one of them is glucose-1-phosphate can be taken as relatively certain in view of the large amount of radioactivity found in this compound, as well as its demonstrated participation in sucrose synthesis by an isolated enzymatic system (5). If the other is fructose-6-phosphate, which has also been identified among the radioactive compounds in the early chromatograms, one might expect a sucrose phosphate in which the phosphorus is attached to the fructose fragment as the intermediate just prior to the formation of free sucrose. Although it is not required that this intermediate be found, since dephosphorylation may take place simultaneously with the condensation to sucrose, there are still a number of unidentified spots in the chromatograms, one of which might well be a sucrose phosphate.

That the fructose phosphates are formed prior to the glucose derivatives is suggested by the fact that the fructose half of the sucrose formed in 30-second photosynthesis by *Chlorella* has approximately twice the specific radioactivity of the glucose half. This was determined by cutting out the sucrose spot from a chromatogram of the total extract, eluting it from the paper, hydrolyzing for 10 minutes in 0.1 N HCl at 80°C and rechromatographing the hydrolyzate after cold evaporation to dryness to remove the HCl. The sucrose formed in 90-second photosynthesis by the same organism is made up of glucose and fructose of equal specific activities (within 5%). This result requires that the functioning reservoirs of precursor hexose phosphates be so small as to achieve equal specific activities in 90 seconds.

Additional evidence for the size of the functioning reservoirs and the speed of turnover may be obtained from a knowledge of the molar specific activity of a compound relative to that of the fed carbon dioxide. One case in which this may readily be determined is that of alanine. Its position on the paper can be defined with reference to the radiogram. The spot is then eluted and the activity determined by counting an aliquot. The alanine content of the remaining solution is then determined colorimetrically. When this is done, the following very approximate values are obtained for the molar specific activity related to that of the starting carbon dioxide for various times of photosynthesis by *Chlorella:* 5 seconds, ~.04; 15 seconds, ~.1; 90 seconds, ~.9; and 5 minutes, ~3.

REFERENCES AND NOTES

* And Radiation Laboratory.

[1] This paper is based on work performed under Contract No. W-7405-Eng-48 with the Atomic Energy Commission in connection with the Radiation Laboratory, University of California, Berkeley.

[2] The solvent is adjusted to separate into two phases if cooled two degrees below the temperature at which it is used.

[3] The details of the methods of identification of the spots will be published elsewhere. ("The Path of Carbon in Photosynthesis. V. Paper Chromatography and

Radioautography of the Products" by A. A. Benson, J. A. Bassham, M. Calvin, V. A. Haas, W. Stepka.)

1. A. A. Benson and M. Calvin, *Proceedings of Cold Spring Harbor Symposia in Quantitative Biology* (1948), in press.

2. _____, *Science* **105**, 648 (1947).

3. _____, V. A. Haas, S. Aronoff, A. G. Hall, J. A. Bassham, John W. Weigl, AAAS monograph on photosynthesis, in press.

4. M. Calvin and A. A. Benson, *Science* **107**, 476 (1948).

5. W. Z. Hassid, M. Doudoroff, H. A. Barker, *J. Amer. Chem. Soc.* **66**, 1416 (1944).

6. W. Stepka, M. Calvin, A. A. Benson, *Science* **108**, 304 (1948).

Assimilatory Power in Photosynthesis

PHOTOSYNTHETIC
PHOSPHORYLATION
BY ISOLATED CHLOROPLASTS IS
COUPLED WITH TPN REDUCTION

Daniel I. Arnon
F. R. Whatley
M. B. Allen*

University of California,
Berkeley

The concept is firmly established in cellular physiology that adenosine triphosphate (ATP) is a universal "energy currency" acting as a link between energy-yielding and energy-consuming metabolic reactions (1). It was natural, therefore, that its possible role in photosynthesis, an energy transformation process par excellence, should receive early scrutiny. The participation of ATP in the overall process of photosynthesis became clear as soon as the enzymatic mechanisms of carbohydrate metabolism were elucidated, when it was recognized that carbohydrates, the main products of photosynthesis, are formed by a series of reactions in which phosphorylation steps with ATP are essential.

The recognition that ATP was needed shed no light on its mode of formation in photosynthesis. That a portion of light energy captured during photosynthesis is transformed into ATP without being first stored in some products of CO_2 assimilation has indeed been envisaged for some time (see review, 2). What remained obscure was the cellular site at which this special phosphorylation occurred and the mechanism by which it was accomplished. From the standpoint of cellular physiology, the important questions were whether ATP used in photosynthesis was formed by some special light-driven assimilation of inorganic phosphate catalyzed by enzymes

Reprinted from *Science* **127**, 1026–1032 (May 2, 1958), by permission of Daniel I. Arnon and *Science*.

45

closely bound to the chlorophyll system or, in mitochondria, by the mechanism of oxidative phosphorylation.

Direct answers to these questions became possible with the discovery of light-induced ATP synthesis (photosynthetic phosphorylation) first in isolated chloroplasts (3) and soon thereafter, by Frenkel, in cell-free preparations of photosynthetic bacteria (4). Photosynthetic phosphorylation revealed a hitherto unrecognized major site of ATP synthesis in the chlorophyll-containing particles of photosynthetic organisms: chloroplasts in green plants and analogous cytoplasmic particles in photosynthetic bacteria. The mechanism of photosynthetic phosphorylation also appeared to differ, notably in its independence from external molecular oxygen, from ATP synthesis by mitochondria.

The purpose of this article is to assess, on the basis of current evidence, the role of photosynthetic phosphorylation in the overall process of photosynthesis and, more particularly, to report new evidence which substantially clarifies the relation of light-induced phosphorylations to other photosynthetic events in chloroplasts.

PHOSPHORYLATION AND CHLOROPHYLL

Prior to the recognition of photosynthetic phosphorylation in chloroplasts, the only cytoplasmic particles known to synthesize ATP were mitochondria. Since green cells contain both types of cytoplasmic particles (5, 6), it becomes of interest to compare them as sites of phosphorylation and to appraise their relative importance as sources of ATP in photosynthesis. This will be attempted presently.

In mitochondrial phosphorylation, ATP synthesis is accomplished at the expense of energy released by the oxidation of foodstuffs. The connection between these two events is indirect. The direct effect of the oxidation of foodstuffs is the formation of reduced diphosphopyridine nucleotide ($DPNH_2$). Adenosine triphosphate is formed while $DPNH_2$ is reoxidized in a stepwise manner by molecular oxygen through the mediation of flavoproteins and cytochromes (7).

In early models of photosynthetic phosphorylation it was shown that if the reduction of a pyridine nucleotide was carried out by illuminated chloroplasts, the resulting reduced pyridine nucleotide could be used by added mitochondria, from either plant or animal sources, for the generation of ATP by oxidative phosphorylation (8). The coupled chloroplast-mitochondrial model system differed from conventional oxidative phosphorylation only in the source of the reduced pyridine nucleotide. In one case DPN was reduced by light, in the other, by a respiratory substrate. The phosphorylation reactions proper, leading to the synthesis of ATP, were in both cases dependent on enzymes localized in mitochondria.

In photosynthetic phosphorylation, isolated chloroplasts were found to be capable of synthesizing ATP without the aid of mitochondria (3, 9). When conditions were so arranged that CO_2 assimilation was excluded, chloroplasts used light energy to esterify inorganic phosphate in accord with the overall reaction:

$$\text{Light} + \text{P} + \text{ADP} \rightarrow \text{ATP} \tag{1}$$

where P represents orthophosphate and ADP and ATP, adenosine diphosphate and triphosphate, respectively.

In the early experiments photosynthetic phosphorylation occurred only in intact chloroplasts; broken plastids which still retained the green water-insoluble chlorophyll pigments but had lost soluble constituents had only feeble phosphorylating activity (3, 9). When in subsequent experiments the phosphorylating capacity was restored to broken chloroplasts by the addition of soluble cofactors such as vitamin K, flavin mononucleotide (FMN), and ascorbate (9, p. 6326; 10; 11), it became clear that the intact structure of whole chloroplasts was not essential to phosphorylation. The enzymes responsible for phosphorylation appeared bound to the water-insoluble chlorophyll pigment system. They were not removed or destroyed by breaking of the chloroplasts but were rendered inactive by the removal of water-soluble constituents (6, 12).

The presence of a phosphorylating system tightly bound to the chlorophyll-containing particles is also seen in experiments with cell-free preparations of photosynthetic bacteria. In these organisms there are no chloroplasts, but the photosynthetic pigments are confined to particles termed chromatophores, much smaller in size than chloroplasts (13). The experiments of Frenkel (14), Williams (15), Geller and Gregory (16), Geller (17), and Mattick and Lindstrom (18) with *Rhodospirillum rubrum* and of Anderson and Fuller (19) and Newton *et al.* (20) with *Chromatium* have shown that in these bacteria the enzymes of photosynthetic phosphorylation are also bound to the particles containing the photosynthetic pigments.

The work with photosynthetic bacteria as well as the recent confirmation of photosynthetic phosphorylation in isolated chloroplasts by Avron and Jagendorf (21, 22), Wessels (23), Krall and Purvis (24), and Chow and Vennesland (25) now provides a broad experimental base for the conclusion that in all photosynthetic organisms the cytoplasmic particles which contain the chlorophyll pigments also contain a phosphorylating system. The phosphorylating system differs from the CO_2-fixing enzymes in chloroplasts in being tightly bound to the chlorophyll pigment system; this suggests a close affinity to the early energy transformation reactions. The CO_2-fixing enzymes are water-soluble and are readily removed from the chloroplast (6, 12, 26).

QUANTITATIVE IMPORTANCE OF PHOTOSYNTHETIC PHOSPHORYLATION

Soon after the demonstration of photosynthetic phosphorylation in isolated chloroplasts, attempts were made to compare its rate with that of CO_2 assimilation by illuminated whole cells. Since, as with most newly discovered cell-free reactions, the rates of photosynthetic phosphorylation were rather low, there was little inclination at first to accord this process quantitative importance (27) as a mechanism for converting light into chemical energy.

A more reliable estimation of the potential magnitude of photosynthetic phosphorylation became possible with further improvement in experimental methods. Using these, Allen *et al.* (28) obtained rates of photosynthetic phosphorylation up to 170 times higher than those originally described (3). A comparison of these maximal rates of photosynthetic phosphorylation by spinach chloroplast fragments (500 micromoles of orthophosphate esterified per hour per milligram of chlorophyll) with the maximum rate (29) of carbon assimilation by intact leaves (180 micromoles of CO_2 per hour per milligram of chlorophyll) leads to the conclusion that the capacity of chloroplasts to convert light energy into ATP is significant. These high rates of phosphorylation were obtained under conditions when CO_2 fixation was excluded. However, as will be discussed later, chloroplasts are also capable of synthesizing ATP at a high rate when light energy is being used for CO_2 assimilation.

High rates of photosynthetic phosphorylation by isolated spinach chloroplasts have also been reported by Jagendorf and Avron. Under experimental conditions similar to those used by our group, they have obtained rates of 200 micromoles of orthophosphate esterified per hour per milligram of chlorophyll (22), but, using a nonphysiological cofactor (phenazine methosulfate), they have observed rates up to 900 micromoles of phosphate esterified per milligram of chlorophyll per hour (30).

It appears therefore that nature has evolved a major mechanism for converting light into useful chemical energy, even under conditions when CO_2 assimilation is curtailed or stopped altogether. The possible physiological significance of this type of energy conversion will be discussed later.

From the standpoint of conventional photosynthesis, the main interest is in those mechanisms for ATP synthesis which can serve not as alternatives but as aids in CO_2 assimilation. The following considerations would suggest that these mechanisms also reside in chloroplasts rather than in mitochondria, which are the major site of ATP synthesis in respiration. (i) The rates of phosphorylation by chloroplasts are, on a nitrogen basis, several times greater than those reported in the literature for oxidative phosphorylation by mitochondria from either plant or animal sources (see 28). (ii) There is a paucity of mitochondria in leaves. The mesophyll of leaves, which contains most of the chloroplasts, is a tissue remarkably specialized for photosynthesis (31). Within the mesophyll cells, especially in the palisade-parenchyma, chloroplasts are the dominant cytoplasmic bodies; mitochondria are relatively few in number (32). On this basis alone, the contribution of mitochondria to the total ATP requirement in photosynthesis would not be expected to be large (6, 33).

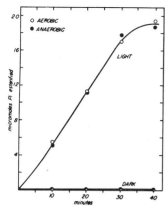

FIGURE 1. Light dependence and oxygen independence of photosynthetic phosphorylation by broken chloroplasts. The reaction mixture contained, in a total volume of 3 ml, "broken" chloroplasts (chlorophyll content 0.5 mg), and, in micromoles: tris(hydroxymethyl)aminomethane, pH 7.4, 40; adenosine-5-phosphate, pH 7.4, 10; potassium phosphate (containing P^{32}), pH 7.2, 20; $MgCl_2$, 10; sodium ascorbate, 10; flavin mononucleotide (FMN), 0.01; and vitamin K_5 (2-methyl-4-amino-1-naphthol hydrochloride), 0.3. The reaction was carried out at 15°C under nitrogen or air. Phosphorylation was measured as described previously (9, 36).

This assessment of the quantitative importance of ATP synthesis by chloroplasts is reached from measurements of rates of phosphorylation in cell-free systems. A different conclusion about the importance of photosynthetic phosphorylation to the overall process of photosynthesis was recently reached by Kandler (34) from experiments with whole cells. However, in these, the estimation of the rate of photosynthetic phosphorylation can only be made indirectly, since it is difficult if not impossible to isolate, with certainty, from the overall phosphorus metabolism of the intact cell, those phases which are solely linked to photosynthetic events.

INDEPENDENCE FROM MOLECULAR OXYGEN

In view of the strict dependence of mitochondrial phosphorylation on oxygen (1, 8), one of the most striking features of photosynthetic phosphorylation is its independence from molecular oxygen. This was perhaps to be expected for cell-free particles of the photosynthetic bacteria mentioned earlier, since in *Rhodospirillum rubrum* normal photosynthesis proceeds anaerobically without any evolution of oxygen, and *Chromatium* is an obligate anaerobic photoautotroph. It was wholly unexpected, however, in chloroplasts of such an eminently aerobic plant as spinach.

The independence from oxygen of photosynthetic phosphorylation by chloroplasts was not apparent in the early experiments (3) prior to the identification of the required cofactors of phosphorylation (9, p. 6326; 10; 11). In later experiments, photosynthetic phosphorylation proceeded anaerobically at rates in no case lower, and in many cases substantially higher, than those observed aerobically, but only when the requisite cofactors of phosphorylation were added. The independence of photosynthetic phosphorylation from molecular oxygen, shown in Figure 1, was established by manometric experiments. This conclusion has recently received strong support from the experiments of Krall *et al.* (35) with labeled oxygen.

Since chloroplasts are able to evolve molecular oxygen in light, it may be useful to define with more precision what we mean by independence from molecular oxygen. We mean that the synthesis of ATP by illuminated chloroplasts occurs (i) when absorption of molecular oxygen cannot be detected either by manometric techniques or by a mass spectrograph (35) or, (ii) in an atmosphere of nitrogen or argon when conditions are so arranged that traces of oxygen originally present or formed during the reaction are eliminated (10). The possibility that a portion of the oxygen generated in photosynthetic reactions may be immediately consumed in back reactions, before it escapes into the gas phase, is further considered unlikely since chloroplasts are unable to carry out the mitochondrial type of phosphorylation with appropriate substrates or reduced pyridine nucleotides when supplied with oxygen in the dark (2, 6, 36).

The independence of photosynthetic phosphorylation from oxygen had certain general implications. First, it distinguished at once between the light-dependent phosphorylation by chloroplasts and the oxidative phosphorylation by mitochondria and suggested that, in the two kinds of cytoplasmic particles, different enzyme systems were involved in at least some of the intermediate steps in ATP synthesis. Second, it pointed to another fundamental similarity in the photosynthetic mechanisms between photosynthesis in aerobic green plants and anaerobic bacteria, in addition to the photodecomposition of water envisaged by van Niel (37).

From the standpoint of photosynthesis in green plants, an interesting question was whether ATP synthesis by chloroplasts is compatible with oxygen *evolution,* which normally accompanies CO_2 assimilation in isolated chloroplasts (5, 38), as in intact leaves. Evidence for photosynthetic phosphorylation accompanied by oxygen evolution has recently been obtained (39, 40). Since the new work clarifies and modifies

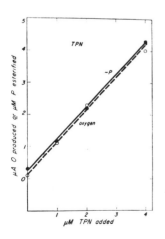

FIGURE 2. Stoichiometry of oxygen evolution and adenosine triphosphate (ATP) formation resulting from the photochemical reduction of triphosphopyridine nucleotide (TPN). The relation between moles of TPN reduced, moles of orthophosphate esterified, and atoms of oxygen produced is 1 : 1 : 1. The reaction mixture contained, in a final volume of 3 ml, "broken" chloroplasts (R_{IS}) containing 0.25 mg of chlorophyll, chloroplast extract (CE) equivalent to 2 mg of chlorophyll, and the following, in micromoles: tris, pH 8.3, 80; $MgCl_2$, 5; ADP, 10; $K_2HP^{32}O_4$, 10; NaCl, 35; and TPN as indicated. The reaction was run at 15°C for 33 minutes, at which time the reduction of TPN was complete. Oxygen evolution was measured manometrically under nitrogen, and the esterification of inorganic phosphate was measured as described previously (36).

the previous concept of photosynthesis by chloroplasts (5, 6, 36), it will now be examined in more detail.

GENERATION OF ASSIMILATORY POWER

Role of pyridine nucleotides. Di- and triphosphopyridine nucleotides (DPN and TPN) were found to enhance CO_2 fixation by isolated chloroplast fragments (26, 12), but experiments to test their participation in photosynthetic phosphorylation had previously yielded only negative results (5, 6, 12, 26). Diphosphopyridine nucleotide occupies a key position in oxidative phosphorylation by mitochondria as the hydrogen or electron carrier in oxidations which lead to phosphorylation. The lack of response to added DPN was therefore regarded in earlier discussions (2, 5, 6) as another feature which distinguished photosynthetic from oxidative phosphorylation. The lack of response to added TPN was not considered significant, since TPN, unlike DPN, was known to be incapable of serving as a hydrogen or electron carrier in phosphorylation by mitochondria (41).

More recently, by changing experimental conditions, we have obtained evidence that TPN, but not DPN, is a catalyst of photosynthetic phosphorylation (39, also compare 42). Substrate amounts of TPN were reduced, and this was accompanied by the evolution of oxygen in accordance with reaction 2. This reaction also requires a TPN-reducing factor which we have identified in an aqueous extract of chloroplasts (CE).

$$2TPN + 4H_2O \xrightarrow[\text{chloroplasts} + CE]{\text{light}} 2TPNH_2 + O_2 + 2H_2O \qquad (2)$$

In the presence of adenosine diphosphate (ADP) and orthophosphate (P), reaction 2 was coupled with the formation of 2 moles of ATP. The overall reaction is summarized by reaction 3:

$$2ADP + 2P + 2TPN + 4H_2O \rightarrow 2ATP + O_2 + 2TPNH_2 + 2H_2O \qquad (3)$$

Under appropriate experimental conditions, which will be described elsewhere, the evolution of 1 mole of oxygen was accompanied by the reduction of 2 moles of TPN and the esterification of 2 moles of orthophosphate.

Reaction 3 and Figure 2 describe a new type of photosynthetic phosphorylation. One mole of orthophosphate is esterified for each mole of TPN reduced. Only part of the light energy absorbed by chlorophyll in this reaction is trapped in the pyrophosphate bond of ATP; the remainder is used for the formation of $TPNH_2$. Thus, the light reaction in chloroplasts consists of the generation of what has previously been termed "assimilatory power" (2), accompanied by the evolution of oxygen. Assimilatory power has two components, both of which are needed for the assimilation of CO_2: the reductant $TPNH_2$ and ATP.

The stoichiometry of reaction 3 (Figure 2) shows that the evolution of 1 mole of oxygen and the synthesis of 2 moles of ATP accompanies the generation of four hydrogen equivalents which are required for the reduction of 1 mole of CO_2 to the level of carbohydrate

$$[\overset{|}{\underset{|}{C}}H(OH)]$$

Reaction 3 would thus account for the well-known photosynthetic ratio CO_2/O_2 of 1, also observed with isolated chloroplasts (5, 38), when CO_2 is assimilated to the level of carbohydrate. A general scheme of photosynthesis in chloroplasts, based on these findings, is shown in Figure 3.

The concept of photosynthesis by chloroplasts represented by Figure 3 shares certain similarities with, but also differs from, the earlier one which it now replaces (5, 6, 26, 36). It is similar in that the chloroplast is regarded as a complete photosynthetic unit containing multienzyme systems divided into three main groups, each controlling an increasingly complex phase of photosynthesis: photolysis of water, photosynthetic phosphorylation, and CO_2 fixation. Carbon dioxide fixation remains, as before, at the apex of this hierarchy and requires the participation of all three groups of enzymes. But photolysis of water is now no longer regarded as resulting *either* in the synthesis of ATP *or* in the reduction of CO_2. Adenosine triphosphate synthesis is *coupled* with the formation of the reductant ($TPNH_2$) required for CO_2 fixation. Thus, the same light quanta which accomplish the reduction of TPN also bring about the synthesis of ATP and generate the assimilatory power needed for the conversion of CO_2 into carbohydrates or analogous end-products of photosynthesis.

The coupling of ATP synthesis with TPN reduction simplifies the con-

FIGURE 3. Scheme for photosynthesis by isolated chloroplasts. Photolysis of water results in the evolution of oxygen and the generation of "assimilatory power" comprising two components: reduced triphosphopyridine nucleotide ($TPNH_2$) and ATP. Assimilatory power is then used for the assimilation of CO_2 in reactions independent of light. [The intermediate X in this scheme is not designated as phosphoglyceric acid, as would be demanded by the theory of Calvin (43). Experiments on carbon fixation with isolated chloroplasts have so far yielded no unequivocal evidence on this point (26, 38; also compare 27, p. 294).]

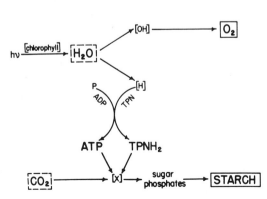

cept of CO_2 assimilation by chloroplasts. If the ATP generated during the TPN reduction step (reaction 3) is sufficient for CO_2 assimilation, it is no longer necessary to visualize a competition for light energy between photosynthetic phosphorylation and CO_2 fixation and to search for appropriate regulatory mechanisms for keeping the two in balance (6). The generation of the two components of assimilatory power, $TPNH_2$ and ATP, goes up and down simultaneously, in accordance with the rate of CO_2 fixation.

Specificity of TPN. The specificity of TPN in photosynthetic phosphorylation (39), together with its previously demonstrated effect on CO_2 assimilation by isolated chloroplasts (12, 26), argues in favor of TPN, rather than DPN, as the pyridine nucleotide *directly* associated with photosynthesis [indirectly, of course, DPN could also be effective in the presence of transhydrogenase (43)].

The preference for TPN rather than DPN in photosynthetic events was hitherto not well established. It was tied to the phosphoglyceric acid theory of carbon assimilation (44) and rested on evidence for the cyclic emergence of light-induced TPN-dependent enzymes (45) concerned in the metabolism of that acid: glyceraldehyde-3-phosphate dehydrogenase (GPD) (46–48) and glyceraldehyde-3-phosphate-TPN reductase (GTR) (49).

The GTR enzyme is known only to oxidize glyceraldehyde-3-phosphate irreversibly to phosphoglycerate (49); the emergence of this enzyme in photosynthetic tissue would thus support not the phosphoglyceric acid theory of Calvin (44) but rather Warburg's view (50) that phosphoglyceric acid is a product of carbohydrate degradation during photosynthesis. The TPN-dependent GPD enzyme which can reduce phosphoglyceric acid offers no compelling evidence for the role of TPN in photosynthesis, since the same function could be performed by the DPN-specific GPD

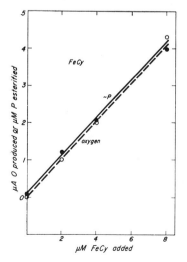

FIGURE 4. Photophosphorylation and oxygen evolution with ferricyanide. The stoichiometric relation between moles of ferricyanide reduced, moles of orthophosphate esterified, and atoms of oxygen produced was 2:1:1. The reaction mixture contained, in a final volume of 3 ml, "broken" chloroplasts (P_{1S}) containing 0.1 mg of chlorophyll and the following, in micromoles: tris, pH 8.3, 80; $MgCl_2$, 5; ADP, 10, $K_2HP^{32}O_4$, 10; NaCl, 35; and ferricyanide as indicated. The reaction was run at 15°C for 18 minutes, at which time the reduction of ferricyanide was complete.

also present in green cells (46–48). However, its specificity in photosynthetic phosphorylation, apart from its other conceivable functions, gives TPN a direct role in photosynthesis, regardless of the validity of the phosphoglyceric acid theory of carbon assimilation.

Improbability of lipoic acid as a TPN reductant. Calvin and his associates (51) have assigned to lipoic (thioctic) acid a key role in photosynthesis as a compound concerned in the primary conversion into chemical energy of the light quanta absorbed by chlorophyll. They have proposed that the reduced lipoic acid (dithiol form) could, in turn, reduce DPN or TPN (52). Lipoic acid could thus fulfill the role of hydrogen carrier in the water-splitting reaction leading to the formation of $TPNH_2$ (Fig. 3).

Reactions in which lipoic acid is a cofactor are very sensitive to arsenite inhibition; the inhibition can be reversed by the addition of dithiols but not of monothiols (53). Peters *et al.* (53) and Gunsalus (54) observed inhibition of the pyruvic oxidation system by concentrations of arsenite of the order of $3 \times 10^{-5} M$; the inhibition was reversed by the dithiol 2,3-dimercaptopropanol (BAL) but not by the monothiol glutathione. In the chloroplast system, $10^{-3} M$ arsenite failed to inhibit the TPN reduction and its coupled phosphorylation. It seems unlikely, therefore, that lipoic acid is a cofactor in this reaction. The TPN reduction and its coupled phosphorylation are sensitive, however, to other sulfhydryl inhibitors, as is evidenced by their inhibition by p-chloromercuribenzoate, an inhibition which was reversed by glutathione.

The improbability that lipoic acid is a participant in photosynthetic phosphorylation is also indicated by the results of Geller (17): $10^{-2} M$ arsenite failed to inhibit phosphorylation by illuminated particles of *Rhodospirillum rubrum.*

Hill reaction as a fragment of a phosphorylating system. Isolated chloroplasts are known (55) to evolve oxygen when they are illuminated in the presence of an artificial electron acceptor (Hill reaction) in accordance with reaction 4, in which *A* represents a nonphysiological substance such as ferricyanide or benzoquinone (56).

$$\text{Light} + A + H_2O \rightarrow H_2A + \tfrac{1}{2}O_2 \qquad (4)$$

The finding of a phosphorylation which is coupled with TPN reduction and oxygen evolution permits us to view the Hill reaction as a measure of photochemical electron transport which is proceeding without its normally associated phosphorylation reaction. The Hill reaction would thus be analogous to those electron transport reactions studied in particulate systems of animal origin in which oxidation has been separated from its normally associated phosphorylation — for example, in the Keilin-Hartree preparations (57) or in the electron transport particles of Green (58).

The validity of this hypothesis was tested with a Hill reagent which is compatible with the phosphorylating activity of chloroplasts. Quinone was found not to fulfill this requirement well, but ferricyanide

FIGURE 5. Diagram representing the generation of "assimilatory power" and the evolution of oxygen by isolated chloroplasts. The components of assimilatory power are reduced triphosphopyridine nucleotide (TPNH$_2$) and adenosine triphosphate (ATP). In the absence of carbon dioxide, TPNH$_2$ and ATP can be generated in substrate amounts in the light by the green fraction of chloroplasts and used subsequently for sugar synthesis in the dark by a colorless chloroplast extract supplied with CO$_2$ (72). (Compare also Figs. 2, 3, and 4.)

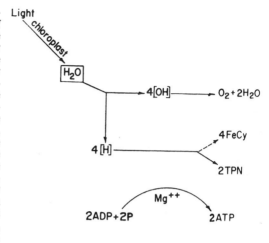

did. Figure 4 shows the esterification of inorganic phosphate coupled with oxygen evolution and the reduction of ferricyanide by illuminated chloroplasts. The stoichiometry of this reaction is the same as in the case of TPN: 1 mole of oxygen is evolved and 2 moles of orthophosphate are esterified in a transfer of four electrons to ferricyanide (compare with reaction 3 and Fig. 2).

The phosphorylation coupled with the photochemical reduction of ferricyanide can thus be regarded as a nonphysiological model for the

FIGURE 6. Effect of phosphate acceptor system on the Hill reaction with ferricyanide. The reaction mixture contained, in a final volume of 3 ml, "broken" chloroplasts (P$_{1S}$), contained 0.1 mg of chlorophyll; and the following in micromoles: tris(hydroxymethyl)aminomethane, 80; sodium chloride, 35; potassium ferricyanide, 15. The vessel with the phosphate acceptor system received, in addition (in micromoles): ADP, 10; K$_2$HPO$_4$, 10; and MgCl$_2$, 5. The oxygen evolution was measured manometrically at 15°C. Gas phase, nitrogen; KOH in the center well of the vessel. Illumination as described previously (38).

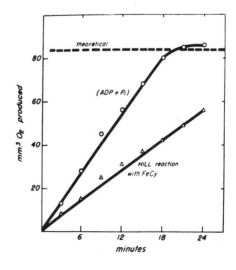

FIGURE 7. Photophosphorylation and oxygen evolution
with TPN in the presence and
absence of FMN. The reaction
mixture was the same as that
described in Figure 2, except
that 15μmole, of K_2HPO_4, 15
μmole of ADP, and 4 μmole of
TPN were used in each vessel.
In the "TPN + FMN" series,
0.1μmole of FMN was added.

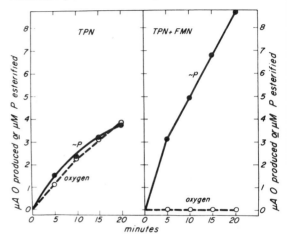

generation of assimilatory power (Fig. 5). (The TPN-reducing factor in
chloroplast extract is not required for the reduction of ferricyanide.)

Further support for the proposal that the Hill reaction is part of an
uncoupled phosphorylation system is seen in Figure 6. With ferricyanide
as a reductant, the rate of oxygen evolution in the Hill reaction was
increased by coupling it with phosphorylation. It seems reasonable to
interpret this effect as indicating that the electron transport system of
chloroplasts is able to function more effectively when it is coupled, as it
would be under physiological conditions, to the synthesis of ATP.

CYCLIC PHOTOPHOSPHORYLATION

In measuring the generation of assimilatory power, the phosphorylation
coupled with the reduction of TPN was accomplished without the
addition of either flavin mononucleotide (FMN) or vitamin K, both of
which have previously been identified as cofactors of photosynthetic
phosphorylation (10, 11). The addition of catalytic amounts of either
FMN or vitamin K altered the system profoundly. The results are shown
in Figures 7 and 8.

Phosphorylation was sharply increased, whereas oxygen evolution and
the accumulation of reduced TPN were abolished. The most direct
explanation of these results is that the addition of catalytic amounts of
either FMN or vitamin K brought about additional phosphorylation
accomplished at the expense of energy liberated by the reoxidation of
$TPNH_2$ by [OH], the oxidized product of photodecomposition of water.

Expressed in another way, the addition of either FMN or vitamin K
has brought about a recombination of the photodecomposition products
of water, [H] and [OH], and a conversion into ATP of all of the light
energy originally trapped in the "water-splitting" reaction. Under these
conditions, when CO_2 assimilation did not occur, the hydrogen atoms
which would have been used in the reduction of CO_2 became a part of a

reconstituted water molecule instead of a newly formed sugar molecule. This type of light-induced phosphorylation is the same as we reported previously under the general name of photosynthetic phosphorylation (2, 5, 6, 10, 26). It will now be designated by the more specific name of *cyclic photophosphorylation* (Fig. 9) to distinguish it from the "one-step" phosphorylation associated with the generation of assimilatory power when only part of the captured light energy is converted into ATP (Fig. 5).

Another explanation of the observed effects of FMN and vitamin K on the "one-step" phosphorylation is possible, and is being tested experimentally, but it appears at this time to be unlikely. It would limit phosphorylation only to the electron transfer step coupled with TPN reduction and would explain the increased phosphorylation which follows the addition of FMN or vitamin K (Figs. 7 and 8) as resulting from a more rapid turnover of the TPN rather than from the activation of additional phosphorylation sites.

Physiological significance. In previous discussions (5, 6, 26, 36), cyclic photophosphorylation was regarded as the sole photosynthetic phosphorylation and its physiological significance was sought in its contribution of ATP to CO_2 assimilation. The identification of a second type of photosynthetic phosphorylation, as a component of assimilatory power, renders the earlier interpretation of cyclic phosphorylation too narrow.

It is tentatively proposed that another physiological role of cyclic photophosphorylation might be the conversion of light energy into ATP under conditions when CO_2 assimilation is, for one reason or another, reduced or even stopped altogether. This might arise during the well-known midday closure of stomata in leaves of higher plants (see 59)

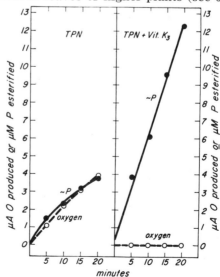

FIGURE 8. Photophosphorylation and oxygen evolution with TPN in the presence and absence of vitamin K_3. Experimental conditions were the same as those described in Figure 7. In the "TPN + vit. K_3," series, 0.2 μmole of vitamin K_3 (menadione) was added.

FIGURE 9. Diagram representing cyclic photophosphorylation induced by the addition of catalytic amounts of riboflaven phosphate (FMN) to a chloroplast system generating assimilatory power (Figs. 3 and 7). The suppression of oxygen evolution and the increase in phosphorylation (Fig. 7) are visualized as resulting from additional phosphorylation steps coupled with the stepwise recombination of the elements of water.

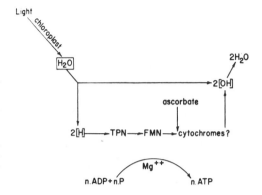

when the supply of CO_2 becomes restricted. The midday closure of stomata often occurs as a result of a water deficit in the plant. Cyclic photophosphorylation, unlike CO_2 assimilation, provides a mechanism for the utilization of light energy without the consumption of water.

It is conceivable that devices other than closure of stomata are also available, both to higher and to lower plants without stomata, for curtailing CO_2 assimilation when the normal photosynthetic products accumulate in the cell. Under such conditions it would greatly benefit the cell to have a supply of ATP generated at the expense of light energy. This ATP of photochemical origin could then be used to drive the many ATP-dependent reactions, notably protein and fat synthesis (1). Another example is the synthesis of glutamine, which provides an important mechanism for the incorporation and transfer of nitrogen in plants, and which was also shown by Elliott (60) to depend on ATP in accordance with reaction 5:

$$\text{Glutamate} + NH_3 + ATP \rightarrow \text{glutamine} + ADP + P \qquad (5)$$

One is tempted to suggest that cyclic phosphorylation itself may, under certain conditions, be a device for diverting light energy into channels other than CO_2 assimilation. Cyclic phosphorylation would thus represent a pattern evolved by photosynthetic cells to use light energy for accomplishing cellular work independently of CO_2 assimilation.

CYCLIC PHOTOPHOSPHORYLATION AND QUANTUM EFFICIENCY MEASUREMENTS

If cyclic photophosphorylation is concurrent with CO_2 assimilation, then the portion of light energy which it consumes will not be accompanied either by oxygen evolution or by CO_2 uptake. Quantum efficiency values for the overall process of photosynthesis, dependent as they usually are on the measurements of these two gases, would therefore be low in proportion to the share of light energy which is diverted to cyclic photophosphorylation. One possible explanation, attractive because of its simplicity, of the high quantum efficiency yield obtained by Warburg *et al.* (*61*) with cells grown in fluctuating light is that they divert little if any of the absorbed light energy from CO_2 assimilation to cyclic photophosphorylation. On the other hand, the seemingly less efficient cells grown under constant illumination may already contain an accumulation of carbohydrates or of other photosynthetic products and would then use a larger share of the absorbed light energy for cyclic photophosphorylation to generate ATP, to be used for protein synthesis and other endergonic processes.

Catalysts of photosynthetic phosphorylation. In previous formulations it was tentatively proposed (*5, 6, 26, 36*) that FMN and vitamin K are members of the same electron transport chain of what is now termed cyclic photophosphorylation. Whatley *et al.* (*62*) have shown, however, that under modified experimental conditions maximal rates of cyclic photophosphorylation are obtained with either FMN or vitamin K as catalysts (Table 1). On the basis of present evidence, vitamin K and FMN are therefore tentatively regarded as participating in alternative pathways for cyclic photophosphorylation. The postulated "FMN pathway" is shown in Figure 9. The "vitamin K pathway" differs from the "FMN pathway"; for example, it is insensitive to $10^{-3}M$ dinitrophenol. Other differences and similarities between these two postulated pathways are now under investigation. This subject is discussed more fully elsewhere (*63, 64*).

The marked stimulating effect of phenazine methosulfate on photosynthetic phosphorylation is sometimes interpreted as casting doubt on the specificity of vitamin K and flavins as the natural cofactors of photosynthetic phosphorylation (*30*). Analogous effects of phenazine methosulfate as an electron carrier in the succinic and other dehydrogenase systems (*65*) have led to no questions about the specificity of the natural cytochrome system in these reactions. We know of no valid reason at this time for questioning the experimentally demonstrated role of vitamin K (*11*, Table 1) and FMN (*10*) in photosynthetic phosphorylation. Both of these substances are normal constituents of chloroplasts; in fact, Dam has shown that in green leaves vitamin K is concentrated in chloroplasts (see review, *63*). We are therefore inclined to favor Geller's interpretation (*17*) that, in photosynthetic phosphorylation, phenazine methosulfate merely "serves as a fast 'by-pass' or 'short circuit' for electron transport around the site which is rate limiting in the system."

Present evidence suggests that the role of ascorbate may be to protect some essential components of the chloroplasts against inactivation (*39*). We are now inclined to assign to ascorbate a protective action and to consider it to be perhaps a poising agent, rather than a catalyst in the electron transport chain (Fig. 9). Contrary to the report of Wessels (*23*), ascorbate, under our experimental conditions (64), markedly increased phosphorylation with either FMN or vitamin K, under anaerobic conditions (Table 1).

The requirements for Mg^{++} and TPN and the possibility that there is a cytochrome requirement in photosynthetic phosphorylation are discussed elsewhere (63, 64).

Several soluble enzymes and other factors contained in chloroplasts have now been identified as likely components of photosynthetic phosphorylation: (i) adenylic acid kinase (24, 28, 39, 66); (ii) a TPN-reducing factor which has the properties of a protein (39) [this factor appears to be the same as that described by San Pietro and Lang (67)]; (iii) a diaphorase, specific for $TPNH_2$ as an electron donor and capable of reducing FMN or vitamin K_3 (68).

PHOSPHORYLATION AND
BIOCHEMICAL EVOLUTION

The presence in green plants of anaerobic mechanisms for generating ATP at the expense of light energy provides another link in the chain of evidence for the basic unity of photosynthetic mechanisms in aerobic green plants and anaerobic photosynthetic bacteria, as proposed by van Niel (37). Photosynthetic phosphorylation is also compatible with the premise that the emergence of photosynthetic organisms in the evolutionary scale was accomplished by their acquisition of a pigment system capable of carrying out the photodecomposition of water (37).

Our present knowledge of photosynthetic phosphorylation (69) suggests that the capacity for harnessing light energy, when first acquired, was probably more closely associated with ATP synthesis than with CO_2 assimilation. This suggestion is based on the close structural association, in both chloroplasts and bacterial chromatophores, of the phosphorylating activity with the chlorophyll pigment system. By contrast, the enzymes responsible for CO_2 assimilation are easily dissociable from the chlorophyll pigment system in the case of chloroplasts (6, 12, 26) and apparently not even structurally joined together in the case of bacterial chromatophores (70).

The direct use of light energy for the synthesis of ATP by a recombination of the products of the photodecomposition of water would be a significant step forward in supplementing the ATP derived from anaerobic fermentations, which were most probably the oldest energy-releasing processes (see 1). If it is agreed that, at an early period in the evolution of life forms, organic compounds were abundant and the earth's atmosphere was a reducing one (71; also see 1, review), then new mechanisms for ATP formation were probably more important than CO_2 fixation to the newly emerging organisms. It is assumed that, at first, the mechanism for the reconstitution of water leading to ATP formation was simpler than that now proposed for cyclic photophosphorylation (Fig. 9).

TABLE 1

Effect of Riboflavin Phosphate (FMN), Vitamin K$_5$ (2-methyl-4-amino-1-naphthol Hydrochloride), and Ascorbate on Photosynthetic Phosphorylation Under Anaerobic Conditions.

| | P esterified (μmole) | |
Treatment	FMN system	Vitamin K$_5$ system
Complete	7.0	5.5
FMN or vitamin K$_5$ omitted	0.9	0.9
Chloroplasts omitted	0.2	0.2
Light omitted	0.2	0.2
Complete	6.2	6.8
Ascorbate omitted	0.9	3.8

The next step in the evolution of photosynthesis might have been the formation of assimilatory power — that is, the conversion of only a portion of the captured light energy into ATP, the remainder being used to generate a reductant for CO_2 assimilation. Here a recombination of the products of photodecomposition of water had to be prevented, since the "hydrogen" derived from the decomposition of water would be required for the reduction of CO_2. The diversion of the "hydrogen" for CO_2 assimilation would have to be accompanied by a mechanism for disposing of the [OH], the oxidized product of the photodecomposition of water. This mechanism was perhaps, at first, generally dependent on an external hydrogen donor, as it still is today in photosynthetic bacteria. In a later stage of evolution, culminating in the emergence of green plants, this mechanism became an enzyme system for the liberation of molecular oxygen (37).

Photosynthetic phosphorylation by chlorophyll-containing particles, being independent of molecular oxygen, could occur before oxidative phosphorylation by mitochondria, which requires molecular oxygen. The only known source for molecular oxygen on earth is photosynthesis by green plants (37, 71). This evolutionary sequence provides another argument against the dependence of photosynthesis on ATP generated by a mitochondrial mechanism. It is an interesting aspect of biochemical evolution that green plants, after evolving a mechanism independent of molecular oxygen for generating ATP in light, have also shared with nongreen organisms the emergence of an oxygen-dependent generation of ATP by oxidative phosphorylation.

REFERENCES AND NOTES

* The authors are, respectively, professor of plant physiology, assistant plant physiologist, and assistant research biochemist, of the University of California, Berkeley. The article is based on a paper presented by Dr. Arnon on September 11, 1957 before the Division of Biological Chemistry of the American Chemical Society at its New York meeting.

1. H. A. Krebs and H. L. Kornberg, *Ergeb. Physiol. biol. Chem. u. exptl. Pharmakol.* **49**, 212 (1957).

2. D. I. Arnon, *Ann. Rev. Plant Physiol.* **7**, 325 (1956).

3. _____, M. B. Allen, F. R. Whatley, *Nature* **174**, 394 (1954).

4. A. W. Frenkel, *J. Am. Chem. Soc.* **76**, 5568 (1954).

5. D. I. Arnon, *Science* **122**, 9 (1955).

6. _____, in *Enzymes: Units of Biological Structure and Function,* O. H. Gaebler, Ed. (Academic Press, New York, 1956).

7. A. L. Lehninger, *J. Biol. Chem.* **190**, 345 (1951).

8. W. Vishniac and S. Ochoa, *ibid.* **198**, 501 (1952).

9. D. I. Arnon, F. R. Whatley, M. B. Allen, *J. Am. Chem. Soc.* **76**, 6324 (1954).

10. F. R. Whatley, M. B. Allen, D. I. Arnon, *Biochim. et Biophys. Acta* **16**, 605 (1955).

11. D. I. Arnon, F. R. Whatley, M. B. Allen, *ibid.* **16**, 607 (1955).

12. F. R. Whatley *et al., ibid.* **20**, 462 (1956).

13. H. K. Schachman, A. B. Pardee, R. Y. Stanier, *Arch. Biochem. Biophys.* **38**, 245 (1952); J. B. Thomas, *Koninkl. Ned. Akad. Wetenschap. Proc. Ser. C* **55**, 207 (1952).

14. A. W. Frenkel, *J. Biol. Chem.* **222**, 823 (1956).

15. A. M. Williams, *Biochim. et Biophys. Acta* **19**, 570 (1956).

16. D. M. Geller and J. D. Gregory, *Federation Proc.* **15**, 260 (1956).

17. D. M. Geller, doctoral dissertation, Division of Medical Science, Harvard Univ., 1957.

18. J. L. Mattick and E. S. Lindstrom, paper presented before the Midwest Section of the American Society of Plant Physiologists, Ann Arbor, Mich., June 1957.

19. E. C. Anderson and R. C. Fuller, *Plant Physiol. Suppl.* **32**, xvi (1957).

20. J. W. Newton, G. A. Newton, M. D. Kamen, paper presented before the Midwest Section of the American Society of Plant Physiologists, Ann Arbor, Mich., June 1957.

21. M. Avron and A. T. Jagendorf, *Nature* **179**, 428 (1957).

22. A. T. Jagendorf and M. Avron, *Plant Physiol. Suppl.* **32**, iv (1957).

23. J. S. C. Wessels, *Biochim. et Biophys. Acta* **25**, 97 (1957).

24. A. R. Krall and M. R. Purvis, *Plant Physiol. Suppl.* **32**, iv (1957).

25. C. T. Chow and B. Vennesland, *ibid.* **32**, iv (1957).

26. D. I. Arnon *et al., Proc. Intern. Congr. Biochem., 3rd. Congr. Brussels, 1955* (1956), p. 227.

27. H. Gaffron, Ed., *Research in Photosynthesis* (Interscience, New York, 1957), pp. 293, 345.

28. M. B. Allen, F. R. Whatley, D. I. Arnon, *Biochim. et Biophys. Acta* **27**, 16 (1958).

29. E. I. Rabinowitch, *Photosynthesis and Related Processes* (Interscience, New York, 1956), II, pt. 2, 1594.

30. A. T. Jagendorf and M. Avron, *J. Biol. Chem.,* in press.

31. K. Esau, *Plant Anatomy* (John Wiley & Sons, New York, 1953), p. 414.

32. W. O. James and V. S. Das, *New Phytologist* **56**, 325 (1957).

33. D. I. Arnon and F. R. Whatley, *Physiol. Plantarum* **7**, 602 (1954).

34. O. Kandler, *Z. Naturforsch.* **126**, 271 (1957).

35. A. R. Krall, M. Avron, A. T. Jagendorf, *Biochim. et Biophys. Acta* **26**, 431 (1957).

36. D. I. Arnon, M. B. Allen, F. R. Whatley, *ibid.* 20, 449 (1956).
37. C. B. van Niel in *Photosynthesis in Plants*, J. Franck and W. E. Loomis, Eds. (Iowa State College Press, Ames, 1949).
38. M. B. Allen *et al., J. Am. Chem. Soc.* 77, 4149 (1955).
39. D. I. Arnon, F. R. Whatley, M. B. Allen, *Nature* 180, 182 (1957).
40. D. I. Arnon, F. R. Whatley, M. B. Allen, in preparation.
41. A. L. Lehninger, *Harvey Lectures Ser.* 49, 176 (1955); N. O. Kaplan *et al., Proc. Natl. Acad. Sci. U.S.* 42, 481 (1956).
42. E. Marré and O. Servettaz, *Nuova giorn. botan. ital.* 64, 1 (1957).
43. N. O. Kaplan, S. P. Colowick, E. F. Neufeld, *J. Biol. Chem.* 205, 1 (1953).
44. M. Calvin, *J. Chem. Soc.* 1956, 1895 (June 1956).
45. R. H. Hageman and D. I. Arnon, *Arch. Biochem. Biophys.* 57, 421 (1955).
46. D. I. Arnon, in *Phosphorus Metabolism* (The Johns Hopkins Press, Baltimore, 1952).
47. M. Gibbs, *Nature* 170, 164 (1952).
48. D. I. Arnon, *Science* 116, 635 (1952).
49. D. I. Arnon, L. L. Rosenberg, F. R. Whatley, *Nature* 73, 1132 (1954); L. L. Rosenberg and D. I. Arnon, *J. Biol. Chem.* 217, 361 (1955).
50. O. Warburg and G. Krippahl, *Svensk Kem. Tidskr.* 69, 143 (1957).
51. J. A. Barltrop, P. M. Hayes, M. Calvin, *J. Am. Chem. Soc.* 76, 4348 (1954).
52. J. A. Bassham and M. Calvin, in *Currents in Biochemical Research*, D. E. Green, Ed. (Interscience, New York, 1956), p. 48.
53. R. A. Peters, H. M. Sinclair, R. H. S. Thompson, *Biochem. J.* 40, 516 (1946).
54. I. C. Gunsalus, *J. Cellular Comp. Physiol. Suppl. I* 41, 113 (1953).
55. R. Hill, *Symposia Soc. Exptl. Biol.* 5, 223 (1951).
56. O. Warburg, in *Heavy Metal Prosthetic Groups and Enzyme Action* (Clarendon Press, Oxford, 1949).
57. D. Keilin and E. F. Hartree, *Proc. Roy. Soc. (London)* 129B, 277 (1940).
58. D. E. Green, *Symposia Soc. Exptl. Biol.* 10, 30 (1957).
59. M. G. Stålfelt, *Physiol. Plantarum* 8, 572 (1955); O. V. S. Heath and B. Orchard, *Nature* 180, 180 (1957).
60. W. H. Elliott, *Biochem. J.* 49, 106 (1951); *J. Biol. Chem.* 201, 661 (1953).
61. O. Warburg, W. Schroder, H. W. Gattung, *Z. Naturforsch.* 11b, 654 (1956).
62. F. R. Whatley, M. B. Allen, D. I. Arnon, *Plant Physiol. Suppl.* 32, iii (1957).
63. D. I. Arnon, in *Encyclopedia of Plant Physiology*, W. Ruhland, Ed. (Springer, Heidelberg), in press.
64. F. R. Whatley, M. B. Allen, D. I. Arnon, in preparation.
65. T. P. Singer and E. B. Kearney, *Biochim, et Biophys. Acta* 15, 151 (1954); *Methods of Biochem. Anal.* 4, 307 (1957).
66. M. Mazelis, *Plant Physiol.* 31, 37 (1956).
67. A. San Pietro and H. M. Lang, *J. Biol. Chem.* 227, 483 (1957).
68. M. Avron and A. T. Jagendorf, *Arch. Biochem. Biophys.* 65, 475 (1957).
69. We were aided in this investigation by grants from the U.S. Public Health Service and the Office of Naval Research.
70. R. C. Fuller and E. C. Anderson, *Plant Physiol. Suppl.* 32, xvi (1957).
71. A. I. Oparin, in *Origin of Life* (Macmillan, New York, 1938); H. C. Urey, in *The Planets* (Yale Univ. Press, New Haven, 1952).
72. A. V. Trebst and D. I. Arnon, unpublished data.

The Isolation of Morphologically Intact Mitochondria from Rat Liver*

George H. Hogeboom
Walter C. Schneider†
George E. Palade

From the Laboratories of
The Rockefeller Institute
for Medical Research,
New York

In previous communications it was reported that the respiratory enzyme systems, cytochrome oxidase and succinoxidase, were associated, probably exclusively, with the "large granule" fraction isolated by differential centrifugation either from water homogenates (1) or from saline extracts (2) of rat liver. The identification of the components making up the large granule fraction presented an important and difficult problem. Microscopical examination of the fraction prepared in isotonic saline revealed the presence of spherical bodies ranging between 0.5 to 2μ in diameter. The corresponding preparation obtained from a water homogenate of liver contained much larger and paler spheres. It was suggested, mainly on the basis of a comparison of the size of the isolated granules with that of known cellular inclusions, that the large granule fraction consisted mostly of mitochondria (2, 3). It was realized, however, that this evidence was not conclusive proof for the hypothesis that large granules were mitochondria, since the isolated large granules did not possess the generally accepted properties of mitochondria, namely, a rod-like shape and the ability to stain vitally with Janus green.

Subsequent investigations showed that isotonic saline solutions were undesirable media for reasons other than the above cytological considerations, in that sodium chloride, as well as certain other electrolytes, caused agglutination of large

Reprinted from *Proceedings of the Society for Experimental Biology and Medicine* **65**, 320–21 (1947), by permission of Walter C. Schneider and the publisher.

granules. This agglutination was reflected in the finding that irregular and usually great amounts of succinoxidase activity were sedimented during the removal, by low-speed centrifugation, of nuclei from saline homogenates. When water was used as the medium, no agglutination was visible, and the loss of succinoxidase in the nuclear fraction was much less.

The question whether the respiratory enzymes are actually associated with mitochondria was thus resolved into the search for a medium that would preserve the morphological and cytological characteristics of mitochondria and permit their isolation in good yields. It was found initially that agglutination did not occur in homogenates prepared in isotonic sucrose (0.25 M). Further studies of the effect of sucrose at different concentrations led to the surprising observation that as the concentration in a series of homogenates was increased, an increasing proportion of the large granules were distinctly rod-like in shape, until at a concentration of 0.80–1.0 M sucrose they could not be distinguished morphologically from the mitochondria of the living cell.

The isolation of morphologically intact mitochondria was effected as follows. Rat liver was homogenized in an all-glass apparatus (4) in 0.88 M sucrose (final liver concentration was 1.0 g in 10 ml homogenate). Free nuclei and residual intact cells were first removed completely by centrifuging the homogenate 3 times at 600 × gravity for 10 minutes. Centrifugation of the supernatant for 20 minutes at 24,000 × gravity resulted in sedimentation of all the free mitochondria, together with a small number of "microsomes" (3). The latter remained in the supernatant when the mitochondria were resuspended in 0.88 M sucrose and resedimented at 24,000 × gravity. Resuspension of this final sediment in 0.88 M sucrose yielded a distinctly yellowish preparation that showed pronounced birefringence of flow and was made up of mitochondria that had retained their original rod-like shape. The washed mitochondria were readily stained with Janus green at a dye concentration of 1/20,000, perceptibly stained at a dye concentration of 1/40,000, and remained morphologically stable in 0.88 M sucrose over a period of several days when kept at 4°C. No extraneous elements could be seen either in preparations stained with Janus green or in preparations fixed with osmium tetroxide and examined at high magnification in the electron microscope. In several experiments, the suspensions of washed mitochondria isolated by this procedure were found to contain 70 to 80% of the succinoxidase activity of the original liver homogenate, the remainder of the enzyme activity being present in the mixture of nuclei and unbroken cells sedimented by the preliminary low-speed centrifugations.

Of some interest is the fact that results obtained with rat kidney homogenates in sucrose solutions paralleled those described above for liver. Furthermore, the morphological alteration of mitochondria within unbroken liver or kidney cells present in homogenates, a phenomenon that occurred very rapidly in isotonic saline or 0.25 M sucrose, was progressively delayed as the concentration of sucrose was increased. In 0.88 M sucrose homogenates, the unbroken cells retained a normal appearance for hours. A possible explanation for the latter finding and for the preservation by concentrated sucrose solutions of mitochondria freed by cell rupture is that the intracellular osmotic pressure at the mitochondrial membrane may be considerably higher than the blood osmotic pressure.

Introduced by J. B. Murphy

REFERENCES AND NOTES

* Aided in part by a grant from the American Cancer Society on the recommendation of the Committee on Growth of the National Research Council.

† Fellow of the Jane Coffin Childs Memorial Fund for Medical Research.

1. W. C. Schneider, *J. Biol. Chem.* **165**, 585 (1946).

2. G. H. Hogeboom, A. Claude, R. D. Hotchkiss, *J. Biol. Chem.* **165**, 615 (1946).

3. A. Claude, *J. Exp. Med.* **84**, 51, 61 (1946).

4. V. R. Potter and C. A. Elvehjem, *J. Biol. Chem.* **114**, 495 (1936).

The Mitochondrion and Biochemical Machines

MITOCHONDRIA OR THEIR EQUIVALENTS ARE THE PRINCIPAL ENERGY TRANSDUCERS IN ALL AEROBIC ORGANISMS

D. E. Green
Y. Hatefi*

University of Wisconsin

Living systems are capable of effecting a wide variety of energy transformations. Even the less-than-complete list of such transformations provided in Table 1 shows that nature has experimented successfully with a considerable number of transducing possibilities. These transformations or transductions of energy are accomplished by highly specialized and complex biochemical systems which can best be described as machines. There is often a reluctance on the part of biologists to speak of parts of living systems as machines because of the connotation of mechanical principles. But if a machine is looked upon merely as a structured device for converting energy from one form to another regardless of the details of mechanism, there need be no objection to the designation of biological transducing systems as machines.

Rarely is there one giant transducing machine in living systems; rather, there are assemblies of many small, identical machines arranged in parallel and in series. To the extent that our present knowledge permits any conclusions, it would appear that the mechanism of biological transducing machines has to be sought at the molecular level. That is to say, the transduction process takes place

Reprinted from *Science* 133, 13–19 (January 6, 1961), by permission of D. E. Green and *Science*. Copyright 1961 by the American Association for the Advancement of Science.

at the level of a single molecule or macromolecule. Indeed, there is now a growing body of knowledge about some of the molecules which are specialized for implementing a particular transduction (see Table 2). In a sense, biochemical machines may be looked upon as structured devices in which the transducing action of specialized molecules is facilitated or made possible. The structure is designed, as it were, for the optimum performance of the molecular transducer, and the structure has to be explained and interpreted from the standpoint of the physicochemical requirements or necessities of the transducing molecules.

Thus, the study of cellular machines is in essence topological enzymology. Function and structure are inextricably intertwined. Before the enzymology (in the sense of catalytic function) can be meaningful, there has to be an adequate and precise biochemical description of the structure of a given machine.

When we say that the transduction takes place at the level of a single molecule, it is implied that the transducing substance accepts energy in one form and transmits or stores energy in another form. For example, retinene (1) is photochemically transformed to a *trans*-isomer and is thus the molecular instrument for converting radiant energy to some form of chemical energy. Actomyosin (2) undergoes either molecular modification in size and shape or positional displacement when acted upon by adenosine triphosphate, thus serving as a molecular instrument for converting chemical energy to mechanical energy. Chlorophyll (3) is the molecular device for converting radiant energy into some as yet undefined form of chemical energy. Thus the operation of cellular machines must involve the integration of the performance of many hundreds or thousands of transducing molecules.

The key problems posed by biochemical machines are covered by the following questions: What are the component parts? How are they

TABLE 1

Biological Transductions.

Energy transduction	Biological transducing system
Sonic to electrical energy	Ear
Radiant to electrical energy	Eye
Mechanical to electrical energy	Skin
Chemical to electrical energy	Nerve
Radiant to chemical energy	Chloroplast
Chemical to radiant energy	Luminescing organisms (firefly)
Chemical to osmotic energy	Kidney, cell membrane
Chemical to mechanical energy	Muscle
Chemical to sonic energy	Vocal cords
Chemical to electrical energy	Electric organs in electric fish
Oxidative to utilizable chemical energy	Mitochondrion

arranged? Which components are the molecular energy transducers and how do they work? In this article we try to give a bird's eye view of the state of progress in the study of one cellular machine—namely, the mitochondrion. The experience which is being gathered in the study of this machine may well be a guide to the problems and pitfalls which can attend exploration of other cellular machines.

FUNCTION OF THE MITOCHONDRIAL SYSTEM

Aerobic cells of animals and plants contain a subcellular body of characteristic shape, size, structure, and staining properties, known as the mitochondrion (4) which serves as the principal generator of chemical energy in utilizable form (5). The corresponding particle in microorganisms (6) is functionally and chemically very similar to the mitochondrion, but it is generally of smaller size.

The universal function of all mitochondria or their structural equivalents in bacteria is to couple the aerobic oxidation of some substance (usually pyruvic acid) to the synthesis of adenosine triphosphate (ATP) from adenosine diphosphate (ADP) and inorganic phosphate. That is to say, these are devices for liberating chemical energy by oxidation and converting or harnessing this energy in the form of the bond energy of ATP (7). In general, the oxidation of pyruvic acid to CO_2 and H_2O by way of the citric acid cycle is the principal, if not the only, oxidative process involved. For each of the five atoms of oxygen used up in the oxidation of one molecule of pyruvic acid, three molecules of ATP are synthesized from ADP and inorganic phosphate. In other words, the

TABLE 2

Components Involved in Biological Transductions.

Component	Transducing system
Retinene 1 and 2	Eye (retina)
Rod opsin	Eye
Cone opsin	Eye
Chlorophyll	Chloroplast
Cytochrome f	Chloroplast
Cytochromes	Mitochondria
Coenzyme Q	Mitochondria
Flavin	Mitochondria
DPN	Mitochondria
Myosin	Muscle
Actomyosin	Muscle
ATP	Muscle
Luciferin	Firefly (*Photinus pyralis*)
Luciferase	Firefly
ATP	Firefly

complete combustion of one molecule of pyruvic acid to CO_2 and H_2O leads to the synthesis of 15 molecules of ATP (8).

Mitochondria can oxidize substances other than members of the citric acid cycle. Some of these substances, such as fatty acids (9) or amino acids (10) ultimately give rise to members of the citric acid cycle, while other substances, such as α-glycerophosphate (11) and β-hydroxybuty-rate (12), have no direct connection at all with the citric cycle. In bacteria even inorganic substances can be oxidized by the particles concerned with terminal respiration (13). The universal element in all mitochondria is the coupling of oxidation to synthesis of ATP — that is, oxidative phosphorylation. The variable element can be the nature of the substances oxidized.

In addition to the basic coupling function, some, but not all, mitochondria catalyze various ATP-dependent synthetic processes, such as synthesis of phospholipid (14), protein (15), hippuric acid (16), and citrulline (17). These are secondary mitochondrial functions which apparently are not involved in the exercise of the primary coupling function.

The terminal electron transport system is one of the invariant universals of aerobic living systems. Whether isolated from heart muscle, *Azobacter,* or mung beans, its basic function is the same; it contains essentially the same catalytic components and exhibits similar, if not identical, structural patterns in all three cases. There is certainly no evidence of convergent evolution as a factor in the development of the mitochondrial system in animals, plants, and microorganisms. It would appear that once the problem of coupling electron flow to ATP synthesis had been solved in a particular fashion early in evolutionary history, no major modification in the underlying principles was introduced thereafter.

MITOCHONDRIAL FORM
AND STRUCTURE

Mitochondria of animal and plant sources share a characteristic form and organization (4) (see the idealized representation in Fig. 1). The

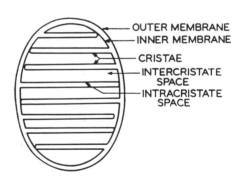

OUTER MEMBRANE
INNER MEMBRANE
CRISTAE
INTERCRISTATE SPACE
INTRACRISTATE SPACE

FIGURE 1.   Idealized structure of the mitochondrion.

long dimension of the rod-shaped mitochondrion may be greater than 10 microns or less than 1 micron, depending upon the source. Surrounding the mitochondrion is an envelope with a double-membrane structure. Within the mitochondrion there is an array of double-membrane structures which usually are at right angles to the long axis of the particle and which may be looked upon as invaginations of the inner membrane of the envelope. These internal structures are known as cristae. External and internal membrane systems form one continuous network. The light area between the electron-dense, twin membranes of cristae and envelope probably is the locus of the internal fluid medium of the mitochondrion. If this is the case, it follows that the internal medium would bathe all the membrane structures of the mitochondrion, and furthermore, that the structured elements would interpose a mechanical barrier to the flow of solutes and solvents either from the external medium inwards or from the internal medium outwards. Thus, there are barriers within barriers which interdict the free flow of substances between the mitochondrion and the external milieu.

The mitochondria of heart muscle are packed with cristae, while those of liver contain relatively few. The greater the number of cristae per unit area, the greater the oxidative rate of the mitochondrion and the fewer are the accessory enzymatic activities — that is, activities other than or unconnected with the primary mitochondrial function. Liver mitochondria surpass all others in wealth of auxiliary functions, and this wealth is accompanied by a low density of cristae in the mitochondrion.

Sonic vibrations comminute mitochondria to much smaller particles which no longer show mitochondrial form and which represent fragments of the mitochondrial cristae and envelope (*18, 19*). Some important correlations have been found between the structure of these derivative particles and the extent to which the original mitochondrial functions are preserved. Let us consider only the three basic functions: citric cycle oxidations, oxidative phosphorylation, and electron transport. As soon as mitochondrial form disappears, the capacity for implementing the complete citric cycle is lost. But as long as the derivative particle retains double membrane structure, even though mitochondrial form has been lost, the capacity for coupling oxidation to synthesis of ATP can be preserved. Finally, when the comminution produces a particle with a single membrane structure, then only the capacity for electron transport is retained. The particle with an intact electron transport chain but lacking the coupling capacity is referred to in our laboratory as the electron transport particle, or ETP (*20*), whereas the comparable particle with coupling capacity is known as ETP_H (*19*) (Fig. 2).

Thus, mitochondrial function can be eliminated or whittled down seriatim, and by similar tactics the structure of the mitochondrion can be reduced in complexity step by step. This technique of seriatim degradation and modification has proved to be the solution to the dilemma of studying a system too complex for direct analysis.

FIGURE 2.   Schematic representation of reactions catalyzed by mitochondria versus ETP_H versus ETP.

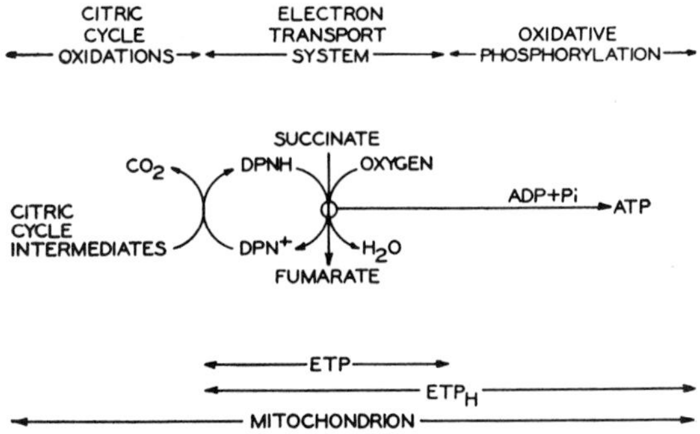

MITOCHONDRION AS A
COMPLETE ENZYMIC UNIT

It cannot be emphasized too strongly that the mitochondrion, when properly isolated, contains the complete repertoire of enzymes, coenzymes, and cofactors required for implementing its wide spectrum of catalytic activities (21). Moreover, the relative proportions of these many components are of a comparable order of magnitude and appear to be fixed. Thus, without any supplementation the mitochondrion is a complete operational unit, in which all the component parts in the proper proportions are fitted together.

Enzymes which are localized outside the mitochondrion are not found in the mitochondrion. That is to say, only enzymes pertinent to the exercise of mitochondrial function are present in any significant amount in the mitochondrion. There is thus no encouragement for the idea that the mitochondrion is a random, heterogeneous particle in which each of a large number of miscellaneous enzymes becomes occluded. On the contrary, the weight of evidence supports the view of the mitochondrion as a highly precise, organized mosaic of a strictly determined number of enzymes and coenzymes arranged in a repeating and invariant pattern.

UNIT OF MITOCHONDRIAL
FUNCTION

Let us consider only one parameter of mitochondrial function — the electron transport chain, or at least that segment thereof which includes all the catalysts between reduced diphosphopyridine nucleotide (DPNH) or succinate at one end and oxygen at the other end. What is the smallest common denominator for the exercise of electron transport?

The mitochondrion, or at least the structured portion thereof, may be looked upon as a polymer of several thousand monomeric repeating units each of which contains a complete electron transport chain as defined above. In theory, then, it should be possible to comminute the electron transport particle to a size which would accommodate only a single unit. Sonic fragmentation of ETP leads to the formation of particles of very small dimensions. This may be a strong indication for the existence of such units. On the other hand, the smallest unit that can couple electron transport to the synthesis of ATP is more complex than the unit which is limited to the exercise only of the electron transport function. The minimal requirement for a particle to exercise the coupling function appears to be double membrane structure.

We may interpret this in the following way. Coupling requires a group of enzymes and factors other than those of the electron transport chain. To conserve these auxiliary enzymes, or perhaps to facilitate their action, it is necessary to have, in effect, a tube with the two ends sealed off to prevent excessive leakage out of the loosely held components in the interior. According to this interpretation, the unit for coupling is merely the unit for electron transport supplemented with a group of easily detachable factors. The double-membrane arrangement may just ensure this close association of the particulate electron transport unit with the complex of enzymes and factors essential for the coupling process.

In the same way, the loss of the capacity for citric cycle oxidations which attends the comminution of mitochondria may be a consequence merely of damage to the cristae and the subsequent leaching out of enzymes and cofactors from the interior of the cristae. In fact, when supplemented with the appropriate enzymes, ETP or ETP_H can carry out the complete citric cycle.

Thus, we may think of the electron transport chain as the ultimate unit. When separated from the milieu of the crista, it is restricted to the electron transport process. When supplemented with some of the cofactors and enzymes, it can couple electron flow to synthesis of ATP, as in ETP_H, and when supplemented with all the enzymes and cofactors, it can couple the oxidations of the citric cycle to synthesis of ATP, as in the mitochondrion.

STRATEGY FOR STUDY OF
MITOCHONDRIAL FUNCTION

By virtue of the complexity (both structural and functional) of the mitochondrion, observations of a gross character cannot penetrate very deeply its underlying chemical and physical principles. The strategy has been to trim down the mitochondrion to a point where the complexity is more manageable (22). In practice this has meant that the starting point for structural and functional studies has been not the mitochondrion but the less complex particle, ETP. Two of the three main facets of mitochondrial function—namely, citric cycle oxidations and the coupling of electron flow to synthesis of ATP—have been set aside, and experimental emphasis has been placed on the elucidation of the electron transport chain. Without a precise knowledge of the electron transport chain it would be difficult to decipher the principles underlying coupling. Once the chain is defined, the road will be clear to achieve this objective.

There is the obvious danger that when the electron transport process is no longer coupled to synthesis of ATP it may not faithfully represent the counterpart process which operates in a coupled system. This possibility has been examined, and it appears that the same electron transport process operates whether coupling takes place or not, in the sense that the sequence of components and the nature of the oxido-reductions are the same. Certain oxidoreductions can take place either with or without phosphate esterification, but there does not seem to be an essential qualitative difference between coupled and uncoupled electron transport processes (23).

SEQUENCE OF COMPONENTS IN THE CHAIN

The electron transport particle (ETP) catalyzes the oxidation of succinate to fumarate and of DPNH to DPN+ by molecular oxygen. Involved in these oxidations are two flavoprotein dehydrogenases (24, 25), four cytochromes (26–28), iron (29) (in a form other than that of porphyrin-bound iron), copper (29, 30), and a benzoquinone derivative known as coenzyme Q (31, 32).

Electrons originating from either succinate or DPNH are transferred eventually to oxygen through a chain involving the cytochromes, co-enzyme Q, nonheme iron, and copper. Our present state of knowledge about the sequence of components in the chain is summarized in Figure 3. Although the idea of a single chain from coenzyme Q to oxygen is more generally accepted, several pieces of information are more consistent with the concept of two interconnecting chains, one for succinic flavoprotein dehydrogenase (f_S) and one for DPNH flavoprotein dehydrogenase (f_D). The bracket in the figure is used to indicate this possibility. Like coenzyme Q, cytochrome b is situated between the flavoproteins and cytochrome c_1. However, its position relative to coenzyme Q is not clear (33).

COMPONENTS OF THE ELECTRON TRANSPORT CHAIN

The two flavoprotein dehydrogenases (succinic and DPNH dehydrogenase) as well as the four cytochromes are proteins which have now been isolated in homogeneous state and defined with respect to molecular weight, spectrum, prosthetic group, and gross composition (see Table 3). Coenzyme Q is not found in close association with any of the six proteins and can be readily extracted and isolated as a crystalline product of molecular weight 863.4 (32, 34).

The succinic dehydrogenase (f_S) (24) and DPNH dehydrogenase (f_D) (25) are both flavoprotein enzymes. The flavin prosthetic group of f_D is

FIGURE 3.   Sequence of components in the electron transport system.

SUCCINATE→FLAVOPROTEIN(f_S)

COENZYME Q

CYTOCHROME $\underline{b}$ →CYT. $\underline{c}_I$→CYT. $\underline{c}$→CYT. $\underline{a}$→O_2

DPNH→FLAVOPROTEIN (f_D)

ELECTRON TRANSPORT SYSTEM

flavinadenine dinucleotide, while that of f_S is a dinucleotide as yet uncharacterized. The flavin group is readily split off by acid from the protein of f_D but not from the protein of f_S, and this difference in behavior is the basis of the method for estimating the proportion of f_S and f_D in a mixture. According to Kearney (35), the flavin prosthetic group of f_S is linked to the protein by a peptide bond which can be ruptured by proteolytic enzymes. Nonheme iron appears to be closely associated with both f_S and f_D in the ratio of at least four atoms of iron per molecule of flavin.

The four cytochromes are hemoproteins which differ in respect to both the protein and heme moieties. The heme group of cytochrome b (36) is protohemin, while that of cytochrome a is a heme derivable from protohemin by replacement of three of the ring substituents with a formyl group and two long-chain carbon residues (37). The heme group of cytochromes c and c_1 is also protohemin, but the heme group of cytochrome c (and probably that of cytochrome c_1) is attached to cysteine residues in the apoprotein by thiol ether links (36). The heme groups of cytochromes a and b are readily extracted from the respective apoproteins

TABLE 3

Components of the Electron Transport System.

Component	Minimal molecular weight	Absorption bands (mμ)	Prosthetic group
f_S	~230,000	450 (oxidized)	Flavin dinucleotide of unknown structure
f_D	~70,000	450 (oxidized)	Flavinadenine dinucleotide
Coenzyme Q	863.4	405, 275 (oxidized in ethanol), 290 (reduced)	
Cytochrome a	~110,000	444, 517, 605, 835* (reduced)	a heme
Cytochrome b	~30,000	429, 530, 562 (reduced)	b heme
Cytochrome c_1	~38,000	418, 540, 554 (reduced)	c_1 heme
Cytochrome c	12,000	415, 521, 550 (reduced)	c heme

* *Present only in the oxidized enzyme.*

by acid acetone, whereas the link of the heme groups of cytochromes c and c_1 to the apoproteins is unaffected by this reagent.

Cytochrome b exists in two forms; one of these forms occurs in close association with succinic dehydrogenase (38) while the other can be isolated as a discrete protein with no functional group other than the heme (28). The succinic dehydrogenase has been isolated by Ziegler and Doeg (39) as a soluble complex containing one molecule of b heme per molecule of flavin, and also lipid in the amount of 18 percent by weight. At present, it is not certain whether the same protein moiety is the bearer of all three functional groups (the flavin, nonheme iron, and heme) or whether the succinic dehydrogenase as isolated is a complex of two or more proteins each with a separate prosthetic group, as has been found to be the case for the component proteins of the pyruvic (40, 41) and α-ketoglutaric dehydrogenase (41, 42) complexes.

Cytochromes a and b are isolated as water-insoluble, polymeric particulates. These can be solubilized in water with bile salts and depolymerized to monomers by reagents such as thioglycollate (43) and cetyldimethylethyl ammonium bromide (28). Cytochromes c and c_1 are water-soluble as isolated, but c_1 occurs in polymeric forms (aggregates of six or more molecules) which can be depolymerized to the monomer by reagents such as thioglycollate (27, 44). Cytochromes a and c_1, as isolated at the highest purity level, contain lipid (27, 45) (about 26 and 10 percent, respectively), whereas b and c can be isolated in lipid-free forms. However, cytochrome c can also be shown to exist in the particle in close association with lipid (46).

Cytochrome a is isolated in the form of a hemoprotein which contains copper (47, 48), the molecular ratio of copper to heme being 1:1 (45, 48). This hemoprotein-copper complex catalyzes the oxidation of reduced cytochrome c by molecular oxygen (45, 49, 50).

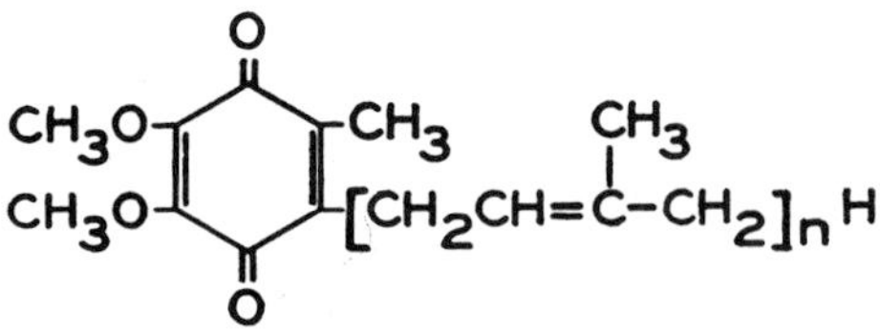

	SOURCE
$n = 10$	BEEF HEART
$n = 9$	RAT, TORULA
$n = 8$	AZOTOBACTER
$n = 7$	TORULA
$n = 6$	SACCHAROMYCES CEREVESIAE

FIGURE 4.   Structure of co-enzymes Q.

Coenzyme Q is a tetrasubstituted benzoquinone with a side chain containing ten isoprenoid units (see Fig. 4) (32, 51). Animal tissues generally contain coenzyme Q_{10} — that is, the coenzyme with a side chain containing ten isoprenoid units — though Q_9 has recently turned out to be the preferred homologue in the tissues of the rat (52). In microorganisms, coenzymes Q_6, Q_7, Q_8, Q_9, and Q_{10} have been found to occur under physiological conditions (32, 53). Coenzyme Q is water-insoluble and is probably solvated in areas of high lipid concentration in the mitochondrion.

STEPWISE FRAGMENTATION OF
THE CHAIN

The sequence of components in the electron transport chain has been deduced from the information obtained by fragmenting the chain into smaller units and determining the composition and the catalytic activity of the derivative segments (see Table 4).

The fragments derived by the cleavage of the mitochondrion or ETP are usually particles, though some of the separation of mixtures of particles which a priori might have been expected to pose a very difficult technical problem has proved to be relatively simple and uncomplicated. The difficulty has been predominantly that of finding the reagent and the conditions which would permit the selective fragmentation of one specific bond. Once this has been achieved, the separation of particles by ultracentrifugation and salt precipitation has been straightforward.

The few reagents which have been found to be efficacious for rupturing the bonds which hold together the components of the chain (see Table 5) are soluble in both water and lipid.

TABLE 4

Subfractions of ETP. In Addition, Cytochromes *b*, *c*, and c_1 and Coenzyme Q Have Been Isolated in Pure Form. Fe, Nonheme Iron; Q, Coenzyme Q; Cyt., Cytochrome.

Enzymic activity of subfraction	*Components*
Succinic dehydrogenase	f_S, Fe
DPNH dehydrogenase	f_D, Fe
Succinic-coenzyme Q reductase	f_S, Fe, cyt. *b*
Succinic-cytochrome *c* reductase	f_S, Fe, Q, cyt. *b*, cyt. c_1
DPNH-cytochrome *c* reductase	f_D, Fe, Q, cyt. *b*, cyt. c_1
Coenzyme Q oxidase	cyt. c_1, cyt. *c*, cyt. *a*, Cu
Cytochrome *c* oxidase	cyt. *a*, Cu

TABLE 5
Fragmenting Reagents.

Cholate	Thioglycollate	Ethanol
Deoxycholate	t-Amyl alcohol	Cetyldimethylethyl ammonium bromide
Duponol	n-Butanol	Triton
		Tweens

LIPID IN RELATION TO MITOCHONDRIAL STRUCTURE AND FUNCTION

Lipid accounts for about 30 percent of the total dry weight of the mitochondrion and of ETP. Recent studies of Fleischer and Klouwen indicate that the composition of the lipid, regardless of the segment of the chain with which it is associated, varies little if at all (54). Phospholipid (55) accounts for the bulk of the lipid (> 90 percent). In addition to coenzyme Q, vitamin E (56), carotenoids (57), and substantial amounts of cholesterol (55) are found in the neutral lipid fraction. The mitochondrial lipids are characterized by fatty acid residues with a high degree of unsaturation (55, 58, 59) and by an unusually high proportion of plasmalogen (55, 59).

Mitochondrial lipid readily assumes, and probably exists, in a state of orientation which, in effect, makes the lipid "soluble" in water (60). This property may be attributed to the phospholipid molecules which constitute the bulk of the mitochondrial lipids. While the role of lipid (except coenzyme Q) in electron transport is far from clear, the close association of lipid with most of the protein components of the chain and its activating effect in some of the catalytic functions of these components (50, 61) are significant indications for the participation of lipid in electron transport and oxidative phosphorylation.

MECHANISM OF ELECTRON FLOW

Electron flow in the mitochondrion or in ETP is an extremely rapid process. Recent studies in our laboratory indicate, for example, that a DPNH oxidase system can be reconstructed from three purified segments [DPNH-cytochrome c reductase (62), cytochrome c, and cytochrome oxidase] and that this system is capable of catalyzing the oxidation of DPNH with a Q_{O_2} of more than 20,000 (20,000 microliters of O_2 per hour per milligram of protein at 38°C).

This rapid flow of electrons does not seem to be the result of simple molecular collision between the components of the electron transport system. The somewhat rigid structure of the electron transport chain does not allow free movement of the electron carriers. The components with larger size, such as the flavoproteins and the cytochromes, seem to be fixed in place and capable of only restricted movement (cytochrome c, which is a homoprotein of relatively small molecular weight, may be an exception). Other components, such as coenzyme Q, nonheme iron, and copper, which have smaller dimensions, facilitate electron transfer between the less mobile carriers.

The sum of the protein contributions by succinic dehydrogenase, DPNH dehydrogenase, and the four cytochromes, as calculated from the purified form of each, represents no more than 25 percent of the total protein of ETP. This is also true for many of the subfractions of ETP. In other words, about 75 percent or more of the protein of ETP cannot be accounted for. Perhaps this excess protein serves a multitude of functions in the mitochondrion which we are as yet unaware of. But it seems that an additional, if not the principal, function of this excess protein is to provide a framework, as it were, for the spatial arrangement of the electron transport components. We may conceive of the electron transport chain as imbedded in a matrix of "framework" proteins and lipid, and the structural arrangement of the unit of the electron transport chain is thus an expression of the close interdigitation of the "framework" proteins with the oxidation-reduction proteins.

It may well be that such an arrangement is common to transducing systems other than the mitochondrion, and the remarkable similarity of the underlying structure of transducing systems suggests that the design of a "framework" protein-lipid continuum has broad applicability (*62a*).

OXIDATIVE PHOSPHORYLATION

Reduced to the most elementary considerations, oxidative phosphorylation may be looked upon as a consequence of three principal reactions, shown in Figure 5. The first reaction is the passage of electrons from a reduced carrier of lower oxidation-reduction potential to an oxidized carrier of higher potential. This process involves a negative free-energy change, which is utilized in converting inorganic phosphate to a so-called "high-energy" organic phosphate (reaction 2). In the third reaction, the "high-energy" phosphoryl group ($\sim P$) is transferred to adenosine diphosphate, resulting in the formation of adenosine triphosphate.

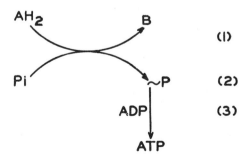

FIGURE 5. Schematic representation of principal reactions in oxidative phosphorylation.

The span in the oxidation-reduction potential ($\Delta E_0'$ at pH 7.0 and 25°C) between DPNH and oxygen is about 1.12 volts and between succinate and oxygen, about 0.8 volt. These values for ΔE correspond to $-\Delta F$ values of about 52,000 and 37,000 calories, respectively. In round numbers, we may say that the synthesis of 1 mole of ATP from ADP and inorganic phosphate requires 12,000 calories (62b). Since the oxidation of 1 mole of DPNH by oxygen is accompanied by the esterification of 3 moles of inorganic phosphate, only about 69 percent of the total free energy change involved in the oxidation is recovered in the form of the bond energy of ATP. The oxidation of succinate by oxygen shows a P/O ratio of 2, which would correspond to about 65 percent efficiency of conversion of oxidation energy to phosphate bond energy.

The experiments of Loomis and Lipmann (63), Copenhaver and Lardy (64), Nielsen and Lehninger (65), Slater (66), and Maley and Lardy (67), as well as those of Chance and Williams (68) and Chance et al. (69), have shown that the phosphorylation occurs in three separate segments of the electron transport chain. These segments are responsible for the following oxidoreductions:

$$\text{DPNH} \longrightarrow \text{flavoprotein}$$
$$\text{flavoprotein} \longrightarrow \text{cytochrome } c$$
$$\text{and cytochrome } c \longrightarrow \text{oxygen}$$

Since these early studies were carried out, a new member of the chain — namely, coenzyme Q — has been discovered. With a better knowledge of the components involved between flavoprotein and cytochrome c, it may now be possible to define more accurately the segment concerned with the second phosphorylation.

Oxidative phosphorylation as a physiological mechanism for the recovery of useful energy was first realized by Kalckar in 1937 (70) (see also 71). It may seem to have taken too long to get where we are today in our understanding of the mechanism of electron transport and oxidative phosphorylation. Admittedly, we do not know all the answers yet, but we know most of the questions that remain to be answered, and we can ask them in great detail (72).

REFERENCES AND NOTES

* The authors are affiliated with the Institute for Enzyme Research of the University of Wisconsin, Madison. Dr. Green is codirector of the institute and Dr. Hatefi is an assistant professor.

1. G. Wald and R. Hubbard in *The Enzymes*, P. D. Boyer, H. Lardy, K. Myrbäck, Eds. (Academic Press, New York, 1960), III, pt. B, 369.

2. A. Szent-Györgyi, *Chemistry of Muscular Contraction* (Academic Press, New York, 1951); J. Hanson and H. E. Huxley, *Symposia Soc. Exptl. Biol.* 9, 228 (1955); M. F. Morales and J. Botts, *Arch. Biochem. Biophys.* 37, 283 (1952); M. F. Morales in *Enzymes: Units of Biological Structure and Function* (Academic Press, New York, 1956), p. 325.

3. H. Gaffron, A. H. Brown, C. S. French, R. Livingston, E. I. Rabinowitch, B. L. Strehler, N. E. Tolbert, Eds., *Research in Photosynthesis* (Interscience, New York, 1957); D. I. Arnon, *Science* **122**, 9 (1955); M. Calvin, *Revs. Modern Phys.* **31**, 147 (1959).

4. G. E. Palade, *Anat. Record* **114**, 427 (1952); *J. Histochem. and Cytochem.* **1**, 188 (1953); in *Enzymes: Units of Biological Structure and Function* (Academic Press, New York, 1956), p. 185; F. S. Sjöstrand in *Fine Structure of Cells: Symposium, Eighth Congress on Cellular Biology, Leyden, 1954* (Interscience, New York, 1955), pp. 16, 222; F. S. Sjöstrand, *Revs. Modern Phys.* **31**, 301 (1959).

5. L. Ernster and O. Lindberg, *Ann. Rev. Physiol.* **20**, 13 (1958); O. Lindberg and L. Ernster, *The Chemistry and Physiology of Mitochondria and Microsomes* (Springer, Vienna, 1954).

6. S. Mudd, L. C. Winterscheid, E. D. Delamater, H. J. Henderson, *J. Bacteriol.* **62**, 459 (1951); S. Mudd, A. F. Brodie, L. C. Winterscheid, P. E. Hartman, E. H. Buetner, R. A. McLean, *ibid.* **62**, 729 (1951).

7. No distinction is being made between biological transducers which convert energy from one type to another and transducers which convert chemical energy from one type to another.

8. S. Ochoa, *J. Biol. Chem.* **151**, 493 (1943).

9. A. L. Grafflin and D. E. Green, *ibid.* **176**, 95 (1948); W. C. Schneider and V. R. Potter, *ibid.* **177**, 893 (1949); A. L. Lehninger and E. P. Kennedy, *ibid.* **179**, 957, (1949).

10. J. V. Taggart and R. B. Krakaur, *ibid.* **177**, 641 (1949); J. L. Still, M. V. Buell, D. E. Green, *Arch. Biochem.* **26**, 406 (1950); ———, *ibid.* **26**, 413 (1950).

11. R. L. Ringler and T. P. Singer, *J. Biol. Chem.* **234**, 2211 (1959).

12. D. E. Green, J. G. Dewan, L. F. Leloir, *Biochem. J.* **31**, 934 (1937); A. L. Lehninger, H. C. Sudduth, J. B. Wise, *J. Biol. Chem.* **235**, 2450 (1960).

13. S. Taniguchi, R. Sato, F. Egami, in *Inorganic Nitrogen Metabolism*, W. D. McElroy and B. Glass, Eds. (The Johns Hopkins Press, Baltimore, 1956), p. 87; M. Ishimoto, J. Koyama, Y. Nagai, *J. Biochem. (Tokyo)* **41**, 763 (1954).

14. E. P. Kennedy, *J. Am. Chem. Soc.* **75**, 249 (1953); ——— and H. M. Bergoff, *J. Biol. Chem.* **201**, 393 (1953).

15. H. M. Bates, V. M. Craddock, M. V. Simpson, *J. Biol. Chem.* **235**, 140 (1960).

16. P. P. Cohen and R. W. McGilvery, *ibid.* **166**, 261 (1946); N. K. Sarkar, H. Beinert, M. Fuld, D. E. Green, *Arch. Biochem.* **37**, 140 (1952).

17. P. P. Cohen and M. Hayano, *J. Biol. Chem.* **170**, 687 (1947).

18. W. McMurry, G. F. Maley, H. Lardy, *ibid.* **230**, 219 (1958); W. W. Kielley and J. R. Bronk, *ibid.* **230**, 521 (1958); D. M. Ziegler, A. W. Linnane, D. E. Green, M. S. Dass, H. Ris, *Biochim. et Biophys. Acta* **28**, 524 (1958).

19. A. W. Linnane and D. M. Ziegler, *Biochim. et Biophys. Acta* **29**, 630 (1958).

20. F. L. Crane, J. L. Glenn, D. E. Green, *ibid.* **22**, 475 (1956).

21. D. E. Green, *Biol. Revs. Cambridge Phil. Soc.* **26**, 410 (1951); ——— and J. Järnfelt, *Perspectives in Biol. and Med.* **2**, 163 (1959).

22. D. E. Green, *Harvey Lectures, Ser. 52 (1956–57)* (1958), p. 177.

23. A. W. Linnane and E. B. Titchner, *Biochim. et Biophys. Acta* **39**, 469 (1960).

24. T. P. Singer and E. B. Kearney in *Methods of Biochemical Analysis*, D. Glick, Ed. (Interscience, New York, 1957), IV, 312.

25. B. De Bernard, *Biochim. et Biophys. Acta* **23**, 510 (1957); D. M. Ziegler, D. E. Green, K. A. Doeg, *J. Biol. Chem.* **234**, 1916 (1959).

26. D. Keilin and E. F. Hartree, *Nature* **176**, 200 (1955); E. Yakushiji and K. Okunuki, *Proc. Imp. Acad. (Tokyo)* **16**, 299 (1940); ———, *ibid.* **27**, 263 (1941); D. Keilin, *Proc. Roy. Soc. (London)* **98B**, 312 (1925); I. Sekuzu and K. Okunuki, *J. Biochem. (Tokyo)* **43**, 107 (1956).

27. D. E. Green, J. Järnfelt, H. D. Tisdale, *Biochim. et Biophys. Acta* **31**, 34 (1959); *ibid.* **38**, 160 (1960).

28. R. Bomstein, R. Goldberger, H. Tisdale, *Biochem. Biophys. Research Comm.* **2**, 234 (1960).

29. D. E. Green in *Enzymes: Units of Biological Structure and Function* (Academic Press, New York, 1956), p. 465; F. L. Crane, J. L. Glenn, D. E. Green, *Biochim. et Biophys. Acta* **22**, 475 (1956).

30. B. Eichel, W. W. Wanio, P. Person, S. J. Cooperstein, *J. Biol. Chem.* **183**, 89 (1950).

31. F. L. Crane, Y. Hatefi, R. L. Lester, C. Widmer, *Biochim. et Biophys. Acta* **25**, 220 (1957); Y. Hatefi, R. L. Lester, F. L. Crane, C. Widmer, *ibid.* **31**, 490 (1959); R. A. Morton, *Nature* **182**, 1764 (1958).

32. R. L. Lester, Y. Hatefi, C. Widmer, F. L. Crane, *Biochim. et Biophys. Acta* **33**, 169 (1959).

33. Y. Hatefi, P. Jurtshuk, A. G. Haavik, in preparation.

34. F. L. Crane, R. L. Lester, C. Widmer, Y. Hatefi, *Biochim. et Biophys. Acta* **32**, 73 (1959).

35. E. B. Kearney, *J. Biol. Chem.* **235**, 865 (1960).

36. K. G. Paul in *The Enzymes*, P. D. Boyer, H. Lardy, K. Myrbäck, Eds. (Academic Press, New York, 1960), III, pt. B, 277.

37. M. Morrison, J. Connelly, J. Petix, E. Stotz, *J. Biol. Chem.* **235**, 1202 (1960).

38. K. A. Doeg, S. Krueger, D. M. Ziegler, *Biochim. et Biophys. Acta* **41**, 491 (1960).

39. D. M. Ziegler and K. A. Doeg, *Biochem. Biophys. Research Comm.* **1**, 344 (1959).

40. V. Jagannathan and R. S. Schweet, *J. Biol. Chem.* **196**, 551 (1952); R. S. Schweet, B. Katchman, R. M. Bock, V. Jagannathan, *ibid.* **196**, 563 (1952).

41. I. C. Gunsalus, in *The Mechanism of Enzyme Action*, W. D. McElroy and B. Glass, Eds. (The Johns Hopkins Press, Baltimore, 1954), p. 545.

42. D. R. Sanadi, J. W. Littlefield, R. M. Bock, *J. Biol. Chem.* **197**, 851 (1952); D. R. Sanadi, M. Langley, R. L. Searls, *ibid.* **234**, 178 (1959); D. R. Sanadi, M. Langley, F. White, *ibid.* **234**, 183 (1959); V. Massey, *Biochim. et Biophys. Acta* **32**, 286 (1959); M. Koike, L. J. Reed, W. R. Carroll, *J. Biol. Chem.* **235**, 1924 (1960); M. Koike and L. J. Reed, *J. Biol. Chem.* **235**, 1931 (1960); M. Koike, P. C. Shah, L. J. Reed, *ibid.* **235**, 1939 (1960).

43. K. S. Ambe and A. Venkataraman, *Biochem. Biophys. Research Comm.* **1**, 133 (1959).

44. R. S. Criddle and R. M. Bock, *ibid.* **1**, 138 (1959).

45. D. E. Griffiths and D. C. Wharton, unpublished studies.

46. C. Widmer and F. L. Crane, *Biochim. et Biophys. Acta* **27**, 203 (1958).

47. C. V. Wende and W. W. Wainio, *J. Biol. Chem.* **235**, PC11 (1960); S. Takemori, I. Sekuzu, K. Okunuki, *Biochim. et Biophys. Acta* **38**, 158 (1960).

48. R. H. Sands and H. Beinert, *Biochem. Biophys. Research Comm.* **1**, 175 (1959).

49. D. Keilin and E. F. Hartree, *Nature* **141**, 870 (1938); L. Smith and E. Stotz, *J. Biol. Chem.* **209**, 819 (1954); K. Okunuki, I. Sekuzu, T. Yonetani, S. Takemori, *J. Biochem. (Tokyo)* **45**, 847 (1958).

50. Y. Hatefi, *Biochim. et Biophys. Acta* 30, 648 (1959).

51. R. A. Morton, G. M. Wilson, J. S. Lowe, W. M. F. Leat, *Chem. & Ind. (London)* 1957, 1649 (1957); D. E. Wolf, C. H. Hoffman, N. R. Trenner, B. H. Arison, C. H. Shunk, B. O. Linn, J. F. McPherson, K. Folkers, *J. Am. Chem. Soc.* 80, 4752 (1958).

52. R. E. Olson and G. H. Dialameh, *Biochem. Biophys. Research Comm.* 2, 198 (1960); D. E. M. Lawson, E. I. Mercer, J. Glover, R. A. Morton, *Biochem. J.* 74, 38P (1960).

53. R. L. Lester, F. L. Crane, Y. Hatefi, *J. Am. Chem. Soc.* 80, 4751 (1958).

54. S. Fleischer and H. Klouwen, unpublished studies.

55. R. E. Basford, *Biochim. et Biophys. Acta* 33, 195 (1959).

56. A. Nason and I. R. Lehman, *J. Biol. Chem.* 222, 511 (1956); J. Bouman and E. C. Slater, *Biochim. et Biophys. Acta* 26, 624 (1957).

57. F. L. Crane, R. L. Lester, C. Widmer, Y. Hatefi, *Biochim. et Biophys. Acta* 32, 73 (1959).

58. R. T. Holman and C. Widmer, *J. Biol. Chem.* 234, 2269 (1959).

59. E. V. Marinetti, J. Erbland, J. Kochen, E. Stotz, *ibid.* 233, 740 (1958); G. D. Joel, M. L. Karnovsky, E. G. Ball, O. Cooper, *ibid.* 233, 1565 (1958).

60. S. Fleischer and H. Kouwen, *Federation Proc.* 19, 33 (1960).

61. W. W. Wainio and J. Greenlees, *Science* 128, 87 (1958); Y. Hatefi, *Biochim. et Biophys. Acta* 34, 183 (1959).

62. Y. Hatefi, A. G. Haavik, P. Jurtshuk, in preparation.

62a. H. Fernández-Morán, *Revs. Modern Phys.* 31, 319 (1959).

62b. L. L. Ingraham and A. B. Pardee in *Metabolic Pathways,* D. M. Greenberg, Ed. (Academic Press, New York, 1960), I, 1.

63. W. F. Loomis and F. Lipmann, *J. Biol. Chem.* 179, 503 (1949).

64. J. H. Copenhaver, Jr., and H. A. Lardy, *ibid.* 195, 225 (1952).

65. S. O. Nielsen and A. L. Lehninger, *J. Am. Chem. Soc.* 76, 3860 (1954).

66. E. C. Slater, *Nature* 174, 1143 (1954).

67. G. F. Maley and H. A. Lardy, *J. Biol. Chem.* 210, 903 (1954).

68. B. Chance and G. R. Williams, *ibid.* 217, 383, 395, 409, 429 (1955).

69. B. Chance, G. R. Williams, W. F. Holmes, J. Higgins, *ibid.* 217, 439 (1955).

70. H. Kalckar, *Enzymologia* 2, 47 (1937).

71. _____, *Biochem. J.* 33, 631 (1939); V. A. Belitzer, *Enzymologia* 6, 1 (1939); _____ and E. T. Tsibakowa, *Biokhimiya* 4, 516 (1939).

72. We wish to thank Dr. H. Fernández-Morán, Mixter Laboratories for Electron Microscopy, Massachusetts General Hospital, Boston, for the electron micrograph of the mitochondria of retinal rods and cones shown on the cover. For the techniques of high-resolution electron microscopy used to obtain this micrograph see H. Fernández-Morán, *J. Appl. Phys.* 30, 2038 (1959), *Ann. N.Y. Acad. Sci.* 85, 689 (1960). Dr. Fernández-Morán has also examined preparations of the electron transport particle (ETP) from our laboratory, and has observed a predominant type of particle 150 to 200 Å in diameter with indications of substructure of the order of 15 to 20 Å (private communication).

The Isolation and Biochemical Characterization of the Mitotic Apparatus of Dividing Cells[*]

Daniel Mazia
Katsuma Dan[†]

Department of Zoology,
University of California,
Berkeley

In this communication, the term "mitotic apparatus" (abbreviated MA) will refer to the ensemble of structures constituting the "chromatic" and "achromatic" figures in the classical descriptions of mitosis, e.g., Flemming (*1*), Wilson (2). It includes spindles, asters, centrioles, nuclei (before breakdown) and chromosomal structures (after breakdown of the nuclear membrane). The classical pattern of mitosis describes the coordinated behavior of these elements without implying that they are integrated into a physical entity to which such a term as "mitotic apparatus" could be applied. Our observations, as will be seen, do indicate the existence of just such a physical association of the various elements, permitting their isolation as a single body, and thus the use of the term seems to be justifiable.

Heretofore, the physical and chemical study of the MA has been rendered difficult by the necessity of studying it *in situ*. Most of the earlier information has been adequately summarized by Hughes (3). The most informative avenues of information have been: (*a*) Staining, e.g., Tahmisian and Brues (4), Mazia, Brewer and Alfert (5); (*b*) polarized light studies, e.g., Inoue and Dan (6), Swann (*19*); (*c*) electron microscopy, e.g., Rozsa and Wykcoff (7); (*d*) hydrostatic pressure studies, e.g., Pease (8); (*e*) measurements

Reprinted from *Proceedings of the National Academy of Sciences* 38, 826–38 (1952), by permission of Daniel Mazia and the National Academy of Sciences.

of anaphase movement of chromosomes, Hughes and Swann (9); (f) correlation of dimensional changes of MA with the progress of cytoplasmic division, Dan (10). An enormous literature on the destruction of the MA by antimitotic agents has yielded little insight into its nature. It is evident that the avenues of information have been entirely visual, and that the MA presents exceptional difficulties because it is a structure without a boundary, whose parts are mingled with other cytoplasmic constituents.

In the following we describe methods for isolation of the MA in quantity from populations of dividing sea urchin eggs. The somewhat unorthodox methods described were developed after numerous failures with procedures involving disruption of living eggs. Such procedures sometimes yield the MA from a few individuals.

Danielli (11) reports briefly on experiences in liberating the MA from eggs by osmotic rupture.

A. THE QUANTITY ISOLATION OF THE MA

The instability of the MA is evident in its natural behavior. It is a structure that seems dramatically to differentiate out of seemingly undifferentiated cytoplasm when division is about to take place and to disappear back into the cytoplasm after division is over. Minor disturbances of the dividing cell cause it to disappear reversibly. It therefore appeared that the best approach to isolation was first to stabilize it, preferably by methods subject to biochemical interpretation.

1. Preparation of Material. The eggs of the sea urchins *Strongylocentrotus franciscanus* and *S. purpuratus* were employed. In order to obtain pure MA preparations, it was necessary to remove the fertilization membranes and this was accomplished, before fertilization, by treatment for 10 minutes with a mixture containing 1–2 mg crystalline trypsin and 1–2 mg crystalline chymotrypsin per 100 ml of sea water. The eggs were inseminated, permitted to develop to the desired stage of the first division in rather dilute populations, then concentrated by centrifugation.

2. "Fixation." After trial of numerous procedures it was found that the MA could be preserved by immersion of the eggs in 30 percent ethanol at about −10°C. From the standpoint of protein chemistry, this is not a drastic procedure. Many proteins will be preserved in the native state.

The eggs could be maintained in 30 percent alcohol at −10° for a period of some weeks, but became more and more resistant to the subsequent treatments on prolonged storage.

The subsequent steps in the isolation were not successful if living eggs were used or if much lower or higher concentrations of alcohol were employed. In the first two cases, the MA apparently disintegrated; when stronger alcohol was used, the cytoplasm coagulated. Therefore, the cold

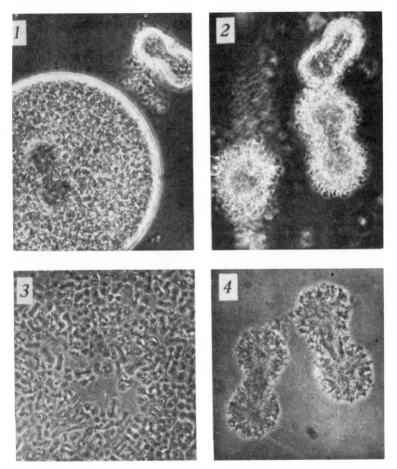

PLATE 1.

FIGURE 1. Mitotic apparatus of *Strongylocentrotus franciscanus* at metaphase. Material "fixed" in sub-zero 30 percent ethanol and dispersed mechanically in water. One MA remains inside unbroken egg, the other is isolated from an egg whose cytoplasm has been dispersed (× 240).

FIGURE 2. Mitotic apparatus isolated by mechanical method at metaphase and later stages. Fibrous structures more clearly shown than in Figure 1 (× 240).

FIGURE 3. Lower power photograph of a mass preparation of MA. Resting nuclei are derived from unfertilized eggs or fertilized eggs whose divisions are retarded (× 60).

FIGURE 4. MA isolated by "high peroxide"–Duponol method. Spindles and cross sections of asters with centrioles are shown. Chromosomes present but not brought out by photograph (× 280).

Figures are photographs of unstained material in water, taken with aid of phase contrast microscope.

alcohol treatment represents a compromise situation where the MA is stabilized without coagulation of the cell contents.‡

3. *Separation of MA.* *(a) Mechanical Method:* Eggs preserved by the above method were suspended in water, placed in a large Luer syringe and rapidly forced through a No. 25 syringe needle. The cytoplasm was largely dispersed, and the MA separated from it. If whole eggs remained, the process was repeated. The MA could then be concentrated by repeated slow centrifugation (Servall SS-1 centrifuge operated at 30 volts), or by sedimentation under gravity, discarding the cytoplasmic granules which remained in the supernatant fluid. Figure 1, Plate 1, shows the appearance of the MA isolated by this method, seen by phase contrast. In this photograph, an isolated MA lies beside an unbroken egg, and the appearance of the MA before and after isolation is evident.

The MA as isolated by this method is rather shrunken, sticky and appears to be contaminated with adhering cytoplasmic material. On close examination, however, the fibrous structure of the spindle region is clearly evident (Fig. 2). If it is an artefact, the artefact results from treatment that is very much milder (from the standpoint of protein chemistry) than the methods of cytological fixation.

The MA prepared by this method may be freed from cytoplasmic particles by washing in alkaline water (pH *ca.* 9).

(b) Solubilization Methods: Considering the possible structure and mechanisms of formation of the MA, an obvious possibility is that it is composed of fibrous proteins which, whether formed by unfolding or by polymerization of corpuscular units, might differ in solubility from other proteins present. In tests with various solubilizing procedures, it was evident that detergents provided a means of dispersing the cell contents, but, with eggs taken from 30 percent alcohol, the MA also dissolved. It seemed possible, from precedents that need not be discussed here, that the establishment of an increased number of S–S bonds might increase the stability of the fibrous MA toward solubilization by detergents, and this proved to be the case.

Briefly, it was found that if the cells, previously preserved in cold 30 percent alcohol, were treated with agents capable of oxidizing –SH groups, the surrounding cytoplasm could simply be dissolved (or, more properly, dispersed) by detergent, leaving the intact MA behind. The agents tested were H_2O_2, I and ferricyanide. All worked, in the sense of making the MA resistant to detergent, but H_2O_2 proved to be best for our purposes because it did not coagulate the cytoplasm. Iodine and ferricyanide rendered the cytoplasm resistant to detergent in the same way as did higher concentration of alcohol or warming; it swelled and became more transparent, but did not disperse into a homogeneous suspension.

A number of detergents was tested, including Nacconol NRSF, Tween, Duponol C, Duponol D, Duponol G, Duponol LS and Duponol ME. Duponol C and Duponol D were finally selected. The former liberated the MA effectively, but in a highly hydrated form that was difficult to observe even in phase contrast. It could be partially dehydrated by addition of electrolyte, but it proved to be more practicable to use Duponol D, a sodium lauryl sulfate preparation containing some electrolyte.

Before describing the details of the method, certain points should be clarified. (1) The cytoplasm is dispersed but not entirely dissolved; a suspension of fine particles is recovered. (2) The isolation of the MA by the selective action of detergent is possible only after previous "fixation" in subzero 30 percent ethanol and treatment with an oxidizing agent. (3) The fact that the treatment with an oxidizing agent produced the desired result does not in itself imply that the reasoning behind the procedure is correct.

While the "fixation" procedure described was essential, its very mildness created a complication. Catalase apparently was not denatured, and when the "fixed" eggs were treated with peroxide a great deal of foaming resulted. Thus the final concentration of peroxide cannot be defined without analysis. Where eggs had been in storage too long, and catalase activity was much reduced, the cytoplasm was correspondingly more resistant to dispersal, and the isolation less successful.

Details of two procedures will be given, which we have termed the "low-peroxide" and "high-peroxide" methods. The difference between the methods tends to support the reasoning underlying their development. After exposure to a low concentration of peroxide, the MA may be isolated by using a small volume of Duponol for a short time, but slowly dissolves in larger amounts of Duponol. After treatment with a higher concentration of peroxide, the MA is isolated only by use of a large amount of detergent for a longer time. The behavior is determined by the amount rather than concentration of detergent, confirming the statement of Putnam (12) that the solubilization of proteins by detergents is a function of weight-to-weight relationships rather than of concentration as such.

(1) "High-Peroxide" Method: The fixed eggs are removed from the cold chamber and immediately mixed with an equal volume of 12–15 percent H_2O_2. There is considerable foaming, but the evolution of oxygen declines as the catalase becomes inactive. The eggs are left in this mixture for 30 minutes at room temperature. In phase contrast, the fibrous elements of the MA appear sharper and more refractile than before treating with H_2O_2. To the mixture, 20–25 volumes of 1–2 percent Duponol D in water are added. The mixture is left at room temperature for 3 hours. The liberation of the MA is aided by stirring, but in any case the cytoplasmic granules spontaneously disperse, leaving the free MA. At the end of the period the MA, which are much heavier, are collected by centrifugation at 500 g for 3 minutes (Servall SS-1 at 30 volts). In cases where undissolved eggs are present (e.g., where process of removal of fertilization membrane was not completely effective) these still heavier bodies may be removed by centrifugation at 500 g for 1 minute. (Times given are periods during which the centrifuge motor was energized, not times at maximum speed.)

The MA preparation is purified by resuspending in water, and centrifuging again in the same way. It is advisable to repeat this at least 3 or 4 times, not only to remove the last granules but also to remove the excess detergent, which forms tactoids at low temperatures and inconveniences observation and analysis. The suspension of MA in water may be stored for several weeks at refrigerator temperatures without drastic changes in morphology.

(2) *"Low-Peroxide" Method:* In this procedure the eggs are placed in an equal volume of 3–4 percent H_2O_2 for 30 minutes at room temperature. To this volume, an equal volume of Duponol D (concentrations ranging from 1 to 2 percent have proved effective) is added. The dispersal of cytoplasm is slower than in a larger volume of Duponol, and vigorous shaking may be employed advantageously without danger of damaging the MA. Following 30 minutes' treatment with Duponol, the MA are separated and washed free of cytoplasmic particles and detergent by the procedure described above.

4. Purity and Yield. Figure 3, Plate 1, shows the appearance of a typical concentrated suspension of MA obtained by the peroxide-detergent methods. Generally there is a slight contamination by cytoplasmic particles, which may be minimized by repeated washing. Close attention has not been paid to yield, but in typical experiments about 10 mg of MA protein was obtained from 10 ml of concentrated eggs, most of which were in metaphase.

B. THE STRUCTURE OF THE
ISOLATED MA

1. Cytological Features. The isolated MA is rather difficult to detect by ordinary microscopic illumination, and all observations and photographs have employed phase contrast microscopy.

The following statements will refer primarily to MA prepared by the peroxide-detergent methods. In general, the MA as isolated conforms in structure to the picture described in the classical cytological observations on sea urchin eggs, e.g., Wilson (*13*). Figure 4, Plate 1, shows several isolated MA from cells in metaphase. The asters, spindles and spindle fibers, and centrioles are evident. The chromosomes also are retained, at least through the earlier stages of isolation, but are rather small and do not appear distinctly in the photographs. The astral rays do not show quite so sharply in Figure 4 because of interference by those oriented along the microscope axis, and are much clearer in Figure 5, which is a similar preparation but slightly compressed.

The synchrony of the division of a population of sea urchin is not perfect, and if, as in all the experiments included in this paper, the cells are collected when the majority are in metaphase, some will be in stages that are earlier or later than this. Cases of earlier stages are clearly evident in Figure 3, Plate 1, since the presence of nuclei with membranes is rather conspicuous. Figure 6 shows a field which contains the MA of a cell with the nuclear membrane remaining and one in telophase. In the former, one sees the growing asters in association with the nucleus. In the latter, it is clear that the asters are larger than in the earlier stages shown in Figures 3 and 4, and near the center of the asters the reconstituting nuclei are seen. An interesting feature of this telophase

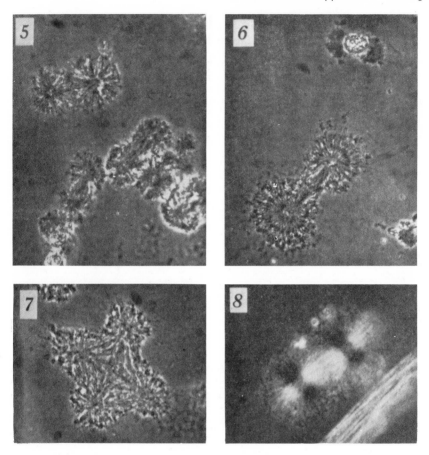

PLATE 2.

FIGURE 5. Preparation similar to Figure 4, but under slight compression to show fibrous structure of asters (× 280).

FIGURE 6. Prophase MA (upper) shows two small astral systems attached to prophase nucleus with intact nuclear membrane. Telophase MA (lower) has a longer spindle and larger asters. Nuclei are reconstituting near centers of asters. Demarcation line at equator of spindle is not an equatorial chromosome plate but the "midbody" ("high peroxide"–Duponol preparation) (× 280).

FIGURE 7. Tetraster spindle derived from polyspermic egg of *S. franciscanus* (× 280).

FIGURE 8. Birefringence picture of isolated MA, showing positive birefringence along fiber axis, as in the living. (Courtesy of Dr. S. Inoue.)

Figures 5–7 are phase contrast photomicrographs.

MA is the suggestion of a plate across the spindle equator, which may correspond to the "midbody" of the classical descriptions — Wilson (*2, 13*).

The behavior of the MA as a single physical entity applies even to mitotic abnormalities such as multipolar spindles. Figure 7 shows an isolated tetrapolar MA resulting from polyspermy. Such configurations of the MA retain their interest because of the difficulties they create for simplified theories that reject the reality of the fibrous elements and appeal to plus-minus attractions, fields of force or tactoid formation.

From the cytological standpoint, the observations thus far permit a number of conclusions. Perhaps the most significant is that the *whole MA, including chromatic and achromatic, nuclear and cytoplasmic elements behaves as a single unit in the isolation procedure.* It is conceivable, of course, that this physical association is some artefact of the method, but the normal expectation would have been that the method would result in the disruption of such associations as that between asters and spindles or asters and fusion nuclei. In addition to the suggestion that the elements of the MA are associated into a single physical entity, the results define a chemical order of unity. Since the method depends on differential resistance to solubilization by detergent, it might have been predicted that some elements of the MA would be preserved while others were dispersed. Instead, we obtain the complete apparatus as defined cytologically.

Occasionally asters were separated from the spindles as a result of handling. Here one often observed in the aster an "insertion cone" where the spindle had been attached, while the spindle poles thus freed from the asters showed convergent ends. In no case were "half-spindles" recovered. It can definitely be said that there are spindle elements which are continuous from pole to pole at all the stages of anaphase and early telophase and are not broken by the mechanical stresses to which they are subjected in these procedures.

2. *The Question of Artefact.* Progress toward an understanding of the mitotic apparatus has been deterred by seemingly endless discussion of artefacts of cytological technique — summarized by Hughes (*3*). The introduction of the electron microscope has merely reduced the size of the alleged artefacts and reintroduced purely visual criteria of "good" and "bad" fixation that had become obsolete in light microscopy. The controversy about the reality of spindle fibers will probably be settled by observations such as Inoue's (*14*) polarization-microscopic records of their appearance in living material.

In the case of the sea urchin egg, the subject of the present study, a number of the elements of the MA are observable in the living (*6*), though obscured by cytoplasm, and, in the development of the present isolation technique, it was possible to follow the major structures through all stages from the living to the final isolated product. Following such a procedure, it is clear that no structures are created in the process, al-

though the structural details may conceivably be modified. The successful isolation of the whole MA as a stable coherent structure would
seem to eliminate such views as that the astral radiations are fluid
channels outlined by cytoplasmic granules or that the spindle fibers are
lines of precipitation due to mechanical stress. At least, a mechanism
whereby treatment with subzero 30 percent alcohol would transform the
postulated liquid channels or lines of stress into strong fibrous units
possessing characteristic arrangement and dimensions at each stage of
mitosis is not obvious. On the contrary, the findings are in accord with
the notions of Dan and collaborators (6, 15) concerning the physical
nature of the spindle and aster.

Perhaps the question of the "normality" of the structure obtained
by isolation is not meaningful; it still contains an element of cyclic
reasoning since the norm is practically derived from fixed material. More
significant is the very fact of the isolation itself, especially by the
peroxide-detergent procedures, for this defines the MA as a coherent
ensemble of structures sharing some chemical properties that differentiate them from everything else in the cell. Taking the structural and
the chemical differentia of the MA together, it is concluded that we can
no longer question the tangible reality of the major elements in the
classical description of the MA, though we may question dimensional
details.

Rozsa and Wyckoff's observation of the absence of distinct spindle
fibers (in dividing plant cells) after formalin fixation is not applicable to
the dividing sea urchin eggs. After fixation in Baker's neutral formalin
and treatment with detergent, the spindle structure appeared essentially
as in the isolated spindles. We could not isolate the formalin-fixed MA.
While the detergent rendered the coagulated cytoplasm swollen and
much more transparent, it did not disperse it.

3. *Birefringence.* Thanks to the cooperation of Dr. Shinya Inoue, of
the University of Washington, polarized-light observations were made
with his microscope. Figure 8 shows the birefringence of the isolated
MA. The sign of birefringence is positive with respect to fiber axes, and
the appearance is essentially the same as is observed in the living
(6, 14).

C. CHEMICAL PROPERTIES

1. *Separation of MA Protein.* The MA prepared by the peroxide-
detergent method is relatively resistant to solution. It is soluble in strong
(*ca.* 0.5 N) NaOH, and the following data concern the material obtained
after solution in this reagent. On back-titration with HCl, an amorphous white precipitate appears at about pH 6, which dissolves as the
pH is taken still lower. It is presumed that the region of pH 6 represents
the isoelectric point of the protein separated, but the exact point of
maximum precipitation has not yet been determined. In most of the
experiments, acetic acid was employed to precipitate the MA protein.

The precipitate may be redissolved at pH 7–8 by suspension in water and addition of alkali, and reprecipitated by addition of acetic acid to pH 6.

Protein Content: Determinations of the protein content of MA suspensions were made by the quantitative biuret method — Robinson and Hogden (*16*). From the biological standpoint, it is most interesting to determine the amount of protein isolated per unit MA. Crystalline bovine serum albumin was used as a standard. The number of MA per unit volume of suspension was determined by the use of a hemocytometer. This was compared with the amount of protein per egg. In the case of the egg of *Strongylocentrotus franciscanus,* the amount of protein recovered after two isoelectric precipitations was 2.4×10^{-6} gm per MA. The amount of protein per egg was 1.4×10^{-4} mg. Thus, about 2 percent of the protein present is used in the formation of the MA. These figures have only order-of-magnitude significance, as the accuracy of the counts is not very high.

2. *Ultraviolet Absorption.* Text Figure 1 shows the ultraviolet absorption curves of the MA protein after the first and second isoelectric precipitations, the material being redissolved each time by addition of sufficient alkali to bring to a pH of about 7.5. The two upper curves coincide, showing complete recovery of the protein on the second precipitation. The absorption spectra, with minima at 255 mμ and a maximum at 275 mμ are those of typical proteins. There is no evidence of other peaks. The lower curve is that of the supernatant solution after the first precipitation. The curve is comparable with the upper curves, since the readings were made at the same dilutions, against the same water blank. The lower curve shows no peaks, and, while it may represent absorption by constituents of the MA that were not precipitated at pH 6, it also will include absorption at short wavelengths by acetate and by whatever Duponol remained in the preparation. Obviously the protein isolated by precipitation at pH 6 accounts for the major part of the UV-absorbing material.

TEXT FIGURE 1. The ultraviolet absorption of the protein of the mitotic apparatus. Upper curves show the absorption spectra at neutral pH of the material recovered from the first (solid circles) and second (crosses) precipitation. Lower curve shows the absorption of the supernatant (including sodium acetate and residual Duponol) from the first precipitation. Water blank.

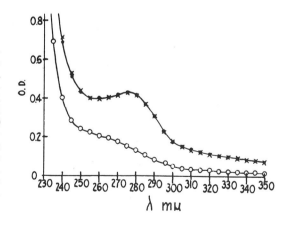

The absence of a nucleic acid peak is not necessarily surprising. At least, the DNA that might be present in the chromosomes (2.3×10^{-9} mg per diploid set) would not be in sufficiently high concentration to be detectable under the conditions of these measurements.

3. *Ultracentrifugation.* The sedimentation pattern of a 0.5 percent solution of twice precipitated MA protein was obtained with the aid of a Spinco analytical ultracentrifgue. We thank Mr. Richard Thomas for making these determinations. The results are shown in Text Figure 2. Only one boundary is apparent. The sedimentation constant was approximately 4.0 svedberg units. A possible particle weight was estimated making the assumption of spherical shape and 30 percent hydration. The weight comes out to be of the order of magnitude of 45,000.

The presence of a single boundary is impressive, in view of the morphological complexity of the MA, but need only imply that other colloidal particles are present only in small amounts. The most reasonable first conclusion would be that we are observing the behavior of a protein constituting the asters and spindle, which accounts for the bulk of the MA. It would be implied that asters and spindles are composed of the same protein even though there is much cytological evidence that they differ in behavior.

The apparent small size of the particles obtained by dissolution of the MA is surprising at first sight, but finds an analogy in the case of actin of muscle, which forms fibrils by polymerization of relatively small particles.

In further work, the MA protein will have to be obtained in solution by a method less drastic than treatment with strong alkali before conclusions allowing physiological interpretations can safely be drawn.

4. *The Role of S–S Linkages.* The MA isolated directly from alcohol is soluble in Duponol. After treatment with dilute H_2O_2 it is less soluble, and after concentrated H_2O_2 quite insoluble. This relationship suggested

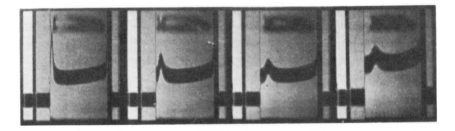

TEXT FIGURE 2. The Ultracentrifugal pattern of the protein recovered from isolated MA after 2 precipitations. Concentration approximately 0.5 percent. Neutral pH. Pictures taken at 569, 1530, 2490, and 3450 seconds after reaching speed (59,780 r.p.m.).

that the stability toward Duponol is related to the number of S–S linkages present, but the practical success of the reasoning does not necessarily prove that it is correct.

If the interpretation is correct, then reduction of S–S linkages should render the isolated MA more soluble in detergent. To test this, MA isolated by the peroxide-Duponol procedures were treated with a 5 percent solution of sodium thioglycollate, at pH 8. The MA did not dissolve, although they gave a visual impression of softening, curling, etc. If 1 percent Duponol was then added, the MA dissolved completely. Alternatively, a solution containing 5 percent thioglycollate and 1 percent Duponol may be used. The MA dissolves immediately in this. Therefore, the characteristic action of H_2O_2 on the stability toward detergent may be reversed by a treatment that would reduce S–S groups.

The alkaline thioglycollate solution used by Goddard and Michaelis (20) to dissolve wool did not dissolve the MA, but made it visibly more flexible and more soluble in stronger alkali and in Duponol. This might suggest that the essential morphology of the MA does not depend on S–S linkages alone.

These results are not surprising in view of the role of S–S linkages in other types of fibrous structures, but do strengthen the view held by a number of workers since Rapkine — summarized by Brachet (17) — that the oxidation and reduction of S plays an important role in mitosis.

D. SUMMARY

1. Methods have been developed for isolating the mitotic apparatus from dividing sea urchin eggs (*Strongylocentrotus franciscanus* and *S. purpuratus*) in quantity.

2. The structure of the MA isolated at various stages of the mitotic cycle corresponds in essential respects to the classical cytological descriptions.

3. The entire MA, including the "chromatic" and "achromatic" elements, behaves as a single physical entity at all stages observed.

4. The isolation processes based on selective solubilization of the surrounding cytoplasm differentiate the MA from the former on chemical as well as morphological grounds.

5. The isolated MA is positively birefringent with respect to fiber axes.

6. A protein has been separated from the MA by isoelectric precipitation. It accounts for most of the mass of the MA and for about 2 percent of all the protein of the egg.

7. The MA protein gives a single boundary in the ultracentrifuge, and the sedimentation rate suggests a small particle (particle weight *ca.* 45,000).

8. Experiments demonstrating the role of S–S linkages in the stability of the MA are described.

Communicated by Curt Stern, June 19, 1952

REFERENCES AND NOTES

* This work was aided by grants from the American Cancer Society, recommended by the Committee on Growth, National Research Council.

† Department of Biology, Tokyo Metropolitan University, Tokyo, Japan. This work was done during tenure of a U.S. Public Health Service Special Fellowship.

‡ It is our present opinion that the subzero ethanol solution is effective not because it alters the MA but because it prevents those reactions which, in the living cell, cause the disappearance of the MA under many abnormal conditions. The procedure may be compared to Szent-Györgyi's (18) technique of preserving the contractile system of muscles by soaking them in cold glycerol solutions.

1. W. Flemming, *Zellsubstanz, Kern- und Zelltheilung* (Vogel, Leipzig, 1882).

2. E. G. Wilson, *The Cell in Development and Inheritance* (Macmillan, New York, 2 ed., 1902).

3. A. F. Hughes, *The Mitotic Cycle* (Academic Press, New York, 1952).

4. T. N. Tahmisian and A. M. Brues, *Trans. Ill. Acad. Sci.* **43**, 259–60 (1950).

5. D. Mazia, P. A. Brewer, M. Alfert, in publication.

6. S. Inoue and K. Dan, *J. Morph.* **89**, 423–56 (1951).

7. G. Rozsa and R. Wyckoff, *Exp. Cell Res.* **2**, 630–41 (1951).

8. D. C. Pease, *J. Morphol.* **69**, 405–41 (1941).

9. A. F. Hughes and M. M. Swann, *J. Exp. Biol.* **25**, 45–47 (1948).

10. J. C. Dan, *Physiol. Zool.* **21**, 191–218 (1948).

11. J. F. Danielli, *Biol. Bull.* **99**, 269 (1950).

12. F. W. Putnam, *Adv. Prot. Chem.* **4**, 79–122 (1948).

13. E. B. Wilson, *Atlas of the Fertilization and Karyokinesis of the Ovum* (Columbia Univ. Press, New York, 1895).

14. S. Inoue, *Exp. Cell Res.*, Supp. 2 (1952), in press.

15. K. Dan, *J. Fac. Sci. Tokyo Imp. U.,* ser. IV 6, 297–321 (1943).

16. A. W. Robinson and C. G. Hogden, *J. Biol. Chem.* **135**, 707–26 (1940).

17. J. Brachet, *Chemical Embryology* (Interscience, New York, 1950).

18. A. Szent-Györgyi, *Biol. Bull.* **96**, 140–61 (1949).

19. M. M. Swann, *J. Exp. Biol.* **28**, 434–44 (1951).

20. D. R. Goddard and L. Michaelis, *J. Biol. Chem.* **106**, 605–13 (1934).

Structural Basis
of the Cross-Striations
in Muscle

Jean Hanson*
Hugh E. Huxley†

*Department of Biology,
Massachusetts Institute
of Technology*

The myofibrils of striated muscle consist largely of protein (more than 90 percent of their dry weight) (1), and it is believed (2) that the only proteins present in significant quantities are myosin, actin and probably a small amount of tropomyosin. We shall describe here evidence that the cross-striation of the myofibrils results from a discontinuous distribution of myosin along their length, the myosin being confined to the A-bands. Previous authors have tentatively suggested that this may be the case (3–6), but we believe that our evidence is more direct and conclusive than any previously presented.

Methods have become available during recent years for extracting successively myosin and actin from muscle, with very little mutual contamination; minced fresh muscle in the form of broken fibres is used as the starting material. We have examined this material microscopically (in phase-contrast illumination, in polarized light and in the electron microscope) at various stages of extraction. We have also modified the procedures to permit their use on isolated myofibrils, where the whole process of extraction can be observed visually on the same single myofibril.

If minced rabbit muscle, before any extraction, is examined either by using normal histological sectioning procedures or else by fixing the material in formalin and fragmenting it to myofibrils in a Waring blender, then the normal band pattern of relaxed muscle is seen. If,

Reprinted from *Nature* **172**, 530–32 (1953, by permission of the authors and the editors of *Nature*, Macmillan (Journals) Limited.

however, the muscle is examined after extraction for twenty minutes either by Guba-Straub solution (0.3 M KCl, 0.15 M phosphate buffer, pH 6.5) or by Hasselbach-Schneider (7) solution (0.47 M KCl, 0.01 M pyrophosphate, 0.1 M phosphate buffer, pH 6.4), then a new band pattern is seen. The A-band has largely disappeared, leaving only a narrow dark line which in favourable circumstances may be resolved into two fine lines lying on either side of the original H-band; the sarcomere-length is unchanged. Apart from the narrow dark band and the Z-line, the sarcomeres now have uniformly low density along their whole length and their birefringence has become very small or zero (cf. the I-band in normal muscle).

If the Hasselbach-Schneider procedure (7) for actin extraction is now carried out (the residue from the myosin extraction being broken up in a Waring blender and stirred for eighteen hours with 0.6 M potassium chloride, pH > 6.0), the organized structure of the muscle disappears and only debris remains. Similarly, few fibrils can be recognized in the residue left after the use of Hasselbach and Schneider's method (7) for the simultaneous extraction of actin and myosin.

In order to observe these processes more closely, we have developed methods for carrying out analogous extractions on isolated myofibrils. Two types of fibrils were used: some were prepared by a modification of the method of Schick and Hass (8) ("trypsin-prepared fibrils") and others by breaking up bundles of glycerinated fibres (3) in a Waring blender. A drop of a suspension of myofibrils is placed on a slide under a cover-slip and observed in phase-contrast illumination or polarized light. Material from the A-band ("A-substance") is then removed from such myofibrils by irrigating the preparations with the following solutions: (1) Hasselbach-Schneider pyrophosphate solution plus $1 \times 10^{-3} M$ MgCl$_2$; (2) Guba-Straub solution plus 4×10^{-4} M ATP. The A-substance disappears in 1–2 sec., leaving a fibril "ghost," consisting of a faint "backbone" with Z-lines and with a pair of lines on either side of each original H-band (Fig.1); the fibrils are no longer distinguishably birefringent and, in contrast to their behaviour before extraction, they will no longer contract in 4×10^{-4} M ATP in 0.1 M KCl, 10^{-3} M MgCl$_2$. The loss of A-substance is accompanied by some swelling of the fibrils: if myofibrils are treated with Guba-Straub solution alone without ATP or with Hasselbach-Schneider's solution without magnesium, then swelling still occurs, but this time it is not accompanied by loss of A-substance or loss of birefringence.

In the case of trypsin-prepared myofibrils, a slower secondary extraction process seems to occur, and the fibril ghosts become progressively fainter with longer treatment; if the extraction is carried out in a test-tube, then the ghosts apparently break up and dissolve, and no recognizable fragments can be recovered. It seems that these fibrils are unstable once the A-substance has been removed, and that any mechanical agitation will destroy them. This would account for the ease with which Hasselbach and Schneider (7) can extract actin when the

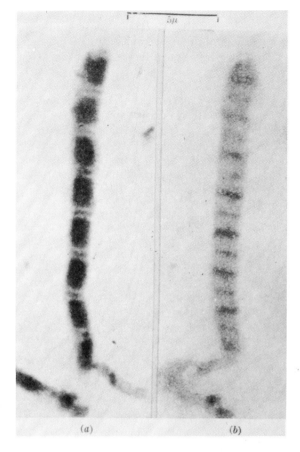

FIGURE 1. Trypsin-prepared fibril under phase-
contrast microscope, (*a*) before and (*b*) after
extraction of *A*-substance by Guba-Straub–ATP.

residue from the myosin extraction is broken up in a Waring blender. In
the case of the glycerinated myofibrils, however, the ghosts are stable
and may be recovered by centrifugation after a test-tube extraction.
Examination of the supernatant in a Beckman ultraviolet spectrophotometer supports the view that protein-like material passes into solution
during this extraction.

We have examined the "ghost" fibrils in the electron microscope and
compared them with normal fibrils. In the first instance this was done on
unstained and unshadowed preparations, and it was found that the
density distribution apparent under phase-contrast illumination in the
light microscope was closely paralleled by that seen in the electron
microscope. For more detailed examination, a thin-sectioning procedure
was used; this technique has been described by Hodge, Huxley and

Spiro (9) in a study of various types of intact muscle; the microtome used was that described by the same authors (10). In these studies on intact muscle a hexagonal array of filaments about 100 Å in diameter was seen in the A-band, together with a good deal of interstitial material. The I-band appeared to have been preserved less satisfactorily; it was much less dense than the A-band and contained much thinner filaments. Later studies by one of us — Huxley (11) — have shown that the interstitial material in the A-band itself consists of filaments, about 30–40 Å in diameter, and that in the absence of ATP these filaments are arranged in a regular six-fold array around each of the larger filaments. These observations confirmed the earlier predictions from low-angle X-ray diffraction studies (12). It was also observed that the secondary six-fold array was absent from the H-band, where the diameter of the thicker filaments was about 130 Å.

FIGURE 2.   Electron micrographs of thin sections through (a) intact glycerinated fibril and (b) glycerinated fibril after removal of A-substance by Guba-Straub–ATP.

We find that, after extraction of the *A*-substance from isolated myofibrils by the methods described above, the thicker filaments which formed the primary array are no longer visible in the *A*-band, and that only fine filaments can now be seen; in the *H*-band, however, the thicker filaments are still present. The Z-lines and the thin dense bands on either side of the *H*-band are also visible (Fig. 2).

To summarize, we believe that the following evidence suggests very strongly that myosin is primarily concentrated in the *A*-bands in muscle and that it is responsible for the high density and the birefringence of these zones, and that actin is present as long filaments which extend continuously through *A*- and *I*-bands.

(*a*) Extraction procedures which are known to remove myosin and little or no actin from whole muscle remove a large amount of material from the *A*-band, and leave it with a low density and birefringence like that of the original *I*-band.

(*b*) If such extraction procedures are followed by the removal of actin, then the remainder of the organized structure of the muscle disappears, leaving only debris.

(*c*) If extraction procedures similar to those used to remove myosin from whole muscle are carried out on myofibrils, then the *A*-substance is removed, and the extraction can be viewed in a single myofibril in phase-contrast illumination or in polarized light. The material which passes into solution can be demonstrated to be protein-like by spectrophotometry.

(*d*) If such extraction procedures (carried out on trypsin-prepared myofibrils) are followed by mechanical agitation, then the fibril ghosts pass into solution.

(*e*) The *A*-bands of intact muscle, as seen in the electron-microscope, contain two sets of filaments. The larger filaments appear to have a total volume three to four times that of the smaller filaments: this is consistent with the view that the larger filaments are composed of myosin and the smaller ones of actin. After extraction of the *A*-substance, the larger filaments disappear.

We do not consider that observations of a shortening of the *I*-band during contraction necessarily imply that both actin and myosin are present there: such observations cannot at present distinguish between a genuine shortening of the filaments in the *A*-band, a migration of *A*-substance into the *I*-band, or a retraction of *I*-band filaments into the *A*-band.

In its simplest form, our picture of muscle is as follows: thin filaments of actin extend from the Z-line through the *I*-band and through one half of the *A*-band, until they join up with the *H*-band filaments, the composition of which is unknown. Myosin is located primarily in the *A*-band, in the form of filaments about 100 Å in diameter, which extend from the *A*–*I* junction up to the *H*-band, where they too join up with the *H*-band filaments. The myosin filaments are arranged in a continuous hexagonal array across the fibrils, with the actin filaments lying between them; in the absence of ATP, the actin filaments are linked to the myosin and form a regular six-fold array around each myosin filament. If the actin-myosin link is broken by the presence of ATP or pyrophosphate, the myosin filaments may be dissolved out from the muscle by solutions of suitable ionic strength, leaving behind a structure principally composed of actin.

We are at present pursuing experiments, similar to those described above, on muscle at various stages of contraction, in order to relate this concept of its structure to the mechanism of contraction.

We are greatly indebted to Prof. Francis O. Schmitt for the encouragement he has given to this research, and to the Rockefeller Foundation and the Commonwealth Fund for their support.

REFERENCES AND NOTES

* Fellow of the Rockefeller Foundation. On leave from the Medical Research Council Biophysics Research Unit, King's College, Strand, London, W.C. 2.

† Fellow of the Commonwealth Fund. On leave from the Medical Research Council Unit for the Study of the Molecular Structure of Biological Systems, Cavendish Laboratory, Cambridge.

1. S. V. Perry, *Biochem. J.* **48**, 257 (1951); _____, *ibid.* **51**, 495 (1952); _____, *Biochim. et Biophys. Acta* **8**, 499 (1952).

2. H. H. Weber and H. Portzehl, Advances in protein chemistry **7**, 161 (1952).

3. A. Szent-Györgyi, *Chemistry of Muscular Contraction* (Academic Press, New York, 2 ed., 1951).

4. A. L. von Muralt and J. T. Edsall, *J. Biol. Chem.* **89**, 351 (1930). H. H. Weber, *Ergebn. Physiol.* **36**, 109 (1934).

5. W. R. Amberson, R. D. Smith, S. Himmelfarb, C. Stout, H. Hoch, *Biol. Bull. Woods Hole* **99**, 314 (1950).

6. C. A. Ashley, K. R. Porter, D. E. Philpott, G. M. Hass, *J. Exp. Med.* **94**, 9 (1951).

7. W. Hasselbach and G. Schneider, *Biochem. Z.* **321**, 461 (1951).

8. A. F. Schick and G. M. Hass, *J. Exp. Med.* **91**, 655 (1950).

9. A. J. Hodge, H. E. Huxley, D. Spiro, in press.

10. _____, in press.

11. H. E. Huxley, in preparation.

12. _____, *Faraday Soc. Symp.*, Size and shape factor in colloidal systems (1951); _____, *Proc. Roy. Soc. London* B **141**, 59 (1953).

C Information transfer

Avery, Oswald T., Colin M. MacLeod, Maclyn McCarty. 1944. Studies on the chemical nature of the substance inducing transformation of pneumococcal types. Induction of transformation by a desoxyribonucleic acid fraction isolated from Pneumococcus Type III. *J. Exp. Med.* **79**, 137–58.

Watson, J. D., and F. H. C. Crick. 1953. Genetical implications of the structure of deoxyribonucleic acid. *Nature* **171**, 964–69.

Watson, J. D. 1963. Involvement of RNA in the synthesis of proteins. *Science* **140**, 17–26.

Studies on the Chemical Nature of the Substance Inducing Transformation of Pneumococcal Types. Induction of Transformation by a Desoxyribonucleic Acid Fraction Isolated from Pneumococcus Type III

Oswald T. Avery
Colin M. MacLeod
Maclyn McCarty*

From the Hospital of
The Rockefeller Institute for
Medical Research, New York

Biologists have long attempted by chemical means to induce in higher organisms predictable and specific changes which thereafter could be transmitted in series as hereditary characters. Among microorganisms the most striking example of inheritable and specific alterations in cell structure and function that can be experimentally induced and are reproducible under well defined and adequately controlled conditions is the transformation of specific types of Pneumococcus. This phenomenon was first described by Griffith (1) who succeeded in transforming an attenuated and non-encapsulated (R) variant derived from one specific type into fully encapsulated and virulent (S) cells of a heterologous specific type. A typical instance will suffice to illustrate the techniques originally used and serve to indicate the wide variety of transformations that are possible within the limits of this bacterial species.

Griffith found that mice injected subcutaneously with a small amount of a living R culture derived from Pneumococcus Type II

Reprinted by permission of M. McCarty and The Rockefeller University Press from *Journal of Experimental Medicine* **79**, 137–58 (1944). The photographs here reproduced from printed halftone copy inevitably show a loss of detail, and the quality of the results is not representative of the originals.

together with a large inoculum of heat-killed Type III (S) cells frequently succumbed to infection, and that the heart's blood of these animals yielded Type III pneumococci in pure culture. The fact that the R strain was avirulent and incapable by itself of causing fatal bacteremia and the additional fact that the heated suspension of Type III cells contained no viable organisms brought convincing evidence that the R forms growing under these conditions had newly acquired the capsular structure and biological specificity of Type III pneumococci.

The original observations of Griffith were later confirmed by Neufeld and Levinthal (2), and by Baurhenn (3) abroad, and by Dawson (4) in this laboratory. Subsequently Dawson and Sia (5) succeeded in inducing transformation *in vitro*. This they accomplished by growing R cells in a fluid medium containing anti-R serum and heat-killed encapsulated S cells. They showed that in the test tube as in the animal body transformation can be selectively induced, depending on the type specificity of the S cells used in the reaction system. Later, Alloway (6) was able to cause specific transformation *in vitro* using sterile extracts of S cells from which all formed elements and cellular debris had been removed by Berkefeld filtration. He thus showed that crude extracts containing active transforming material in soluble form are as effective in inducing specific transformation as are the intact cells from which the extracts are prepared.

Another example of transformation which is analogous to the interconvertibility of pneumococcal types lies in the field of viruses. Berry and Dedrick (7) succeeded in changing the virus of rabbit fibroma (Shope) into that of infectious myxoma (Sanarelli). These investigators inoculated rabbits with a mixture of active fibroma virus together with a suspension of heat-inactivated myxoma virus and produced in the animals the symptoms and pathological lesions characteristic of infectious myxomatosis. On subsequent animal passage the transformed virus was transmissible and induced myxomatous infection typical of the naturally occurring disease. Later Berry (8) was successful in inducing the same transformation using a heat-inactivated suspension of washed elementary bodies of myxoma virus. In the case of these viruses the methods employed were similar in principle to those used by Griffith in the transformation of pneumococcal types. These observations have subsequently been confirmed by other investigators (9).

The present paper is concerned with a more detailed analysis of the phenomenon of transformation of specific types of Pneumococcus. The major interest has centered in attempts to isolate the active principle from crude bacterial extracts and to identify if possible its chemical nature or at least to characterize it sufficiently to place it in a general group of known chemical substances. For purposes of study, the typical example of transformation chosen as a working model was the one with which we have had most experience and which consequently seemed best suited for analysis. This particular example represents the transformation of a non-encapsulated R variant of Pneumococcus Type II to Pneumococcus Type III.

EXPERIMENTAL

Transformation of pneumococcal types *in vitro* requires that certain cultural conditions be fulfilled before it is possible to demonstrate the reaction even in the presence of a potent extract. Not only must the broth medium be optimal for growth but it must be supplemented by the addition of serum or serous fluid known to possess certain special properties.

Moreover, the R variant, as will be shown later, must be in the reactive phase in which it has the capacity to respond to the transforming stimulus. For purposes of convenience these several components as combined in the transforming test will be referred to as the *reaction system*. Each constituent of this system presented problems which required clarification before it was possible to obtain consistent and reproducible results. The various components of the system will be described in the following order: (1) nutrient broth, (2) serum or serous fluid, (3) strain of R Pneumococcus, and (4) extraction, purification, and chemical nature of the transforming principle.

1. *Nutrient Broth.* Beef heart infusion broth containing 1 percent neopeptone with no added dextrose and adjusted to an initial pH of 7.6–7.8 is used as the basic medium. Individual lots of broth show marked and unpredictable variations in the property of supporting transformation. It has been found, however, that charcoal adsorption, according to the method described by MacLeod and Mirick (10) for removal of sulfonamide inhibitors, eliminates to a large extent these variations; consequently this procedure is used as routine in the preparation of consistently effective broth for titrating the transforming activity of extracts.

2. *Serum or Serous Fluid.* In the first successful experiments on the induction of transformation *in vitro,* Dawson and Sia (5) found that it was essential to add serum to the medium. Anti-R pneumococcal rabbit serum was used because of the observation that reversion of an R pneumococcus to the homologous S form can be induced by growth in a medium containing anti-R serum. Alloway (6) later found that ascitic or chest fluid and normal swine serum, all of which contain R antibodies, are capable of replacing antipneumococcal rabbit serum in the reaction system. Some form of serum is essential, and to our knowledge transformation *in vitro* has never been effected in the absence of serum or serous fluid.

In the present study human pleural or ascitic fluid has been used almost exclusively. It became apparent, however, that the effectiveness of different lots of serum varied and that the differences observed were not necessarily dependent upon the content of R antibodies, since many sera of high titer were found to be incapable of supporting transformation. This fact suggested that factors other than R antibodies are involved.

It has been found that sera from various animal species, irrespective of their immune properties, contain an enzyme capable of destroying the transforming principle in potent extracts. The nature of this enzyme and the specific substrate on which it acts will be referred to later in this paper. This enzyme is inactivated by heating the serum at 60°–65°C, and sera heated at temperatures known to destroy the enzyme are often rendered effective in the transforming system. Further analysis has shown that certain sera in which R antibodies are present and in which the enzyme has been inactivated may nevertheless fail to support transformation. This fact suggests that still another factor in the serum is essential. The content of this factor varies in different sera, and at present its identity is unknown.

There are at present no criteria which can be used as a guide in the selection of suitable sera or serous fluids except that of actually testing their capacity to support transformation. Fortunately, the requisite properties are stable and remain unimpaired over long periods of time; and sera that have been stored in the refrigerator for many months have been found on retesting to have lost little or none of their original effectiveness in supporting transformation.

The recognition of these various factors in serum and their role in the reaction system has greatly facilitated the standardization of the cultural conditions required for obtaining consistent and reproducible results.

3. *The R Strain (R36A).* The unencapsulated R strain used in the present study was derived from a virulent "S" culture of Pneumococcus Type II. It will be recalled that irrespective of type derivation all "R" variants of Pneumococcus are characterized by the lack of capsule formation and the consequent loss of both type specificity and the capacity to produce infection in the animal body. The designation of these variants as R forms has been used to refer merely to the fact that on artificial media the colony surface is "rough" in contrast to the smooth, glistening surface of colonies of encapsulated S cells.

The R strain referred to above as R36A was derived by growing the parent S culture of Pneumococcus Type II in broth containing Type II antipneumococcus rabbit serum for 36 serial passages and isolating the variant thus induced. The strain R36A has lost all the specific and distinguishing characteristics of the parent S organisms and consists only of attenuated and non-encapsulated R variants. The change S → R is often a reversible one provided the R cells are not too far "degraded." The reversion of the R form to its original specific type can frequently be accomplished by successive animal passages or by repeated serial subculture in anti-R serum. When reversion occurs under these conditions, how-ever, the R culture invariably reverts to the encapsulated form of the same specific type as that from which it was derived (*11*). Strain R36A has become relatively fixed in the R phase and has never spontaneously reverted to the Type II S form. Moreover, repeated attempts to cause it to revert under the conditions just men-tioned have in all instances been unsuccessful.

The reversible conversion of S ⇌ R within the limits of a single type is quite different from the transformation of one specific type of Pneumococcus into another specific type through the R form. Trans-formation of types has never been observed to occur spontaneously and has been induced experimentally only by the special techniques outlined earlier in this paper. Under these conditions, the enzymatic synthesis of a chemically and immunologically different capsular polysaccharide is specifically oriented and selectively determined by the specific type of S cells used as source of the transforming agent.

In the course of the present study it was noted that the stock culture of R36 on serial transfers in blood broth undergoes spontaneous dissociation giving rise to a number of other R variants which can be distinguished one from another by colony form. The significance of this in the present instance lies in the fact that of four different variants isolated from the parent R culture only one (R36A) is susceptible to the transforming action of potent extracts, while the others fail to respond and are wholly inactive in this regard. The fact that differences exist in the responsiveness of different R variants to the same specific stimulus em-phasizes the care that must be exercised in the selection of a suitable R variant for use in experiments on transformation. The capacity of this R strain (R36A) to respond to a variety of different transforming agents is shown by the readiness with which it can be transformed to Types I, III, VI, or XIV, as well as to its origi-nal type (Type II), to which, as pointed out, it has never spontaneously reverted.

Although the significance of the following fact will become apparent later on, it must be mentioned here that pneumococcal cells possess an enzyme capable of destroying the activity of the transforming principle. Indeed, this enzyme has been found to be present and highly active in the autolysates of a number of different strains. The fact that this intracellular enzyme is released during auto-lysis may explain, in part at least, the observation of Dawson and Sia (5) that it is essential in bringing about transformation in the test tube to use a small inoculum of young and actively growing R cells. The irregularity of the results and often the failure to induce transformation when large inocula are used may be attributable to the release from autolyzing cells of an amount of this enzyme sufficient to destroy the transforming principle in the reaction system.

In order to obtain consistent and reproducible results, two facts must be borne in mind: first, that an R culture can undergo spontaneous disso-ciation and give rise to other variants which have lost the capacity to respond to the transforming stimulus; and secondly, that pneumococcal cells contain an intracellular enzyme which when released destroys the activity of the transforming principle. Consequently, it is important to select a responsive strain and to prevent as far as possible the destruc-tive changes associated with autolysis.

Method of Titration of Transforming Activity. In the isolation and purification of the active principle from crude extracts of pneumococcal cells it is desirable to have a method for determining quantitatively the transforming activity of various fractions.

The experimental procedure used is as follows: Sterilization of the material to be tested for activity is accomplished by the use of alcohol since it has been found that this reagent has no effect on activity. A measured volume of extract is pre-cipitated in a sterile centrifuge tube by the addition of 4 to 5 volumes of absolute ethyl alcohol, and the mixture is allowed to stand 8 or more hours in the re-frigerator in order to effect sterilization. The alcohol precipitated material is centrifuged, the supernatant discarded, and the tube containing the precipitate is allowed to drain for a few minutes in the inverted position to remove excess alcohol. The mouth of the tube is then carefully flamed and a dry, sterile cotton plug is inserted. The precipitate is redissolved in the original volume of saline. Sterilization of active material by this technique has invariably proved effective. This procedure avoids the loss of active substance which may occur when the solution is passed through a Berkefeld filter or is heated at the high temperatures required for sterilization.

To the charcoal-adsorbed broth described above is added 10 percent of the sterile ascitic or pleural fluid which has previously been heated at 60°C for 30 minutes, in order to destroy the enzyme known to inactivate the transforming principle. The enriched medium is distributed under aseptic conditions in 2.0 cc amounts in sterile tubes measuring 15 × 100 mm. The sterilized extract is diluted serially in saline neutralized to pH 7.2–7.6 by addition of 0.1 N NaOH, or it may be similarly diluted in M/40 phosphate buffer, pH 7.4. 0.2 cc of each dilution is added to at least 3 or 4 tubes of the serum medium. The tubes are then seeded with a 5- to 8-hour blood broth culture of R36A. 0.05 cc of a 10^{-4} dilution of this culture is added to each tube, and the cultures are incubated at 37°C for 18 to 24 hours.

The anti-R properties of the serum in the medium cause the R cells to agglutinate during growth, and clumps of the agglutinated cells settle to the bottom of the tube leaving a clear supernatant. When transforma-tion occurs, the encapsulated S cells, not being affected by these anti-bodies, grow diffusely throughout the medium. On the other hand, in the

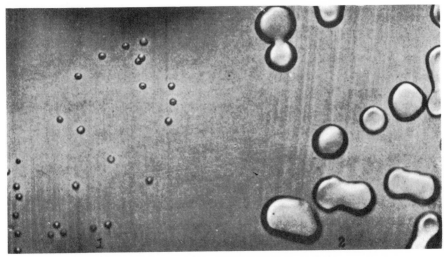

The photograph was made by Mr. Joseph B. Haulenbeek.

PLATE 1.

FIGURE 1 [*l*]. Colonies of the R variant (R36A) derived from Pneumococcus Type II. Plated on blood agar from a culture grown in serum broth in the absence of the transforming substance (× 3.5).

FIGURE 2 [*r*]. Colonies on blood agar of the same cells after induction of transformation during growth in the same medium with the addition of active transforming principle isolated from Type III pneumococci. The smooth, glistening, mucoid colonies shown are characteristic of Pneumococcus Type III and readily distinguishable from the small, rough colonies of the parent R strain illustrated in Figure 1 (× 3.5).

absence of transformation the supernatant remains clear, and only sedimented growth of R organisms occurs. This difference in the character of growth makes it possible by inspection alone to distinguish tentatively between positive and negative results. As routine all the cultures are plated on blood agar for confirmation and further bacteriological identification. Since the extracts used in the present study were derived from Pneumococcus Type III, the differentiation between the colonies of the original R organism and those of the transformed S cells is especially striking, the latter being large, glistening, mucoid colonies typical of Pneumococcus Type III. Figures 1 and 2 illustrate these differences in colony form.

A typical protocol of a titration of the transforming activity of a highly purified preparation is given in Table 4.

PREPARATIVE METHODS

Source Material. In the present investigation a stock laboratory strain of Pneumococcus Type III (A66) has been used as source material for obtaining the active principle. Mass cultures of these organisms are grown in 50 to 75 liter lots of plain beef heart infusion broth. After 16 to 18 hours' incubation at 37°C the bacterial cells are collected in a steam-driven sterilizable Sharples centrifuge. The centrifuge is equipped with cooling coils immersed in ice water so that the culture fluid is thoroughly chilled before flowing into the machine. This procedure retards autolysis during the course of centrifugation. The sedimented bacteria are removed from the collecting cylinder and resuspended in approximately 150 cc of chilled saline (0.85 percent NaCl), and care is taken that all clumps are thoroughly emulsified. The glass vessel containing the thick, creamy suspension of cells is immersed in a water bath, and the temperature of the suspension rapidly raised to 65°C. During the heating process the material is constantly stirred, and the temperature maintained at 65°C for 30 minutes. Heating at this temperature inactivates the intracellular enzyme known to destroy the transforming principle.

Extraction of Heat-Killed Cells. Although various procedures have been used, only that which has been found most satisfactory will be described here. The heat-killed cells are washed with saline 3 times. The chief value of the washing process is to remove a large excess of capsular polysaccharide together with much of the protein, ribonucleic acid, and somatic "C" polysaccharide. Quantitative titrations of transforming activity have shown that not more than 10 to 15 percent of the active material is lost in the washing, a loss which is small in comparison to the amount of inert substances which are removed by this procedure.

After the final washing, the cells are extracted in 150 cc of saline containing sodium desoxycholate in final concentration of 0.5 percent by shaking the mixture mechanically 30 to 60 minutes. The cells are separated by centrifugation, and the extraction process is repeated 2 or 3 times. The desoxycholate extracts prepared in this manner are clear and colorless. These extracts are combined and precipitated by the addition of 3 to 4 volumes of absolute ethyl alcohol. The sodium desoxycholate being soluble in alcohol remains in the supernatant and is thus removed at this step. The precipitate forms a fibrous mass which floats to the surface of the alcohol and can be removed directly by lifting it out with a spatula. The excess alcohol is drained from the precipitate which is then redissolved in about 50 cc of saline. The solution obtained is usually viscous, opalescent, and somewhat cloudy.

Deproteinization and Removal of Capsular Polysaccharide. The solution is then deproteinized by the chloroform method described by Sevag (12). The procedure is repeated 2 or 3 times until the solution becomes clear. After this preliminary treatment the material is reprecipitated in 3 to 4 volumes of alcohol. The precipitate obtained is dissolved in a larger volume of saline (150 cc) to which is added 3 to 5 mg of a purified preparation of the bacterial enzyme capable of hydrolyzing the Type III capsular polysaccharide (13). The mixture is incubated at 37°C, and the destruction of the capsular polysaccharide is determined by serological tests with Type III antibody solution prepared by dissociation of immune precipitate according to the method described by Liu and Wu (14). The advantages of using the antibody solution for this purpose are that it does not react with other serologically active substances in the extract and that it selectively detects the presence of the capsular polysaccharide in dilutions as high as 1:6,000,000. The enzymatic breakdown of the polysaccharide is usually complete within 4 to 6 hours, as evidenced by the loss of serological reactivity. The digest is then precipitated in 3 to 4 volumes of ethyl alcohol, and the precipitate is redissolved in 50 cc of saline. Deproteinization by the chloroform process is again used to remove the added enzyme protein and remaining traces of pneumococcal protein. The procedure is repeated until no further film of protein-chloroform gel is visible at the interface.

Alcohol Fractionation. Following deproteinization and enzymatic digestion of the capsular polysaccharide, the material is repeatedly fractionated in ethyl alcohol as follows. Absolute ethyl alcohol is added dropwise to the solution with constant stirring. At a critical concentration varying from 0.8 to 1.0 volume of alcohol the active material separates out in the form of fibrous strands that wind themselves around the stirring rod. This precipitate is removed on the rod and washed in a 50 percent mixture of alcohol and saline. Although the bulk of active material is removed by fractionation at the critical concentration, a small but appreciable amount remains in solution. However, upon increasing the concentration of alcohol to 3 volumes, the residual fraction is thrown down together with inert material in the form of a flocculent precipitate. This flocculent precipitate is taken up in a small volume of saline (5 to 10 cc) and the solution again fractionated by the addition of 0.8 to 1.0 volume of alcohol. Additional fibrous material is obtained which is combined with that recovered from the original solution. Alcoholic fractionation is repeated 4 to 5 times. The yield of fibrous material obtained by this method varies from 10 to 25 mg per 75 liters of culture and represents the major portion of active material present in the original crude extract.

Effect of Temperature. As a routine procedure all steps in purification were carried out at room temperature unless specifically stated otherwise. Because of the theoretical advantage of working at low temperature in the preparation of biologically active material, the purification of one lot (preparation 44) was carried out in the cold. In this instance all the above procedures with the exception of desoxycholate extraction and enzyme treatment were conducted in a cold room maintained at 0–4°C. This preparation proved to have significantly higher activity than did material similarly prepared at room temperature.

Desoxycholate extraction of the heat-killed cells at low temperature is less efficient and yields smaller amounts of the active fraction. It has been demonstrated that higher temperatures facilitate extraction of the active principle, although activity is best preserved at low temperatures.

ANALYSIS OF PURIFIED
TRANSFORMING MATERIAL

General Properties. Saline solutions containing 0.5 to 1.0 mg per cc of the purified substance are colorless and clear in diffuse light. However, in strong transmitted light the solution is not entirely clear and when stirred exhibits a silky sheen. Solutions at these concentrations are highly viscous.

Purified material dissolved in physiological salt solution and stored at 2–4°C retains its activity in undiminished titer for at least 3 months. However, when dissolved in distilled water, it rapidly decreases in activity and becomes completely inert within a few days. Saline solutions stored in the frozen state in a CO_2 ice box ($-70°C$) retain full potency for several months. Similarly, material precipitated from saline solution by alcohol and stored under the supernatant remains active over a long period of time. Partially purified material can be preserved by drying from the frozen state in the lyophile apparatus. However, when the same procedure is used for the preservation of the highly purified substance, it is found that the material undergoes changes resulting in decrease in solubility and loss of activity.

The activity of the transforming principle in crude extracts withstands heating for 30 to 60 minutes at 65°C. Highly purified preparations of active material are less stable, and some loss of activity occurs at this temperature. A quantitative study of the effect of heating purified material at higher temperatures has not as yet been made. Alloway (6), using crude extracts prepared from Type III pneumococcal cells, found that occasionally activity could still be demonstrated after 10 minutes' exposure in the water bath to temperatures as high as 90°C.

The procedures mentioned above were carried out with solutions adjusted to neutral reaction, since it has been shown that hydrogen ion concentrations in the acid range result in progressive loss of activity. Inactivation occurs rapidly at pH 5 and below.

Qualitative Chemical Tests. The purified material in concentrated solution gives negative biuret and Millon tests. These tests have been done directly on dry material with negative results. The Dische diphenylamine reaction for desoxyribonucleic acid is strongly positive. The orcinol test (Bial) for ribonucleic acid is weakly positive. However, it has been found that in similar concentrations pure preparations of desoxyribonucleic acid of animal origin prepared by different methods give a Bial reaction of corresponding intensity.

Although no specific tests for the presence of lipid in the purified material have been made, it has been found that crude material can be repeatedly extracted with alcohol and ether at −12°C without loss of activity. In addition, as will be noted in the preparative procedures, repeated alcohol precipitation and treatment with chloroform result in no decrease in biological activity.

Elementary Chemical Analysis.[1] Four purified preparations were analyzed for content of nitrogen, phosphorus, carbon, and hydrogen. The results are presented in Table 1. The nitrogen-phosphorus ratios vary from 1.58 to 1.75 with an average value of 1.67 which is in close agreement with that calculated on the basis of the theoretical structure of sodium desoxyribonucleate (tetranucleotide). The analytical figures by themselves do not establish that the substance isolated is a pure chemical entity. However, on the basis of the nitrogen-phosphorus ratio, it would appear that little protein or other substances containing nitrogen or phosphorus are present as impurities, since if they were, this ratio would be considerably altered.

Enzymatic Analysis. Various crude and crystalline enzymes[2] have been tested for their capacity to destroy the biological activity of potent bacterial extracts. Extracts buffered at the optimal pH, to which were added crystalline trypsin and chymotrypsin or combinations of both,

TABLE 1

Elementary Chemical Analysis of Purified Preparations of the Transforming Substance.

Preparation No.	Carbon *percent*	Hydrogen *percent*	Nitrogen *percent*	Phosphorus *percent*	N/P ratio
37	34.27	3.89	14.21	8.57	1.66
38B	—	—	15.93	9.09	1.75
42	35.50	3.76	15.36	9.04	1.69
44	—	—	13.40	8.45	1.58
Theory for sodium desoxyribonucleate	34.20	3.21	15.32	9.05	1.69

suffered no loss in activity following treatment with these enzymes. Pepsin could not be tested because extracts are rapidly inactivated at the low pH required for its use. Prolonged treatment with crystalline ribonuclease under optimal conditions caused no demonstrable decrease in transforming activity. The fact that trypsin, chymotrypsin, and ribonuclease had no effect on the transforming principle is further evidence that this substance is not ribonucleic acid or a protein susceptible to the action of tryptic enzymes.

In addition to the crystalline enzymes, sera and preparations of enzymes obtained from the organs of various animals were tested to determine their effect on transforming activity. Certain of these were found to be capable of completely destroying biological activity. The various enzyme preparations tested included highly active phosphatases obtained from rabbit bone by the method of Martland and Robison (15) and from swine kidney as described by H. and E. Albers (16). In addition, a preparation made from the intestinal mucosa of dogs by Levene and Dillon (17) and containing a polynucleotidase for thymus nucleic acid was used. Pneumococcal autolysates and a commercial preparation of pancreatin were also tested. The alkaline phosphatase activity of these preparations was determined by their action on β-glycerophosphate and phenyl phosphate, and the esterase activity by their capacity to split tributyrin. Since the highly purified transforming material isolated from pneumococcal extracts was found to contain desoxyribonucleic acid, these same enzymes were tested for depolymerase activity on known samples of desoxyribonucleic acid isolated by Mirsky[3] from fish sperm and mammalian tissues. The results are summarized in Table 2 in which the phosphatase, esterase, and nucleodepolymerase activity of these enzymes is compared with their capacity to destroy the transforming principle. Analysis of these results shows that irrespective of the presence of phosphatase or esterase only those preparations shown to contain an enzyme capable of depolymerizing authentic samples of desoxyribonucleic acid were found to inactivate the transforming principle.

TABLE 2

The Inactivation of Transforming Principle by Crude Enzyme Preparations.

| | Enzymatic activity | | | |
Crude enzyme preparations	Phosphatase	Tributyrin esterase	Depolymerase for desoxy- ribonucleate	Inactivation of transforming principle
Dog intestinal mucosa	+	+	+	+
Rabbit bone phosphatase	+	+	−	−
Swine kidney phosphatase	+	−	−	−
Pneumococcus autolysates	−	+	+	+
Normal dog and rabbit serum	+	+	+	+

Greenstein and Jenrette (*18*) have shown that tissue extracts, as well as the milk and serum of several mammalian species, contain an enzyme system which causes depolymerization of desoxyribonucleic acid. To this enzyme system Greenstein has later given the name desoxyribonucleodepolymerase (*19*). These investigators determined depolymerase activity by following the reduction in viscosity of solutions of sodium desoxyribonucleate. The nucleate and enzyme were mixed in the viscosimeter and viscosity measurements made at intervals during incubation at 30°C. In the present study this method was used in the measurement of depolymerase activity except that incubation was carried out at 37°C and, in addition to the reduction of viscosity, the action of the enzyme was further tested by the progressive decrease in acid precipitability of the nucleate during enzymatic breakdown.

TABLE 3

Differential Heat Inactivation of Enzymes in Dog and Rabbit Serum Which Destroy the Transforming Substance.

	Heat treatment of serum	Dilution*	Triplicate tests					
			1		2		3	
			Diffuse growth	*Colony form*	*Diffuse growth*	*Colony form*	*Diffuse growth*	*Colony form*
	Unheated	Undiluted	−	R only	−	R only	−	R only
		1:5	−	R only	−	R only	−	R only
		1:25	−	R only	−	R only	−	R only
Dog serum	60°C for 30 min	Undiluted	+	SIII	+	SIII	+	SIII
		1:5	+	SIII	+	SIII	+	SIII
		1:25	+	SIII	+	SIII	+	SIII
	65°C for 30 min	Undiluted	+	SIII	+	SIII	+	SIII
		1:5	+	SIII	+	SIII	+	SIII
		1:25	+	SIII	+	SIII	+	SIII
	Unheated	Undiluted	−	R only	−	R only	−	R only
		1:5	−	R only	−	R only	−	R only
		1:25	−	R only	−	R only	−	R only
Rabbit serum	60°C for 30 min	Undiluted	−	R only	−	R only	−	R only
		1:5	−	R only	−	R only	−	R only
		1:25	−	R only	−	R only	−	R only
	65°C for 30 min	Undiluted	+	SIII	+	SIII	+	SIII
		1:5	+	SIII	+	SIII	+	SIII
		1:25	+	SIII	+	SIII	+	SIII
Control (no serum)	None	Undiluted	+	SIII	+	SIII	+	SIII
		1:5	+	SIII	+	SIII	+	SIII
		1:25	+	SIII	+	SIII	+	SIII

* *Dilution of the digest mixture of serum and transforming substance.*

The effect of fresh normal dog and rabbit serum on the activity of the transforming substance is shown in the following experiment.

Sera obtained from a normal dog and normal rabbit were diluted with an equal volume of physiological saline. The diluted serum was divided into three equal portions. One part was heated at 65°C for 30 minutes, another at 60°C for 30 minutes, and the third was used unheated as control. A partially purified preparation of transforming material which had previously been dried in the lyophile apparatus was dissolved in saline in a concentration of 3.7 mg per cc. 1.0 cc of this solution was mixed with 0.5 cc of the various samples of heated and unheated diluted sera, and the mixtures at pH 7.4 were incubated at 37°C for 2 hours. After the serum had been allowed to act on the transforming material for this period, all tubes were heated at 65°C for 30 minutes to stop enzymatic action. Serial dilutions were then made in saline and tested in triplicate for transforming activity according to the procedure described under Method of titration. The results given in Table 3 illustrate the differential heat inactivation of the enzymes in dog and rabbit serum which destroy the transforming principle.

From the data presented in Table 3 it is evident that both dog and rabbit serum in the unheated state are capable of completely destroying transforming activity. On the other hand, when samples of dog serum which have been heated either at 60°C or at 65°C for 30 minutes are used, there is no loss of transforming activity. Thus, in this species the serum enzyme responsible for destruction of the transforming principle is completely inactivated at 60°C. In contrast to these results, exposure to 65°C for 30 minutes was required for complete destruction of the corresponding enzyme in rabbit serum.

The same samples of dog and rabbit serum used in the preceding experiment were also tested for their depolymerase activity on a preparation of sodium desoxyribonucleate isolated by Mirsky from shad sperm.

A highly viscous solution of the nucleate in distilled water in a concentration of 1 mg per cc was used. 1.0 cc amounts of heated and unheated sera diluted in saline as shown in the preceding protocol were mixed in Ostwald viscosimeters with 4.0 cc of the aqueous solution of the nucleate. Determinations of viscosity were made immediately and at intervals over a period of 24 hours during incubation at 37°C.

The results of this experiment are graphically presented in Chart 1. In the case of unheated serum of both dog and rabbit, the viscosity fell to that of water in 5 to 7 hours. Dog serum heated at 60°C for 30 minutes brought about no significant reduction in viscosity after 22 hours. On the other hand, heating rabbit serum at 60°C merely reduced the rate of depolymerase action, and after 24 hours the viscosity was brought to the same level as with the unheated serum. Heating at 65°C, however, completely destroyed the rabbit serum depolymerase.

Thus, in the case of dog and rabbit sera there is a striking parallelism between the temperature of inactivation of the depolymerase and that of the enzyme which destroys the activity of the transforming principle. The fact that this difference in temperature of inactivation is not merely a general property of all enzymes in the sera is evident from experiments

CHART 1   Differential Heat Inactivation
of Desoxyribonucleodepolymerase
of Dog and Rabbit Serum

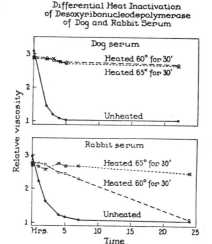

on the heat inactivation of tributyrin esterase in the same samples of serum. In the latter instance, the results are the reverse of those observed with depolymerase since the esterase of rabbit serum is almost completely inactivated at 60°C while that in dog serum is only slightly affected by exposure to this temperature.

Of a number of substances tested for their capacity to inhibit the action of the enzyme known to destroy the transforming principle, only sodium fluoride has been found to have a significant inhibitory effect. Regardless of whether this enzyme is derived from pneumococcal cells, dog intestinal mucosa, pancreatin, or normal sera its activity is inhibited by fluoride. Similarly it has been found that fluoride in the same concentration also inhibits the enzymatic depolymerization of desoxyribonucleic acid.

The fact that transforming activity is destroyed only by those preparations containing depolymerase for desoxyribonucleic acid and the further fact that in both instances the enzymes concerned are inactivated at the same temperature and inhibited by fluoride provide additional evidence for the belief that the active principle is a nucleic acid of the desoxyribose type.

Serological Analysis. In the course of chemical isolation of the active material it was found that as crude extracts were purified, their serological activity in Type III antiserum progressively decreased without corresponding loss in biological activity. Solutions of the highly purified substance itself gave only faint trace reactions in precipitin tests with high titer Type III antipneumococcus rabbit serum.[4] It is well known that pneumococcal protein can be detected by serological methods in dilutions as high as 1:50,000 and the capsular as well as the somatic polysaccharide in dilutions of at least 1 : 5,000,000. In view of these facts, the loss of serological reactivity indicates that these cell constituents have been almost completely removed from the final preparations. The fact that the transforming substance in purified state exhibits little or no serological reactivity is in striking contrast to its biological specificity in inducing pneumococcal transformation.

Physicochemical Studies.[5] A purified and active preparation of the transforming substance (preparation 44) was examined in the analytical ultracentrifuge. The material gave a single and unusually sharp boundary indicating that the substance was homogeneous and that the molecules were uniform in size and very asymmetric. Biological activity was found to be sedimented at the same rate as the optically observed boundary, showing that activity could not be due to the presence of an entity much different in size. The molecular weight cannot be accurately determined until measurements of the diffusion constant and partial specific volume have been made. However, Tennent and Vilbrandt (20) have determined the diffusion constant of several preparations of thymus nucleic acid, the sedimentation rate of which is in close agreement with the values observed in the present study. Assuming that the asymmetry of the molecules is the same in both instances, it is estimated that the molecular weight of the pneumococcal preparation is of the order of 500,000.

Examination of the same active preparation was carried out by electrophoresis in the Tiselius apparatus and revealed only a single electrophoretic component of relatively high mobility comparable to that of a nucleic acid. Transforming activity was associated with the fast moving component giving the optically visible boundary. Thus in both the electrical and centrifugal fields, the behavior of the purified substance is consistent with the concept that biological activity is a property of the highly polymerized nucleic acid.

Ultraviolet absorption curves showed maxima in the region of 2600 Å and minima in the region of 2350 Å. These findings are characteristic of nucleic acids.

Quantitative Determination of Biological Activity. In its highly purified state the material as isolated has been found to be capable of inducing transformation in amounts ranging from 0.02 to 0.003 µg. Preparation 44, the purification of which was carried out at low temperature and which had a nitrogen-phosphorus ratio of 1.58, exhibited high transforming activity. Titration of the activity of this preparation is given in Table 4.

A solution containing 0.5 mg per cc was serially diluted as shown in the protocol. 0.2 cc of each of these dilutions was added to quadruplicate tubes containing 2.0 cc of standard serum broth. All tubes were then inoculated with 0.05 cc of a 10^{-4} dilution of a 5- to 8-hour blood broth culture of R36A. Transforming activity was determined by the procedure described under Method of titration.

TABLE 4

Titration of Transforming Activity of Preparation 44.

Transforming principle Preparation 44*		Quadruplicate tests							
		1		2		3		4	
Dilution	Amount added	Diffuse growth	Colony form	Diffuse growth	Colony form	Diffuse growth	Colony form	Diffuse growth	Colony form
	μg.								
10⁻²	1.0	+	SIII	+	SIII	+	SIII	+	SIII
10⁻²·⁵	0.3	+	SIII	+	SIII	+	SIII	+	SIII
10⁻³	0.1	+	SIII	+	SIII	+	SIII	+	SIII
10⁻³·⁵	0.03	+	SIII	+	SIII	+	SIII	+	SIII
10⁻⁴	0.01	+	SIII	+	SIII	+	SIII	+	SIII
10⁻⁴·⁵	0.003	−	R only	+	SIII	−	R only	+	SIII
10⁻⁵	0.001	−	R only	−	R only	−	R only	−	R only
Control	None	−	R only	−	R only	−	R only	−	R only

* Solution from which dilutions were made contained 0.5 mg per cc of purified material. 0.2 cc of each dilution added to quadruplicate tubes containing 2.0 cc of standard serum broth. 0.05 cc of 10⁻⁴ dilution of a blood broth culture of R36A is added to each tube.

The data presented in Table 4 show that on the basis of dry weight 0.003 μg. of the active material brought about transformation. Since the reaction system containing the 0.003 μg. has a volume of 2.25 cc, this represents a final concentration of the purified substance of 1 part in 600,000,000.

DISCUSSION

The present study deals with the results of an attempt to determine the chemical nature of the substance inducing specific transformation of pneumococcal types. A desoxyribonucleic acid fraction has been isolated from Type III pneumococci which is capable of transforming unencapsulated R variants derived from Pneumococcus Type II into fully encapsulated Type III cells. Thompson and Dubos (21) have isolated from pneumococci a nucleic acid of the ribose type. So far as the writers are aware, however, a nucleic acid of the desoxyribose type has not heretofore been recovered from pneumococci nor has specific transformation been experimentally induced *in vitro* by a chemically defined substance.

Although the observations are limited to a single example, they acquire broader significance from the work of earlier investigators who demonstrated the interconvertibility of various pneumococcal types and showed that the specificity of the changes induced is in each instance determined by the particular type of encapsulated cells used to evoke the reaction. From the point of view of the phenomenon in general, therefore, it is of special interest that in the example studied, highly purified and protein-free material consisting largely, if not exclusively, of desoxyribonucleic acid is capable of stimulating unencapsulated R variants of Pneumococcus Type II to produce a capsular polysaccharide identical in type specificity with that of the cells from which the inducing substance was isolated. Equally striking is the fact that the substance evoking the reaction and the capsular substance produced in response to it are chemically distinct, each belonging to a wholly different class of chemical compounds.

The inducing substance, on the basis of its chemical and physical properties, appears to be a highly polymerized and viscous form of sodium desoxyribonucleate. On the other hand, the Type III capsular substance, the synthesis of which is evoked by this transforming agent, consists chiefly of a non-nitrogenous polysaccharide constituted of glucose-glucuronic acid units linked in glycosidic union (22). The presence of the newly formed capsule containing this type-specific polysaccharide confers on the transformed cells all the distinguishing characteristics of Pneumococcus Type III. Thus, it is evident that the inducing substance and the substance produced in turn are chemically distinct and biologically specific in their action and that both are requisite in determining the type specificity of the cell of which they form a part.

The experimental data presented in this paper strongly suggest that nucleic acids, at least those of the desoxyribose type, possess different specificities as evidenced by the selective action of the transforming principle. Indeed, the possibility of the existence of specific differences in biological behavior of nucleic acids has previously been suggested (23, 24) but has never been experimentally demonstrated owing in part at least to the lack of suitable biological methods. The techniques used in the study of transformation appear to afford a sensitive means of testing the validity of this hypothesis, and the results thus far obtained add supporting evidence in favor of this point of view.

If it is ultimately proved beyond reasonable doubt that the transforming activity of the material described is actually an inherent property of the nucleic acid, one must still account on a chemical basis for the biological specificity of its action. At first glance, immunological methods would appear to offer the ideal means of determining the differential specificity of this group of biologically important substances. Although the constituent units and general pattern of the nucleic acid molecule have been defined, there is as yet relatively little known of the possible effect that subtle differences in molecular configuration may exert on the biological specificity of these substances. However, since nucleic acids free or combined with histones or protamines are not known to function antigenically, one would not anticipate that such differences would be revealed by immunological techniques. Consequently, it is perhaps not surprising that highly purified and protein-free preparations of desoxyribonucleic acid, although extremely active in inducing transformation, showed only faint trace reactions in precipitin tests with potent Type III antipneumococcus rabbit sera.

From these limited observations it would be unwise to draw any conclusion concerning the immunological significance of the nucleic acids until further knowledge on this phase of the problem is available. Recent observations by Lackman and his collaborators (25) have shown that nucleic acids of both the yeast and thymus type derived from hemolytic streptococci and from animal and plant sources precipitate with certain antipneumococcal sera. The reactions varied with different lots of immune serum and occurred more frequently in antipneumococcal horse serum than in corresponding sera of immune rabbits. The irregularity and broad cross reactions encountered led these investigators to express some doubt as to the immunological significance of the results. Unless special immunochemical methods can be devised similar to those so successfully used in demonstrating the serological specificity of simple non-antigenic substances, it appears that the techniques employed in the study of transformation are the only ones available at present for testing possible differences in the biological behavior of nucleic acids.

Admittedly there are many phases of the problem of transformation that require further study and many questions that remain unanswered largely because of technical difficulties. For example, it would be of interest to know the relation between rate of reaction and concentration of the transforming substance; the proportion of cells transformed to those that remain unaffected in the reaction system. However, from a bacteriological point of view, numerical estimations based on colony counts might prove more misleading than enlightening because of the aggregation and sedimentation of the R cells agglutinated by the antiserum in the medium. Attempts to induce transformation in suspensions of resting cells held under conditions inhibiting growth and multiplication have thus far proved unsuccessful, and it seems probable that transformation occurs only during active reproduction of the cells. Important in this connection is the fact that the R cells, as well as those that have undergone transformation, presumably also all other variants and types of pneumococci, contain an intracellular enzyme which is released during autolysis and in the free state is capable of rapidly and completely destroying the activity of the transforming agent. It would appear, therefore, that during the logarithmic phase of growth when cell division is most active and autolysis least apparent, the cultural conditions are optimal for the maintenance of the balance between maximal reactivity of the R cell and minimal destruction of the transforming agent through the release of autolytic ferments.

In the present state of knowledge any interpretation of the mechanism involved in transformation must of necessity be purely theoretical. The biochemical events underlying the phenomenon suggest that the trans-forming principle interacts with the R cell giving rise to a coordinated series of enzymatic reactions that culminate in the synthesis of the Type III capsular antigen. The experimental findings have clearly demon-strated that the induced alterations are not random changes but are predictable, always corresponding in type specificity to that of the en-capsulated cells from which the transforming substance was isolated. Once transformation has occurred, the newly acquired characteristics are thereafter transmitted in series through innumerable transfers in artificial media without any further addition of the transforming agent. Moreover, from the transformed cells themselves, a substance of identical activity can again be recovered in amounts far in excess of that originally added to induce the change. It is evident, therefore, that not only is the capsular material reproduced in successive generations but that the primary factor, which controls the occurrence and specificity of capsular development, is also reduplicated in the daughter cells. The induced changes are not temporary modifications but are permanent alterations which persist, provided the cultural conditions are favorable for the maintenance of capsule formation. The transformed cells can be readily distinguished from the parent R forms not alone by serological reactions but by the presence of a newly formed and visible capsule which is the immunological unit of type specificity and the accessory structure essential in determining the infective capacity of the micro-organism in the animal body.

It is particularly significant in the case of pneumococci that the experi-mentally induced alterations are definitely correlated with the develop-ment of a new morphological structure and the consequent acquisition of new antigenic and invasive properties. Equally if not more significant is the fact that these changes are predictable, type-specific, and heritable.

Various hypotheses have been advanced in explanation of the nature of the changes induced. In his original description of the phenomenon Griffith (1) suggested that the dead bacteria in the inoculum might furnish some specific protein that serves as a "pablum" and enables the R form to manufacture a capsular carbohydrate.

More recently the phenomenon has been interpreted from a genetic point of view (26, 27). The inducing substance has been likened to a gene, and the capsular antigen which is produced in response to it has been regarded as a gene product. In discussing the phenomenon of transformation Dobzhansky (27) has stated that "If this transformation is described as a genetic mutation — and it is difficult to avoid so describ-ing it — we are dealing with authentic cases of induction of specific mutations by specific treatments. . . ."

Another interpretation of the phenomenon has been suggested by Stanley (28) who has drawn the analogy between the activity of the transforming agent and that of a virus. On the other hand, Murphy (29) has compared the causative agents of fowl tumors with the transforming principle of Pneumococcus. He has suggested that both these groups of agents be termed "transmissible mutagens" in order to differentiate them from the virus group. Whatever may prove to be the correct interpretation, these differences in viewpoint indicate the implications of the phenomenon of transformation in relation to similar problems in the fields of genetics, virology, and cancer research.

It is, of course, possible that the biological activity of the substance described is not an inherent property of the nucleic acid but is due to minute amounts of some other substance adsorbed to it or so intimately associated with it as to escape detection. If, however, the biologically active substance isolated in highly purified form as the sodium salt of desoxyribonucleic acid actually proves to be the transforming principle, as the available evidence strongly suggests, then nucleic acids of this type must be regarded not merely as structurally important but as functionally active in determining the biochemical activities and specific characteristics of pneumococcal cells. Assuming that the sodium desoxyribonucleate and the active principle are one and the same substance, then the transformation described represents a change that is chemically induced and specifically directed by a known chemical compound. If the results of the present study on the chemical nature of the transforming principle are confirmed, then nucleic acids must be regarded as possessing biological specificity, the chemical basis of which is as yet undetermined.

SUMMARY

1. From Type III pneumococci a biologically active fraction has been isolated in highly purified form which in exceedingly minute amounts is capable under appropriate cultural conditions of inducing the transformation of unencapsulated R variants of Pneumococcus Type II into fully encapsulated cells of the same specific type as that of the heat-killed microorganisms from which the inducing material was recovered.

2. Methods for the isolation and purification of the active transforming material are described.

3. The data obtained by chemical, enzymatic, and serological analyses together with the results of preliminary studies by electrophoresis, ultracentrifugation, and ultraviolet spectroscopy indicate that, within the limits of the methods, the active fraction contains no demonstrable protein, unbound lipid, or serologically reactive polysaccharide and consists principally, if not solely, of a highly polymerized, viscous form of desoxyribonucleic acid.

4. Evidence is presented that the chemically induced alterations in cellular structure and function are predictable, type-specific, and transmissible in series. The various hypotheses that have been advanced concerning the nature of these changes are reviewed.

CONCLUSION

The evidence presented supports the belief that a nucleic acid of the desoxyribose type is the fundamental unit of the transforming principle of Pneumococcus Type III.

Received for publication, November 1, 1943

REFERENCES AND NOTES

* Work done in part as Fellow in the Medical Sciences of the National Research Council.

1 The elementary chemical analyses were made by Dr. A. Elek of The Rockefeller Institute.

2 The authors are indebted to Dr. John H. Northrop and Dr. M. Kunitz of The Rockefeller Institute for Medical Research, Princeton, N.J., for the samples of crystalline trypsin, chymotrypsin, and ribonuclease used in this work.

3 The authors express their thanks to Dr. A. E. Mirsky of the Hospital of The Rockefeller Institute for these preparations of desoxyribonucleic acid.

4 The Type III antipneumococcus rabbit serum employed in this study was furnished through the courtesy of Dr. Jules T. Freund, Bureau of Laboratories, Department of Health, City of New York.

5 Studies on sedimentation in the ultracentrifuge were carried out by Dr. A. Rothen; the electrophoretic analyses were made by Dr. T. Shedlovsky, and the ultraviolet absorption curves by Dr. G. I. Lavin. The authors gratefully acknowledge their indebtedness to these members of the staff of The Rockefeller Institute.

1. F. Griffith, *J. Hyg.* (Cambridge, Eng.) **27**, 113 (1928).

2. F. Neufeld and W. Levinthal, Z. *Immunitätsforsch.* **55**, 324 (1928).

3. W. Baurhenn, *Centr. Bakt., 1. Abt., Orig.* **126**, 68 (1932).

4. M. H. Dawson, *J. Exp. Med.* **51**, 123 (1930).

5. _____ and R. H. P. Sia, *J. Exp. Med.* **54**, 681 (1931).

6. J. L. Alloway, *J. Exp. Med.* **55**, 91 (1933); **57**, 265 (1932).

7. G. P. Berry and H. M. Dedrick, *J. Bact.* **31**, 50 (1936).

8. G. P. Berry, *Arch. Path.* **24**, 533 (1937).

9. E. W. Hurst, *Brit. J. Exp. Path.* **18**, 23 (1937). R. E. Hoffstadt and K. S. Pilcher, *J. Infect. Dis.* **68**, 67 (1941). R. E. Gardner and R. R. Hyde, *J. Infect. Dis.* **71**, 47 (1942). R. B. Houlihan, *Proc. Soc. Exp. Biol. and Med.* **51**, 259 (1942).

10. C. M. MacLeod and G. S. Mirick, *J. Bact.* **44**, 277 (1942).

11. M. H. Dawson, *J. Exp. Med.* **47**, 577 (1928); **51**, 99 (1930).

12. M. G. Sevag, *Biochem. Z.* **273**, 419 (1934). M. G. Sevag, D. B. Lackman, J. Smolens, *J. Biol. Chem.* **124**, 425 (1938).

13. R. J. Dubos and O. T. Avery, *J. Exp. Med.* **54**, 51 (1931). R. J. Dubos and J. H. Bauer, *J. Exp. Med.* **62**, 271 (1935).

14. S. Liu and H. Wu, *Chinese J. Physiol.* **13**, 449 (1938).

15. M. Martland and R. Robison, *Biochem. J.* **23**, 237 (1929).

16. H. Albers and E. Albers, Z. *physiol. Chem.* **232**, 189 (1935).

17. P.A. Levene and R. T. Dillon, *J. Biol. Chem.* **96**, 461 (1933).

18. J. P. Greenstein and W. Y. Jenrette, *J. Nat. Cancer Inst.* **1**, 845 (1940).

19. J. P. Greenstein, *J. Nat. Cancer Inst.* **4**, 55 (1943).

20. H. G. Tennent and C. F. Vilbrandt, *J. Am. Chem. Soc.* **65**, 424 (1943).

21. R. H. S. Thompson and R. J. Dubos, *J. Biol. Chem.* **125**, 65 (1938).

22. R. E. Reeves and W. F. Goebel, *J. Biol. Chem.* **139**, 511 (1941).

23. J. Schultz, in Genes and chromosomes. Structure and organization, Cold Spring Harbor Symp. Quant. Biol. 9, 55 (1941).

24. A. E. Mirsky, in *Advances in Enzymology and Related Subjects of Biochemistry*, F. F. Nord and C. H. Werkman, Eds. (Interscience, New York, 1943), III, 1.

25. D. Lackman, S. Mudd, M. G. Sevag, J. Smolens, M. Wiener, *J. Immunol.* **40**, 1 (1941).

26. R. A. Gortner, *Outlines of Biochemistry* (John Wiley & Sons, New York, 2 ed., 1938), p. 547.

27. T. Dobzhansky, *Genetics and the Origin of the Species* (Columbia Univ. Press, New York, 1941), p. 47.

28. W. M. Stanley, in R. Doerr, and C. Hallauer, *Handbuch der Virusforschung* (Springer, Vienna, 1938), I, 491.

29. J. B. Murphy, *Tr. Assn. Am. Physn.* **46**, 182 (1931); *Bull. Johns Hopkins Hosp.* **56**, 1 (1935).

Genetical Implications of the Structure of Deoxyribonucleic Acid

J. D. Watson
F. H. C. Crick

*Cavendish Laboratory, Cambridge**

The importance of deoxyribonucleic acid (DNA) within living cells is undisputed. It is found in all dividing cells, largely if not entirely in the nucleus, where it is an essential constituent of the chromosomes. Many lines of evidence indicate that it is the carrier of a part of (if not all) the genetic specificity of the chromosomes and thus of the gene itself. Until now, however, no evidence has been presented to show how it might carry out the essential operation required of a genetic material, that of exact self-duplication.

We have recently proposed a structure (1) for the salt of deoxyribonucleic acid which, if correct, immediately suggests a mechanism for its self-duplication. X-ray evidence obtained by the workers at King's College, London (2), and presented at the same time, gives qualitative support to our structure and is incompatible with all previously proposed structures (3). Though the structure will not be completely proved until a more extensive comparison has been made with the X-ray data, we now feel sufficient confidence in its general correctness to discuss its genetical implications. In doing so we are assuming that fibres of the salt of deoxyribonucleic acid are not artefacts arising in the method of preparation, since it has been shown by Wilkins and his co-workers that similar X-ray patterns are obtained from both the isolated fibres and certain intact biological materials such as sperm head and bacteriophage particles (2, 4).

Reprinted from *Nature* 171, 964–69 (1953), by permission of the authors and the editors of *Nature,* Macmillan (Journals) Limited.

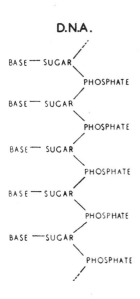

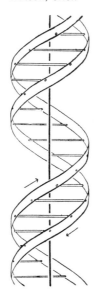

FIGURE 1. Chemical formula of a single chain of deoxyribonucleic acid.

FIGURE 2. This figure is purely diagrammatic. The two ribbons symbolize the two phosphate-sugar chains, and the horizontal rods the pairs of bases holding the chains together. The vertical line marks the fibre axis.

The chemical formula of deoxyribonucleic acid is now well established. The molecule is a very long chain, the backbone of which consists of a regular alternation of sugar and phosphate groups, as shown in Figure 1. To each sugar is attached a nitrogenous base, which can be of four different types. (We have considered 5-methyl cytosine to be equivalent to cytosine, since either can fit equally well into our structure.) Two of the possible bases — adenine and guanine — are purines, and the other two — thymine and cytosine — are pyrimidines. So far as is known, the sequence of bases along the chain is irregular. The monomer unit, consisting of phosphate, sugar and base, is known as a nucleotide.

The first feature of our structure which is of biological interest is that it consists not of one chain, but of two. These two chains are both coiled around a common fibre axis, as is shown diagrammatically in Figure 2. It has often been assumed that since there was only one chain in the chemical formula there would only be one in the structural unit. However, the density, taken with the X-ray evidence (2), suggests very strongly that there are two.

The other biologically important feature is the manner in which the two chains are held together. This is done by hydrogen bonds between the bases, as shown schematically in Figure 3. The bases are joined

FIGURE 3. Chemical formula of a pair of deoxyribonucleic acid chains. The hydrogen bonding is symbolized by dotted lines.

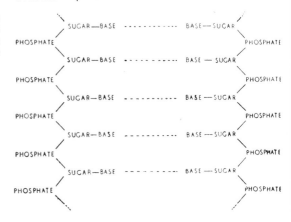

together in pairs, a single base from one chain being hydrogen-bonded to a single base from the other. The important point is that only certain pairs of bases will fit into the structure. One member of a pair must be a purine and the other a pyrimidine in order to bridge between two chains. If a pair consisted of two purines, for example, there would not be room for it.

We believe that the bases will be present almost entirely in their most probable tautomeric forms. If this is true, the conditions for forming hydrogen bonds are more restrictive, and the only pairs of bases possible are:

adenine with thymine

guanine with cytosine

The way in which these are joined together is shown in Figures 4 and 5. A given pair can be either way round. Adenine, for example, can occur on either chain; but when it does, its partner on the other chain must always be thymine.

This pairing is strongly supported by the recent analytical results (5), which show that for all sources of deoxyribonucleic acid examined the amount of adenine is close to the amount of thymine, and the amount of guanine close to the amount of cytosine, although the cross-ratio (the ratio of adenine to guanine) can vary from one source to another. Indeed, if the sequence of bases on one chain is irregular, it is difficult to explain these analytical results except by the sort of pairing we have suggested.

The phosphate-sugar backbone of our model is completely regular, but any sequence of the pairs of bases can fit into the structure. It follows that in a long molecule many different permutations are possible, and it therefore seems likely that the precise sequence of the bases is the code which carries the genetical information. If the actual order of

FIGURE 4. Pairing of adenine and thymine. Hydrogen bonds are shown dotted. One carbon atom of each sugar is shown.

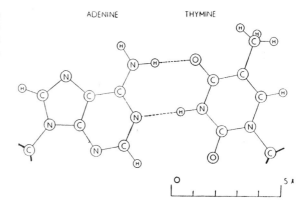

FIGURE 5. Pairing of guanine and cytosine. Hydrogen bonds are shown dotted. One carbon atom of each sugar is shown.

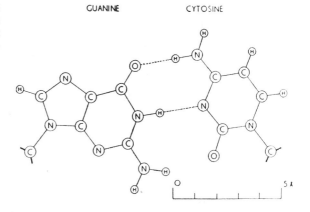

the bases on one of the pair of chains were given, one could write down the exact order of the bases on the other one, because of the specific pairing. Thus one chain is, as it were, the complement of the other, and it is this feature which suggests how the deoxyribonucleic acid molecule might duplicate itself.

Previous discussions of self-duplication have usually involved the concept of a template, or mould. Either the template was supposed to copy itself directly or it was to produce a "negative," which in its turn was to act as a template and produce the original "positive" once again. In no case has it been explained in detail how it would do this in terms of atoms and molecules.

Now our model for deoxyribonucleic acid is, in effect, a *pair* of templates, each of which is complementary to the other. We imagine that prior to duplication the hydrogen bonds are broken, and the two chains unwind and separate. Each chain then acts as a template for the formation on to itself of a new companion chain, so that eventually we shall have *two* pairs of chains, where we only had one before. Moreover, the sequence of the pairs of bases will have been duplicated exactly.

A study of our model suggests that this duplication could be done most simply if the single chain (or the relevant portion of it) takes up the helical configuration. We imagine that at this stage in the life of the cell, free nucleotides, strictly polynucleotide precursors, are available in quantity. From time to time the base of a free nucleotide will join up by hydrogen bonds to one of the bases on the chain already formed. We now postulate that the polymerization of these monomers to form a new chain is only possible if the resulting chain can form the proposed structure. This is plausible, because steric reasons would not allow nucleotides "crystallized" on to the first chain to approach one another in such a way that they could be joined together into a new chain, unless they were those nucleotides which were necessary to form our structure. Whether a special enzyme is required to carry out the polymerization, or whether the single helical chain already formed acts effectively as an enzyme, remains to be seen.

Since the two chains in our model are intertwined, it is essential for them to untwist if they are to separate. As they make one complete turn around each other in 34 Å, there will be about 150 turns per million molecular weight, so that whatever the precise structure of the chromosome a considerable amount of uncoiling would be necessary. It is well known from microscopic observation that much coiling and uncoiling occurs during mitosis, and though this is on a much larger scale it probably reflects similar processes on a molecular level. Although it is difficult at the moment to see how these processes occur without everything getting tangled, we do not feel that this objection will be insuperable.

Our structure, as described (*1*), is an open one. There is room between the pair of polynucleotide chains (see Fig. 2) for a polypeptide chain to wind around the same helical axis. It may be significant that the distance between adjacent phosphorus atoms, 7.1 Å, is close to the repeat of a fully extended polypeptide chain. We think it probable that in the sperm head, and in artificial nucleoproteins, the polypeptide chain occupies this position. The relative weakness of the second layer-line in the published X-ray pictures (*3a, 4*) is crudely compatible with such an idea. The function of the protein might well be to control the coiling and uncoiling, to assist in holding a single polynucleotide chain in a helical configuration, or some other nonspecific function.

Our model suggests possible explanations for a number of other phenomena. For example, spontaneous mutation may be due to a base occasionally occurring in one of its less likely tautomeric forms. Again, the pairing between homologous chromosomes at meiosis may depend on pairing between specific bases. We shall discuss these ideas in detail elsewhere.

For the moment, the general scheme we have proposed for the reproduction of deoxyribonucleic acid must be regarded as speculative. Even if it is correct, it is clear from what we have said that much remains to be discovered before the picture of genetic duplication can be described in detail. What are the polynucleotide precursors? What makes the pair of chains unwind and separate? What is the precise role of the protein? Is the chromosome one long pair of deoxyribonucleic acid chains, or does it consist of patches of the acid joined together by protein?

Despite these uncertainties we feel that our proposed structure for deoxyribonucleic acid may help to solve one of the fundamental biological problems — the molecular basis of the template needed for genetic replication. The hypothesis we are suggesting is that the template is the pattern of bases formed by one chain of the deoxyribonucleic acid and that the gene contains a complementary pair of such templates.

One of us (J. D. W.) has been aided by a fellowship from the National Foundation for Infantile Paralysis (U.S.A.).

REFERENCES AND NOTES

* Medical Research Council Unit for the Study of the Molecular Structure of Biological Systems.

1. J. D. Watson and F. H. C. Crick, *Nature* 171, 737 (1953).
2. M. H. F. Wilkins, A. R. Stokes, H. R. Wilson, *Nature* 171, 738 (1953). R. E. Franklin and R. G. Gosling, *Nature* 171, 740 (1953).
3. W. T. Astbury, *Symp. No. 1 Soc. Exptl. Biol.* 66 (1947). b. S. Furberg, *Acta Chem. Scand.* 6, 634 (1952). c. L. Pauling and R. B. Corey, *Nature* 171, 346 (1953: *Proc. Nat. Acad. Sci. U.S.* 39, 84 (1953). d. R. D. B. Fraser, in preparation.
4. M. H. F. Wilkins and J. T. Randall, *Biochim. et Biophys. Acta* 10, 192 (1953).
5. E. Chargaff, for references see S. Zamenhof, G. Brawerman, E. Chargaff, *Biochim. et Biophys. Acta* 9, 402 (1952). G. R. Wyatt, *J. Gen. Physiol.* 36, 201 (1952).

Involvement of RNA in the Synthesis of Proteins

THE ORDERED INTERACTION OF THREE CLASSES OF RNA CONTROLS THE ASSEMBLY OF AMINO ACIDS INTO PROTEINS

J. D. Watson[*]

I arrived in Cambridge in the fall of 1951. Though my previous interests were largely genetic, Luria had arranged for me to work with John Kendrew. I was becoming frustrated with phage experiments and wanted to learn more about the actual structures of the molecules which the geneticists talked about so passionately. At the same time John needed a student and hoped that I would help him with his X-ray studies on myoglobin. I thus became a research student of Clare College with John as my supervisor.

But almost as soon as I set foot in the Cavendish Laboratory I knew I would never be of much help to him, for I had already started talking with Francis Crick. Perhaps even without Francis, I would have quickly tired of myoglobin. But with Francis to talk to, my fate was sealed, for we quickly discovered that we thought the same way about biology. The center of biology was the gene and its control of cellular metabolism. The main challenge in biology was to understand gene replication and the way in which genes control protein synthesis. It was obvious that these problems could be logically attacked only when the structure of the gene became known. This meant solving the

Reprinted from *Science* **140** 17–26 (April 5, 1963), by permission of the author and *Science*. Copyright 1963 by the American Association for the Advancement of Science.

structure of DNA. This objective then seemed out of reach to the interested geneticists. But in our cold, dark Cavendish room we thought the job could be done, quite possibly within a few months. Our optimism was partly based on Linus Pauling's feat (*1*) in deducing the α-helix, largely by following the rules of theoretical chemistry so persuasively explained in his classical *The Nature of the Chemical Bond*. We also knew that Maurice Wilkins had crystalline X-ray diffraction photographs of DNA, and so DNA must have a well-defined structure. There was thus an answer for somebody to get.

During the next 18 months, until the double-helical structure became elucidated, we frequently discussed the necessity that the correct structure have the capacity for self-replication. And in pessimistic moods we often worried that the correct structure might be dull — that is, that it would suggest absolutely nothing and excite us no more than something inert like collagen.

The finding of the double helix (*2*) thus brought us not only joy but great relief. It was unbelievably interesting and immediately allowed us to make a serious proposal (*3*) for the mechanism of gene duplication. Furthermore, this replication scheme involved thoroughly understood conventional chemical forces. Previously, some theoretical physicists, among them Pascual Jordan (*4*), had proposed that many biological phenomena, particularly gene replication, might be based on long-range forces arising from quantum-mechanical resonance interactions. Pauling (*5*) thoroughly disliked this conjecture and firmly insisted that known short-range forces between complementary surfaces would prove to be the basis of biological replication.

The establishment of the DNA structure reinforced our belief that Pauling's arguments were sound and that neither long-range forces nor, for that matter, any form of mysticism was involved in protein synthesis. But for the protein-replication problem, mere inspection of the DNA structure then gave no immediate bonus. This, however, did not worry us, since there was much speculation that RNA, not DNA, was involved in protein synthesis.

The notion that RNA is involved in protein synthesis goes back over 20 years to the pioneering experiments of Brachet and Casperson (*6*), who showed that cells actively synthesizing protein are rich in RNA. Later, when radioactive amino acids became available, this conjecture was strengthened by the observation (*7*) that the cellular site of protein synthesis is the microsomal component, composed in large part of spherical particles rich in RNA. Still later experiments (*8*) revealed that these ribonucleoprotein particles (now conveniently called ribosomes), not the lipoprotein membranes to which they are often attached, are the sites where polypeptide bonds are made. Most ribosomes are found in the cytoplasm, and, correspondingly, most cellular protein synthesis occurs without the direct intervention of the DNA located in the nucleus. The possibility was thus raised that the genetic specificity present in

DNA is first transferred to RNA intermediates, which then function as templates controlling assembly of specific amino acids into proteins.

We became able to state this hypothesis in more precise form when the structure of DNA became known in 1953. We then realized that DNA's genetic specificity resides in the complementary base sequences along its two intertwined chains. One or both of these complementary chains must serve as templates for specific RNA molecules whose genetic information again must reside in specific base sequences. These RNA molecules would then assume three-dimensional configurations containing surfaces complementary to the side groups of the 20 specific amino acids.

X-RAY STUDIES ON RNA AND
RNA-CONTAINING VIRUSES

The direct way to test this hypothesis was to solve the RNA structure. Already in 1952 I had taken some preliminary X-ray diffraction pictures of RNA. These, however, were very diffuse, and it was not until I returned to the United States in the fall of 1953 that serious X-ray studies on RNA began. Alexander Rich and I, then both at California Institute of Technology, obtained RNA samples from various cellular sources. We (9) were first very much encouraged to find that all the RNA samples, no matter what their cellular origin, gave similar X-ray diffraction patterns. A general RNA structure thus existed. This gave us hope that the structure, when solved, would be interesting. Our first pictures already showed large systematic absences of reflections on the meridian, suggesting a helical structure. But despite much effort to obtain native undegraded samples of high molecular weight, no satisfactory X-ray diffraction pattern was obtained. The reflections were always diffuse; no evidence of crystallinity was seen. Though there were marked similarities to the DNA pattern, we had no solid grounds for believing that these arose from a similar, helical molecule. The problem of whether RNA was a one-chain or a several-chain structure remained unanswered.

We then considered the possibility that RNA might have a regular structure only when combined with protein. At that time (1955) there was no good evidence for RNA's existing free from protein. All RNA was thought to exist either as a viral component or to be combined with protein in ribonucleoprotein particles. It thus seemed logical to turn attention to a study of ribonucleoprotein particles (ribosomes), since upon their surfaces protein was synthesized. Our hope, again, was that the establishment of their structure would reveal the long-sought cavities specific for the amino acids.

Then we were struck by the morphological similarity between ribosomes and small RNA-containing viruses like turnip yellow mosaic virus and poliomyelitis virus. By then (1955–56) I was back in Cambridge with Crick to finish formulating some general principles of viral structure (10). Our main idea was that the finite nucleic-acid content of viruses severely restricted the number of amino acids they could code for. As a consequence, the protein coat could not be constructed from a very large number of different protein molecules. Instead, it must be constructed from a number of identical small subunits arranged in a regular manner. These ideas already held for TMV, a rod-shaped virus, and we were very pleased when D. L. D. Caspar (*11*), then working with us at the Cavendish Laboratory, took some elegant diffraction pictures of bushy stunt virus crystals and extended experimental support to the spherical viruses.

STRUCTURAL STUDIES OF RIBOSOMES

At that time almost no structural studies had been done with ribosomes. They were chiefly characterized by their sedimentation constants; those from higher organisms (*12*) were in the 70S to 80S range, while those from bacteria (*13*) appeared smaller and to be of two sizes (30S and 50S). Because the bacterial particles seemed smaller, they seemed preferable for structural studies. Thus, when Alfred Tissières and I came to Harvard's Biological Laboratories in 1956, we initiated research on the ribosomes of the commonly studied bacteria *Escherichia coli*. We hoped that their structure would show similarities to the structures of the small spherical RNA viruses. Then we might have a good chance to crystallize them and eventually to use X-ray diffraction techniques to establish their three-dimensional structure.

But from the beginning of our Harvard experiments it was obvious that ribosome structure was more complicated than RNA virus structure. Depending upon the concentration of divalent cations (in all our experiments, Mg^{++}), four classes of *E. coli* ribosomes were found, characterized by sedimentation constants of 30S, 50S, 70S, and 100S. Our first experiments with $10^{-4}M$ Mg^{++} revealed 30S and 50S ribosomes. At the same time Bolton and his co-workers (*14*), at the Carnegie Institute of Washington, employing higher levels of Mg^{++}, saw ribosomes with a higher rate of sedimentation and suggested that they were observing aggregates of the smaller particles. Soon after, more experiments (*15–17*) revealed that, as the concentration of Mg^{++} is raised, one 30S particle and one 50S particle combine to form a 70S ribosome. At still higher concentrations of Mg^{++} two 70S ribosomes dimerize to form a 100S ribosome (Figs. 1 and 2).

FIGURE 1. Diagrammatic representation of *E. coli* ribosome subunits and their aggregation products. The values in the bottom line indicate the molecular weight with a factor of 10^{-6}. The data are from Tissières *et al.* (*15*). All particles are composed of 64 percent RNA and 36 percent protein.

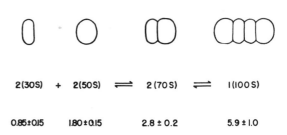

2(30S)	+	2(50S)	⇌	2(70S)	⇌	1(100S)
0.85±0.15		1.80±0.15		2.8 ± 0.2		5.9 ± 1.0

FIGURE 2. Electron micrograph of negatively stained *E. coli* ribosomes (Huxley and Zubay, *17*). Two particle types are predominant: (i) 70*S*, containing two subunits of unequal size, and (ii) 100*S*, consisting of two 70*S* ribosomes joined together at their smaller (30*S*) subunits.

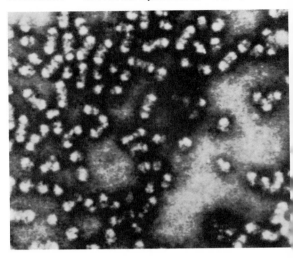

Ribosomes from every cellular source have a similar subunit construction. In all cases the level of divalent cations determines which ribosomes are predominent. Bacterial ribosomes require higher levels of Mg^{++} in order to aggregate into the larger sizes. Conversely, they break down much faster to the 30*S* and 50*S* forms when the Mg^{++} level is lowered. It is often convenient (*18*) when using mammalian ribosomes to add a chelating agent to rapidly break down the 80*S* ribosomes (homologous to the 70*S* ribosomes of bacteria) to their 40*S* and 60*S* subunits. Bacterial ribosomes are thus not significantly smaller than mammalian ribosomes. It is merely easier to observe the smaller subunits in bacterial systems.

Already in 1958 there were several reports (*19*) that ribosomal RNA sedimented as two distinct components (18*S* and 28*S*). We thought that the smaller molecules most likely arose from the smaller subunit, while the faster-sedimenting RNA came from the larger of the ribosomal

FIGURE 3. Molecular weights of RNA isolated from *E. coli* ribosomes. This picture is diagrammatic and does not represent the true conformation of ribosomal RNA.

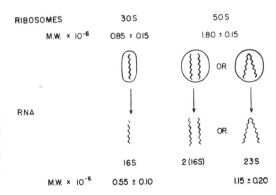

subunits. Experiments of Kurland (20) quickly confirmed this hunch. The *Escherichia coli* 30S ribosome was found to contain one RNA chain (16S) with a molecular weight of 5.5×10^5. Correspondingly, a larger RNA molecule (23S) of molecular weight 1.1×10^6 was found in most 50S ribosomes (Fig. 3).

RIBOSOME PROTEINS

Analysis of the protein component revealed a much more complicated picture. In contrast to the small RNA viruses, where the protein coat is constructed from the regular arrangement of a large number of identical protein molecules, each ribosome most likely contains a large number of different polypeptide chains. At first our results suggested a simple answer when Waller and J. I. Harris analyzed *E. coli* ribosomes for their amino terminal groups. Only alanine and methionine, with smaller amounts of serine, were present in significant amounts. This hinted that only several species of protein molecules were used for ribosome construction. Further experiments by Waller (21), however, suggested the contrary. When ribosomal protein fractions were analyzed by starch-gel electrophoresis, more than 20 distinct bands were seen. Almost all these proteins migrated toward the anode at pH 7, confirming the net basic charge of ribosomal protein (22). A variety of control experiments suggested that these bands represented distinct polypeptide chains, not merely aggregated states of several fundamental subunits. Moreover, the band pattern from 30S ribosomes was radically different from that of 50S proteins.

As yet we have no solid proof that each 70S ribosome contains all the various protein components found in the total population. But so far, all attempts by Waller to separate chromatographically intact ribosomes into fractions with different starch-gel patterns have failed. The total protein component of a 70S ribosome amounts to about 9×10^5 daltons. Since the end group analysis suggests an average molecular weight of about 30,000, approximately 20 polypeptide chains must be used in the construction of the 50S ribosome, and ten for the 30S ribosome. It is possible that all the polypeptide chains in a 30S particle are different. Waller already has evidence for ten distinct components in 30S ribosomes, and the present failure to observe more in the 50S protein fraction may merely mean that the same electrophoretic mobility is shared by several polypeptide chains.

We believe that most, if not all, these basic proteins have primarily a structural role. That is, they are not enzymes but function largely to hold the ribosomal RNA and necessary intermediates in the correct position for peptide bond formation. In addition, a number of enzymes are bound tightly to ribosomes. As yet their function is unclear. One such enzyme is a bacterial ribonuclease found by Elson (23) to be specifically attached to 30S ribosomes in a latent form. No ribonuclease activity is present prior to ribosome breakdown. Spahr (24) in our laboratories has purified this enzyme and shown its specificity, and from specific activity measurements he concludes that it is present on less than one 30S particle in 20. It is clear that this enzyme, if present in a free active form, would be rapidly lethal to its host cell. Thus its presence in latent form is to be expected. But why it is stuck to ribosomes is still a complete mystery.

CHEMICAL INTERMEDIATES
IN PROTEIN SYNTHESIS

Our early experiments with ribosomes were almost unrelated to the efforts of biochemists. At that time our research objectives seemed very different. The enzymologically oriented biochemists hoped to find the intermediates and enzymes necessary for peptide bond formation. On the contrary, those of us with a genetic orientation wanted to see the template and discover how it picked out the correct amino acid. Very soon, however, these separate paths came together, partly because of a breakthrough in work on the nature of the amino acid intermediates and partly because of an incisive thought of Crick's.

The biochemical advances arose largely from work (25) in Paul Zamecnik's laboratory at Massachusetts General Hospital. There was developed a reproducible *in vitro* system containing ribosomes, supernatant factors, and adenosine triphosphate (ATP) which incorporated amino acids into proteins. Using this system, Hoagland helped make two important discoveries. First, he showed (26) that amino acids are initially activated by ATP to form high-energy complexes of amino acid and adenosine monophosphate. Second, together with Zamecnik he demonstrated (27) that the activated amino acids are then transferred to low-molecular-weight RNA molecules (now known as soluble or transfer RNA), again in an activated form. These amino-acyl-sRNA compounds then function as the intermediates for peptide bond formation (Fig. 4).

It had previously been obvious that amino acid activation would have to occur. However, Hoagland and Zamecnik's second discovery (in 1956) of the involvement of a hitherto undiscovered RNA form (sRNA) was unanticipated by almost everybody. Several years previously (in 1954), Leslie Orgel and I had spent a quite frustrating fall attempting to construct hypothetical RNA structures which contained cavities complementary in shape to the amino acid side groups. Not only did plausible configurations for the RNA backbone fail to result in good cavities, but even when we disregarded the backbone, we also failed to find convincing holes which might effectively distinguish between such similar amino acids as valine and isoleucine. Crick at the same time (early 1955) sensed the same dilemma and suggested a radical solution to the paradox. He proposed (28) that the amino acids do not combine with the template. Instead each should first combine with a specific adaptor molecule, capable of selectively interacting with the hydrogen

FIGURE 4. Enzymatic steps in protein peptide bond formation. Steps *a* and *b* are catalyzed by single enzymes. The number of enzymes required in *c* is unknown.

a) $AA + ATP \longrightarrow AMP{\sim}AA + PP$

b) $AMP{\sim}AA + SRNA \longrightarrow AA{\sim}SRNA + AMP$

c) $(AA{\sim}SRNA)_n + GTP \xrightarrow{\text{ribosomes}}$

$AA_1 - AA_2 .... AA_n + GDP \text{ (GMP ?)} + (SRNA)_n$

bonding surfaces provided by RNA's purine and pyrimidine bases. This scheme requires at least 20 different adaptors, each specific for a given amino acid. These are very neatly provided by the specific sRNA molecules. Soon after the discovery of sRNA, many experiments, particularly by Hoagland and Paul Berg (29), established that the sRNA molecules are in fact specific for a given amino acid. It thus became possible to imagine, in accordance with Crick's reasoning, that the ribosomal template for protein synthesis combined not with the amino acid side groups but, instead, with a specific group of bases on the soluble RNA portion of the amino-acyl-sRNA precursors.

PARTICIPATION OF ACTIVE RIBOSOMES IN PROTEIN SYNTHESIS

Very little protein synthesis occurred in the cell-free system developed by the Massachusetts General Hospital group. Only by using radioactive amino acids could they convincingly demonstrate amino acid incorporation into proteins. This fact initially seemed trivial, and there was much hope that when better experimental conditions were found, significant net synthesis would occur. But despite optimistic claims from several laboratories, no real improvement in the efficiency of cell-free synthesis resulted. Some experiments (1959) of Tissières and Schlessinger (30) with *Escherichia coli* extracts illustrate this point well. At 30°C, cell-free synthesis occurs linearly for 5 to 10 minutes and then gradually stops. During this interval the newly synthesized protein amounts to 1 to 3 micrograms of protein per milligram of ribosomes. Of this, about one-third is released from the ribosomes, the remainder being bound to the ribosomes.

Cell-free synthesis in *E. coli* extracts requires the high ($\sim 10^{-2}M$) Mg^{++} levels which favor the formation of 70S ribosomes from their 30S and 50S subunits. After incorporation, the ribosomes possessing nascent polypeptide chains become less susceptible to breakdown to 30S and 50S ribosomes. When cell-free extracts (after synthesis) are briefly dialyzed against $10^{-4}M$ Mg^{++}, about 80 to 90 percent of the 30S and 50S ribosomes become free. There remain, however, 10 to 20 percent of the original 70S ribosomes, and it is upon these "stuck" ribosomes that most ribosomal-bound nascent protein is located. This suggests, first, that protein synthesis occurs on 70S ribosomes, not upon free 30S or 50S ribosomes. Second, in the commonly studied *E. coli* extract, only a small ribosome fraction is functional. Tissières and Schlessinger named these particles "active ribosomes" and suggested that they contained a functional component lacking in other ribosomes.

Each active ribosome synthesizes on the average between 15,000 and 50,000 daltons of protein. This is in the size range of naturally occurring polypeptide chains. Thus, while we remained unsatisfied by the small net synthesis, sufficient synthesis occurred to open the possibility that some complete protein molecules had been made. This encouraged us to look for synthesis of β-galactosidase. None, however, was then found (*31*), despite much effort.

Another important point emerged from these early (1959) incorporation studies with *E. coli* extracts. The addition of small amounts of purified deoxyribonuclease decreased protein synthesis to values 20 to 40 percent of those found in untreated extracts (*30*). This was completely unanticipated, for it suggested that DNA functions in the commonly studied bacterial extracts. But since a basal level of synthesis remains after DNA is destroyed by deoxyribonuclease, the DNA itself must not be directly involved in the formation of peptide bonds. This finding suggested, instead, synthesis of new template RNA upon DNA in untreated extracts. This raised the possibility, previously not seriously considered by biochemists, that the RNA templates themselves might be unstable, and hence a limiting factor in cell-free protein synthesis.

METABOLIC STABILITY OF RIBOSOMAL RNA

In all our early ribosome experiments we had assumed that the ribosomal RNA was the template. Abundant evidence existed that proteins were synthesized on ribosomes, and since the template must be RNA, it was natural to assume that it was ribosomal RNA. Under this hypothesis ribosomal RNA was a collection of molecules of different base sequences, synthesized on the functioning regions of chromosomal DNA. After synthesis, they combined with the basic ribosomal proteins to form ribosomes. We thus visualized that the seemingly morphologically identical ribosomes were, in fact, a collection of a very large number of genetically distinct particles masked by the similarity of their protein components.

At that time there existed much evidence suggesting that ribosomal RNA molecules were stable in growing bacteria. As early as 1949, experiments showed that RNA precursors, once incorporated into RNA, remained in RNA. The distinction between ribosomal and soluble RNA was not then known, but later experiments by the ribosome group of the Carnegie Institute of Washington and at Harvard indicated similar stabilities for both fractions. In these experiments, however, the fate of single molecules was not followed; and the possibility remained that a

special trick allowed ribosomal RNA chains to be broken down to fragments that were preferentially reused to make new ribosomal RNA
molecules. Davern and Meselson (32), however, ruled out this possibility
by first growing bacteria in heavy (C^{13}, N^{15}) medium, and then transferring the cells to light (C^{12}, N^{14}) medium for several additional generations of growth. They then separated the light from the heavy ribosomal
RNA in cesium formate density gradients and showed that the heavy
molecules remained completely intact for at least two generations. This
result predicts, if ribosomes are assumed to be genetically specific,
that the protein templates will persist indefinitely in growing bacteria.

But already, by the time of the Davern and Meselson experiment
(1959), evidence had begun to accumulate, chiefly at the Institut
Pasteur, that some, if not all, bacterial templates were unstable, with
lives of only several percent of a generation time. None of these experiments, by themselves, were convincing. Each could be interpreted in
other ways which retained the concept of stable templates. But taken
together, they argued a strong case.

These experiments were of several types. In one, the effect of suddenly
adding or destroying specific DNA molecules was studied. Sudden introduction was achieved by having a male donor introduce a molecule
from a specific chromosomal region absent in the recipient female.
Simultaneously, the ability of the male gene to function (to produce an
enzymatically active protein) in the female cell was measured. Riley,
Pardee, Jacob, and Monod (33) obtained the striking finding that β-
galactosidase, genetically determined by a specific male gene, begins to
be synthesized at its maximum rate within several minutes after gene
transfer. Thus, the steady-state number of β-galactosidase templates
was achieved almost immediately. Conversely, when the E. coli chromosome was inactivated by decay of P^{32} atoms incorporated into DNA,
they observed that active enzyme formation stopped within several
minutes. It thus appeared that the ribosomal templates could not function without concomitant DNA function.

At the same time, François Gros discovered (34) that bacteria grown in
5-fluorouracil produced abnormal proteins, most likely altered in amino
acid sequences. 5-Fluorouracil is readily incorporated into bacterial
RNA, and its presence in RNA templates may drastically raise the
"mistake" level. More unexpected was the observation that after addition of 5-fluorouracil the production of all normal proteins ceases within
several minutes. This again argues against the persistence of *any*
stable templates.

UNSTABLE RNA MOLECULES
IN PHAGE-INFECTED
CELLS

At first it was thought that no RNA synthesis occurred in T2-infected
cells. But in 1952 Hershey (35) observed that new RNA molecules are
synthesized at a rapid rate. But no net accumulation occurs since there
is a correspondingly fast breakdown. Surprisingly, almost everybody

ignored this discovery. This oversight was partly due to the tendency, then still prevalent, to suspect that the metabolism of virus-infected cells might be qualitatively different from that of uninfected cells.

Volkin and Astrachan (36) were the first (1956) to treat Hershey's unstable fraction seriously. They measured its base composition and found it different from that of uninfected *E. coli* cells. It bore a great resemblance to the infecting viral DNA, a finding which suggested that it was synthesized on T2 DNA templates. Moreover, and most importantly, this RNA fraction must be the template for phage-specific proteins. Unless we assume that RNA is not involved in phage protein synthesis, it necessarily follows that the Volkin-Astrachan DNA-like RNA provides the information for determining amino acid sequences in phage-specific proteins.

Not till the late summer of 1959 was the physical form of this DNA-like RNA investigated. Then Nomura, Hall, and Spiegelman (37) examined its relationship to the already characterized soluble and ribosomal RNA's. Immediately they observed that none of the T2 RNA was incorporated into stable ribosomes. Instead, in low concentrations of Mg^{++} ($10^{-4}M$) it existed free, while in $10^{-2}M$ Mg^{++}, they thought, it became part of 30S ribosomal-like particles. At the same time, Risebrough in our laboratories began studying T2 RNA, also using sucrose gradient centrifugation. He also found that T2 RNA was not typical ribosomal RNA. In addition, he was the first to notice (in the early spring of 1960) that in $10^{-2}M$ Mg^{++} most T2 RNA sedimented not with 30S particles but with the larger 70S and 100S ribosomes.

Risebrough's result leads naturally to the hypothesis that phage protein synthesis takes place on genetically nonspecific ribosomes to which are attached metabolically unstable template RNA molecules. Independently of our work, Brenner and Jacob, motivated by the aforementioned metabolic and genetic experiments at the Institut Pasteur, were equally convinced that conditions were ripe for the direct demonstration of the existence of metabolically unstable RNA templates, to which Jacob and Monod (38) gave the name "messenger RNA." In June of 1960 Brenner and Jacob traveled to Pasadena for a crucial experiment in Meselson's laboratory. They argued that all the T2 messenger RNA should be attached to old ribosomes synthesized before infection. This they elegantly demonstrated (39) by infecting heavy (C^{13} and N^{15}) labeled bacteria in light (C^{12} and N^{14}) medium with T2. Subsequent CsCl equilibrium centrifugation revealed that most of the T2 messenger RNA was indeed attached to "old" ribosomes, as was all the ribosomal-bound nascent protein, labeled by pulse exposure to radioactive amino acids.

MESSENGER RNA MOLECULES
IN UNINFECTED BACTERIA

We were equally convinced that similar messenger RNA would be found in uninfected bacteria. Its demonstration presented greater problems because of the simultaneous synthesis of ribosomal and soluble RNA. François Gros had then (May 1960) just arrived for a visit to our laboratory. Together with Kurland and Gilbert, we decided to look for labeled messenger molecules in cells briefly exposed to a radioactive RNA precursor. Experiments with T2-infected cells suggested that the T2 messenger comprised about 2 to 4 percent of the total RNA and that most of its molecules had lives of less than several minutes. If a similar situation held for uninfected cells during any short interval most RNA synthesized would be messenger RNA. There would be no significant accumulation, since the RNA would be broken down almost as fast as it was made.

Again, the messenger hypothesis was confirmed (40). The RNA labeled during pulse exposures was largely attached to 70S and 100S ribosomes in $10^{-2}M$ Mg^{++}. In low concentrations of Mg^{++} ($10^{-4}M$) it came off the ribosomes and sedimented free, with an average sedimentation constant of 14S. Base ratio analysis revealed DNA-like RNA molecules, in agreement with the expectation that such RNA is produced on very many DNA templates along the bacterial chromosome.

Soon afterwards, Hall and Spiegelman (see 41) formed artificial T2 DNA–T2 messenger RNA hybrid molecules, and in several laboratories (42) hybrid molecules were subsequently formed between *E. coli* DNA and *E. coli* pulse RNA. The DNA-template origin for messenger RNA was thus established beyond doubt.

ROLE OF MESSENGER RNA IN CELL-FREE PROTEIN SYNTHESIS

It was then possible to suggest why deoxyribonuclease partially inhibits amino acid incorporation in *E. coli* extracts. The messenger hypothesis prompts the idea that DNA in the extract is a template for messenger RNA. This newly made messenger then attaches to ribosomes, where it serves as additional protein templates. Since deoxyribonuclease only destroys the capacity to make messenger RNA, it has no effect upon the messenger RNA present at the time of extract formation. Hence, no matter how high the deoxyribonuclease concentration employed, a residual fraction of synthesis will always occur. Experiments by Tissières and Hopkins (43) in our laboratories and by Berg, Chamberlain, and Wood (44) at Stanford confirmed these ideas. First it was shown that the addition of DNA to extracts previously denuded of DNA significantly increased amino acid incorporation. Second, RNA synthesis occurs simultaneously with *in vitro* protein synthesis. This RNA has a DNA-like composition, attaches to ribosome in $10^{-2}M$ Mg^{++}, and physically resembles messenger RNA synthesized *in vivo*.

Furthermore, Tissières showed that addition of fractions rich in messenger RNA increased *in vitro* protein synthesis two- to five-fold. More striking results came from Nirenberg and Matthaei (45). They reasoned that *in vitro* destruction of messenger RNA might be the principal reason why cell-free systems stop synthesizing protein. If so, previously

FIGURE 5. Stepwise growth of a polypeptide chain. Initiation begins at the free NH_2 end, the growing point being terminated by an sRNA molecule.

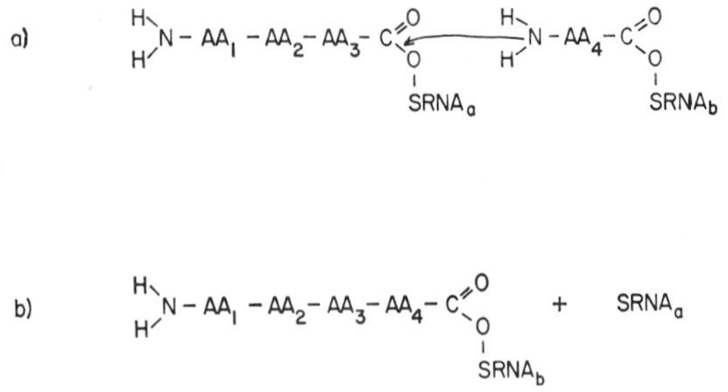

incubated extracts deficient in natural messenger RNA should respond more to the addition of new messenger RNA than other extracts. This way they were able to demonstrate a 20-fold increase in protein synthesis after the addition of a phenol-purified E. coli RNA. Like Tissières's active fraction, their stimulating fraction sedimented heterogeneously, arguing against an effect due to either ribosomal or soluble RNA. More convincing support came when they next added TMV RNA to previously incubated extracts of E. coli. Again there was a 10- to 20-fold increase. Here there could be no confusion with possible ribosomal RNA templates. Even more dramatic (46) was the effect of adding polyuridylic acid (like TMV RNA, single-stranded). This specifically directed incorporating phenylalanine into polyphenylalanine. With this experiment (June 1961) the messenger concept became established. Direct proof then existed that single-stranded messenger RNA was the protein template.

In in-vitro systems ordinarily only 10 to 20 percent of E. coli ribosomes contain attached messenger RNA. This was first shown in experiments of Risebrough (47), who centrifuged extracts of T2-infected cells through a sucrose gradient. Ribosomes containing labeled messenger RNA were found to centrifuge faster than ordinary ribosomes. Similarly, Gilbert (48) showed that these faster-sedimenting ribosomes are "active" — that is, they are able to incorporate amino acids into proteins. A fresh cell-free extract was centrifuged through a sucrose gradient. Samples along the gradient were collected and then tested for their ability to make protein. A complete parallel was found between "activity" and the presence of messenger RNA.

Furthermore, if an extract is centrifuged after it has incorporated amino acids, the nascent protein chains also sediment attached to a small fraction of fast-sedimenting ribosomes (47). These ribosomes still contain messenger RNA. For when the messenger RNA molecules are destroyed by ribonuclease (ribosomes remain intact in the presence of microgram amounts of ribonuclease), the ribosomal-bound nascent protein sediments as 70S ribosomes. The nascent protein is thus not attached to messenger RNA but must be directly bound to ribosomes.

FIGURE 6. Diagrammatic summary of ribosome participation in protein synthesis. The active complex is shown schematically in Figure 7. SDS, sodium dodecyl sulfate (Duponal).

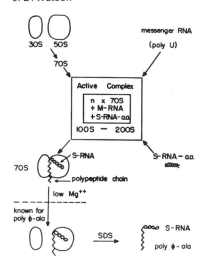

BINDING OF sRNA TO RIBOSOMES

Experiments by Schweet (49) and Dintzes (50) show that proteins grow by the stepwise addition of individual amino acids, beginning at the amino terminal end. Since the immediate precursors are amino-acyl-sRNA molecules, Schweet and Dintzes's result predicts that the polypeptide chain is terminated at its carboxyl growing end by an sRNA molecule (Fig. 5). To test this scheme, we began some studies to see whether sRNA was bound specifically to ribosomes. Cannon and Krug (51) first examined binding in the absence of protein synthesis. They showed that, in $10^{-2}M$ Mg^{++}, each 50S subunit of the 70S ribosome reversibly bound one sRNA molecule. The same amount of reversible binding occurs with amino-acyl-sRNA or with free sRNA, and in the presence or absence of protein synthesis.

Protein synthesis, however, effects the binding observed in $10^{-4}M$ Mg^{++}. In the absence of protein synthesis no sRNA remains bound to the ribosomes when the Mg^{++} level is lowered from $10^{-2}M$ to $10^{-4}M$. On the contrary, after amino acid incorporation, sRNA molecules become tightly fixed to the "stuck" 70S ribosomes, whose nascent polypeptide chains hinder dissociation to 30S and 50S ribosomes. One sRNA molecule appears to be attached to each stuck ribosome. Prolonged dialysis against $10^{-4}M$ Mg^{++} eventually breaks apart the stuck ribosomes. Then all the bound sRNA, as well as almost all the nascent protein, is seen to be attached to the 50S component — an observation which supports the hypothesis that these bound sRNA molecules are directly attached to nascent chains (Fig. 6). Direct proof comes from recent experiments in which Gilbert (52) used the detergent Duponol to further dissociate the 50S ribosomes into their protein and RNA components. Then the nascent protein and bound sRNA remained together during both sucrose gradient centrifugation and separation on G200 Sephadex columns. After exposure, however, to either weak alkali or hydroxylamine (treatments known to break amino-acyl bonds), the sRNA and nascent proteins move separately.

The significance of the reversible binding by nonactive (no messenger) ribosomes is not known. Conceivably, inside growing cells, all ribosomes have attached messenger RNA and synthesize protein. Under these conditions only those sRNA molecules corresponding to the specific messenger sequence can slip into the ribosomal cavities. But when most ribosomes lack messenger templates, as in our *in vitro* extracts, then any sRNA molecule, charged or uncharged, may fill the empty site.

All the evidence suggests that covalent bonds are not involved in holding nascent chains to ribosomes. Instead, it seems probable that the point of firm attachment involves the terminal sRNA residue, bound by Mg^{++}-dependent secondary forces to a cavity in the 50S ribosome. Extensive dialysis against $5 \times 10^{-5}M$ Mg^{++} (which leaves intact 30S and 50S ribosomes) strips the nascent chains off the 50S ribosomes (52, 53). The released polypeptides have a sedimentation constant of about 4S, and if the latent ribonuclease is not activated, they most likely still have terminally bound sRNA. When the Mg^{++} level is again brought to $10^{-2}M$, many released chains again stick to ribosomes.

MOVEMENT OF THE MESSENGER
TEMPLATE OVER THE
RIBOSOMAL SURFACE

At any given time, each functioning ribosome thus contains only one nascent chain. As elongation proceeds, the NH_3-terminal end moves away from the point of peptide bond formation and, conceivably, may assume much of its final three-dimensional configuration before the terminal amino acids are added to the carboxyl end. The messenger RNA must be so attached that only the correct amino-acyl-sRNA molecules are inserted into position for possible peptide bond formation. This requirement demands formation of specific hydrogen bonds (base pairs?) between the messenger template and several (probably three) nucleotides along the sRNA molecule. Then, in the presence of the necessary enzymes, the amino-acyl linkage to the then-terminal sRNA breaks and a peptide bond forms with correctly placed incoming amino-acyl-RNA (Fig. 5). This must create an energetically unfavorable environment for the now free sRNA molecule, causing it to be ejected from the sRNA binding site. The new terminal sRNA then moves into this site, completing a cycle of synthesis. It is not known whether the messenger template remains attached to the newly inserted amino-acyl-sRNA. If it does, the messenger necessarily moves the correct distance over the ribosomal surface to place its next group of specific nucleotides in position to correctly select the next amino acid. But no matter what the mechanism is, the messenger tape necessarily moves over the ribosome. It cannot remain in static orientation if there is only one specific ribosomal site for peptide bond formation.

ATTACHMENT OF SINGLE MESSENGER RNA MOLECULES

Addition of the synthetic messenger polyuridylic acid to extracts containing predominantly 70S ribosomes creates new active ribosomes which sediment in the 150 to 200S region (54). Fixation of a single polyuridylic acid molecule (molecular weight, 100,000) to a 70S ribosome (molecular weight, 3×10^6) should not significantly increase ribosomal sedimentation. Nor is it likely that a very large number of polyuridylic acid molecules have combined with individual ribosomes; in these experiments the molar ratio of fixed polyuridylic acid to 70S ribosomes was less than 1/5. Instead, the only plausible explanation is formation of ribosomal aggregates attached to single polyuridylic acid molecules. The 300 nucleotides in a polyuridylic acid molecule of molecular weight $\sim 10^5$ will have a contour length of about 1000 angstroms if the average internucleotide distance is 3.4 angstroms. Simultaneous attachment is thus possible to groups of four to eight ribosomes (diameter, ~ 200 Å), depending upon the way the messenger passes over (or through) the ribosomal surface. This estimate agrees well with the average aggregate size suggested by the sedimentation rate of the "active" complexes. Sedimentation of extracts *after* incorporation reveals that most polyphenylalanine is attached to the rapidly sedimenting "active" ribosomes.

Single messenger molecules thus most likely move simultaneously over the surfaces of several ribosomes, functioning on each as protein templates (Fig. 7). A progression of increasingly long polypeptide chains should be attached to successive ribosomes, depending upon the fraction of the messenger tape to which they were exposed. When all the messenger has moved across the site of synthesis, some mechanism, perhaps itself triggered by a specific template nucleotide sequence, must release

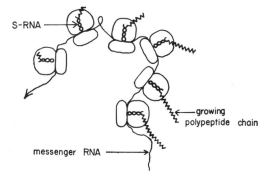

FIGURE 7. Messenger RNA attachment to several ribosomes. This illustration is schematic, since the site of messenger attachment to ribosomes is not known.

the finished protein. The now vacant ribosome then becomes competent to receive the free end of another (or perhaps even the same) messenger molecule and start a new cycle of protein synthesis.

The realization that a single messenger molecule attaches to many ribosomes resolves a bothersome paradox which accompanied the messenger hypothesis. About 2 to 4 percent of *E. coli* RNA is messenger RNA (42, 55). Its average sedimentation constant of 14S (56) suggests an average molecular weight of about 500,000. This value may be too low, since it is very difficult to completely prevent all enzymatic degradation. There thus must be at least six to eight 70S ribosomes for every messenger molecule. It was very difficult to believe that only 10 to 20 percent of the ribosomes functioned at a given moment, for under a variety of conditions the rate of protein synthesis is proportional to ribosome concentration (57). Instead it seems much more likely that, *in vivo*, almost all ribosomes are active. During the preparation of cell extracts, however, many ribosomes may lose their messenger RNA and become inactive. If this is the case, we may expect that use of more gentle techniques to break open *E. coli* cells will reveal larger fractions of fast-sedimenting active material. Already there are reports (58) that over 50 percent of mammalian reticulocyte ribosomes exist as aggregates of five to six 80S particles. Furthermore, it is these aggregated ribosomes which make protein, both *in vivo* and *in vitro*.

TEMPLATE LIFETIME

Under the scheme just described, a messenger molecule might function indefinitely. On the contrary, however, the unstable bacterial templates function on the average only 10 to 20 times. This fact comes from experiments done in Levinthal's laboratory (59), where synthesis of new messenger RNA was blocked by addition of the antibiotic actinomycin D. Pre-existing messenger (*Bacillus subtilus* growing with a 60-minute generation time) then broke down with a half-life of 2 minutes. Correspondingly, protein synthesis ceased at the expected rate. A mechanism (or mechanisms) must thus exist to specifically degrade messenger molecules. Several enzymes (polynucleotide phosphorylase and a K^+-dependent diesterase) which rapidly degrade free messenger RNA are active in bacterial cell extracts (60). They function, however, much less efficiently when the messenger is attached to ribosomes (61). Conceivably, a random choice exists, whether the free forward-moving end of a messenger tape attaches to a vacant ribosome or is enzymatically degraded. If this is the case, this important decision is settled by a chance event unrelated to the biological need for specific messengers.

CONCLUSION

We can now have considerable confidence that the broad features of protein synthesis are understood. The involvement of RNA is very much more complicated than was imagined in 1953. There is not one functional RNA. Instead, protein synthesis demands the ordered interaction of three classes of RNA — ribosomal, soluble, and messenger. Many important questions, however, remain unanswered. For instance, there is no theoretical framework for the ribosomal subunits, nor for that matter, do we understand the functional significance of ribosomal RNA. Most satisfying is the realization that all the steps in protein replication will be shown to involve well-understood chemical forces. As yet we do not know all the details. For example, are the DNA base pairs involved in messenger RNA selection of the corresponding amino-acyl-sRNA? With luck, this will soon be known. We can thus have every expectation that future progress in understanding selective protein synthesis (and its consequences for embryology) will have a similarly well-defined and, when understood, easy-to-comprehend chemical basis (62).

REFERENCES AND NOTES

* The author is affiliated with the Harvard Biological Laboratories, Cambridge, Massachusetts. This article is adapted from the lecture which he delivered in Stockholm, Sweden, December 11, 1962, on receiving the Noble prize in medicine and physiology, a prize which he shared with Francis H. C. Crick and Maurice H. F. Wilkins. It is published with the permission of the Nobel Foundation. It will also be included in the complete volume of Nobel lectures in English which is published yearly by the Elsevier Publishing Company, Amsterdam and New York.

1. L. Pauling and R. B. Corey, *Proc. Nat. Acad. Sci. U.S.* **37**, 235 (1951).

2. J. D. Watson and F. H. C. Crick, *Nature* **171**, 737 (1953).

3. _____, *ibid.*, p. 964.

4. P. Jordan, *Phys. Z.* **39**, 711 (1938); the reader is also referred to the discussion of possible implications of long-range forces in biology by H. J. Muller in his 1946 Pilgrim Trust lecture, *Proc. Roy. Soc. London* **B** (1947).

5. A sample of Pauling's views is found in his note with M. Delbrück, *Science* **92**, 77 (1940).

6. J. Brachet, *Arch. Biol. Liege* **53**, 207 (1942); T. Casperson, *Naturwissenschaften* **28**, 33 (1941).

7. H. Borsook, C. L. Deasy, A. J. Hagen-Smit, G. Keighley, P. H. Lowy, *J. Biol. Chem.* **187**, 839 (1950); T. Hultin, *Exptl. Cell Res.* **1950–I**, 376 (1950).

8. J. W. Littlefield, E. B. Keller, J. Gross, P. C. Zamecnik, *J. Biol. Chem.* **217**, 111 (1955); V. G. Allfrey, M. M. Daly, A. E. Mirsky, *J. Gen. Physiol.* **37**, 157 (1953).

9. A. Rich and J. D. Watson, *Nature* **173**, 995 (1954); *Proc. Nat. Acad. Sci. U.S.* **40**, 759 (1954).

10. F. H. C. Crick and J. D. Watson, *Nature* **177**, 473 (1956); _____, in *Ciba Foundation Symposium on the Nature of Viruses*, G. E. W. Wolstenholme and C. M. O'Connor, Eds. (Little, Brown, Boston, 1957).

11. D. L. D. Caspar, *Nature* **177**, 475 (1956).

12. M. L. Petermann and M. G. Hamilton, *J. Biol. Chem.* **224**, 725 (1957); P. Tso, J. Bonner, J. Vinograd, *J. Biophys. Biochem. Cytol.* **2**, 451 (1956).

13. H. K. Schachman, A. B. Pardee, R. Y. Stanier, *Arch. Biochem. Biophys.* **38**, 245 (1952).

14. E. T. Bolton, B. H. Hoyer, D. B. Ritter, *Microsomal Particles and Protein Synthesis* (Pergamon, New York, 1958), p. 18.

15. A. Tissières and J. D. Watson, *Nature* 182, 778 (1958); A. Tissières, J. D. Watson, D. Schlessinger, B. R. Hollingsworth, *J. Mol. Biol.* 1, 221 (1959).

16. C. E. Hall and H. S. Slayeter, *J. Mol. Biol.* 1, 329 (1959).

17. H. E. Huxley and G. Zubay, *ibid.* 2, 10 (1960).

18. H. Lamfrom and E. R. Glowacki, *J. Mol. Biol.* 5, 97 (1962); P. Tso and J. Vinograd, *Biochim. et Biophys. Acta* 49, 113 (1961).

19. B. Hall and P. Doty, *J. Mol. Biol.* 1, 111 (1959); U. Z. Littauer and H. Eisenberg, *Biochim. et Biophys. Acta* 32, 320 (1959); S. M. Timasheff, A. Brown, J. S. Colter, M. Davies, *ibid.* 27, 662 (1958).

20. C. G. Kurland, *J. Mol. Biol.* 2, 83 (1960).

21. J. P. Waller and J. I. Harris, *Proc. Nat. Acad. Sci. U.S.* 47, 18 (1961).

22. P. F. Spahr, *J. Mol. Biol.* 4, 395 (1962).

23. D. Elson, *Biochim. et Biophys. Acta* 27, 216 (1958); *ibid.* 36, 372 (1959).

24. P. F. Spahr and B. R. Hollingsworth, *J. Biol. Chem.* 236, 823 (1961).

25. J. W. Littlefield, E. B. Keller, J. Gross, P. C. Zamecnik, *ibid.* 217, 111 (1955); J. W. Littlefield and E. B. Keller, *ibid.* 224, 13 (1957); P. C. Zamecnik and E. B. Keller, *ibid.* 209, 337 (1954); E. B. Keller and P. C. Zamecnik, *ibid.* 221, 45 (1956).

26. M. B. Hoagland, P. C. Zamecnik, M. L. Stephenson, *Biochim. et Biophys. Acta* 24, 215 (1957).

27. M. B. Hoagland, M. L. Stephenson, J. F. Scott, L. I. Hecht, P. C. Zamecnik, *J. Biol. Chem.* 231, 241 (1958).

28. F. H. C. Crick, *Symp. Soc. Exptl. Biol.* 12, 138 (1958).

29. P. Berg and E. J. Ofengand, *Proc. Nat. Acad. Sci. U.S.* 44, 78 (1958).

30. A. Tissières, D. Schlessinger, F. Gros, *ibid.* 46, 1450 (1960).

31. F. Gros and D. Schlessinger, unpublished experiments (1961–62).

32. C. I. Davern and M. Meselson, *J. Mol. Biol.* 2, 153 (1960).

33. M. Riley, A. Pardee, F. Jacob, J. Monod, *ibid.* 2, 216 (1960).

34. S. Naono and F. Gros, *Compt. Rend.* 250, 3889 (1960).

35. A. D. Hershey, J. Dixon, M. Chase, *J. Gen. Physiol.* 36, 777 (1953).

36. E. Volkin and L. Astrachan, *Virology* 2, 149 (1956).

37. M. Nomura, B. D. Hall, S. Spiegelman, *J. Mol. Biol.* 2, 306 (1960).

38. F. Jacob and J. Monod, *ibid.* 3, 318 (1961).

39. S. Brenner, F. Jacob, M. Meselson, *Nature* 190, 576 (1961).

40. F. Gros, H. Hiatt, W. Gilbert, C. G. Kurland, R. W. Risebrough, J. D. Watson, *ibid.*, p. 581.

41. B. D. Hall and S. Spiegelman, *Proc. Nat. Acad. Sci. U.S.* 47, 137 (1961).

42. M. Hayashi and S. Spiegelman, *ibid.*, p. 1564. F. Gros, W. Gilbert, H. Hiatt, G. Attardi, P. F. Spahr, J. D. Watson, *Cold Spring Harbor Symp. Quant. Biol.* 26 (1961).

43. A. Tissières and J. W. Hopkins, *Proc. Nat. Acad. Sci. U.S.* 47, 2015 (1961).

44. M. Chamberlin and P. Berg, *ibid.* 48, 81 (1962); W. B. Wood and P. Berg, *ibid.* 48, 94 (1962).

45. M. W. Nirenberg and J. H. Matthaei, *Biochem. Biophys. Res. Commun.* 4, 404 (1961).

46. _____, *Proc. Nat. Acad. Sci. U.S.* 47, 1588 (1961).

47. R. W. Risebrough, A. Tissières, J. D. Watson, *ibid.* 48, 430 (1962).

48. W. Gilbert, *J. Mol. Biol.*, in press.

49. J. Bishop, J. Leahy, R. Schweet, *Proc. Nat. Acad. Sci. U.S.* 46, 1030 (1960).

50. H. Dintzes, *ibid.* **47**, 247 (1961).
51. M. Cannon, R. Krug, W. Gilbert, in preparation.
52. W. Gilbert, *J. Mol. Biol.,* in press.
53. D. Schlessinger and F. Gros, in preparation.
54. S. H. Barondes and M. W. Nirenberg, *Science* **138**, 813 (1962); G. J. Spyrides and F. Lipman, *Proc. Nat. Acad. Sci. U.S.* **48**, 1977 (1962); W. Gilbert, *J. Mol. Biol.,* in press.
55. S. S. Cohen, H. D. Barner, J. Lichtenstein, *J. Biol. Chem.* **236**, 1448 (1961).
56. R. Monier, S. Naono, D. Hayes, F. Hayes, F. Gros, *J. Mol. Biol.* **5**, 311 (1962); K. Asano, unpublished experiments (1962).
57. O. Maaløe, *Cold Spring Harbor Symp. Quant. Biol.* **26**, 45 (1961); F. C. Neidhardt and D. Fraenkel, *ibid.,* p. 63.
58. A. Gierer, *J. Mol. Biol.,* in press; J. R. Warner, P. M. Knopf, A. Rich, *Proc. Nat. Acad. Sci. U.S.,* in press.
59. C. Levinthal, A. Keynan, A. Higa, *ibid.* **48**, 1631 (1962).
60. S. S. Cohen, *J. Biol. Chem.,* in press. D. Schlessinger and P. F. Spahr, in preparation.
61. R. Gesteland and J. D. Watson, in preparation.
62. I have been very fortunate in having the collaboration of many able students and colleagues. The work of Dr. C. G. Kurland, Dr. David Schlessinger, and Dr. Robert Risebrough established many of the ideas reported here. Equally significant have been experiments by Drs. Kimiko Asano, Michael Cannon, Walter Gilbert, François Gros, Françoise Gros, Johns Hopkins, Masayasu Nomura, Pierre François Spahr, Alfred Tissières, and Jean-Pierre Waller. The visit of François Gros in the spring of 1960 was crucial in focusing attention on messenger RNA. Most importantly, I wish to mention my long collaboration with Alfred Tissières. Since 1960 I have had the good fortune, also, to work closely with Walter Gilbert.

SECTION TWO
Development of Organisms

Developmental biology is in the spotlight at the moment because in this study of how cells specialize, the lessons of molecular biology can be used to the greatest advantage. A good deal is known about how proteins are made, but an essential question in the study of development is how specific proteins are made at specific rates and at specific times. It is this series of events which results in cell specificity, and when we talk about cell differentiation, we are really talking about the increasing specificity or the unlikeness of cells. Differentiation is not the only event in a developmental sequence since growth and changes in form are also involved. Development is a complex series of interactions which have proven resistant to easy explanation, but many biologists are confident that our relative ignorance in this field will soon be a thing of the past. How will increased insight into developmental processes help us in our previously stated goal of understanding the process of evolution? Development is really the expression of the phenotype, and if we can understand how the phenotype is controlled, we will have the secret of individual variation. This information will in turn increase our understanding of how organisms have evolved.

It might be thought that the zygote, or fertilized egg, is a logical starting point for the study of development, but the behavior of the zygote is to a certain extent influenced by the previous history of the egg. We know, for example, that a polarity,

153

or sense of direction, is already present in some unfertilized eggs and that the pattern of subsequent development is initiated by this polarity. Such factors as the direction of the entrance path of the sperm may also influence zygote polarity. The factors controlling the differentiation of gametes, or sex cells, and the events of fertilization are, therefore, the proper concern of the developmental biologist.

The electron microscope has revolutionized our view of the cell, and the fertilization process as described by D. G. Szollosi and H. Ris* is an example of the kind of information it has allowed us to obtain. It had been possible to follow the sperm up to the point of contact with the egg under the light microscope, but the details of the union of the two gametes were hidden from view. Fusion of the egg and sperm membranes soon after contact is an example of the kind of observations which stimulated reinterpretations of fertilization and influenced subsequent descriptive and experimental work in this field.

Invertebrates and amphibians have been favorite organisms for studying fertilization because the gametes are easily isolated and are subject to experimental manipulation. Studies on mammalian fertilization, on the other hand, have been hampered because access to the eggs is difficult. M. C. Chang's studies* on fertilization of rabbit eggs outside the organism are especially intriguing for this reason. The development of techniques permitting routine *in vitro* mammalian fertilization would have great significance both for studies on mammalian development and for practical breeding programs.

Species are often defined as members of a population which freely interbreed with one another. The inability of one population to interbreed with another sets them apart as separate species, and the mechanism of reproductive incompatibility has always been of great interest because of its importance to our understanding of evolution. The recent research of Boris Ephrussi and Mary C. Weiss* is spectacular for many reasons, and one of the most important is that it shows that the incompatibility between gametes of species does not extend to somatic cells. Their work proves that it is quite possible for cells from different species to fuse and that the artificial zygotes can divide and give rise to clones of cells. The chromosome complements from the two parental cells appear to be quite happy with one another's company. Mouse and rat cells were combined by Ephrussi and Weiss, but it is also possible to produce somatic hybrids between distantly related cells. Henry Harris of Oxford University has succeeded in fusing mouse cells with human cells, and the hybrid cells continue to divide. This tremendously interesting work, though in its infancy, promises to have a very bright future.

An attempt to explore the problem of nuclear differentiation apparently gave birth to the discipline of experimental embryology. In 1882, German biologist Wilhelm Roux plunged a red hot needle into one

_____

* An asterisk indicates that the paper is included in this section.

cell of a two-celled frog embryo. He wished to know if the two cells had the same potential for development. The result of his experiment was a half embryo, which suggested that there had been a segregation of genetic determinants. Many ingenious and increasingly sophisticated experiments have been performed over the following eighty years to test the question whether nuclei become differentiated during development. The most elegant experiments designed to test this basic question have been performed by Robert Briggs and Thomas J. King.* Their experiment is simple to understand but difficult to execute. They took a nucleus out of an activated egg and replaced it with a nucleus from an embryonic cell and waited to see if this new combination resulted in a normal frog embryo. Their first paper describes experiments with nuclei taken from young embryos. Most of the embryos resulting from this kind of experiment were normal, which suggests that nuclei from young embryos are totipotent — they have all the information to support the full development of the organism. The results reported in their second paper cast some cold water on this interpretation: When nuclei from cells of older embryos are placed in enucleated eggs, the majority of resulting embryos are abnormal. This means either the nuclei from older embryos had become specialized or their age had made them more susceptible to damage during the experimental treatment. A small percentage of normal embryos were produced in the later experiments, so the question of nuclear differentiation in older embryos is still unsettled. It will, however, remain with us as a central problem. While this question has not been completely answered for animals, it has been answered for plants. The work of F. C. Steward and his co-workers* shows conclusively that cells from some mature plants are totipotent. Their nuclei have not differentiated and they are capable of supporting the development of complete plants.

Tissue differentiation, unlike nuclear differentiation, can be clearly demonstrated at every point in the development of an organism. The problem here is to uncover the mechanism for differentiation, and this is a quest which has proved most difficult. The fact that tissue specificity has little to do with species' specificity is clearly shown in A. Moscona's paper.* It appears that the cell's first loyalty is to its tissue type rather than to its species. Since embryonic animal cells are notoriously perambulatory, and since a cell's eventual fate has a good deal to do with where it happens to be in the embryo at certain critical times, it is important to know how certain cells recognize each other as they move about. One hypothesis states that each cell type has its specific glue which permits common types to stick together. The contrasting hypothesis states that the glue may be the same, but that differences in amount can influence rates of movement. It is too early to tell which is the right explanation, but the answer will probably come from experiments similar to the ones in the Moscona paper.

Some of the most influential experiments ever done in biology were performed by German embryologist Hans Spemann and his students during the 1920's and 1930's. They succeeded in showing that one kind of embryonic tissue could induce the other kinds of tissue to differentiate in a specific fashion. The search for the "inducing" substance or substances has continued to the present day. For many years it was not possible to induce one tissue with another if there was a barrier or substantial distance between the two tissues. M. C. Niu and V. C. Twitty* were finally able to show that a specific type of differentiation could be induced in the absence of the inducing tissue. A great variety of experiments by a large number of workers have been concerned with the identity of the mechanism of induction since the work of Niu and Twitty, and in some cases compounds which are effective inducers have been identified. Even though a convincing general theory explaining induction of differentiated tissues during development has not been presented, this central problem in developmental biology will continue to intrigue biologists, and the future holds bright promise for progress. This progress might first result from experiments with plants; they are generally less complex organisms than animals, and their responses to experimental manipulation often reflect a wider spectrum than is found in experiments with animals. The paper by F. Skoog and C. O. Miller* reflects this point. They were able to control the induction of different organs from undifferentiated tissue by means of specific chemical treatment, and were able to order up buds or roots at will by regulating the concentration of known chemical growth regulators. This is the kind of experiment which captures the imagination of biologists, because it indicates how difficult and important problems might be solved. It now remains to discover how particular ratios of certain chemicals cause undifferentiated cells to select a pathway leading either to buds or to roots. Such a discovery would provide insights into how cells differentiate in all organisms.

We have been speaking mostly about differentiation, but other components of development can also be identified. Changes in form usually accompany increase in the complexity associated with development. These changes in form are referred to as morphogenesis, and they are the most difficult problems in development. It has not been possible to provide many answers about the mechanisms of morphogenesis, and in many cases it has even been difficult to ask meaningful questions. Even newly acquired knowledge of the genetic code does not help much here. Form is determined by changes in planes of cell division and by localized differences in rates of cell division and enlargement, and knowing how DNA replicates and how amino acids are assembled into protein molecules does not tell us how the mitotic spindle decides to align itself along a particular cell axis.

Like all difficult situations, the problems of morphogenesis should whet our appetite for research. That considerable progress in this field is possible is shown in the papers on the flowering of plants and the metamorphosis of animals. The first three papers in this group provide insight into one of the most exciting stories in modern biology as they reflect a progression in the investigation of a morphogenic phenomenon from the initial discovery to the underlying mechanism. W. W. Garner and H. A. Allard* discovered that flowering in certain plants was regulated by the relative length of the light and dark periods, and termed this phenomenon photoperiodism. Their experiments possessed great significance because they established that plants had a way of telling time. It has since been found that many organisms exhibit a periodicity in their metabolism or behavior and these endogenous rhythms are initially set by a particular photoperiod. We are just beginning to realize the role biological clocks play in regulating the lives of plants and animals. Garner and Allard worked for the United States Department of Agriculture, and their original experiments were designed to produce a bigger and better tobacco plant; their work is an excellent example of how applied research can provide significant new inputs for basic research.

M. Ch. Čajlachjan's paper* deals with the ability of the plant to recognize the changes in the relative length of the light and dark periods. It was found that leaves are the organs which detect the changes, and the information is relayed from the leaves to the stem apex. The apical meristem consists of a cluster of actively dividing cells; and leaves, lateral buds, and stem tissue are derived from this meristem. Flowers are produced when this meristem produces petals and other floral parts instead of leaves. Leaves and floral parts are merely different forms of a basic derivative of the apical meristem. Čajlachjan demonstrated that photo-induced leaves produce a stimulus which induced the apical meristem to produce flowers instead of leaves. The nature of this stimulus is still unknown despite many attempts to identify it.

Light cannot influence chemical reactions unless it is absorbed. Visible light is absorbed by pigments; we call various compounds pigments because they exhibit colors. The specific color is determined by the wave length of light which is reflected instead of absorbed. The fact, proved by Čajlachjan, that plants flowered in response to light indicates that the leaves contained a pigment absorbing particular kinds of visible light. Flowering is not the only aspect of plant development influenced by light. A dark-grown plant is a very different organism from a light-grown plant, and most of the features we associate with green plants are due to the action of light. The germination of many seeds is also regulated by light. After the discovery that most of these light-induced responses were due to red light, it appeared, therefore, that such diverse reactions as flowering, stem length, and seed germination were controlled by a similar pigment. W. L. Butler and his co-workers* succeeded in isolating and identifying this pigment which they called phytochrome, and this provided the capstone for the research initiated by Garner and Allard many years before. Many people are working on the next act in this drama of discovery: they want to know how phytochrome influences plant metabolism.

Everyone is familiar with the metamorphosis of a caterpillar into a butterfly or of a tadpole into a frog. These changes from the juvenile to the adult life forms cannot help but excite the most listless observer. The triggering mechanisms in metamorphosis are as interesting as the changes in external form. The triggering effect of insect hormones is demonstrated in a classic set of experiments by C. M. Williams.* The role of hormones in controlling insect development has been an active field of research, and the principal hormones have now been isolated and identified. We will see a little later that the work with insect hormones may provide us with our most complete explanation for the mechanism of hormone action. In addition to promoting our understanding of development, this work holds great promise for providing practical methods for controlling certain kinds of insects.

The change in body form seen in amphibian metamorphosis reflects the difficulty in analyzing such complex events. Morphogenesis and cell differentiation are so correlated at all stages of metamorphosis that it is impossible to consider either of these aspects of development in isolation. The kind of research reported by Jerome Gross* shows how this complex phenomenon can be untangled and how certain aspects of metamorphosis can be discussed in molecular terms.

It was stated at the beginning of this introduction that molecular biology has provided developmental biologists with the tools for victory, i.e., explaining development in molecular terms. The papers by W. Beermann* and by J. E. Varner and G. Ram Chandra* present models for this kind of discussion. Beermann presents evidence that the role of insect hormones is to activate parts of the chromosomes. These turned-on regions would synthesize specific RNA (ribonucleic acid), which would act as templates for the synthesis of specific proteins. Knowledge about the synthesis of specific proteins at specific times is basic to an understanding of development. This dictum is clearly illustrated in Varner and Chandra's paper on enzyme synthesis in barley endosperm. Gibberellic acid affects plants in many ways, but one effect is to induce the synthesis of the starch-digesting enzyme, α-amylase, from a cell layer in barley seeds. The enzyme digests starch in the endosperm, and the germinating embryo, which produces the hormone utilizes the digestion products for growth. These experiments are perhaps the most convincing ones to date illustrating that hormones can work by inducing the synthesis of a specific protein. The present work on control mechanisms for developmental processes provides few final answers, but it has provided promising techniques and convincing models which bode well for future progress.

SUGGESTIONS FOR FURTHER READING

Austin, C. R. 1965. *Fertilization.* Prentice-Hall, Englewood Cliffs, N.J.

Balinsky, B. I. 1968. *An Introduction to Embryology.* 2nd ed. W. B. Saunders, Philadelphia.

Barth, L. F. 1964. *Development: Selected Topics.* Addison-Wesley, Reading, Mass.

Bell, E. 1967. *Molecular and Cellular Aspects of Development.* Harper & Row, New York.

Ebert, J. D. 1965. *Interacting Systems in Development.* Holt, Rinehart & Winston, New York.

Laetsch, W. M., and R. E. Cleland. 1967. *Papers on Plant Growth and Development.* Little, Brown, Boston.

Leopold, C. A. 1964. *Plant Growth and Development.* McGraw-Hill, New York.

Locke, M. 1966. *Major Problems in Developmental Biology.* Academic Press, New York.

Moore, J. A. 1963. *Heredity and Development.* Oxford University Press, New York.

Sinnott, E. W. 1960. *Plant Morphogenesis.* McGraw-Hill, New York.

Thompson, D. W. 1961. *On Growth and Form.* Cambridge University Press, New York.

Torrey, J. G. 1967. *Development in Flowering Plants.* Macmillan, New York.

Twitty, V. C. 1966. *Of Scientists and Salamanders.* W. H. Freeman, San Francisco.

A Fertilization

Szollosi, Daniel G., and Hans Ris. 1961. Observations on sperm penetration in the rat. *Jour. Biophys. Biochem. Cytol.* **10**, 275–83.

Chang, M. C. 1959. Fertilization of rabbit ova *in vitro*. *Nature* **184**, 446–67.

Ephrussi, Boris, and Mary C. Weiss. 1965. Interspecific hybridization of somatic cells. *Proc. Nat. Acad. Sci. U.S.* **53**, 1040–1042.

Observations on
Sperm Penetration
in the Rat

Daniel G. Szollosi
Hans Ris

*Department of Zoology,
University of Wisconsin*

There are only a few investigations that deal with the process of sperm penetration through the plasma membrane of the egg. In general, studies of fertilization are concerned with the approach of the gametes or the penetration of the extraneous layers of the ovum. Originally, penetration was thought to be accomplished by active movements of the sperm itself, but doubts were soon raised about this simple explanation. Wilson (24), for instance, concluded that "another and more important factor lies in some physical action that causes the sperm to be drawn passively into and through the membrane."

Allen, in his recent review (2), concludes that "there is no evidence that the movements themselves play any role in sperm entry," and ascribes the major role in sperm penetration to the acrosome filament, which may function as a "handle" by which the sperm is drawn into the egg. The acrosome filament itself, or the cytoplasm in which it is anchored, is thought to play the active role, while the plasma membrane proper is presumed to be broken mechanically.

Allen's view on sperm entry agrees with that previously expressed by Lillie (12) pertaining to sperm entrance in *Nereis*. After attachment of the spermatozoon to the egg membrane, the cortical cytoplasm

Reprinted by permission of Daniel G. Szollosi and The Rockefeller University Press from *The Journal of Biophysical and Biochemical Cytology* 10, 275–83 (1961). The photographs here reproduced from printed halftone copy inevitably show a loss of detail, and the quality of the results is not representative of the originals.

of the egg is said to become denser at the point of attachment. This is followed by an active streaming of the surrounding cortical cytoplasm toward the sperm head, which is then carried into the egg by a centripetal movement of the condensed cytoplasmic mass.

From phase contrast microscope observations of sperm entrance into the rat egg, Austin (3) concluded that the sperm plays a passive role and that penetration is due to some membrane activity through which the sperm head "sinks" into the vitellus. Ludwig (13) also believes that the egg cytoplasm is the active factor in sperm penetration. These observers, then, agree in principle in that they emphasize the role of the egg surface in sperm penetration.

Following the extensive studies on the reactive systems of fertilizin-antifertilizin and other surface agents, the idea developed that sperm attachment and activation of the ovum were due to specific surface reactions followed by a phagocytotic process which was responsible for the engulfment of the spermatozoon. Tyler (22) has recently proposed an elaborate pinocytotic scheme.* A similar process has been suggested by Bennett (5) in his "membrane flow" hypothesis for active transport of particles, even ions, into or out of cells.

While this hypothesis of sperm penetration is very attractive, there is no evidence for it. Indeed, in the electron micrograph of a recently penetrated sea urchin sperm published by Lord Rothschild (19), no membrane is seen surrounding the sperm. If the process of penetration involves phagocytosis or membrane flow, there should be at least one membrane around the sperm, namely that of the phagocytotic vesicle. None is visible, however.

The purpose of this paper is to examine with the help of electron micrographs the process of sperm penetration in the albino rat, *Rattus rattus*.

MATERIALS AND METHODS

Rats 70 to 100 days old were kept on daily 14-hour light and 10-hour dark periods in an artificially lighted, air-conditioned room. The estrus cycle of the female rats was followed by means of vaginal smears. Each female in proestrus was placed overnight with two vigorous males. The following morning the animals were examined for copulation plugs, and the presence of sperm was detected by vaginal smears. If there was evidence of mating, the females were sacrificed by cerebral dislocation. The eggs were collected between 8 and 10:30 A.M. by flushing the oviducts with hyaluronidase (Alidase, G. D. Searle and Co., Chicago, 150 USP/ml) and were transferred into a buffered 2 percent OsO_4 solution. This solution was prepared by dissolving 4 percent OsO_4 in veronal acetate buffer at pH 7.8 and diluting it just before use with an equal volume of Tyrode's solution. Sucrose to yield a 0.25 M concentration was added.

After 30 minutes to 1 hour fixation, the eggs were rinsed with Tyrode's solution and embedded in 1 percent bacto-agar. The agar block was dehydrated in increasing concentrations of ethanol and passed through *n*-butyl methacrylate. The eggs, surrounded with a small amount of agar, were embedded in a 3:1 mixture of *n*-butyl and methyl methacrylate. Three percent benzoyl peroxide was added as a curing agent. Sections were prepared with a Porter-Blum microtome and a diamond knife, and were mounted on 200 mesh grids with carbon films. The specimens were examined in a Siemens Elmiskop II B. A 30 μ objective aperture was used. Some sections were stained with lead hydroxide (23).

It was found that the time of ovulation, sperm penetration, and early pronuclear development in the Holzman strain rats used in this study agree well with the schedules published by Austin (4) and by Odor and Blandau (14).

RESULTS

Figure 1 shows a longitudinal section of a recently penetrated sperm near the surface of a rat egg following normal mating conditions. The chromatin material is beginning to be dispersed and is much less electron opaque than the nucleus of a mature sperm (Fig. 3). The apparent granular structure of the sperm nucleus is reminiscent of a late spermatid (6). Near the caudal region of the nucleus the chromatin is further dispersed into finer components, showing fibrils about 40 Å thick. These correspond to the smallest chromosomal fibrils that were observed in elongating spermatids of several species (18). At the apex of the nucleus no changes can be observed as yet in the electron opacity of the nuclear material. No acrosome is visible. Some dense fragments near the sperm nucleus may represent remnants of it. The centriolar complex and the midpiece are still attached at the base of the nucleus.

The most striking finding is that no plasma membrane appears to cover the sperm head on the side facing toward the vitellus. A plasma membrane is distinctly visible on the side facing toward the zona pellucida, however. The membrane makes a deep fold at the apex of the spermatozoon (arrows, left, Fig. 1) and another fold where the midpiece of the sperm moves out of the plane of section (arrows, right, Fig. 1). At both folds the plasma membrane of the egg is apparently continuous with the plasma membrane of the spermatozoon. This situation is represented diagrammatically in Figure 2. The plasma membrane surrounding the egg is continuous with the membrane of the sperm along the axial filament which still protrudes into the perivitelline space. Another example of the continuity of the cell membranes of the two gametes is presented in Figure 4.

Figures 5 to 8 show cross sections at different levels along the tail of a sperm penetrating an egg. These figures correspond to cross sections at the places marked *A, B, C,* and *D,* in Figure 2. In Figure 5, the midpiece lies in the perivitelline space and a continuous plasma membrane is clearly visible around the mitochondrial complex. The plasma membrane of the egg is still intact. Figure 6 shows the attachment of the plasma membrane of the midpiece to that of the ovum. At the arrow, a

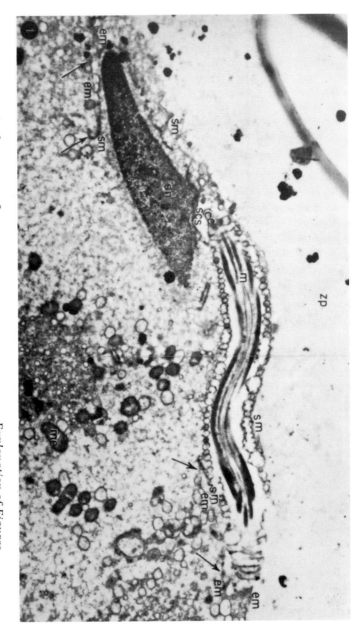

FIGURE 1. Rat sperm in the process of penetrating the egg. The arrows point to the folds
where the plasma membranes of the egg and
sperm are continuous. The section was stained
with lead hydroxide for 5 minutes. The dark
spots are deposits of lead carbonate (× 15,000).

Explanation of Figures

cc, centriolar complex
em, egg plasma membrane
m, midpiece
me, mitochondria of egg cytoplasm
ps, perivitelline space

scs, supracentriolar sheet
sm, sperm plasma membrane
sn, sperm nucleus
zp, zona pellucida

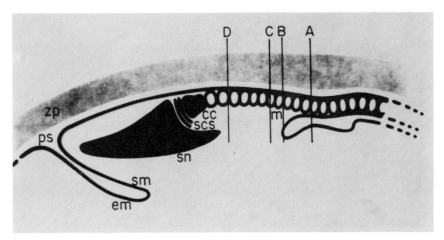

FIGURE 2. A diagrammatic representation of the sperm shown in Figure 1, illustrating the behavior of egg and sperm plasma membranes during sperm entrance. The lines *A, B, C,* and *D* correspond to the planes of section through the midpiece shown in Figures 5 to 8.

FIGURE 3. A spermatozoon in the perivitelline space. Observe the very dense nucleus and the cell membrane surrounding it (× 22,000).

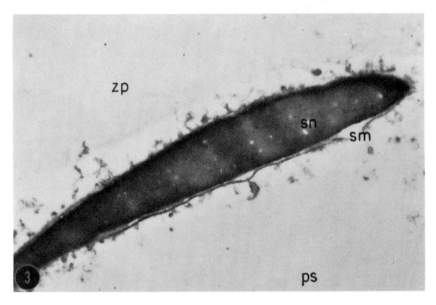

continuity between the two membranes is suggested. Figure 7 presents a view of the midpiece partially incorporated into the vitellus. The plasma membrane of the egg is continuous with the membrane enclosing the still protruding portion of the axial filament. In Figure 8 the midpiece is completely within the vitellus. No plasma membrane surrounds the mitochondria of the midpiece in this case, but a plasma membrane is continuous above the incorporated portion of the spermatozoon.

Further sections of the same ovum (Fig. 9) show the sperm nucleus with the centriolar complex (or juxtanuclear body) and the "supracentriolar sheet" of Sotelo and Trujillo-Cenoz (21). This egg is the most advanced in its development of any described in this study. Neither a sperm plasma membrane nor a nuclear membrane is visible at any point. The nucleus of the spermatozoon has changed considerably. The swollen sperm nucleus now shows masses of 100 Å fibers. Each fiber can be resolved into two parallel 40 Å subfibrils (circles in Fig. 9). Three eggs were sectioned which showed the sperm in the process of penetration. In each case a fusion of the sperm and egg plasma membranes was visible. More than one hundred eggs were studied in which the sperm was already entirely inside the vitellus. No plasma membrane was ever seen to surround any part of these sperm. Parallel studies of eggs of the golden hamster indicate that the same process of sperm penetration is found here. The newly introduced paternal genome is thus exposed rapidly to the egg cytoplasm. This observation may lead to interesting theoretical considerations. Studies on further developments with regard to the sperm nucleus will be published elsewhere.

DISCUSSION

The electron micrographs presented here show that the sperm has no plasma membrane after it has penetrated the egg. During the process of penetration, however, a plasma membrane is still visible on the outer surface of the sperm. This membrane is continuous with the egg plasma membrane and forms a deep fold around the sperm. On the side facing toward the egg interior, the sperm has no visible plasma membrane. Serial cross sections through the midpiece show all stages of penetration: in the region outside the vitellus, the midpiece is surrounded by a membrane; then comes the region where the egg and sperm plasma membranes fuse; finally, within the vitellus the midpiece is without a plasma membrane. These observations suggest the following hypothesis for sperm penetration.

The sperm head comes to lie against the plasma membrane of the egg. At a certain point the apposed plasma membranes rupture and the egg plasma membrane fuses with the sperm plasma membrane so that a continuous membrane is formed over the egg and around the outer surface of the sperm. In the regions where egg and sperm membranes have joined, the continuous membrane at first forms a deep fold around the

FIGURE 4. A sperm penetrating the rat egg. The plasma membrane of the egg is continuous with the membrane surrounding the sperm tail (arrows) (× 37,000).

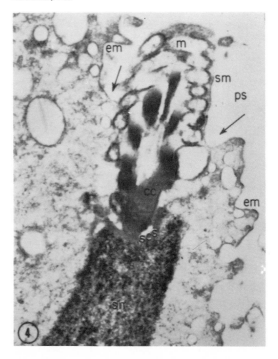

sperm. This fusion of membrane proceeds from the point of attachment near the anterior end of the sperm toward the tail until the entire sperm lies inside the egg.

Figure 10 illustrates schematically our hypothesis of sperm entry and contrasts it with the phagocytotic scheme suggested by Tyler (22). The solid black line corresponds to the plasma membrane of the spermatozoon, while the finely dotted line represents the plasma membrane of the egg.

It is clear that the phagocytotic scheme is not supported by our electron micrographs of sperm entry into the rat egg. If phagocytosis were the mechanism of sperm penetration, we would expect to find not only an intact sperm plasma membrane, but also a surrounding membrane of the phagocytotic vesicle. In fact, there are no membranes at all around the sperm after penetration.

A recent electron microscope study of conjugation in *Paramecium aurelia* (20) indicates that in the formation of the cytoplasmic bridge between conjugants a fusion of the cell membranes of the two cells occurs. This process resembles the fusion of egg and sperm plasma membranes, except for the restriction in space and time.

The process of sperm entrance by membrane fusion can be compared with the interesting membrane phenomenon described by Palade (16) for the discharge of the zymogen granules into the acinar lumen; he

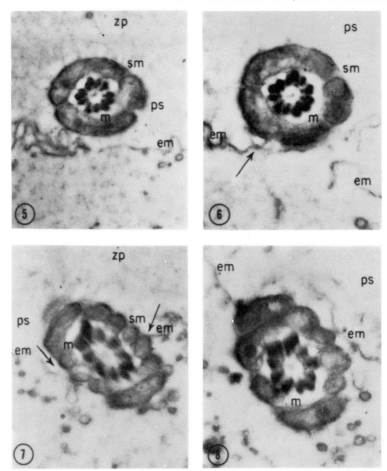

FIGURES 5 to 8. Cross sections through the midpiece of an entering sperm at different levels.

FIGURE 5. The posterior region still in the perivitelline space. The intact plasma membranes of the egg and sperm are clearly visible (× 28,000).

FIGURE 6. The egg and sperm plasma membranes touch and apparently fuse at the arrow (× 34,000).

FIGURE 7. The midpiece is partially incorporated into the vitellus. The continuity of the plasma membrane of the egg with the sperm plasma membrane is visible at the arrows (× 31,000).

FIGURE 8. The midpiece is now entirely within the vitellus. The plasma membrane is continuous outside the incorporated spermatozoon (× 35,000).

states that "the membrane of the zymogen granules becomes continuous with the cell membrane at the apical pole of the exocrine cell." The membrane phenomena in both of these processes would seem to be identical except for their direction.

Fusion of cellular membrane systems is a widely distributed phenomenon. Palade (15), in his studies on "The Endoplasmic Reticulum," reports that smooth surfaced vesicles of the endoplasmic reticulum establish contact with the cell membrane in many different cell types. He further suggests that, in the case of cells which are involved actively in pinocytosis or phagocytosis, large quantities of membrane material will be incorporated into the cytoplasm and that a unidirectional flow of membrane material is unlikely. Palade suggests also that the membrane is repeatedly circulated between the cell surface and the interior of the cell.

Hodge *et al.* (9) propose that the lamellar systems of plant cells are generated by fusion or coalescence of vesicular elements. The most important example they give is the formation of the internal membrane systems in developing chloroplasts.

Other examples of membrane fusion during fat absorption in the intestinal epithelium have been described by Palay (17).

Close contact of egg and sperm plasma membranes can be seen in electron micrographs published by Afzelius and Murray (1) in the case of the sea urchin, and by Colwin *et al.* (7) and Colwin and Colwin (8) for annelids. These investigators, however, did not show later stages of sperm penetration.

The hypothesis we have presented above allows us to examine in a new light other questions related to sperm penetration. The formation of the fertilization cone and its creeping up along the acrosome filament (cf. 8, 10) may be interpreted as cytoplasmic streaming or redistribution of the egg cytoplasm after membrane fusion has taken place. This allows the sperm head to "sink" gradually into the egg. Kille's (10) recent description of the penetration of the lamprey sperm provides a good example of such a process. Fertilization in *Nereis,* as described by Lillie (12), can be interpreted in the same fashion.

Such membrane fusion may take place only between membranes of similar molecular organization. The reasons for species specificity in fertilization may be sought in part in a specificity of membrane structure. Similarly, the block to polyspermy could be the reflection of a reorientation of the reactive sites within the membrane following the fusion of egg and sperm membranes.

ABSTRACT

The structural aspects of sperm penetration in the rat egg were investigated by electron microscopy. Eggs were recovered at intervals between 8 and 10:30 A.M. from females which had mated during the previous night. The oviducts were flushed with hyaluronidase and the eggs trans-

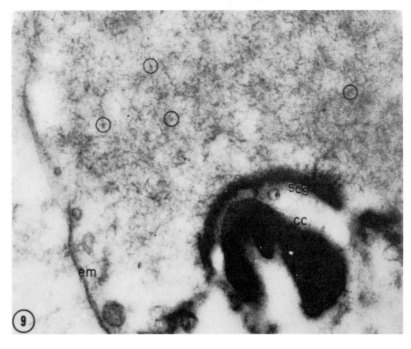

FIGURE 9. The sperm nucleus with the centriolar complex is shown in further sections of the same egg that is illustrated in Figures 5 to 8. On the left the egg plasma membrane is visible. Inside, no sperm plasma membrane or nuclear membrane around the sperm chromatin mass can be observed. At the base of the nucleus is the "supracentriolar sheet" which is the only membrane associated with the nucleus. The sperm nucleus shows masses of 100 Å fibers, each of which is composed of two 40 Å subfibrils (circles). The section was stained with lead hydroxide for 5 minutes ($\times$ 65,000).

FIGURE 10. A diagrammatic representation of sperm penetration by phagocytosis (A) and by membrane fusion (B).

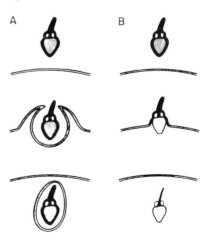

ferred into a 2 percent osmium tetroxide solution, buffered at pH 7.8. After fixation, the eggs were mounted individually in agar, dehydrated in ethyl alcohol, and embedded in butyl-methyl methacrylate (3:1). The sperm penetrating the egg is covered by a plasma membrane which is present only on the side facing toward the zona pellucida; no membrane is visible on the side facing toward the vitellus. The sperm plasma membrane becomes continuous with the egg plasma membrane and forms a deep fold around the entering sperm. Cross sections through the sperm midpiece in the perivitelline space show an intact plasma membrane. At the place of entrance, the plasma membrane of the sperm appears to fuse with the egg plasma membrane. After the sperm has penetrated the vitellus, it has no plasma membrane at all. The nuclear membrane is also absent. These observations suggest a new hypothesis for sperm penetration. After the sperm has come to lie on the plasma membrane of the egg, the egg and sperm plasma membranes rupture and then fuse with one another to form a continuous cell membrane over the egg and the outer surface of the sperm. As a result the sperm comes to lie inside the vitellus, leaving its own plasma membrane incorporated into the egg membrane at the surface of the egg.

Received for publication, February 1, 1961

REFERENCES AND NOTES

This investigation was supported in part by research grant no. RG-4738 from the National Institutes of Health, United States Public Health Service, and by a grant from the Research Committee of the University of Wisconsin from funds contributed by the Wisconsin Alumni Research Foundation.

* Lewis (*11*) defined pinocytosis as "drinking by cells," and phagocytosis as "eating by cells," in describing the incorporation of fluids versus solids. Phagocytosis would be more accurate here than the term pinocytosis used by Tyler.

1. B. A. Afzelius and A. Murray, *Exp. Cell Research* 12, 325 (1957).

2. R. D. Allen, in *A Symposium on the Chemical Basis of Development,* W. D. McElroy and B. Glass, Eds. (The Johns Hopkins Press, Baltimore, 1958), p. 17.

3. C. R. Austin, *Australian J. Sc. Research, series B* 4, 581 (1951).

4. _____, *J. Roy. Micr. Soc.* 71, 295 (1951).

5. H. S. Bennett, *J. Biophysic. and Biochem. Cytol.* 2, No. 4, suppl. 99 (1956).

6. M. G. Burgos and D. W. Fawcett, *J. Biophysic. and Biochem. Cytol.* 1, 287 (1955).

7. A. L. Colwin, L. H. Colwin, D. F. Philpott, *J. Biophysic. and Biochem. Cytol.* 3, 489 (1957).

8. L. H. Colwin and A. L. Colwin, *J. Biophysic. and Biochem. Cytol.* 7, 315 (1960).

9. A. J. Hodge, J. D. McLean, F. V. Mercer, *J. Biophysic. and Biochem. Cytol.* 2, 597 (1956).

10. R. A. Kille, *Exp. Cell Research* 20, 17 (1960).

11. W. H. Lewis, *Bull. Johns Hopkins Hosp.* 49, 17 (1931).

12. F. R. Lillie, *J. Exp. Zool.* 12, 413 (1912).

13. R. S. Ludwig, *Arch. biol.* **65**, 135 (1954).
14. D. L. Odor and R. J. Blandau, *Am. J. Anat.* **89**, 29 (1951).
15. G. E. Palade, *J. Biophysic. and Biochem. Cytol.* **2**, No. 4, suppl. 85 (1956).
16. _____, in *Subcellular Particles,* T. Hayashi, Ed. (Ronald Press, New York, 1959).
17. S. L. Palay, *J. Biophysic. and Biochem. Cytol.* **5**, 373 (1959).
18. H. Ris, Chemie der Genetik, *9. Colloq. Ges. Physiol. Chem.* (Springer, Berlin, 1959), p. 1.
19. Lord Rothschild, *Discovery* **18**, 65 (1957).
20. L. Schneider, *Naturwissenschaften* **47**, 543 (1960).
21. J. R. Sotelo and O. Trujillo-Cenoz, Z. *Zellforsch.* **48**, 565 (1958).
22. A. Tyler, *Exp. Cell Research* Suppl. 7, p. 183 (1959).
23. M. L. Watson, *J. Biophysic. and Biochem. Cytol.* **4**, 727 (1958).
24. E. B. Wilson, *The Cell in Development and Heredity* (Macmillan, New York, 1928).

Fertilization of
Rabbit Ova *in vitro*

M. C. Chang

Worcester Foundation for
Experimental Biology and
Department of Biology,
Boston University

In reviews of the evidence for mammalian fertilization *in vitro*, Austin and Bishop (*1*) stated that "it seems best for the present to regard the case as *sub judice*." Chang (*2*) concluded that "up till now we still do not have a repeatable procedure to fertilize mammalian eggs *in vitro*." Since the recognition of "capacitation" of spermatozoa in the female tract by Chang (*3*) and Austin (*4*), Thibault and his associates (*5–7*) have reported cytological evidence of fertilization of rabbit ova *in vitro* by capacitated sperms. It was thought that unless living young are obtained by transplanting such fertilized ova into recipient rabbits, fertilization *in vitro,* as determined by cytological evidences, may not be sufficiently proved because such ova may be abnormally and/or incompletely fertilized, may die during the process, or may not be fertilized at all. This note reports a procedure to fertilize rabbit ova *in vitro* and the probability of normal development *in vivo* of such *in vitro* fertilized rabbit ova.

An œstrous rabbit was bred three times by fertile bucks at about 9.00 P.M. for the recovery of capacitated sperms, and two other rabbits were injected intravenously with sheep pituitary extract to induce ovulation for the recovery of unfertilized ova. Next day at about 9.00 A.M., before killing, an animal was bled by heart puncture or from the carotid artery in order to obtain fresh serum for the culture of ova. About 3–5 ml of freshly prepared

Reprinted from *Nature* 184, 466–67 (1959), by permission of the author and the editors of *Nature,* Macmillan (Journals) Limited.

Krebs-Ringer bicarbonate solution containing 0.25 percent of glucose was injected into one uterine horn of the mated rabbit and the fluid withdrawn immediately and placed into 1.5 ml capacity small Carrel flasks. Progressive motile sperms from the uterine washings could be seen in most cases. The Fallopian tubes of the other two rabbits were flushed with Krebs-Ringer bicarbonate solution and the ova (still in mucous clot) were placed into a small Carrel flask that contained uterine sperms. These flasks were stopped with rubber and attached to a gentle rocking device placed inside an incubator at 38°C. After about 3–4 hours, the ova, free from the mucous clot but with corona cells still attached, were picked up with a capillary pipette and transferred into an 8 ml capacity Carrel flask containing 4 ml of 50 percent heated rabbit serum (at 55°C for 20 minutes) in saline. After culture for another 18 hours the ova were picked out, separated, mounted *in toto* on a slide (8) and examined under a compound microscope before fixation to determine the location of sperms. After fixation with acetic alcohol they were examined for the polar bodies, pronuclei, and the second maturation spindle, and then stained with Lacmoid for checking details.

The ova thus examined were classified into four groups: (*a*) Unfertilized; the ova that had definite second maturation spindles irrespective of the presence sperms. (*b*) Uncertain; those ova having no second maturation spindles but the nuclear configuration of which was at variance; some had one pronucleus, some had two groups of chromosomes, and some had several pronuclei. They may have been parthenogenetically activated, or fertilized, but died at an early stage. (*c*) Fertilized but dead; ova showing sperms on the zona or in the perivitelline space and with the nucleus at the anaphase of the second maturation division; some had a definite second polar body and had either cleaved into two cells or had two pronuclei, but most of them had fragmented. (*d*) Fertilized and cleaved normally; those cleaved into 4 cells and with either a second polar body or sperms in the perivitelline space.

Of 266 rabbit ova examined, 166 (62 percent) were unfertilized, 23 (8.7 percent) were uncertain, 22 (8.3 percent) seemed to have been fertilized but died at an early stage, and 55 (21 percent) cleaved normally and were considered definitely fertilized. Of these 51 ova, 36 were transplanted (9) into the tubes of 6 recipient rabbits that had been injected with pituitary extract 18 hours previously. The recipient animals were allowed to deliver in term. Two recipients did not become pregnant; but 4 delivered 15 living healthy young. The probability of normal development of such *in vitro* fertilized ova is then about 42 percent.

The procedure used in the present study is similar to that recommended by Thibault (10), and the proportion of ova fertilized is similarly low. The concentration of sperms in the uterine washings ranged from 10,000 to 26,000 per ml and the proportion of fertilized ova was not correlated with the concentration of sperms. Furthermore, when uterine washings were centrifuged to concentrate sperms, or when a small amount of saline was used to wash the uterine horns the proportion of ova fertilized was not increased. The proportion of fertilized ova was also not increased by using sperms recovered from the tubes of a mated animal (at 10,000 to 15,000 sperms per ml). In this case only 5 out of 41 ova (12.2 percent) were fertilized. Autologous serum seems to be better than heterologous serum for culturing newly fertilized ova: when autologous serum was used 50 out of 102 ova (49 percent) were fertilized and 43 of the 102 (42 percent) cleaved normally; but in heterologous serum 18 of 109 ova (17 percent) were fertilized and 11 of the 109 (10 percent) cleaved normally.

Due to the thick layer of corona cells on the zona pellucida, it was not possible to observe the penetration of sperm through the zona. Judging from their rate of cleavage, as compared with those ova recovered from the mated rabbit and cultured similarly, penetration of sperms probably occurred when the ova were in saline rather than in serum. In some experiments, the zona pellucida at the time of examination was very soft or partially dissolved. This may be due to a reaction between the zona and some factors in the uterine washing, as it was shown that the zona of unfertilized ova dissolved in a few hours when transplanted into the uterus (*11*) or it may be that certain factors in the serum of a particular animal affect the zona in this way. At the time of examination the general appearance of a fertilized ovum is better than that of an unfertilized ovum. This shows that fertilization increases the resistance of the ovum to the artificial medium.

Although the proportion of fertilized ova is relatively low and sometimes no fertilization occurred due to infection or other unknown reasons under the present experimental conditions, it can be said that at least we have a repeatable procedure for fertilizing mammalian ova *in vitro* and that such ova are truly fertilized and able to develop into normal young. Further studies are planned to elucidate the mechanisms of mammalian fertilization *in vitro*.

REFERENCES

This work was supported by the Population Council and the Dickinson Research Memorial, Planned Parenthood Federation of America. Thanks are due to Miss Dorothy M. Hunt for assistance, and to Dr. G. Pincus for constant interest.

1. C. R. Austin and M. W. H. Bishop, *Biol. Rev.* **32**, 296 (1957).

2. M. C. Chang, in "The Beginnings of Embryonic Development," Amer. Assoc. Adv. Sci. Symposium, Washington, D.C. (1957), p. 109.

3. ———, *Nature* **168**, 697 (1951).

4. C. R. Austin, *Aust. J. Sci. Res.* B **4**, 581 (1951).

5. L. Dauzier, C. Thibault, S. Winterberger, *C. R. Acad. Sci.* **238**, 844 (1954).

6. C. Thibault, L. Dauzier, S. Winterberger, *C. R. Soc. Biol.* **148**, 789 (1954).

7. L. Dauzier and C. Thibault, Third Int. Congr. Anim. Reprod., Cambridge, Sect. I, 58 (1956).

8. M. C. Chang, *J. Exp. Zool.* **128**, 379 (1955).

9. ———, *J. Exp. Zool.* **144**, 197 (1950).

10. C. Thibault, personal communication (1956).

11. M. C. Chang, in *La Fonction Tubaire et ses Troubles* (Masson et Cie, Paris, 1955), p. 140.

Interspecific Hybridization of Somatic Cells[*]

Boris Ephrussi[†]
Mary C. Weiss[‡]

Western Reserve University Developmental Biology Center

Hybridization of somatic cells *in vitro*, first described in 1960 by Barski, Sorieul, and Cornefert (*1*), has since been shown to occur in mixed cultures of many different pairs of cultured mouse cells. A recent review (*2*) lists 12 different "crosses" of mouse cells resulting in the formation of viable hybrids. This list includes crosses between cells of permanent lines as well as crosses between the latter and freshly explanted normal diploid cells. In this paper we describe the first interspecific cross giving rise to rapidly multiplying monucleate somatic hybrids (*3*).

The two cell types involved are: (1) clone LM(TK⁻)1D, a 5-bromo-deoxyuridine-resistant thymidine kinase-deficient subclone of *mouse* L cells, kindly given to us by Dr. S. Kit; (2) recently explanted Wistar *rat* embryo diploid cells.

The detection and identification of the hybrids was facilitated by the use of a recently established selective technique for the isolation of hybrids between biochemically deficient L cells and normal mouse cells (*5*) and by the characteristically different karyotypes of the "parental" cells. The karyotype of the mouse cells (Fig. 1) is characterized by a modal number of 53 chromosomes, 7 to 11 of which are long biarmed chromosomes, which have median or submedian centromeres, and are clearly different from those of rat cells. Ninety percent of the mouse cells carry one biarmed chromo-

Reprinted from *Proceedings of the National Academy of Sciences* **53**, 1040–1042 (1965), by permission of the authors and the National Academy of Sciences.

FIGURE 1. Metaphase of a cell of mouse cell line LM (TK⁻) 1D with 53 chromosomes. Note the presence of 9 long biarmed chromosomes with median or submedian centromeres; the arrow points to the "D chromosome" with a characteristic secondary constriction.

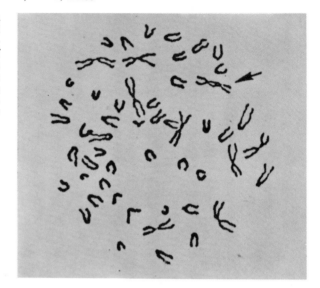

FIGURE 2. Metaphase of a diploid rat cell (42 chromosomes). Note the small biarmed chromosomes and the characteristic long ones, indicated by arrows.

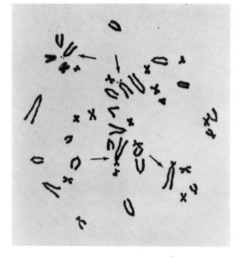

some presenting a characteristic secondary constriction. The karyotype of the rat ($2n = 42$) is characterized by the presence of 20 small and 4 long biarmed chromosomes, the latter with subterminal centromeres (Fig. 2).

Trypsinized suspensions of the two cell types are prepared and mixed to give a 1:1 mouse/rat cell ratio. Two million cells of this mixed population are inoculated into a 20-ml plastic bottle containing 5 ml of modified Eagle's minimal medium, supplemented with 5 percent calf serum, and incubated for 24–48 hours at 37°C. During this period the cells attach to the bottom of the flask. The medium is then replaced by the selective medium, which differs from the above by the addition of $1 \times 10^{-4}M$ hypoxanthine, $4 \times 10^{-7}M$ aminopterin, and $1.6 \times 10^{-5}M$ thymidine, and the culture is further incubated at 37°C (6).

In the selective medium, the LM cells degenerate (because they lack thymidine kinase and therefore cannot utilize exogenous thymidine which must be used since the *de novo* synthesis of thymidine is blocked by aminopterin) while the rat cells grow and form a monolayer. On this background, the hybrid cells, unhampered by the selective medium, form, in the course of the next few days, discrete, multilayered colonies which can easily be isolated and subcultured. Karyological examination of the subcultured hybrid cells clearly shows the presence of chromosomes characteristic of each of the parents (Fig. 3).

At the present date, the hybrid cells have been maintained under conditions of continuous multiplication for 1 month, going through at least 25 cell generations. The evolution of their karyotype and some of their enzymatic characteristics are being investigated.

Communicated March 24, 1965

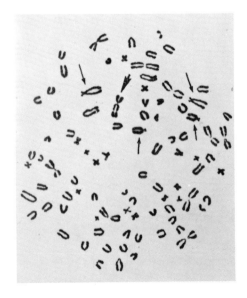

FIGURE 3. Metaphase of a hybrid cell with 89 chromosomes. Note the presence of 10 long biarmed mouse chromosomes (among them the "D chromosome," indicated by a large arrow) and of 4 long rat biarmed chromosomes (small arrows). Many small biarmed rat chromosomes can also be recognized.

REFERENCES AND NOTES

We wish to thank Dr. L. J. Scaletta and Mr. M. C. Yoshida for their help in karyological analysis and for preparing the microphotographs, and Miss Patricia Mendez for her able technical assistance.

* This work was supported by grant no. G-23129 of the National Science Foundation.

† On leave from the University of Paris.

‡ Graduate fellow of the National Science Foundation.

1. G. S. Barski, S. Sorieul, F. Cornefert, *Compt. Rend.* **251**, 1825 (1960).

2. B. Ephrussi, *19th Symposium on Fundamental Cancer Research,* Houston, Texas, in press.

3. It has recently been shown by Harris and Watkins (4) that human and mouse cells can be caused to fuse into heterokaryons by the action of UV-inactivated Sendai virus. Whether these heterokaryons are capable of (limited or indefinite) multiplication appears to be unknown at the present time.

4. H. Harris and J. F. Watkins, *Nature* **205**, 640 (1965).

5. R. L. Davidson and B. Ephrussi, *Nature* **205**, 1170 (1965).

6. J. W. Littlefield, *Science* **145**, 709 (1964).

B Differentiation of the nucleus

Briggs, Robert, and Thomas J. King. 1952. Transplantation of living nuclei from blastula cells into enucleated frogs' eggs. *Proc. Nat. Acad. Sci. U.S.* **38**, 455–63.

King, Thomas J., and Robert Briggs. 1955. Changes in the nuclei of differentiating gastrula cells, as demonstrated by nuclear transplantation. *Proc. Nat. Acad. Sci. U.S.* **41**, 321–25.

Steward, F. C., L. M. Blakely, Ann E. Kent, and Marion O. Mapes. 1963. Growth and organization in free cell cultures. *Brookhaven Symp. Biol.* **16**, 73–88.

Transplantation of Living Nuclei from Blastula Cells into Enucleated Frogs' Eggs[*]

Robert Briggs
Thomas J. King

Institute for Cancer
Research and Lankenau
Hospital Research Institute,
Philadelphia

Introduction. The role of the nucleus in embryonic differentiation has been the subject of investigations dating back to the beginnings of experimental embryology. At first it was supposed by Roux, Weismann and others that differentiation is the result of qualitative nuclear divisions, different blastomeres thereby receiving the different kinds of nuclei which determine their subsequent differentiation. Later on this theory was disproved by numerous experiments showing that, during early cleavage at least, the distribution of the nuclei can be changed at will without altering the pattern of development. The cleavage nuclei have, therefore, been regarded as identical, and differentiation has been ascribed primarily to the well-known localizations in the egg cytoplasm.

This evidence, it should be emphasized, relates only to the early phases of development. During this time it is definitely true that the nuclei in the various blastomeres are equivalent. However, whether they remain equivalent or become differentiated as the various parts of the embryo differentiate has never been tested. The possibility that nuclei might differentiate in response to regional differences in the cytoplasm, and that such nuclear changes might have reciprocal effects on the cytoplasm during cell differentiation, was

Reprinted from *Proceedings of the National Academy of Sciences* 38, 455–63 (1952), by permission of the authors and the National Academy of Sciences.

suggested by Morgan (*1*). More recently Schultz (*2–4*) has discussed the problem more fully, indicating the known cytogenetical mechanisms that could account for nuclear differentiation, and Weisz (*5*) has reviewed it in relation to ciliate morphogenesis.

Obviously this problem can be solved only by the development of a method for testing directly whether nuclei of differentiating embryonic cells are or are not themselves differentiated. This sort of test could be obtained, as suggested to us several years ago by Schultz, if it were possible to transplant nuclei. Ideally, this type of experiment should be carried out by transplanting the nucleus from an irreversibly differentiated cell into an enucleated egg. The egg cytoplasm when normally nucleated is, of course, capable of giving rise to the complete range of differentiated cell types, while in the absence of the nucleus it may cleave but fails completely to differentiate (*6–8*). In other words, its differentiation, while potentially complete, is still nucleus-dependent. Therefore, if the egg nucleus could be replaced by one from a differentiated cell, the nature of the ensuing development should reveal the character of the transplanted nucleus — complete differentiation would indicate that irreversible nuclear differentiation had not occurred, while limited differentiation would indicate that it had.

In order to make such tests of nuclear differentiation it is first necessary to develop a method of transplantation that leaves both the transplanted nucleus and the recipient egg cytoplasm in undamaged condition. The only way to determine if this can be done is to work first with nuclei from undifferentiated cells which, if transplanted properly, should give rise to normal embryos. In the Amphibia the cells of choice for this purpose are those of the late blastula. They are almost as small as the differentiated cells of slightly older embryos and so present the same technical problems. At the same time they are, with the exception of the future dorsal lip cells, still undetermined and therefore their nuclei cannot be irreversibly differentiated. For these reasons we have worked out a method for transplanting nuclei from these cells into enucleated frogs' eggs. These eggs cleave and in a significant proportion of the cases develop into complete embryos.

Method. The transplantation of nuclei is carried out in the following steps: First the recipient egg is pricked with a clean glass needle. This activates the egg and causes it to rotate so that the animal pole is uppermost and the egg nucleus can be taken out with a glass needle by Porter's (*9*) technique. The outer jelly coats are then removed and the egg is placed in a depression in a wax-bottomed dish in Niu-Twitty's (*10*) solution. A blastula or early gastrula (St. 8 to 10, Shumway, *11*), placed in the same dish, is then opened up and one of the subsurface animal pole cells is dissected free from its neighbors. The cell is now drawn up into the mouth of a thin-walled glass micropipette, the lumen of which is somewhat smaller than the diameter of the cell. The pipette is held in a Leitz-Chambers holder connected via rubber pressure tubing to an ordinary 5-ml syringe. All of the system except the tip of the needle is filled with air. The tip contains the column of solution drawn up with the cell. Provided the needle is really clean the movements of the column can be controlled accurately. Now, as the cell is drawn up into the needle it is compressed and distorted in such a way as to break the cell surface without dispersing the cell contents. The needle is then inserted into the enucleated egg and the broken cell is injected, thus liberating the nucleus within the egg. The injection can be controlled by watching the meniscus of the fluid column within the needle, things being arranged so that the broken cell is kept near the tip of the needle while the meniscus of the column is higher up but still within the field of the microscope. Following the injection the needle is slowly withdrawn. Usually as it is withdrawn it pulls the surface coat up against the vitelline membrane so that a small canal is formed through which the egg substance may subsequently leak. This can be prevented by cutting the connection between the egg surface and the vitelline membrane with glass needles. The egg is then removed from the operating dish and placed in a small Stender dish in spring water.

Results. When eggs (*R. pipiens*) are simply pricked with a clean glass needle they rotate, form the ephemeral "black dots" localizing the second maturation division spindle, and within a few hours show puckering of the surface or abortive and irregular cleavage furrows. There is no genuine cleavage or blastula formation. In our experiments 99% (2831 out of 2853) of the pricked eggs behaved in this way. By contrast, eggs which are pricked *and* enucleated fail to give any signs of cleavage. When observed a few hours after activation these eggs show none of the puckerings, etc., which are present in practically all of the pricked eggs at this time. Thus, 631 out of 638 enucleated eggs behaved in this way, indicating that 99% of the operations for removal of the egg nucleus were successful. Actually, the 7 eggs which did show puckers were ones in which the exovate, which forms when the egg is enucleated and which contains the egg nucleus, still retained a connection with the egg. In these the egg proper may have been enucleated, the puckers forming through the influence of the nucleus in the attached exovate.

In order to check further on the success of the operation for enucleation we always enucleated some normally inseminated eggs at the end of each experiment. From these we should obtain androgenetic haploids when the operation is successful, and normal diploids when it is not. Out of 358 operations, regarded at the time as successful, we obtained 337 embryos, all of them haploids. An additional 169 operations, regarded as not absolutely certain, gave 161 embryos of which 160 were haploids.

From these results we can say that eggs which are pricked and then enucleated will practically never retain the egg nucleus by mistake, and will never develop. When these eggs are now each injected with a diploid blastula cell nucleus more than half of them cleave, giving rise to

TABLE 1

Cleavage of Enucleated Eggs Injected with Blastula Cell Nuclei.

No. of eggs injected	197
Cleavage	
None	45
Abortive	48
Cleaved	104
Blastulae	
Partial	
$< \frac{1}{2}$	12
$> \frac{1}{2}$	29
Complete	63

Notes: *Each egg was activated, enucleated and then injected with a diploid nucleus from an animal hemisphere cell of an advanced blastula or early gastrula. Of the blastulae obtained from the injected eggs, 13 of the complete ones and 17 of the partial ones were fixed during the first day of development. The remainder were allowed to develop and gave rise to embryos as shown in Table 2.*

partial and complete blastulae as summarized in Table 1. Some of these blastulae were fixed. The remainder developed as shown in Table 2. Of the complete blastulae the majority (74%) gastrulated normally and formed complete embryos. Approximately half of these were normal in appearance when fixed at stages ranging from stage 19 (5-mm embryo) to the tadpole stage. The remainder formed complete neurulae but later on displayed slight to moderate abnormalities such as growth retardation, microcephaly in some cases, larger than normal heads in others and so on. Of the 15 abnormal embryos listed in Table 2, 14 were diploids and 1 was polyploid as judged from the ectodermal cell size. Among the 15 normal embryos there were 7 diploids and 8 polyploids. The only other embryos that developed far enough to give clear indications of chromosome number were 4 of the 5 abnormal neurulae listed in the table. These also were diploid (2 cases) or polyploid (2 cases). Thus, among the 35 embryos obtained there were no haploids. Had they occurred they would have been hard to account for in these experiments, since the injected nucleus was diploid. The polyploids, on the other hand, may be explained. The blastula cell nuclei are undoubtedly in various stages of mitosis when transplanted, and there should be ample opportunity for a doubling of chromosomes to occur after the nucleus has been transplanted and before the egg cytoplasm is prepared to cleave.

In order to get cytological evidence of the removal of the egg nucleus 22 of the injected eggs were fixed at stages ranging from morula to gastrula, and were sectioned and stained with the Feulgen reagent. In 21 of these eggs the exovate could be seen trapped in the inner jelly layer but separated from the egg proper. In 9 cases the egg nucleus was

TABLE 2

Development of Blastulae Derived from Enucleated Eggs Injected with Blastula Cell Nuclei.

1	2	3	4		5		6		
							Post-Gastrula Development		
					Effective Total		Abn.	Post-Neurula	
Type of	Total	Arrested	—Gastrulae—		—Gastrulae—		Neu-	—Embryos—	
Blastula	No.	Blastulae	Normal	Abn.	Normal	Abn.	rulae	Normal	Sl. Abn.
Complete	50	3	37	10	30	2	2	15	15
> ½	20	7	0	13	0	3	3	0	0
< ½	4	4	0	0	…	…	…	…	…

Notes: *Of the total number of gastrulae obtained (col. 4) some were fixed, leaving the numbers given in column 5. These were developed into embryos as listed in column 6.*

found in the exovate, while the egg proper consisted of cells containing normal nuclei which could only have been derived from the transplanted nucleus. In 6 additional cases Feulgen positive material was seen in the exovate, but it could not be definitely recognized as the egg nucleus. The remaining 6 cases showed no Feulgen positive material. In these the egg nucleus may have been lost from the exovate, or it could have been obscured by the pigment of the surface coat surrounding the exovate.

The evidence summarized above shows quite conclusively that living nuclei can be transplanted from blastula cells into enucleated eggs.

TABLE 3

Development of Enucleated *Pipiens* Eggs Injected with *Catesbeiana* Nuclei.

1	2	3				4			5	
	No. of	—Cleavage—				—Blastulae—			Arrested in	Arrested in Early
Type of	Eggs		Abortive			—Partial—			Blastula	Gastrula
Nucleus	Injected	None	Cleavage	Cleaved	< ½	> ½	Complete	Stage	Stage
Cates-beiana (haploid)	119	27	26	66	12	31	23	66	0
Cates-beiana × *pipiens* (diploid)	46	17	7	22	1	7	14	11	11

Notes: *The nuclei used for transplantation were taken from animal hemisphere cells of hybrid blastulae 17–18 hours old (18°C). The diploid hybrid nuclei were from the cross,* pipiens ♀ × catesbeiana ♂. *The* catesbeiana *haploid nuclei were from the androgenetic haploid hybrid,* pipiens (♀) × catesbeiana ♂.

However, in order to get an additional proof of the success of the technique we have transplanted *R. catesbeiana* nuclei into *R. pipiens* enucleated eggs. It is known from hybridization experiments (8, 12, 13) that this combination is lethal. The diploid hybrid is arrested in late blastula or early gastrula stage and dies in about 3 days, while the androgenetic haploid hybrid is always arrested in late blastula stage but dies later — at about 4 to 5 days. Thus, if the transplantation of the foreign nucleus is successful we should obtain a uniform arrest of development followed at the appropriate interval by the death of the embryo.

The experiments were done as follows: Donor blastulae were produced by inseminating *pipiens* eggs with *catesbeiana* sperm. The egg nucleus was removed from some of these, giving us androgenetic haploid hybrids. The rest of the eggs were allowed to develop as diploid hybrids. After about 18 hours at 18° both types of hybrids had developed to stage 8 (mid to late blastula), and were usually used to provide nuclei for transplantation at this time. The hybrids are, of course, arrested shortly thereafter and we have evidence, not presented here, that nuclei taken from older blastulae (stage 9) generally will not cause enucleated eggs to cleave.

The results of the transplantations of nuclei from hybrid blastulae are summarized in Table 3. About half of the enucleated eggs which were injected with the *catesbeiana* haploid nucleus cleaved and developed into partial or complete blastulae, as indicated in the table. The complete blastulae, it should be emphasized, looked perfectly normal. Yet none of them showed any signs of gastrulation. They were all arrested in late blastula stage, as were the androgenetic haploid hybrid controls, and later on they all died at approximately the same time as did the controls (Fig. 1).

Enucleated eggs injected with diploid hybrid nuclei also cleaved and gave rise to blastulae, as shown in Table 3. These corresponded to the diploid hybrid controls in their development. That is, they were all arrested either in late blastula or early gastrula stages, and died when their controls did (Fig. 1).

In order to see whether the nuclear phenomena associated with the arrest and death of the blastulae were occurring in the same way in the experimental and control blastulae, we fixed several of each at ages of 42 to 72 hours. The controls consisted of 9 androgenetic haploid hybrids [*pipiens* (♀) × *catesbeiana* ♂]; the 17 experimental blastulae were all derived from enucleated *pipiens* eggs injected with haploid *catesbeiana* nuclei taken from androgenetic haploid hybrid blastulae.

A study of the arrested control blastulae revealed a variety of nuclear abnormalities. The majority of the nuclei were in an abnormal interphase condition characterized by an accumulation of chromatin around the periphery of the nucleus in the form of thick threads, leaving the central portion free of Feulgen-positive material. In addition there were

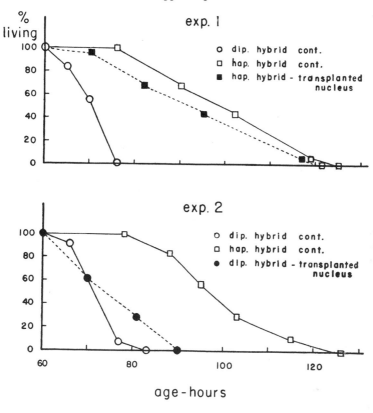

FIGURE 1.

EXP. 1. Mortality curves for (1) haploid hybrid controls, *pipiens* (♀) × *catesbeiana* ♂; (2) enucleated *pipiens* eggs injected with haploid *catesbeiana* nuclei; and (3) control diploid hybrids, *pipiens* ♀ × *catesbeiana* ♂.

Based on 55 haploid hybrid controls, 28 experimental haploid hybrids, and 147 diploid hybrid controls.

EXP. 2. As for experiment 1, except for the experimental embryos which in this experiment are derived from enucleated *pipiens* eggs injected with diploid (*pipiens* ♀ × *catesbeiana* ♂) hybrid nuclei.

Based on 119 diploid hybrid controls, 21 experimental diploid hybrids, and 73 haploid hybrid controls.

arrested and abnormal metaphases, and a few anaphases which always showed bridges. In some of these figures the chromosomes were clumped. Finally, some cells contained small groups of chromosomes, or small pycnotic nuclei, presumably derived from irregular divisions that had occurred earlier.

In the majority (14 out of 17) of the experimental blastulae the nuclear abnormalities were exactly the same as those described above for the controls. In 3 cases, however, the condition was different, with the nuclei all in an abnormal interphase condition characterized by a rather diffuse Feulgen staining. We do not know yet how to account for these exceptional cases. It may be that in a larger series of cases the same type of nuclear phenomenon might appear among the controls, or occasionally there may be some effect of the transplantation on the subsequent behavior of the nuclei. In any case, in the large majority of the experimental blastulae the appearance of the nuclei is the same as it is in the controls. This fact, taken together with the fact that the extent of development and the time of death are also the same in the experimental and control blastulae provides convincing evidence of the successful transplantation of the foreign nucleus.

Discussion. Nuclear transplantation has been accomplished previously in amoebae (*14, 15*), but to our knowledge has not been reported for other forms. The evidence summarized in this paper shows that blastula cell nuclei may now be transplanted into enucleated frogs' eggs, giving rise to nucleated embryos which differentiate normally. This means that the nuclei are not significantly damaged, and indicates that the technique of nuclear transplantation may now be used in testing nuclei from various differentiated parts of the Amphibian embryo. The advantages of being able to study the problem of nuclear differentiation with this embryo are considerable. It is one of the classical objects of experimental embryology and thereby provides us with the opportunity of correlating the properties of the nuclei, as they may be revealed by nuclear transplantation, with the known properties of the different parts of the embryo as demonstrated by the numerous transplantation and explantation experiments recorded in the literature.

The method of nuclear transplantation, described in this paper, involves transferring the cytoplasm as well as the nucleus of the blastula cell into the enucleated egg. This does not, however, bring about a significant dilution of the egg cytoplasm. The total volume of the donor blastula cell is about 2×10^{-4} cu mm, while the average volume of the *pipiens* egg is about 3.4 cu mm — giving a ratio of 1:17,000. We have not calculated the volume of the blastula cell cytoplasm but it would be significantly smaller than that of the whole cell and the ratio of it to the egg cytoplasm volume is therefore probably smaller than 1:20,000. Nonetheless, some cytoplasm is transferred along with the nucleus by this method. Refinements may make it possible to eliminate most of the cytoplasm, but it will be extremely difficult, if not impossible, to devise a method for obtaining nuclei which can be said to be completely free of cytoplasm. However, this is not important at present. The method as it stands should allow us to detect such irreversible changes in nuclei as may be limiting with respect to differentiation. And in the future the role of the cytoplasm may be explored by combining in transplantation nuclei and cytoplasm from different types of cells, or from the same type at different stages of differentiation.

Although the method of nuclear transplantation should be valuable principally for the study of nuclear differentiation, it may also have other uses. In particular, it can provide us with a test of whether nuclei which have been treated in various ways still retain their capacity for mitosis. This is the best if not the only test of a normal nucleus, and we hope that it may eventually be applied to the problem of developing an optimal nuclear medium — a matter which should have real importance for future studies of nuclear biochemistry.

Summary. In this paper a method is described for transplanting nuclei from advanced blastula cells into *enucleated* eggs of *Rana pipiens*. When the nucleus is from the same species as the egg cytoplasm the egg then cleaves and can develop into a normal embryo. When the nucleus is from a different species (*R. catesbeiana*) the enucleated *pipiens* egg which receives it forms a blastula which is then arrested and subsequently dies, exactly as do the normally produced hybrids between the two species. These and other experiments prove that the blastula cell nucleus can be transplanted in undamaged condition, indicating that the technique of nuclear transplantation is now sufficiently well developed so that it may be used in studies of nuclear differentiation and possibly in other studies of nuclear function as well.

Communicated by C. W. Metz, March 15, 1952

REFERENCES AND NOTES

Acknowledgement. We wish to thank Miss Marie DiBerardino for her skilful assistance in this work.

* This investigation was supported in part by a research grant from the National Cancer Institute, of the National Institutes of Health, Public Health Service; and in part by an institutional grant from the American Cancer Society.

1. T. H. Morgan, *Embryology and Genetics* (Columbia Univ. Press, New York, 1934).
2. J. Schultz, *Proc. Seventh Internat. Genet. Congress*, 257 (1939).
3. J. Schultz, *Cancer Research* 7, 41 (1947).
4. J. Schultz, in press.
5. P. B. Weisz, *Am. Nat.* 85, 293 (1951).
6. G. Fankhauser, *J. Exp. Zool.* 67, 349 (1934).
7. E. B. Harvey, *Biol. Bull.* 71, 101 (1936).
8. R. Briggs, E. U. Green, T. J. King, *J. Exp. Zool.* 116, 455 (1951).
9. K. R. Porter, *Biol. Bull.* 77, 233 (1939).

10. Referred to in R. A. Flickinger, Jr., *J. Exp. Zool* **112**, 465 (1949).
11. W. Shumway, *Anat. Rec.* **78**, 139 (1940).
12. R. Rugh and F. Exner, *Proc. Am. Phil. Soc.* **83**, 607 (1940).
13. J. A. Moore, *J. Exp. Zool.* **86**, 405 (1941).
14. J. Comandon and P. de Fonbrune, *Compt. Rend.* **130**, 744 (1939).
15. I. J. Lorch and J. F. Danielli, *Nature* **166**, 329 (1950).

Changes in the Nuclei of Differentiating Gastrula Cells, as Demonstrated by Nuclear Transplantation

Thomas J. King
Robert Briggs

Institute for Cancer Research and Lankenau Hospital Research Institute, Philadelphia

The hypothesis that the nucleus controls the differentiation of embryonic cells dates back to the time of Roux and Weismann. Originally it involved the assumption of a segregation of nuclear determiners of differentiation during cleavage. When put to the test, the hypothesis was found wanting (1). Embryological experimentation showed that the distribution of nuclei during the early cleavages could be altered without producing a corresponding alteration of the developmental pattern. Furthermore, cytological evidence of the equational nature of mitosis was against any theory of differentiation involving somatic segregation. Finally, modifications of the hypothesis which required permanent changes in gene activity were difficult to accept. So far as was known, such changes (i.e., mutations) occur infrequently and unpredictably, while what was required was a coordinated series of directed gene changes. Taken together, this evidence indicated that somatic cells contain identical nuclei. However, definite proof of this fact was obtained only for the early cleavage stages, and the possibility remained that nuclear changes, perhaps of a type not heretofore recognized, might occur later in development (2).

In an effort to detect changes in the properties of nuclei during differentiation, we have developed a method for

Reprinted from *Proceedings of the National Academy of Sciences* **41**, 321–25 (1955), by permission of the authors and the National Academy of Sciences.

191

transferring nuclei of embryonic cells into enucleated eggs of the frog *Rana pipiens* (3, 4). The earlier work with this procedure showed that living nuclei of undifferentiated blastula cells could be successfully transplanted. The recipient eggs developed into normal embryos, demonstrating that there had been no irreversible changes in the nuclei during pregastrula development.

More recently, nuclei of chorda-mesoderm and presumptive medullary plate of the late gastrula were similarly tested (5). The donor cells were small and difficult to handle, and fewer of the attempted transfers were successful than had been the case in the previous experiments. About 8 percent of the test eggs developed into normal blastulae which, on the basis of their appearance, would have been expected to differentiate normally. Instead of so developing, about half the blastulae were arrested in blastula and gastrula stages. Of the remainder, a few developed into larvae, while the majority were arrested in various embryonic stages. At the time there were two possible interpretations of this result. One was that the nuclei of determined areas of the late gastrula had undergone a change restricting their capacity to promote certain of the varied types of differentiation required for the coordinated development of the egg. Such a nuclear change could easily account for the cessation of the development of the test eggs. The second possibility was that the nuclei might have been damaged in the course of the transfer in such a way as to lead to the same result. Since this possibility could not be excluded, we adopted it as the more conservative interpretation and emphasized the fact that some of the test eggs did develop normally. This indicated that at least some, and possibly all, of the late gastrula nuclei were unchanged, despite the fact that the tissues were determined.

Recently the experiments mentioned above have been repeated and extended, using an improved procedure for nuclear transplantation. The improvement consists mainly of the use of trypsin and versene (ethylenediamine tetra acetic acid) to aid in dissecting the embryo and isolating individual cells of known type in undamaged condition (6). The embryo is first placed in 0.5 percent commercial (Difco) trypsin made up in a Niu-Twitty solution (7) lacking Ca^{++} and Mg^{++} and buffered at pH 7.1 with phosphate. The trypsin has a preferential action on the material cementing the embryonic layers together. As it acts, the layers can be neatly separated. A portion of the desired layer is now placed in $5 \times 10^{-4} M$ versene, also made up in the modified Niu-Twitty solution. The versene quickly affects the intercellular material — within 5–10 minutes the cells round up and are transferred to the regular Niu-Twitty solution. They can now be picked up singly in the transfer pipette, and the nuclei can be transplanted in the manner previously described (4).

The improved transplantation procedure was first tested on nuclei of undifferentiated early gastrula cells, with gratifying results (Table 1).

TABLE 1

Transplantability of Nuclei as Influenced by Method of Donor Cell Isolation (Donor Cells from Animal Hemisphere of Early Gastrulae).

| Method of Donor Cell Isolation | No. Eggs Injected with Nuclei | Complete Blastulae | Development of Blastulae | | |
			Arrested Blastulae and Gastrulae	Arrested Neurulae and Postneurulae	Larvae (10–12 Mm)
Dissection with glass needles*	135 (100%)	29 (21%)	10	12	7
Trypsin plus versene	71 (100%)	29 (41%)	1	3	25

Note: *There is no difference in the type of cleavage that can be correlated with the sources of nuclei. In all cases some nuclear transfers fail completely; others give rise to abortive or "nucleusless" blastulae which never develop further. The remainder, which comprise the genuinely cleaved eggs, give rise to partial or complete blastulae. In this and the following tables we will consider only the formation and development of the complete blastulae.*

* T. J. King and R. Briggs, J. Embryol. Exptl. Morphol. 2, 78 (1954).

The proportion of attempted transfers resulting in normal cleavage of the recipient eggs was increased from 21 to 41 percent. There was also a pronounced improvement in the later development of the test eggs, as indicated in the table.

The experiments with late gastrula chorda-mesoderm nuclei were now repeated. With the new procedure the proportion of recipient eggs displaying normal cleavage and blastula formation was more than doubled — from 8 to 22 percent — indicating that more of the nuclei were being transplanted in undamaged condition (Table 2). On this basis one would expect a definite improvement in the later development of the blastulae. However, no such improvement was observed. The majority of the blastulae were still arrested in blastula, gastrula, or abnormal postneurula stages. Sections of the latter embryos showed that the inductor system (notochord and somites) was differentiated, while the central nervous system was very deficient and occasionally absent. These experiments indicated that the deficiencies in the development of the "chorda-mesoderm embryos" were not, as we had previously thought, entirely the result of nuclear damage but rather reflected an intrinsic change in the "differentiative" properties of the chorda-mesoderm nuclei.

In order to obtain more decisive evidence of nuclear changes during cell differentiation, a series of experiments was done on nuclei of the presumptive mid-gut region of late gastrulae. The cells in this region (floor of archenteron) are large and are easily handled during the trans-

TABLE 2

Transplantability of Nuclei as Influenced by Method of Donor Cell Isolation (Donor Cells from Chorda-Mesoderm of Late Gastrulae).

Method of Donor Cell Isolation	No. Eggs Injected with Nuclei	Complete Blastulae	—————Development of Blastulae—————		
			Arrested Blastulae and Gastrulae	Arrested Neurulae and Postneurulae	Larvae (10–12 Mm)
Dissection with glass needles*	242 (100%)	20 (8%)	10	6	4
Trypsin plus versene	83 (100%)	18 (22%)	8	8	2

* See Table 1.

plantation operation, which can therefore be carried out with minimal risk of damage to the nuclei. The results of these experiments showed, first, that the endoderm nuclei elicited normal cleavage and blastula formation in 40 percent of the test eggs — this being almost exactly the same result as was obtained in control experiments with nuclei of undifferentiated early gastrula cells (Table 3). However, the later development of the two groups of blastulae was quite different. Most of the control blastulae developed into larvae, while the "endoderm blastulae" were usually arrested in blastula, gastrula, or abnormal embryonic stages.

The abnormal embryos were very interesting. They grew to a length of about 6 mm and displayed a combination of deficiencies which we have not observed in other embryos. This syndrome is characterized by a loss of the integrity of the epidermis, which becomes thickened in some places and thin or absent in others. Internally, the notochord is well developed, somites are large but abnormal in forms and the gut is developed as well as the general condition of the embryo allows. All ectodermal derivatives, however, are very poorly developed and display degenerative nuclear changes. It should be added that these effects on development are not observed when endoderm cytoplasm alone is injected into either enucleated or normally nucleated eggs.

From the results described above it now appears definite that nuclei undergo certain changes during differentiation. These have been best worked out for the endoderm nuclei of late gastrulae. The transplantation tests show that these nuclei have retained the ability to participate normally in cleavage but are usually restricted in their potentiality for differentiation. In some cases chorda-mesoderm is formed, and some attempt at the differentiation of central nervous system and other ectodermal derivatives ensues. In others, development stops sooner, before any neural structures appear. Finally, experiments not reported here reveal that at later developmental stages there is a loss of the capacity of these nuclei to enter into cleavage of egg cytoplasm. All together, this suggests a progressive specialization of nuclear function

TABLE 3

Development of Eggs Injected with Endoderm
Nuclei of Late Gastrulae.

Source of Nuclei	No. Eggs Injected with Nuclei	Complete Blastulae	————Development of Blastulae————		
			Arrested Blastulae and Gastrulae	Arrested Neurulae and Postneurulae	Larvae (10–12 Mm)
Early gastrula (St. 10), animal hemisphere	71 (100%)	29 (41%)	1	3	25
Late gastrula (St. 12), doderm	67 (100%)	26* (40%)	8	13	5

* There is some variation in the results in the separate experiments. In one experiment 3 out of 11 complete blastulae developed into larvae. In the other two experiments 1 out of 10, and 1 out of 5 blastulae developed into larvae, respectively.

during cell differentiation. Concerning its nature there is as yet very little known. How it may differ in different tissues, whether it depends upon alterations in chromosomal or other aspects of nuclear function, and the question of correlated changes in cytoplasmic elements are among the problems remaining to be worked out.

A more detailed account of these experiments, and of those involving nuclear transfers from later developmental stages, is in preparation.

Summary. Nuclei of chorda-mesoderm and endoderm of late gastrulae *(R. pipiens)* were transferred to enucleated eggs. In the successful cases the recipient eggs cleaved normally and developed into complete blastulae, the majority of which were arrested in blastula, gastrula, or abnormal embryonic stages. Evidence is presented to indicate that the failure of the test eggs to differentiate normally is due to intrinsic restrictions in potentiality for differentiation on the part of the nuclei of the late gastrula.

Communicated by David R. Goddard, March 2, 1955

REFERENCES AND NOTES

We are indebted to Miss Marie DiBerardino for her valuable assistance in this work. This investigation was supported in part by a research grant from the National Cancer Institute of the National Institutes of Health, United States Public Health Service, and in part by an institutional grant from the American Cancer Society.

1. For a review of early literature on this subject see E. B. Wilson, *The Cell in Development and Heredity* (Macmillan, New York, 3 ed., 1925).

2. J. Schultz, *Cancer Research* 7, 41 (1947).

3. R. Briggs and T. J. King, these *Proceedings* 38, 455 (1952).

4. _____, *J. Exptl. Zool.* 122, 485 (1953).

5. T. J. King and R. Briggs, *J. Embryol. Exptl. Morphol.* 2, 78 (1954).

6. P. Rous and F. S. Jones, *J. Exp. Med.* **23**, 549 (1916); P. B. Medawar, *Nature* **148**, 783 (1941); A. Moscona, *Exptl. Cell Research* **3**, 535 (1952); C. Grobstein, *J. Morphol.* **93**, 19 (1953); E. C. Slater and K. W. Cleland, *Nature* **170**, 118 (1952); N. G. Anderson, *Science* **117**, 627 (1953).

7. M. C. Niu and V. C. Twitty, these *Proceedings* **39**, 985 (1953).

Growth and Organization
in Free Cell Cultures

F. C. Steward
with L. M. Blakely
Ann E. Kent
Marion O. Mapes

*Department of Botany,
Cornell University*

Spores and zygotes are the outstanding examples of single cells from which growth and development stems in plants. In angiosperms these cells form and grow in highly specialized milieux with distinctive nutritional qualities. Nevertheless they link one phase of development (in the case of spores) or one generation (in the case of zygotes) to another through cells which are essentially without organic connection with their neighbors and which develop independently. With a full knowledge of all the requirements for growth, it would seem possible to start with these free single cells already endowed with the capacity to grow and to foster their growth and development outside the organs in which this normally occurs in the plant body. Although frequently attempted for the young embryo, this task is fraught with greater difficulty the younger the embryo isolated. Indeed, except for such embryos as orchid that normally grow without endosperm, the isolated cultivation of anything as simple as a true zygote or even a globular embryo usually fails.

The facts of equational cell division and the ideas on genetic determination being what they are, each divided cell should be genetically an exact facsimile of its predecessor. This being so, the problems of differentiation and morphogenesis require that this essentially "built-in" genetic information be controlled, restrained, or modulated in its expression by the special nutrition and stimuli to which the cells

Reprinted from *Brookhaven Symposia in Biology* 16, 73–88 (1963), by permission of F. C. Steward and the Brookhaven National Laboratory.

are exposed in the environment of the living plant body. Although Haberlandt (6) is usually credited with the foresight to perceive the gains that might accrue from the culture of isolated cells of higher plants, he nevertheless encountered its obstacles and recognized its difficulties. In retrospect, Haberlandt's perception was even more acute than is generally conceded, for his final paragraphs, freely translated, read as follows: "Without permitting myself to pose more questions, or to prophesy too boldly, I believe, in conclusion, that it will be possible *to grow*, in this manner, *artificial embryos from vegetative cells.** In any case the method of growing isolated plant cells in nutrient solutions could be a new experimental approach to various important problems." Only recently can it be claimed that Haberlandt's original ideas have been fulfilled by examples of the culture of free cells and by the demonstrable totipotency of their behavior. This is the outcome of the long history of plant organ and tissue culture, culminating in recent years in a better knowledge of the biochemical stimuli to make cells grow and divide.

Many examples may be cited of situations in which, in greater or lesser degree, organs of plants may arise from otherwise mature initiating cells. In the normal environment of the embryo some cells, other than zygotes, may be stimulated to grow apomictically, without the need of fertilization, and these may form adventive or nucellar embryos, the subsequent development of which is indistinguishable from that of normal embryos from zygotes. The organized growing regions of lateral roots are traceable to divisions that occur in individual cells of the pericycle. Classical examples, like those of *Kalanchoe,* disclose that some cells of some leaves may initiate what are sometimes called foliar embryos and these may develop into individual plantlets. In all such situations the genetic information which is inherent apparently in any diploid cell of the plant body is released for freer expression than in the tissue in which the cell normally occurs. A recent review (26) analyzed these situations from the standpoint that the initiating cells must respond to external stimuli that make them divide and grow but that they must also do so as though they were, in effect, isolated. However, in the work now to be described it can be shown that, when free, the cells of some angiosperms (e.g., of carrot, *Daucus carota*) not only divide but display a remarkable degree of totipotent development, so much so that they really behave like zygotes. In fact, one now sees that the zygote is unique only from the genetic point of view; developmentally it is to be regarded rather as a diploid cell which can grow, in a medium fully competent to make it grow and in a space which provides the conditions in which it can grow. To the extent that these latter conditions can be met with otherwise mature cells isolated from the plant body, such cells also can behave like zygotes. It will be shown that, to a remarkable degree, this is so, at least for the carrot plant.

The salient features of this cell growth and morphogenesis that need to be summarized or discussed are (1) the stimuli to cell growth and cell division; (2) the modes of cell division and cell multiplication in isolated or free cells: the formation of colonies; (3) organization, or growth from cells to plants; and (4) embryonic development from somatic cells. The ensuing discussion will be based on the work of this laboratory; no attempt will be made to deal completely with the work of others, for this is more appropriately attempted elsewhere.

THE STIMULI TO CELL DIVISION

The development which ultimately made it possible to cultivate, in this laboratory, cells of many angiosperms freely suspended in liquid or isolated on an agar medium was a better understanding of the stimuli which make cells divide at their most rapid rate and which induce cell division in otherwise quiescent cells. Over and above all the known nutrients (inorganic salts required to furnish major nutrient elements, trace elements, sugars, vitamins), chemical stimuli are required. These stimuli work in ways which put the idling metabolism of resting cells into gear so that they grow. The sources *par excellence* of such stimuli are fluids or extracts derived from the environment of embryos such as the liquid endosperm of the coconut (coconut milk or coconut water) or extracts from immature grains of corn (corn in the milk stage) or from the young fruits of *Aesculus* (horse chestnut). Added to a normal, basal, tissue culture medium, such as that of White, these fluids or extracts cause a far more rapid growth than any other known means. A 2 to 2.5-mg explant of carrot secondary phloem will grow, under the conditions prescribed (4), to some 200 to 300 mg in 3 weeks, whereas in their absence only sluggish expansion ensues. The most significant feature, however, is that an initial 25,000 to 28,000 cells may give rise to some $2\frac{1}{2}$ million much smaller, actively dividing cells in this period (27). It is especially significant that these stimuli, which restore resting carrot cells to the actively dividing state, derive principally from the immediate nutritional environment of immature embryos. Some have claimed that very complex media, which are regarded as defined (30), will also support this growth at a rapid rate. However, direct comparisons between such media and the coconut milk supplemented White's medium, made in this laboratory and under our experimental conditions, have never substantiated these claims except to a minimal degree. It is neither necessary or appropriate to dwell here on the chemical constituents of the liquid endosperm which evokes the growth response. Suffice it to say that it consists of three separate parts. First, there is a nonspecific source of reduced nitrogen compounds which is entirely replaceable by amino acids or casein hydrolysate. Second, there is a so-called neutral fraction which, though inactive in cell division itself, is nevertheless essential to create the milieu in which the active substances proper may work. This neutral fraction consists of hexitols, three of which (myo-inositol, scyllo-inositol, and sorbitol) have been isolated and identified

(12). These hexitols seem to act independently of each other, and the effect of the neutral fraction may be largely, if not entirely, reproduced by myo-inositol. Lastly, there is a complex and not yet completely identified category of substances which constitutes the so-called active fraction. These substances induce cell division in the presence of the neutral fraction when they themselves are at a dilution of the order of 50 ppm (28). If all other requirements are met, carrot explants do not require exogenous indoleacetic acid, or even any known substitute for it.

Not all explants of angiosperms, even of dicotyledonous plants, will respond by growth to coconut milk or similar sources, although many will do so. A successful culture of the potato tuber was made possible only by a synergistic combination (22) of coconut milk and 2,4-dichlorophenoxyacetic acid (2,4-D), and this was the forerunner of many examples in which the 2,4-D was replaced by a variety of other substances, some of which are more effective than 2,4-D (19).

Other work and other workers have produced other evidence of chemically induced growth in cells of angiosperms. The classical case of crown gall tumors, as investigated by Braun (3), suggests that, from a cell initially altered, as by wound healing, the rapid growth of the tumor may be simulated by chemical stimuli of which amino acids and myo-inositol are at least a part, along with some "kinin-like" cell division substance as described by Skoog.

Especially in the large cells of tobacco pith, internal cell divisions may be chemically induced by the substance called kinetin, now known to be 6-furfurylaminopurine, as detected, isolated, and identified in Skoog's laboratory (16). Characteristically this substance acts only in the presence of indoleacetic acid. When tested on carrot explants or some other tissue (Jerusalem artichoke tumor), under the conditions in use in this laboratory, kinetin itself is only a weakly active substance, although some of its even less natural analogues (6-benzylaminopurine, azakinetin) are more active. However, a curious substance, 2-benzthiazolyloxyacetic acid, is often unexpectedly effective in causing cell divisions when added in lieu of coconut milk to an otherwise defined tissue culture medium (27). The substances known as gibberellins have also been tested, and, although several of them do lead to some cell divisions, the evidence does not as yet suggest that their primary role is the causation of cell division in the manner attributable to the stimuli present in the liquid endosperms like coconut milk. Thus, it is now clear that cells exercise their full and innate capacity for cell division only when they are subjected to appropriate exogenous chemical stimuli over and above the usual nutrients (organic and inorganic) and vitamins.

Against the above background, the technique for effective culture of free angiosperm cells emerged. When many small explants of tissue are caused to proliferate rapidly in the same slowly rotated flask or tube (27), some surface cells are gently rubbed off and, being in a medium fully competent to make them grow, they divide (25). From such a dilute inoculum of cells a vigorous growth of free cells develops, and from this subcultures may be made and cell strains continued, like microorganisms, virtually indefinitely. In this way free cell cultures of carrot, potato, Jerusalem artichoke, *Haplopappus gracilis,* tobacco, asparagus, banana, *Kalanchoe,* etc., have been established and grown (Fig. 1), though any one of these may require a subtle combination of growth factors (e.g., coconut milk and a suitable synergist) for its maximum growth rate.

CELL DIVISION AND MULTIPLICATION IN FREE CELLS: THE FORMATION OF COLONIES

Freed from the restraints of the plant body, cells which grow assume a different form and divide in unfamiliar ways. In the plant body, cell division in apical growing regions is often conveniently visualized in terms of the efficient partitioning of space by similar polygons, and these approximate to 14-sided figures. Large vesicles of certain algae, e.g., *Valonia,* have protoplasts which subdivide by "segregative cell division" and then as spheres; then separate entities (aplanospores) enlarge until they fill the original vesicle with a morulloid mass of cells and fill all the available space by mutual compression (26).

A spherical free cell, treated as a liquid drop, dividing in a symmetrical environment in accordance with Sachs' or Errera's laws could be expected to divide in such a way as to produce predictable patterns which have been worked out by D'Arcy Thompson (29) and others. The first surprise was that the cell forms and cell divisions encountered in free cell cultures of carrot or *Haplopappus gracilis* were unpredictable and little like those that follow from the general rules and considerations referred to above (2, 24, 25). This could be attributed to the following possibilities: (a) the cells are not to be likened to liquid drops in a symmetrical environment with which they are in equilibrium, or (b) the cells were already endowed with certain innate or intrinsic capacities for growth which, when freed, they were able to exercise. Whatever the explanation, the following means of growth from the unicellular to the multicellular colony were recognized: (i) the formation of giant cells which become multinucleate and divide internally by septa along preformed cytoplasmic strands or surfaces, and subsequent enlargement of the marginal cells; (ii) equational divisions in isodiametric cells which soon produce major and minor axes of growth which lead to an ellipsoidal mass of cells; (iii) the formation of filaments which grow at their tip and also by transverse and intercalary divisions; (iv) budding of small from large cells, in a manner not too dissimilar from that which is familiar in yeast. With variations on these themes, individual cells or small preformed cell clusters produce colonies which grow freely suspended in a liquid nutrient medium of the kind described.

Free cell cultures can now be manipulated by microbiological methods (1). A mass culture of cells, obtained as described, may be filtered through cheesecloth layers to yield a concentrated suspension consist-

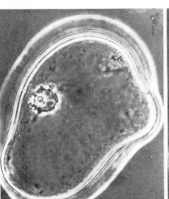
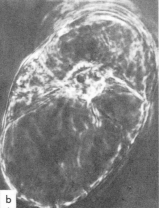
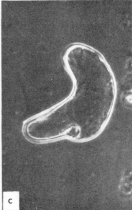
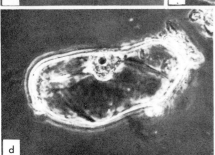
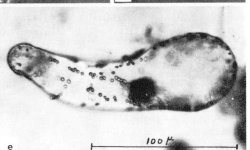

FIGURE 1. Some examples of freely suspended cells in culture (*a* to *d*, photographed under phase microscope; *e*, in bright field; all at the same magnification). *a.* Cell of *Kalanchoe daigremontiana* in a culture which originated from a stem. *b.* Cell of *Nicotiana tabacum* in a culture which originated from tobacco pith. *c.* Cell of *Asparagus officinalis* in a culture which originated from a shoot tip. *d.* Cell of *Haplopappus gracilis* in a culture which originated from the stem. *e.* Cell of *Nicotiana rustica* in a culture which originated from the embryo. Note prominent nuclei and nucleoli and other cytoplasmic inclusions; active protoplasmic streaming could be seen along the cytoplasmic strands.

ing of a very high percentage (80%) of single cells and of very small cell clusters (up to about 30 cells) themselves derived originally from free single cells. If these cells are appropriately spread on an agar medium, they will grow, and unquestionably single cells do divide and go on to form colonies. For the first few divisions in such isolated cells and small colonies, the cell generation time seems to be of the order of 24 hours. Very sparsely distributed cells show a low proportion of cells that divide and form colonies; cells somewhat more densely distributed on the plates may show a critical density at which their viability is greatest; and in very dense distributions viability falls off. All this suggests that the products of some cells promote divisions in others even over and above the coconut milk stimulus. This is also indicated by the very much greater frequency of division of cells attached to colonies

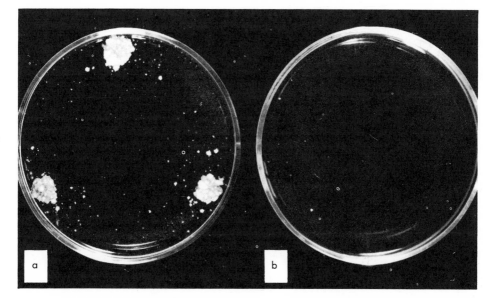

FIGURE 2. Effect of the proximity of free cells to cultured explants on the viability on an agar medium containing coconut milk. *a*. Plate with a uniform distribution of free cells and three precultured explants. *b*. Control plate lacking the precultured explants. Note the occurrence of visible colonies from free cells in the proximity of the explants.

or explants than of free cells (20), and by the very much greater viability of even small cell colonies than of single cells. Thus the nondividing cells of a colony stimulated by a coconut milk medium may contribute significantly to the cell divisions of its dividing members. This idea led to the dramatic demonstration shown in Figure 2 (*1*). Free carrot cells were distributed on an agar medium containing coconut milk. Various pregrown carrot explants, containing the original 2.5-mg piece surrounded by actively proliferating tissue, were placed on the plates as shown. Around each such cultured explant there is a significant concentration of successful viable colonies grown from free cells, although, when the explant density is too great, their growth is suppressed. In the most favorable cases more than 30% of the single cells in the vicinity of such explants will divide. This is analogous to the "nurse-tissue" technique of Muir *et al.* (*11*) carried out in a more quantitative and more convenient way. It shows that the parts of a colony which are not themselves able to grow may nevertheless contribute nutrients, or stimuli, to those cells that can divide. This result is very significant with respect to the cells of quiescent regions in growing points, for they may likewise contribute stimuli to the adjacent growing cells — cf. Clowes (5) and also Steward and Mohan Ram (26). The nature of this stimulus, over and above coconut milk, is not yet known.

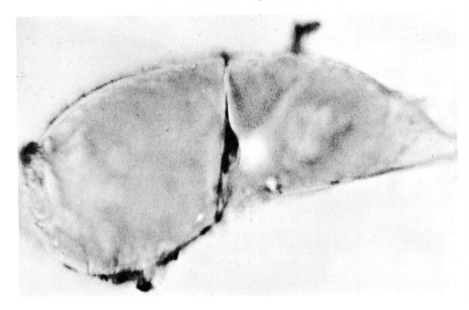

FIGURE 3. Two-celled stage after division of a free cell of carrot in a liquid medium. Note the asymmetrical development of the two cells and the resemblance to a two-celled proembryo of carrot.

ORGANIZATION OR GROWTH
FROM FREE CELLS TO PLANTS

Even in the most uniform environment the two daughter cells from a single carrot cell are rarely identical. One often tends to be more rounded and larger, the other often tends to be smaller and more pointed (Fig. 3). The cause of this asymmetry is hard to stipulate. As the familiar facts of embryogeny show, even small plant embryos are rarely spheres — polarity enters in at an early stage, and attachment via a suspensor is an important feature. In fact the resemblance of certain glandular hairs, with their basal cells, short filament stalks, and a multicellular "head" composed of growing cells, to certain plant embryos has been noted (26); both grow out into a free space from an initiating cell and a point of attachment. Even the initially spherical, naked mass of cytoplasm which constitutes a *Valonia ventricosa* aplanospore cannot grow indefinitely by mere radial expansion into a completely spherical vesicle. In fact it will not grow into a *Valonia* plant until it becomes attached, and from then on it has polarity and assumes an ellipsoidal shape (17). Gravity, light, and diurnal fluctuations all enter in to make this simple organism what in fact it grows to be.

The first point to be made with respect to carrot free cell cultures is at first unexpected but on reflection appears entirely logical. So long as cells proliferate around a central mass of preformed tissue and grow at their maximum rates, almost inevitably this is incompatible with organization. In fact, under these conditions secondary phloem root explants, free of cambium and lateral root initials, so rarely form roots that when they do so this is remarked upon among the many thousands of such explants which have been grown. On the other hand free cells, after forming colonies or clusters, organize with very great ease to form roots even while they are in liquid and rotated around a horizontal shaft (24). To do this, however, a colony of cells of finite size is needed, and then all cells of the colony are not equally placed; in fact hardly any two such cells are so placed, for gradients become established within the mass. Root formation, from root cells, was first obtained in small "nodules" of growing cells. These spherical nodules are bounded by a cambium-like layer of growing cells. The dividing cells which border the globules form at a critical point along a gradient. This gradient was interpreted (18) as having at one extreme the stimuli that emanated from cells which lost their contents to form lignified xylem-like elements and at the other, the coconut milk stimulus toward rapid proliferation that was in the solution outside. Thus a spherical globular mass of growing tissue was formed and roots originated in the cambium-like layer. To form shoots the cell clusters which had already originated nodule-like centers and formed roots were sown on stationary agar cultures containing coconut milk. Under these conditions shoot growing points originated at the opposite end of the axis where they could grow in air. These embryo-like structures (embryoids) from which plants developed recapitulated to a surprising degree the form of zygotic embryos in the ovule even though they originated from large, cultivated free cells — so much so that the parallelism between normal embryogeny and the development of embryo plantlets from free cells has been pointed out (18, 19, 26).

All this points clearly to the totipotency of the free cells which, suitably nourished by the chemicals which represent the special nurture of young embryos, grow to plants. Thus the conclusion is that to release the totipotency of any diploid carrot cell it is necessary (a) to obtain it, like the zygote, as a free cell, and (b) to cause it to divide under the influence of the special nutrients drawn from the environment of natural, immature, zygotic embryos.

However, the totipotency of single carrot cells is now amply verified because vegetative "life cycles" can be repeatedly traversed in such a way that one cycle and another are linked not through fertilization and seed formation but through embryoids developed on each cycle from free cells grown initially from the storage parenchyma of the root (Figs. 4 and 6). Even so, however, the plants grown in this way eventually form flowers and normal viable seed (23).

It is not necessary here to comment upon the nuclear cytology during these events. Free cells are subject to a variety of nuclear changes which have been described (9, 10). These even include somatic reduction and the formation of pseudochiasmata which provide a physical basis for somatic crossing over. Although the genetic possibilities are obvious, they are largely undeveloped, for as yet all the plants which have been

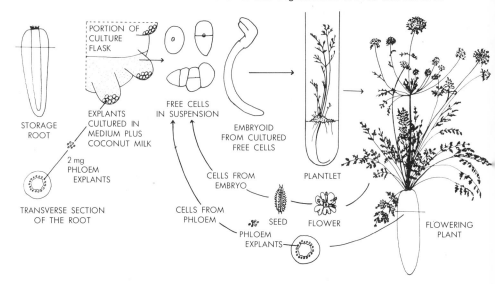

FIGURE 4. Diagram to show the sequence of growth from tissue explants isolated from the secondary phloem of the root to proliferating cultures which give rise, in liquid medium, to freely suspended cells which develop into embryoids, plantlets, and mature carrot plants, repeating the cycle indefinitely. Free cells which originate from the embryo may also behave in a similar way.

grown from cells have proved to be normal diploids. Also, *Haplopappus gracilis,* which presents unusual features for the observation of chromosomes during these operations, has not yet produced embryo-like forms which have advanced beyond the early stages (*10*).

A characteristic feature of early organization in cell cultures of *Haplopappus* is the occurrence of local areas of small cells showing nonrandom divisions (*2*) (also see Figs. 5*a* and *b*). In the cultures of *Kalanchoe daigremontiana,* derived from the stem callus, nodules similar in appearance to those described in the carrot culture are produced in the cell clusters. Nodules are produced singly, in small clusters, or in greater numbers in larger cell clusters, and when roots do appear, they arise from one of the nodules (Figs. 5*c* and *d*). Thus far no shoots have appeared in the rooted cultures. In the *Nicotiana rustica* culture of embryo origin, discrete areas of small cells showing nonrandom arrangements (Fig. 5*e*) were detected, but no distinct nodules or organized roots have been formed.

EMBRYOGENY IN CELL POPULATIONS
DERIVED FROM EMBRYOS

This new development is of great interest. It has been observed that long continued cell cultures may lose their capacity to organize. Even the cell strains which first yielded the typical embryoids eventually failed to do so. However, the plants which are grown from such cells in turn yield root phloem cells which do organize. Knowing that callus tissue cultures may be readily grown from embryos (7, 8, 13–15) and having converted one of these, obtained from Dr. H. Y. Mohan Ram of Delhi, India, to a rapidly growing, free cell culture of tobacco (*Nicotiana rustica*), we considered it an obvious development to convert carrot embryos into free cells. This was first done from young embryos dissected from the ovule of the wild strain of *Daucus carota*. These were grown in the same medium and in the same manner as explants from the root, and, when they were actively proliferating, free cell cultures

FIGURE 5. Evidence of organization in a colony of cells grown from free cell cultures. *a* and *b*. Nonrandom divisions in a culture of *Haplopappus gracilis* (*a*) in the vicinity of an internal cavity in a vesicular type of culture, and (*b*) in the vicinity of a necrotic region in a compact type of culture. *c* and *d*. Cell clusters of *Kalanchoe daigremontiana* showing nodular growth centers which give rise to typical roots: (*c*) one of the nodules with root primordium, and (*d*) a nodule with elongating root tip. *e*. Nonrandom divisions in cell clusters of *Nicotiana rustica*.

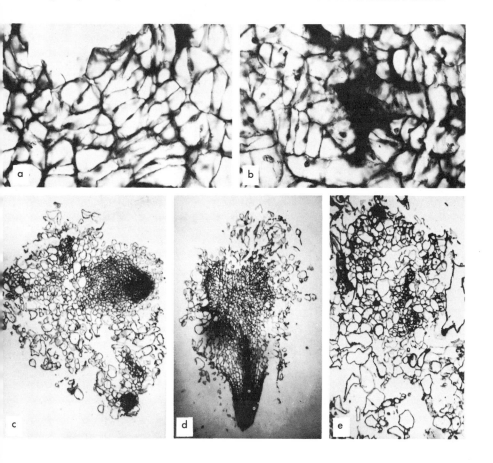

FIGURE 6. Carrot cells to carrot plants. *a.* Suspension of carrot cells from root phloem explants. *b.* Suspension of carrot cells from phloem root explants from a plant grown from *a. c.* Roots from cell clusters grown from *a. d.* Plantlets from cell clusters grown from *b. e.* Group of plants, in flower, raised from cell cultures shown in *a. f.* Second "generation" plant with flowers grown from the cell suspension shown in *b. g.* Plant grown from an embryo excised from the flowers shown in *f. h.* Heart-shaped embryoid grown from a free cell in a culture established from an embryo excised from the flowers in *f. i.* Torpedo-shaped embryo of similar origin as *h.*

were established in the usual way. The same has been done repeatedly from the embryos which form in the flowers of carrot plants also grown from cells, as shown in Figures 6*f* to *i* (23). However, the striking result is that a cell population established from a young carrot embryo produces, very readily, viable and very normal embryos. By actual count an aliquot of the cells grown from a single *Daucus carota* embryo formed up to 100,000 young embryos on a single Petri dish! The appearance of such a dish is shown in Figures 7*b* to *d*, and the highly typical globular, heart-shaped torpedo, and later stages of embryogeny are shown in Figures 7*a* and 7*e* to *h*. It can also be seen how easily the marginal cells of these young embryos swell and proliferate in the medium, and these may slough off and repeat the process.

The conclusion, therefore, is that the free cells derived from young embryos are virtually all totipotent and, when they grow in the appropriate medium, they simulate normal embryogeny so closely that one must conclude that the ovule has been effectively replaced. It is in fact now far easier to make somatic cells from carrot embryos behave like zygotes and grow to form plants than it would be to dissect the zygote from the embryo sac and to cultivate it separately. In fact, that operation now seems superfluous.

Although such cells, whether zygotes or parenchyma, possess this innate totipotency, they express it only during growth in response to the conditions in which they are placed. The nutrients required to nourish the growth become more specific as the size of the growing piece is reduced and especially when it is reduced to free cells. It is here that the fluids that nourish immature embryos have proved their use. But, as growth ensues, the tissue mass inevitably acquires its own internal specialization and a measure of "division of labor" between internal and external cells; also, cells and organs respond to a variety of environmental conditions which modulate the degree to which their innate genetic potentialities are expressed. It is clear, however, from work on the culture of cells, that these effects may be mediated by simple, soluble, exogenous substances. But how these substances intervene to modify the effectiveness of the genetic information is the crux of the problem of differentiation and morphogenesis. Perhaps clues may be seen if the growth-regulating substances can be shown to activate local regions of chromosomes after the manner which it has been possible to see in the polytene chromosomes of insect larvae during metamorphosis.

A still not wholly explained and yet curious feature of the cell cultures obtained from embryos is as follows. They consist of both an elongated weft of large or filamentous cells (not unlike those previously encountered) and curious tight globular masses (Figs. 7*i* to *j*) of small highly cytoplasmic or granular cells. It is the latter that readily give rise, like globular embryos, to heart-shaped and torpedo-shaped embryos. The precise origin and early development of these curious globular forms have not yet been fully worked out. The significant feature is that the origin of embryoids from an embryo culture differs from their origin in a phloem culture from the storage root. However, in some way the globular mass, like the nodule, behaves as an independent unit which does not proliferate at random, even in the presence of coconut milk. Thus, in both the nodules previously described and the globular masses here described, the proliferating effect of the coconut milk is brought under control in the formation of a "proembryo."

The work of Skoog on the regeneration of tobacco stem segments has shown that the appropriate combination of substances which behave as "kinins" or as "auxins" exercises control over the form of growth (i.e.,

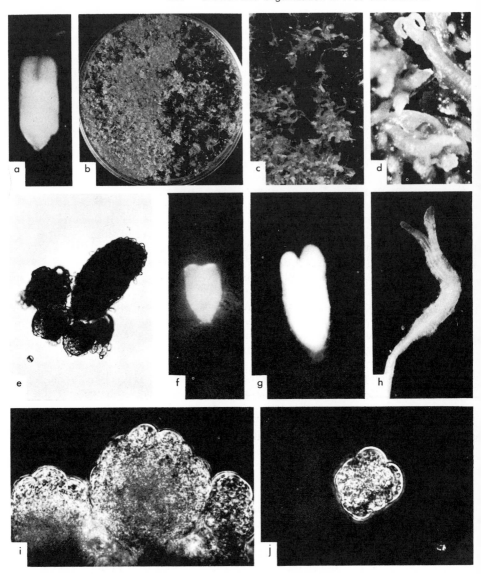

whether shoot or root or callus) which ensues. A difference between
the tobacco stem system as used by Skoog and that here shown for carrot is in the size of the tissue explant which supports the growth in
question. Even a small (2.5-mg) preformed explant of carrot phloem pro-
liferates as a callus under the conditions in which it grows best. The
tobacco tissue of Skoog, when exposed to the same medium, begins to

FIGURE 7. Embryonic development in free cell suspensions established from an embryo from the wild strain of carrot (*Daucus carota*). *a.* A typical carrot embryo dissected from the ovule. (From such an embryo, or from even a younger and more globular stage, cell suspensions have been developed.) *b.* Growth on an agar plate with complete medium plus coconut milk of a free cell suspension generally dispersed on the agar surface. (Material was removed from the barer regions.) *c.* Higher magnification of a field from *b* showing evidence of organized growth into numerous embryoids. *d.* Embryoids at higher magnification (note cotyledons, hypocotyls, and root tips). *e.* Embryo-like development from free cells showing several globular stages and one later stage. *f.* Typical heart-shaped embryoid developed from free cell. *g.* Typical torpedo-shaped embryoid from free cell. Compare with zygotic embryo shown at *a.* *h.* Typical plantlet which has developed from an embryoid. *i.* Colony of globular masses grown from embryo cells of wild carrot. *j.* Freely suspended globular mass which developed in a free cell culture and from which a typical embryoid developed.

---

grow by internal divisions (not unlike some giant free cells of carrot) and forms nests of cells which are then nourished in part by the external medium, in part by the tissue segment upon which they grow. It is interesting that the measure of independence which the regenerant exhibits over the host tissue upon which it is borne, as shown by the way it grows, is controlled by the balance of chemical growth factors to which it is exposed. Again, therefore, the original cells contained the necessary genetic information to be shoots or roots or whole plants or callus, and the way this information is expressed can be controlled or modulated by a variety of exogenous, simple substances which induce the growth of the cells.

One conclusion is inescapable. One should no longer seek any mystic root-forming or shoot-forming or leaf-forming substances which exogenously evoke these structures. The individual carrot cell is fully totipotent. Subtle, balanced proportions of growth regulating substances may, and do, produce the best conditions for cell growth by division or by enlargement. This is analogous to Skoog's combination (*16*) of a "kinin" and an "auxin." Nevertheless, these treatments stimulate the cells to grow; they do not of themselves evoke shoots or roots. The individual carrot cells which grow, especially when they start free, produce the organization spontaneously. This occurs in response to intrinsic, not extrinsic, factors; for any free diploid cell, endowed with a "built-in" capacity to grow, may, with the right nurture, behave like a zygote. But when, with the formation of organized shoot and root growing regions, tissues and lateral organs are formed, it is obvious that each cell of the growing point can no longer express its full totipotency. Restraints and limitations are placed upon what a given cell does in the special milieu in which it then occurs. What each cell then does, as a temporary part of the continuing organization which is termed a meristem, is as much a function of *where it is* as of *what it is*. The challenge of morphogenesis and differentiation is to translate these restraints and limitations which restrict the otherwise totipotent behavior of the cells into defined chemical and physical stimuli.

REFERENCES AND NOTES

* ". . . aus vegetativen Zellen künstliche Embryonen zu züchten."

1. L. M. Blakely, Ph. D. Thesis, Cornell University, Ithaca, N.Y. (1963).
2. _____ and F. C. Steward, *Am. J. Botany* 48, 351–58 (1961).
3. A. C. Braun, *Proc. Nat. Acad. Sci. U.S.* 45, 932–38 (1959).
4. S. M. Caplin and F. C. Steward, *Nature* 163, 920 (1949).
5. F. A. L. Clowes, *Apical Meristems* (Blackwell, Oxford, 1961), p. 217.
6. G. Haberlandt, *Sitzber. Akad. Wiss. Wien, Math-naturw. Kl. Abt.* I, Cl. III, 69–92 (1902).
7. B. M. Johri and C. B. Sehgal, in *Plant Tissue and Organ Culture — A Symposium* (University of Delhi, India), P. Maheshwari and N. S. Ranga Swami, Eds., Intern. Soc. Plant Morphol. (1963), pp. 245–56.
8. P. Maheshwari and N. S. Ranga Swami, *ibid.*, pp. 390–419.
9. J. Mitra, M. O. Mapes, F. C. Steward, *Am. J. Botany* 47, 357–68 (1959).
10. _____ and F. C. Steward, *Am. J. Botany* 48, 358–68 (1961).
11. W. H. Muir, A. C. Hildebrandt, A. J. Riker, *Science* 119, 877–78 (1954).
12. J. K. Pollard, E. M. Shantz, F. C. Steward, *Plant Physiol.* 36, 492–501 (1961).
13. H. Y. Ram Mohan, in *Plant Tissue and Organ Culture* (1963), pp. 159–67 (see ref. 7).
14. A. N. Rao, *ibid.*, pp. 332–43.
15. P. S. Sabharwal, *ibid.*, pp. 265–74.
16. F. Skoog and C. O. Miller, *Symp. Soc. Exptl. Biol.* 11, 118–31 (1957).
17. F. C. Steward, *Carnegie Inst. Wash. Publ.* 517, 87–98 (1939).
18. _____, *Am. J. Botany* 45, 709–13 (1958).
19. _____, *et al.*, in *Synthesis of Molecular and Cellular Structure (19th Growth Symp.)*, D. Rudnick, Ed. (Ronald Press, New York, 1961), pp. 193–246.
20. _____, in *Plant Tissue and Organ Culture* (1963), pp. 1–25 (see ref. 7).
21. _____, *ibid.*, pp. 178–97.
22. _____ and S. M. Caplin, *Science* 113, 518–20 (1951).
23. _____ and M. O. Mapes, *Phytomorphology*, in press.
24. _____, M. O. Mapes, K. Mears, *Am. J. Botany* 45, 705–708 (1958).
25. _____, M. O. Mapes, J. Smith, *Am. J. Botany* 45, 693–703 (1958).
26. _____ and H. Y. Ram Mohan, *Advan. Morphogenesis* 1, 189–265 (1961).
27. _____ and E. M. Shantz, in *The Chemistry and Mode of Action of Plant Growth Substances (Proc. Symp. Univ. London, 1955)*, R. F. Wain and F. Wightman, Eds. (Butterworth's Scientific Pub., London, 1956), pp. 165–86.
28. _____ and E. M. Shantz, *Ann. Rev. Plant Physiol.* 10, 379–404 (1959).
29. D'Arcy W. Thompson, *On Growth and Form*, Vol. 2 (The University Press, Cambridge, 1952).
30. J. G. Torrey and J. Reinert, *Plant Physiol.* 36, 483–91 (1961).

DISCUSSION

BERLYN: What do you think of some of the concepts being presented today with regard to whether the fundamental thing in morphogenesis is form or division? In the work of Haber and his colleagues, and as suggested by Dr. Ball this morning, form is fundamental and cell division is merely a consequence of morphogenesis. However, other workers have had the concept that division itself is fundamental and that form is a result of division.

STEWARD: Isn't it a little like the hen and the egg? How do you have form without division? I have shown that the milieu of the cells determines to some extent the way the cells divide. I don't have the ultimate answers to these questions, but I think we must be very careful not to invent a lot of words and phrases which don't mean very much. If we can grow whole plants out of single cells, I find it very difficult to put limitations in terms of these phrases about form, about determining division, etc. What I hope we can ultimately do is not merely to leave all this vague, in conventional morphological terminology, but to say what it means in terms of physical and chemical stimuli. If we know that in a leaf-forming group of cells the internal cells do something by virtue of some exogenous stimuli which they receive, then I think I can understand it; but merely to say that the cells do something because they are part of a preformed leaf doesn t help me very much. I am still a physiologist and a biochemist at heart, because I want to translate this type of expression into either substances or stimuli which can be physiologically measured, isolated, or handled.

HALPERIN: We have also been studying adventive embryony in wild carrot tissue cultures, and our observations have been similar to yours. I would like to make two points, however. First, the callus which gives rise to adventive embryos does not itself have to be derived from an excised seed embryo. We have found that callus tissue derived from both petioles and storage roots also gives rise to adventive embryos in large numbers. Second, we have not found that a physical isolation of individual cells, such as you have achieved by growing carrot tissue in liquid suspensions, is required for the subsequent production of adventive embryos. We have observed that pieces of callus tissue, maintained on semisolid media, will grow in the undifferentiated form for a period of time and will then, for reasons we do not understand at present, spontaneously give rise to proembryos in every conceivable position within the body of the callus. Microtome sections show that the proembryos are sometimes touching each other and sometimes separated by varying numbers of parenchyma cells. Many of the proembryos form normal mature embryos, but physical separation does not seem to be a requirement.

STEWARD: I hope I didn't leave the impression that only the cells derived from the embryo do this. What I said was that if you have free cell cultures obtained from the embryo and, as in our case, from carrot root, the former do it much more directly and efficiently. They recapitulate more freely and faithfully the normal embryogeny. From a mere aliquot of a free cell suspension obtained from a single embryo, the people in my laboratory counted 100,000 embryoids on one Petri dish plate! That is, potentially every cell in the suspension of embryo origin may form an embryo. Embryogenesis does not happen anything like as spontaneously and easily when the same technique is used with previously mature, isolated phloem cells. That was the main point. Obviously, if, as I am saying, individual cells are totipotent to different degrees, there will be a variety of conditions which release this totipotency, and I would be interested in seeing any conditions that do so, for either carrot or anything else.

TAKATS: In your very young carrot roots, do you get a quiescent center?

STEWARD: We have not studied those particular roots from that point of view. I have looked at the other dicotyledon roots, where we do find it. I would be surprised if there was anything unusual in these roots grown from cells; that is, if a normal carrot root has a quiescent region, I'm sure these do also, although we haven't looked for it.

FORMAN: Have you ever isolated an immature embryo and brought it, as a natural embryo, to a seedling?

STEWARD: Yes, I showed some.

FORMAN: In the young stage?

STEWARD: We isolated an immature embryo out of the ovules grown on carrot plants, which had themselves been reared from a cell suspension; that embryo grew as an embryo. But, from such a young embryo cells can be made to proliferate as free cells, and it is such free cell cultures which so dramatically form embryonal plantlets. There is nothing unusual about an immature embryo formed in the seeds of a plant grown from free cells compared with embryos from field plants. It can either be grown as an embryo or made to form a free cell culture.

TULECKE: Among all the cells observed, was there any evidence for pinocytosis?

STEWARD: That is another matter not directly related to this paper. I have a strong feeling about pinocytosis. Whenever I have looked at cells under the phase microscope, and I have looked at many, I have not been able to see, in the membrane surface just within the cell wall, anything that we could authentically describe as pinocytosis. That doesn't mean to say it isn't there, but the place where I would look for it is in another situation. We have always had a great deal of difficulty in understanding how the solutes, once they get into the vacuole, get out again. The vacuole surface is constantly rippling and in motion, and I myself feel that the higher plant analog of pinocytosis may be here and its function is to get what is in the vacuole back into the cytoplasm. But that is a further question.

TULECKE: We have observed some cell proliferation from the pollen of *Torreya nucifera* and find it quite different from tissue growths we have observed from *Ginkgo* or *Taxus* pollen. In *Ginkgo* there is regular cell wall formation; in *Taxus* there are elongated cells which divide unequally. Cell proliferation in *Torreya*, however, takes the form of yeast-like division in which budding occurs and new cells are pinched off. All these are haploid tissues derived from pollen.

HALPERIN: Dr. Steward, I would like to ask your opinion of the relationship between the phenomenon you observed in liquid cultures of the domestic carrot, in which roots form from cell clumps, followed by shoot formation when the root-bearing nodules are transferred to a solid medium, and the phenomenon of embryogenesis that you have observed in wild carrot tissue cultures. You have compared the cell clumps, which ultimately give rise to roots and then shoots, to proembryos. Do you feel that the formation of a root from a clump of cells in liquid medium, followed by a shoot some time later on solid medium, is a situation analogous to embryogenesis? This type of root formation, from cell clumps containing vascular tissue, seems to occur in many species of callus, and you might have to extend your interpretation to these other types of callus.

STEWARD: If I understand the question right, I don't think there is any essential difference between the two types of phenomena. There may be differences of degree, or in how the ends are accomplished, but I don't think there is any difference in principle.

HALPERIN: But isn't this formation of roots in the domestic carrot cell cultures more directly comparable to the development of secondary roots than it is to the development of primary roots which originate in an embryo? In other words, the roots in the tissue cultures are secondary since they originate in something that approximates a stele.

STEWARD: I suppose you may have to call them all adventitious roots, don't you? But clearly the roots which are eventually part of the main axis of the subsequent plantlet form from masses of cells in which there is no stele — merely a group of cells which initiate a growing point that becomes a root tip.

BALL: This has some philosophical implications. I am inclined to think that, on the basis of recent studies which are just beginning on free cells similar to those which Dr. Steward has studied so magnificently, there is a profound difference between the physiologic state of the free cells and that of the shoot apex. These free cells indeed have totipotency, whereas the cells of a terminal meristem such as the shoot apex do not. In this beginning of understanding of the differences between these categories of meristematic cells I think that we have made a significant beginning in a logical approach to the fundamental problem of differentiation.

STEWARD: Obviously, while the cell is in the meristem, it is not totipotent, because each cell does not form a whole plant. There is the essential problem. But if you could take the central apical dome — and I'm sure you have the ingenuity to do this — and break it down into its free cells and really grow them, I suspect that they would form embryos.

BALL: I don't know. I will only say that our attempts have proved unsuccessful We can't get the cells apart in the state in which they occur in nature.

STEWARD: Try the carrot.

C Differentiation of tissues

Moscona, A. 1957. The development *in vitro* of chimeric aggregates of dissociated embryonic chick and mouse cells. *Proc. Nat. Acad. Sci. U.S.* **43**, 184–94.

Niu, M. C., and V. C. Twitty. 1953. The differentiation of gastrula ectoderm in medium conditioned by axial mesoderm. *Proc. Nat. Acad. Sci. U.S.* **39**, 985–89.

Skoog, Folke, and Carlos O. Miller. 1957. Chemical regulation of growth and organ formation in plant tissues cultured *in vitro*. *Soc. Exper. Biol. Symp.* **11**, 118–31.

The Development *in vitro* of Chimeric Aggregates of Dissociated Embryonic Chick and Mouse Cells[*]

A. Moscona

Laboratory of Developmental Biology, The Rockefeller Institute for Medical Research, New York

Various embryonic tissues and organ rudiments can be dissociated into suspensions of discrete, viable cells following treatment with Ca- and Mg-free saline and trypsin (*1–3*). When cultivated *in vitro* under appropriate conditions, such cells reaggregate into compact clusters (Figs. 1–6), which subsequently reestablish tissue-like relationships and differentiate histotypically (*2, 3*). These findings, orginally established for chondrogenic, nephrogenic, and myogenic cells, have recently been extended to other embryonic tissues (*3–8*).

If two different types of embryonic chick cells are intermingled in the same suspension, the resulting aggregates incorporate both types of cells; however, in the course of the further development of such heterotypic aggregates,† the diverse types of cells form distinct, histogenetically uniform groupings (*2*). The problem of grouping of animal cells in its relation to morphogenesis was discussed in detail by Weiss (*9*) in reference to the concepts of "affinities" (*10*) and "coaptation" (*11*); its experimental implications were explored in the chick embryo (*12*) and in amphibian embryos (*13, 14*) and larvae (*15–17*) and also under conditions of tissue culture (*3, 18–20*). Several of these studies strongly suggested that cells of diverse lineages manifested characteristic preferences in establishing intercellular contacts and tissue contiguity. This view was further sup-

Reprinted from *Proceedings of the National Academy of Sciences* 43, 184–94 (1957), by permission of the author and the National Academy of Sciences.

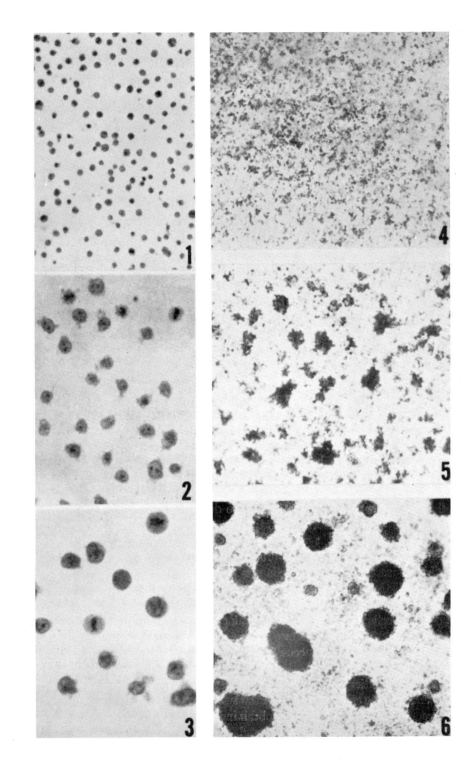

FIGURE 1. Suspension of chondrogenic cells from limb-buds of chick (4-day) and mouse (12-day) embryos. Ehrlich's hematoxylin–Biebrich's ($\times$ 160).
FIGURE 2. Suspension of chick chondrogenic cells ($\times$ 460).
FIGURE 3. Suspension of mouse chondrogenic cells ($\times$ 460).
FIGURE 4. Dissociated chondrogenic cells beginning to aggregate. 2-hour culture; living ($\times$ 50).
FIGURE 5. A similar culture to that in Figure 4, after 12 hours.
FIGURE 6. A similar culture to that in Figure 4, after 36 hours.

ported by the results of recent experiments on heterotypic aggregates of chick cells (2) which convincingly demonstrated a type-specific grouping of cells in the formation and development of such aggregates. These observations fell short of proof, however, due to the difficulty of identifying early embryonic chick cells when dissociated into discrete units in suspension; under these conditions, nearly all types of such cells look alike, and their identities in heterotypic mixtures are therefore not readily determined. The obvious solution to this impasse was to have cells marked in a way which would make them individually distinguishable in a mixed population. In searching for suitable "marker cells," an attempt was made to exploit the morphological differences between chick and mouse cells; mouse cell nuclei are larger than chick cell nuclei and stain differently with basic stains and hematoxylin. Previous studies have shown that mouse and chick tissues can be successfully cultured in heterologous media (21, 22) and maintained simultaneously in culture without apparent incompatibility (23–25); it has further been noticed that under such conditions the differences of size and staining properties of the cells and nuclei of the two species are retained.

Accordingly, the feasibility of obtaining composite aggregates, consisting of both chick and mouse cells, was explored. Preliminary experiments (26) demonstrated that aggregates formed in suspensions of intermingled chick and mouse cells incorporated, under appropriate conditions, cells of both species. Upon further cultivation, such heterologous aggregates developed histogenetically in accordance with the origin of their cellular components. Due to the differences in size and the staining properties of chick and mouse nuclei, the two types of cells could be easily distinguished and their precise distribution in the aggregates determined. As a further variation along this line, dissociated mouse tumor cells were introduced into suspensions of embryonic chick cells, and the structure and composition of the resulting aggregates were examined. With the aid of these differential cellular systems, various aspects of tissue reconstruction and development in cell aggregates were studied. Some of the observations bearing on the problem of cellular grouping are reported below.

MATERIALS AND METHODS

The preparation by treatment with trypsin of cell suspensions from embryonic organ rudiments and tumor tissue followed procedures described previously (*1–3*). The experiments reported here were made with chondrogenic, mesonephric, and hepatic cells from chick and mouse embryos. Different age combinations of these tissues were tried, as it turned out that embryonic chick and mouse cells of diverse ages and types migrated and aggregated at different rates. This communication reports on tissues from 3- to 5-day chick embryos and from 11- to 13-day mouse embryos. The tumor tissue used was pigmented melanoma S91, maintained in a DBA/2JN strain of mice. Suspensions of cells were mixed in the desired proportions, and aliquots of the heterologous mixtures were distributed into hollow-ground (Maximow) slides with 1.0 cc liquid culture medium in each. The medium consisted of 40 percent chicken serum, 40 percent embryo extract (freshly prepared from 10- to 12-day chick embryos), and 20 percent Earl's balanced salt solution. Horse serum was sometimes added in proportions not exceeding 4 percent of the total quantity of the medium. The culture medium was kept at room temperature for about an hour before being used. The slides with the cell suspensions were sealed and incubated at 38° C for twenty-four hours. The medium was then changed, and the cultures maintained for an additional day or two. The aggregates which had formed by that time were then transferred to a plasma clot for further cultivation in watch glasses. After fixation in Zenker's fixative, the cultures were sectioned at 6 or 8 μ, and the sections were stained briefly with Ehrlich's hematoxylin and Biebrich's scarlet, which rendered cell nuclei of the chick a light purple tint, while mouse nuclei stained a deep blue.

ISOTOPIC COMBINATIONS OF CHICK
AND MOUSE CELLS

Dissociated chondrogenic cells from the limb-buds of 4-day chick embryos were thoroughly intermingled in suspension with chondrogenic cells from the limb-buds of 12-day mouse embryos (Figs. 1–3). The amount of mouse cells was about double that of chick cells. At this stage of development, the presumptive chondroblasts of the limb-bud are still in the form of stellate mesenchyme cells. The aggregates that formed in such suspensions were cultured for 6 days. Histological sections showed that they consisted of typical cartilage formed by chick and mouse cells

FIGURE 7. Cartilage masses composed of interspersed chick and mouse chondrogenic cells (× 120). (Figures 7–19. Stained with Ehrlich's hematoxylin–Biebrich's scarlet.)

FIGURE 8. Same at × 280. Compare with Figure 9.

FIGURE 9. Outlines of nuclei of Figure 8 to show the distribution of mouse (*circles*) and chick (*dark*) nuclei.

FIGURE 10. Full differentiated, composite cartilage, showing chick and mouse chondrocytes in a common matrix (× 980).

FIGURE 11. Aggregate of mouse liver and chick chondrogenic cells, showing a "capsule" of hepatic tissue surrounding the globule of cartilage. Four-day culture (× 80).

FIGURE 12. A 5-day culture of an aggregate of mouse hepatic and chondrogenic cells, showing the cells separated according to types (× 620).

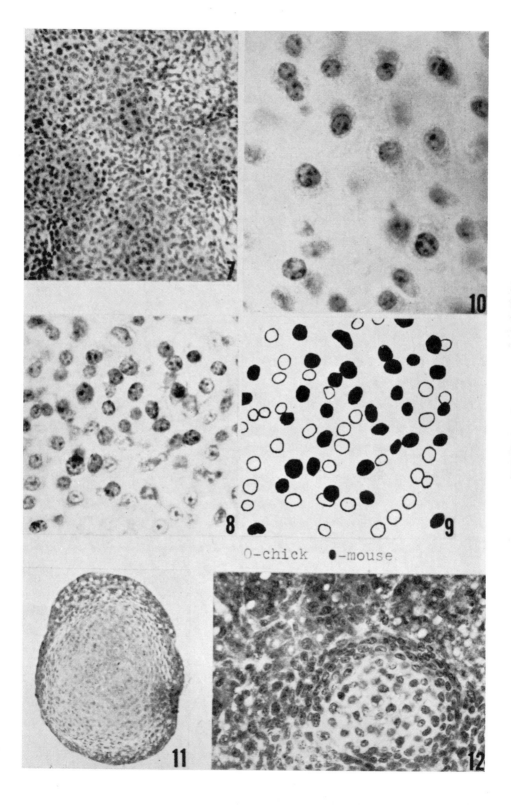

O-chick ●-mouse

interspersed with each other (Fig. 7). Both types of cells were intimately associated and bound by the common cartilaginous matrix into a uniform tissue fabric: the matrix surrounding a mouse cell merged quite imperceptibly with that around the chick cell next to it (Figs. 8–10). Cultures of such aggregates were maintained for periods up to one month without evidence of deterioration or incompatibility between the chick and mouse cells. Evidently the common histogenetic fabric reconstructed by the cells under these conditions was acceptable to both chick and mouse cells and suitable for their histotypical development.

An additional instance of such formative integration of interspersed chick and mouse cells was observed in combinations of liver cells. Liver tissue was obtained from 5-day chick embryos and from 13-day mouse embryos. The dissociated cells from both sources aggregated to form hepatic cords that consisted of interspersed chick and mouse cells producing glycogen or fat. In this case as well, the cells, regardless of their generic origin, reconstructed a common tissue fabric which developed in accordance with their preestablished properties.

HETEROTYPIC COMBINATIONS OF CHICK AND MOUSE CELLS

The cellular architecture of aggregates formed by cells of two diverse histogenetic types was quite different from that of isotypic cell aggregates. Mixtures of dissociated chick chondrogenic cells and mouse liver cells formed aggregates in which, after 4 days in culture, both cartilage and hepatic tissue were present. In this case, however, the two cell types had become regionally separated: the cartilage cells formed one or more central clusters, and the hepatic cells were situated around the periphery of the cartilage. In the present case, contrary to isotypic combinations, the two constituent tissues were not of mixed, chimeric composition, but each contained cells of the species that had furnished the respective cell type; that is, cartilage consisted solely of chick cells, hepatic tissue exclusively of mouse cells (Figs. 11, 12). This spatial arrangement was quite characteristic for the heterologous, as well as the homologous, combinations of these two types of cells (see also Wolff, 24).

Such type-specific grouping of cells was perhaps even more striking in combinations of mesonephric and chondrogenic cells, because of the structural characteristics of nephric tissue. In composite aggregates of 4-day chick mesonephric cells and 12-day mouse chondrogenic cells, cultured for 5 days, both kidney and cartilage cells reconstituted their recognizable tissue patterns (Figs. 13–16). The cells became consistently grouped according to type: chick chondroblasts formed areas of cartilage, mouse nephroblasts built nephric tubules. Careful examination of this material revealed no chick cells that had become chondrocytes or mouse cells that had turned into nephrocytes. Single cells that were occasionally trapped in a nonmatching environment, if they took and multiplied, developed according to their original identities. In the reversed combination of cells, namely, in aggregates of mouse meso-nephric with chick chondrogenic cells, similar type-specific, separate groupings of the corresponding tissues were formed. The reconstituted nephric and chondrified [cells] showed no regular distribution within the aggregates such as was typical of combinations of hepatic and chondrogenic cells.

COMBINATIONS OF EMBRYONIC CHICK CELLS AND MOUSE MELANOMA CELLS

In another aspect of this study of the grouping properties of embryonic cells, observations were made on their behavior in the presence of tumor cells. Dissociated hepatic or chondrogenic cells of the chick embryo were intermingled in suspension with dissociated cells of pigmented melanoma S91 of mice (Figs. 17, 18). Embryonic and tumor cells became incorporated in common clusters, which were then further cultured for 3–5 days. Aggregates of chondrogenic chick cells and S91 cells were found to consist of a central core of cartilage surrounded by S91 cells. In older cultures, scattered melanoma cells had infiltrated into the cartilage. Aggregates of hepatic chick cells and S91 cells consisted of a central core of melanoma cells surrounded by a compact capsule of hepatic parenchyma (Fig. 19). It appears, then, that also when intermixed with tumor cells of this type, the embryonic cells clearly manifested their tendency for typewise association as well as for type-specific localization — cartilage centrally, liver peripherally.

COMMENT

The experiments reported in the foregoing demonstrated the following facts. (a) Chick and mouse cells, when cultured together *in vitro*, retained characteristics by which they could be identified as to their origins. (b) When cells from both species, belonging to the *same* histogenetic type, were cultured in random mixtures, they combined to form uniform chimeric tissues. (c) Chick and mouse cells belonging to *different* histogenetic types, however, did not readily combine but gave rise each to its discrete type-specific differentiation. Previous experiments with heterotypic cell combinations from a single species (chick embryo) had already suggested that dissociated cells tended to preserve their original type specificities and to sort out and differentiate accordingly (2); these observations, together with the results obtained presently with cells marked clearly as to their species origin, lead to the conclusions that, under the experimental conditions explored, (1) type specificity prevailed over species specificity in guiding the association and grouping of embryonic cells of the given types of differentiation and (2) no transformation of cells of one type into another had taken place. It should be stressed at this point that these conclusions apply to cells which had evidently reached determination prior to their being dissociated, although they had not, at that time, become typically differen-

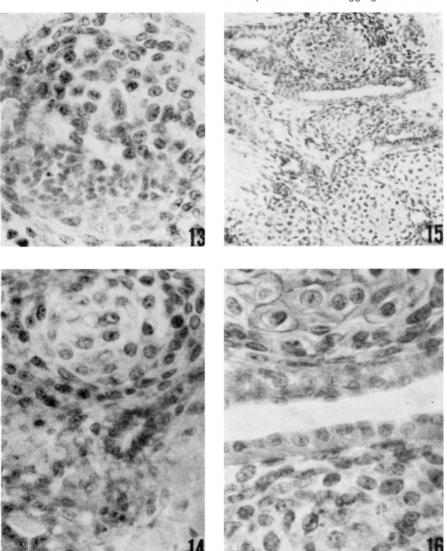

FIGURE 13. Aggregate of mouse chondrogenic and chick mesonephric cells, showing groups of cells with beginning differentiation. Three-day culture (× 250).
FIGURE 14. Four-day culture of a chimeric aggregate as in Figure 13, showing advanced histodifferentiation (× 250).
FIGURE 15. Six-day culture of a chimeric aggregate as in Figure 13, showing mosaic distribution of the cellular groupings (× 100).
FIGURE 16. Enlarged part of Figure 15 to show the topographical proximity of the reconstituted chick and mouse tissues (× 830).

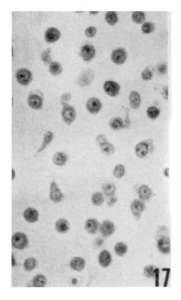

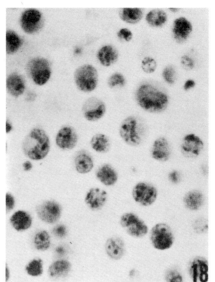

FIGURE 17. Suspension of chick liver cells (× 530).
FIGURE 18. Suspension of S91 melanoma cells (× 530).
FIGURE 19. Section through a composite aggregate of hepatic chick and S91 cells, cultured for 4 days and showing a "capsule" of liver tissue surrounding the cluster of melanoma cells (× 530).

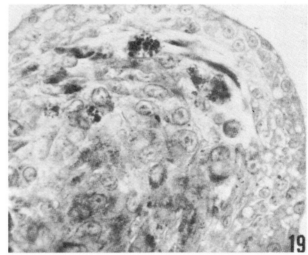

tiated. It is thus conceivable that different results may be obtained with cells from earlier or later stages of development as well as with other types of cells, or different experimental conditions.

The problem of type-specific development in these experiments, as in the earlier ones, has two different aspects. One refers to the formation of the primary aggregates of cells, and the other to the sorting out of the cells according to kind, concurrently with or following aggregation and their subsequent differentiation. The former aspect, concerned mainly with the mechanisms of aggregation, has been only parenthetically mentioned here, and its discussion will therefore be postponed. In view of the pertinence of these problems to the observations reported, the following brief comment should be included. The formation of all types of aggregates and their histogenesis *in vitro* may be markedly affected by a variety of factors. Environmental changes, such as of the physical and chemical properties of the medium or the substrate, markedly influence cellular aggregation by their differential effects on the diverse types of cells. Changes in the proportionate concentrations of different cell types intermixed in the same culture become reflected in the histological development of the ensuing aggregates (2). As mentioned before, the rates of migration of different types of cells, as well as of cells of different generic origin, vary considerably under identical conditions. For instance, mouse mesonephric cells migrate at a slower rate than chick mesonephric cells; in cultures containing both types of cells, this difference leads eventually to the formation of aggregates in which chick mesonephric cells predominate. Whether the different rates of migration are due to intrinsic cellular factors, to a differential response by the cells to culture conditions, or to specific activating stimuli is presently not clear.

Following formation of the primary cell aggregates, or perhaps concurrently with it, histologically identifiable tissues begin to develop, and eventually the cluster of cells becomes an organized tissue fabric. The available evidence suggests strongly that the processes of tissue formation are preceded or accompanied by a reshuffling of the aggregated cells; when more than one type of cell is incorporated in the cluster, they become sorted out to form type-specific cell groupings. The precise manner in which this occurs is still obscure, but time-lapse motion pictures, presently being undertaken in this laboratory, are expected to furnish pertinent information.

The structural differences between iso- and heterotypic cell combinations provide a striking indication of the specificities involved in cellular interactions which lead to grouping. In the tissues reconstituted from isotypic chick and mouse cells, the cells remained intermingled and interspersed in the form of cellular mosaics, without becoming segregated according to species origin. On the other hand, in aggregates of heterotypic cells the different types of cells became arranged in separate groups, so that the aggregates assumed the appearance of tissue mosaics. Thus, under the present experimental conditions, the type identities, rather than the generic identities, of the cells determined the manner of grouping. Typical grouping selectivity was also manifested by the dissociated embryonic cells when confronted with cells of the S91 tumor. However, following histogenesis of the embryonic tissue, S91 cells began, in some cases, secondarily to infiltrate between the normal cells. The nature of such manifestations, as well as the generality of such interactions, will become clearer when more is known of other combinations of dissociated normal and tumor cells and their patterns of aggregation.

The interpretation of cellular grouping in chimeric aggregates in terms of preferential, type-specific interactions between cells conforms well with observations on the tissue-specific localization of cells injected into the chick embryo (*12*) and into irradiated mice (*27–31*). That the properties involved are effective across generic differences, not only under conditions of culture but in the organism as well, may be inferred from the successful implantations in the bone marrow of rat blood cells injected intravenously into irradiated mice (*28*). In this connection, the question of the stability of chimeric cell aggregates is of interest. The successful persistence *in vitro* of cartilage chimeras beyond the embryonic age of their constituent cells suggested that, under such conditions, the cells, although generically alien, remained histocompatible. The response of heterologous combinations to suitable immune environments and to implantation into embryos and adults should provide additional information on the stability or the differential susceptibility of the cells under such conditions. Studies in this direction might also furnish information on the nature of histogenetic interactions between cells and the "recognition" (Weiss) effects involved, i.e., whether they function on the same basis as antibody-antigen systems (*11, 32, 33*) or whether they reflect specific properties, typical of this particular aspect of cellular behavior.

SUMMARY

1. Dissociated cells from various organ rudiments of chick and mouse embryos when intermixed in suspension cultures, readily aggregated and combined to form composite, chimeric tissues. Under suitable conditions of culture, such reconstituted tissues differentiated histotypically. This communication reports on combinations of chondrogenic, nephrogenic, and hepatogenic cells of chick and mouse embryos and S91 mouse melanoma cells.

2. In aggregates of intermixed chick and mouse cells of same type (i.e., chick and mouse chondrogenic cells) the cells reconstructed a uniform fabric which differentiated histotypically into a chimeric tissue consisting of interspersed chick and mouse cells.

3. In aggregates of intermixed chick and mouse cells of different types (i.e., chick nephrogenic and mouse chondrogenic cells) the cells became associated according to type and formed separate groupings which developed in accordance with the original histogenetic properties of the cells.

4. Due to the clear morphological differences between chick and mouse cells, it was possible precisely to identify and localize them in the chimeric aggregates. The evidence thus obtained suggested conclusively that (*a*) in the course of tissue reconstruction the dissociated embryonic cells became grouped preferentially, according to their

original type identities, regardless of their generic origin, and *(b)* under the present experimental conditions no transformation of one cell type to another was observed.

Communicated by Paul Weiss, November 14, 1956

REFERENCES AND NOTES

The author wishes to thank Dr. Paul Weiss, head of the Laboratory of Developmental Biology, for his interest and indispensable advice throughout this study. The aid of Dr. Dorothea Bennett in some phases of this work is gratefully acknowledged.

* Research aided by grants (Paul Weiss, principal investigator) from the American Cancer Society (through the Committee on Growth, National Research Council) and the Public Health Service, National Institutes of Health.

† The following terms will be used: (1) *isotypic* and (2) *heterotypic* to designate suspensions consisting of (1) predominantly one type of cell and (2) two or more cell types; (3) *homologous* and (4) *heterologous* for cells from embryos of the same specie (3) or (4) a mixture of cells from two species (i.e., chick and mouse cells).

1. A. Moscona, *Exptl. Cell Research* 3, 535 (1952).

2. _____, *Proc. Soc. Exptl. Biol. Med.* 92, 410 (1956).

3. _____ and H. Moscona, *J. Anat.* 86, 287 (1952).

4. P. Weiss and R. James, *Exptl. Cell Research,* Suppl. 3 (1955), p. 381.

5. M. W. Cavanaugh, *J. Exp. Zool.* 128, 573 (1955).

6. _____, *Exptl. Cell Research* 9, 42 (1955).

7. C. Grobstein, *J. Exp. Zool.* 130, 319 (1955).

8. J. P. Trinkaus and P. W. Groves, these *Proceedings* 41, 784 (1955).

9. P. Weiss, *Yale J. Biol. Med.* 19, 235 (1947).

10. J. Holtfreter, *Arch. f. exptl. Zellforsch.* 23, 620 (1939).

11. P. Weiss, *Quart. Rev. Biol.* 25, 177 (1950).

12. _____ and G. Andres, *J. Exp. Zool.* 121, 449 (1952).

13. J. Holtfreter, *J. Morphol.* 80, 25 (1947).

14. P. L. Townes and J. Holtfreter, *J. Exp. Zool.* 128, 53 (1955).

15. J. J. Chiakulas, *J. Exp. Zool.* 121, 383 (1952).

16. F. Baltzer, *Rev. suisse Zool.* 48, 413 (1941).

17. G. Andres, *Genetica* 24, 1 (1949).

18. M. A. Willmer, in *Essays on Growth and Form* (Oxford University Press, Oxford, 1945).

19. V. C. Twitty and M. C. Niu, *J. Exp. Zool.* 108, 405 (1948).

20. M. Abercrombie and J. E. M. Heaysman, *Exptl. Cell Research* 5, 111 (1953).

21. H. B. Fell and H. Gruneberg, *Proc. Roy. Soc. London, B* 127, 257 (1939).

22. H. B. Fell, *Science Progr.,* No. 162, p. 212 (1953).

23. C. Grobstein and J. S. Younger, *Science* 110, 501 (1949).

24. E. Wolff, *Bull. Soc. Zool. France* 79, 357 (1954).

25. _____ and D. Bresch, *Compt. Rend.* (Paris) 240, 1014 (1955).

26. Reported at the International Congress of Developmental Biology at Brown University, Providence, Rhode Island, July 1956.

27. D. L. Lindsley, T. T. Odell, Jr., F. G. Tausche, *Proc. Soc. Exptl. Biol. Med.* 90, 512 (1955).

28. C. E. Ford, J. Hamerton, D. W. H. Barnes, J. F. Loutit, *Nature* **177**, 452 (1956).
29. C. L. Miller, *Nature* **178**, 142 (1956).
30. N. A. Mitchison, *Brit. J. Exptl. Pathol.* **37**, 239 (1956).
31. E. S. Russel, L. J. Smith, F. A. Lawson, *Science* **124**, 1076 (1956).
32. R. E. Billingham, L. Brent, P. B. Medawar, *Nature* **172**, 603 (1953).
33. A. Tyler, in *Analysis of Development* (W. B. Saunders Co., Philadelphia, 1955).

The Differentiation of Gastrula Ectoderm in Medium Conditioned by Axial Mesoderm

M. C. Niu
V. C. Twitty

Stanford University

The widely accepted conclusion that embryonic "inductors" can transmit their stimuli only when in direct physical contact with the reacting cells has seemed to rest on the best of evidence. Separation of the two tissues by the smallest gap, or interposition of the thinnest cellular or artificial barriers, invariably proved to block inductive action. In fact, so consistent have been the findings in this respect that it has not been warranted, in spite of the great amount of work on the chemistry of inductors, to assert positively that diffusible substances are involved in the inductive control of differentiation. The results of Holtfreter (1) and others on the neuralization of young gastrula ectoderm in solutions of various substances do not constitute true exceptions, since according to Holtfreter the action of these agents was probably indirect, through toxic damage which activates strictly endogenous mechanisms.

The present study was originally undertaken with the object of investigating inductive relationships in very small cell populations. Encouraged by earlier success in the cultivation of propigment cells isolated singly or in groups of two or more (2), it was hoped that it might be possible to work on a similar scale with dissociated chordamesoderm and gastrula ectoderm cells, perhaps bringing together

Reprinted from *Proceedings of the National Academy of Sciences* 39, 985–89 (1953), by permission of M. C. Niu and the National Academy of Sciences.

representatives of each in small groups or even single pairs to test for any demonstrable effects upon their differentiation. At first technical difficulties, and later other considerations, led to the gradual modification of this approach, and the procedure eventually adopted was to isolate minute pieces of young gastrula ectoderm, the smallest that can readily be excised by ordinary microsurgical methods, together with pieces of axial mesoderm of more substantial size. The mesodermal explants consisted variously of: dorsal blastoporal lip; posterior medullary plate (the portion which invaginates during late gastrulation and forms the mesodermal structures of the tail and posterior part of the trunk); and blocks of mesodermal somites taken from embryos in young tailbud stages of development. In preliminary trials the mesodermal and ectodermal explants were placed in close apposition and often underwent intimate fusion, but it is important to emphasize that in this paper we are concerned only with experiments in which the two tissues were separately situated and had no physical contact with one another.

The species employed were *Triturus torosus, T. rivularis,* and *T. granulosus;* and *Amblystoma tigrinum* and *A. mexicanum.* The culture medium was a modified physiological salt solution devised by us some years ago. Its formula, first published by Flickinger (3), is repeated here:

Solution A (500cm³)		Solution B (250cm³)		Solution C (250cm³)	
NACl	3400 mg	Na_2HPO_4	110 mg	$NaHCO_3$	200 mg
KCl	50	KH_2PO_4	20		
$Ca(NO_3)_2{\cdot}4H_2O$	80				
$MgSO_4$	100				

Solutions A, B, and C are brought to a boil separately, and mixed after cooling.

When small pieces of young gastrula ectoderm are isolated alone in drops of this medium, they attach temporarily to the glass substratum and spread into very thin epithelial sheets which commonly release a few migrating ameboid cells. Later these scattered cells round up and lose their attachment to the glass, and the intact sheet also eventually retracts and falls free from the cover slip. Except for the development of ciliation, in no case have the explant or the emigrating cells shown any evidence of histological or cytological differentiation.

The ectodermal explant likewise fails to differentiate if a piece of mesoderm has been introduced simultaneously into the same drop. There is active outgrowth from the mesodermal explant, notably of myoblasts, but the behavior of the ectodermal isolate is essentially indistinguishable from that when it is cultivated alone.

The results are very different, however, when the ectodermal piece is introduced into a drop in which a mesodermal explant has already been developing for a period of approximately one week. In the complete

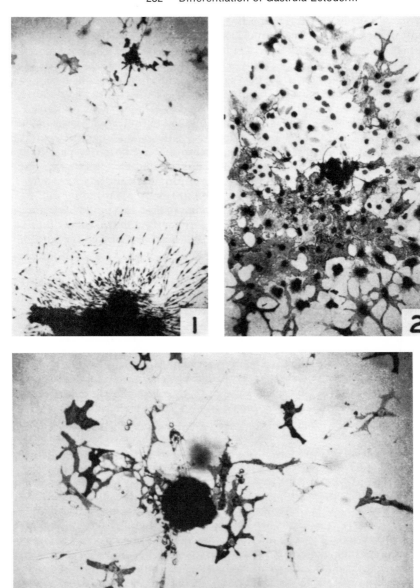

absence of physical contact between the two explants, and independently of the distance separating them, the ectodermal piece undergoes striking histological differentiation in well over half the cases tested.

In the most representative cases the behavior is remarkably similar to that of neural crest explants. The ectodermal pieces attach intimately to the cover slip, but spread somewhat less extensively than in "unconditioned" medium, and after a few days begin to give outgrowths of ameboid cells. A variable number of these may later round up and fall free from the glass, but the majority remain attached and eventually differentiate into highly branched chromatophores (Figs. 1 and 2). Meanwhile nerve fibers usually grow out, often in profusion, from the residual explant mass. Occasionally the explant may disperse completely into chromatophores, and at the other extreme are rare cases in which the explant remains compact and forms only nervous tissue. When ectoderm is placed in even older (about 14–18 days) cultures of mesoderm, particularly cultures of embryonic somites, there is a noticeable change in the quality of its differentiation. In general, fewer pigment cells and more nervous tissue are formed, and frequently clearly identifiable myoblasts emerge.

It appears highly improbable that the differentiation of the explants is attributable merely to nonspecific toxic effects of the medium. The explants appear to be completely healthy, and cell dissociation or other evidences of injury are definitely rarer than in unconditioned medium, in which no differentiation occurs. It is also significant that no differentiation ensues when ectoderm pieces are introduced into cultures of endoderm, or into drops containing massive pieces of young epidermis.

The physical presence of the mesodermal explant is not essential to the differentiation of the ectodermal pieces. This has been demonstrated repeatedly by cases in which explants have differentiated into chromatophores and nervous tissue after isolation in cell-free medium drawn from established mesodermal cultures (Fig. 3). In a few series,

---

FIGURE 1. Below, explant of *T. torosus* posterior medullary plate, with outgrowth of differentiating myoblasts. Above, scattered chromatophores which have originated from a small piece of torosus gastrula ectoderm (Harrison, stage 10) introduced into the culture 10 days after isolation of the posterior medullary plate. Nerve fibers have grown out of the residual portion of the ectodermal isolate. Photographed 23 days after isolation of the ectoderm.

FIGURE 2. Chromatophores formed from a piece of black axolotl gastrula ectoderm (stage 10) after introduction into a 10-day-old culture of *T. torosus* posterior medullary plate. The two explants were situated remotely from one another in the drop. Photographed 12 days after introduction of the ectodermal isolate.

FIGURE 3. Chromatophores and neural tissue (note nerve fibers) formed from a piece of young *T. torosus* gastrula ectoderm isolated in cell-free medium withdrawn from a 6-day-old culture of torosus posterior medullary plate. Photographed 20 days after isolation.

after the medium had been withdrawn from the latter cultures, it was replaced by fresh physiological salt solution and the mesoderm allowed to continue its differentiation for another week or ten days. When this medium was in turn withdrawn and tested, it often induced ectodermal pieces to give rise to myoblasts in addition to nervous tissue and chromatophores.

The results of the investigation thus seem to indicate clearly that inductor tissues indeed contain, and under the conditions of these experiments can release, diffusible substances capable of effecting "at a distance" the inductive control of ectodermal differentiation; they suggest further that the inductive specificity of the substances released changes with the age or degree of differentiation of the inductor.

The modified physiological salt solution employed for this study has the incidental property of causing ectoderm to attach intimately and spread extensively upon a glass substratum, and it is believed that this fact may have contributed importantly to the positive outcome of the tests. Pieces of ectoderm isolated in Holtfreter's standard salt solution characteristically round up into unattached vesicles, which by virtue of the intact "surface coat" investing them are undoubtedly impervious to larger molecules. This insulating coat is probably torn and disrupted, under the conditions of the present experiments, by the tensions and cellular rearrangements incidental to spreading of the explants into thin sheets, with the result that the constituent cells are partly denuded and thus more accessible to diffusible substances in the medium.

Samples of conditioned medium examined by Dr. Hubert S. Loring of the Department of Chemistry show appreciable light absorption in the ultraviolet with maxima and minima at 265 and 245 respectively, suggestive of nucleic acid or certain of its components. Various experiments are in progress to determine the nature of the substance or substances present.

Communicated June 23, 1953

REFERENCES

1. J. Holtfreter, *J. Exp. Zool.* 98, 161–209 (1945).
2. V. C. Twitty, *Science* 113, 476 (1951).
3. R. A. Flickinger, Jr., *J. Exp. Zool.* 112, 465–84 (1949).

Chemical Regulation of Growth and Organ Formation in Plant Tissues Cultured *in vitro**

Folke Skoog
Carlos O. Miller

Department of Botany,
University of Wisconsin

I. INTRODUCTION

In the context of the symposium this report is to deal with the biological action of growth substances as revealed in organ formation, especially bud formation in plant tissues cultured *in vitro*. This emphasis on technique may give the impression that we are dealing with a concise, rigidly defined subject, perhaps even too technical and artificial to be of general biological interest or usefulness. Actually the problems of growth encountered in studies of tissue and organ cultures are essentially as complex as in those of intact organisms, but a brief consideration of the experimental approach itself as well as of the results is called for. The vast domain of morphogenesis has been explored for a long time from different points of view and staked out into separate fields of highly specialized disciplines. Each of these which has been intensively studied has yielded its share of information for the development of such general concepts and understanding of growth as we now have.

The "formal" biochemical approach. In dealing with biochemical aspects of morphogenesis, Needham has distinguished between (1) morphogenetic substratum, (2) morphogenetic stimuli and (3) morphogenetic mechanisms. The validity of such categories, especially the existence of the third as set apart from

Reprinted from *Society for Experimental Biology Symposium* 11, 118–31 (1957), by permission of the Society for Experimental Biology.

the first two, is debatable; and if this third category is at all logically justifiable, it must be as a very temporary scaffold for the elaboration of the others. Nevertheless, arbitrary as this classification may be, these first two categories at least serve to draw attention to distinctions between problems of raw materials and energy supplies for growth on the one hand, and the finer regulation of rates and coordination of component processes on the other. At the present time major emphasis seems to be on aspects of the former of these categories, i.e., metabolism. Especially intermediary carbohydrate metabolism is being studied extensively and scrutinized intensively for possible clues to the secret of growth. From this line of approach come reports in which differences between normal development and uncontrolled growth of cancer are considered as being due merely to the funnelling of the energy-providing substrate into alternative aerobic or anaerobic, that is, respiratory, fermentative or otherwise grossly different pathways of degradation. Somewhat more subtle and now extremely popular are working hypotheses based on the assumption that the relative quantitative activities of key enzyme systems in the general respiratory chain are decisive in the regulation of growth. When it is considered, however, that complete cessation of growth may be achieved, at least in plants, by lowering the total respiratory rate by as little as 10–20% through the intervention of various inhibitors, it would appear that the energy-supplying mechanism as such, although it is a prerequisite for growth, can hardly act as a sensitive governor of the processes involved in normal differentiation and development. It seems rather that biochemistry in its preoccupation with metabolic cycles has revealed the general nature of the energy-furnishing machinery but not yet the finer points of its operation. This is said, not to detract from the great achievements in this field, but to emphasize the necessity, in analyses of growth, of working also at higher levels of structural organization, i.e., of using more complex systems than it has been possible to handle effectively so far with chemical tools exclusively.

The physiological approach with plants. (a) General physiological analyses. From the more physiological approach to the analysis of growth, students of plants early postulated separate factors for the regulation of successive phases of development. Sachs spoke of specific organ-forming substances. At the cellular level a sharp distinction was made between increase in size and numbers. Much effort has been spent in studies of cell elongation and cell division as processes separate and distinct from one another, and in attempts to determine the additive contributions and interactions of the two in tissue differentiation and in organ formation, especially as observed in regeneration phenomena.

(b) Search for growth hormones. A natural consequence of this reasoning has been a deliberate search for a specific chemical regulator of cell elongation and a specific regulator of cell division as well as, of

course, the continuing search for specific organ-forming substances. It is said that he who seeks shall find. We now have the auxins, the very definition of which is based on physiological activity (hormone action) leading to cell enlargement. Also for a long time there has been good indirect evidence for a cell-division hormone (Haberlandt, 1921), and recently the term kinin has been proposed as a generic name for substances with physiological activity promoting cell division in plant tissues under certain specified conditions (Miller, Skoog, Okumura, von Saltza and Strong, 1956; Strong, Okumura, von Saltza, Miller and Skoog, unpublished). Further investigations into the manner in which the known growth regulators exert their specific effects in cell elongation and division respectively have led to a blank wall. Instead of finding their intimate and unique nature, we have found that they are involved indirectly in a wide variety of biochemical activities or physiological functions and lead to most heterogeneous histological and morphological end-results. For example, under appropriate conditions auxins have been shown on the one hand to promote root formation and even cell division in the cambium (Snow, 1935); and, on the other hand, to inhibit root elongation and bud development. Thus we do not yet know the specific organ-forming substances, but instead evidence is accumulating against their existence; although various claims and specifications for calines (in the sense of Went's proposal, 1951), for rhizocaline (Bouillenne, 1950), florigens, vernalins, etc., are still being made.

(c) In vitro *studies of nutrient and growth-factor relationships.* The complexity and variability in growth responses indicated above obviously mean that the interaction of many factors must be considered, and that some of these perhaps might be revealed in studies of the simplest possible material capable of "multiple growth responses" and grown under as rigidly standardized conditions as reasonably could be attained. The present experimental approach utilizing stem segments, pith and callus tissues grown on inorganic nutrient media with added organic substrates and various growth factors was intended to eliminate some of the extraneous features and variables which are difficult to control in intact plants. Because valid comparisons and integration of results obtained with different tissue-culture methods and materials are still very difficult, if not impossible, the present discussion will be confined mainly to work carried out in our laboratory, with only brief consideration given to pertinent work in other laboratories. Details of the methodology, media, etc., have been reported (Skoog and Tsui, 1948; Miller and Skoog, 1953; Jablonski and Skoog, 1954). It is hoped that the evidence to be presented will convincingly demonstrate that this approach does in fact permit a closer examination of individual factors and their interaction in various growth processes than has been possible so far with intact plants. For a more general review of the tissue-culture approach in studies of growth see Gautheret (1955).

II. GENERAL RESULTS

The present work was started in an attempt to account for the dual, stimulatory and inhibitory, action of auxin (IAA) as exemplified in its promotion of growth of the terminal shoot and inhibition of lateral buds. A study particularly of the latter process led to the recognition of a parallel function of auxin in the initial formation of organ primordia and in the subsequent development of buds.

Interaction of IAA, adenine and other factors in bud formation. Experiments with tobacco callus and stem tissues cultured *in vitro* have shown that a delicate, quantitative balance between IAA and adenine and between these and other factors will determine the types of growth and organ formation which occur (Skoog and Tsui, 1951; Miller and Skoog, 1953; Skoog, 1954a). For example, with reference to the induction of bud formation in tobacco-stem segment cultures, the addition of 5 $\mu g/l$. IAA to the medium was enough to prevent completely spontaneous bud formation in control segments, and about 40 mg of adenine must be supplied to restore bud formation to the same level as in controls. Computations on the basis of numerous experiments of this type indicated that under the conditions used about 15,000 molecules of adenine were required to counterbalance 1 molecule of IAA. Further-more, by the use of purine-type inhibitors such as 2,6-diaminopurine and the reversal of their effects (Miller, 1953), it could be clearly shown that adenine as well as auxin is required for each of the several types of growth tested, including cell elongation. The interaction of adenine with IAA, therefore, can hardly be one of competitive inhibition. Also other naturally occurring purines and pyrimidines may enhance or modify the effect of adenine in bud formation (Skoog, 1954b).

Isolation of kinetin; kinins. In view of the above, a search was made for possible reaction products or complexes of IAA and adenine within the tobacco tissues. In this connection it was found that excised pith tissue responds differently to IAA in the absence and presence of vascular tissue; in the former case there is only cell enlargement, whereas in the latter case some cell division and eventually root forma-tion occur as well. The presence of a factor in the vascular tissue which induces division in the pith cells (especially in the presence of added

TEXT FIGURE 1. Structural formula of kinetin.

auxin) was demonstrated and was shown to be present also in various natural products (Jablonski and Skoog, 1954). Later a crystalline substance with properties of this type was isolated from commercial DNA preparations, identified as 6-(furfurylamino) purine, and synthesized (Miller *et al.,* 1956). The structural formula is given in Text Figure 1. Because of its activity in promoting cell division it was named kinetin. More than twenty analogues (all adenine derivatives) have since been found to possess similar activity to varying degrees, but none has been markedly more active than the furfuryladenine (Okumura, von Saltza, Strong, Miller and Skoog, 1955). The following are among the more active derivatives (active in tobacco callus or pith cultures in concentrations of 1–10 μg/l.): benzyl-, phenyl-, 2-thenyl-, butyl-, amyl-, hexyl-. Of the alkyl derivatives ethyl- and heptyl- were slightly active, but methyl-, octyl- and decyl- were not active in our tests. Substitutions of polar groups in the side chain has led to inactivation. Substitutions in the purine nucleus almost invariably had led to complete loss in activity, but in the case of $-NH_2$ substituted in the 2 position some activity was retained. Further details will be published by Strong *et al.* As mentioned, these substances with physiological activity similar to that of kinetin have been named kinins. This generic term may also include structurally different substances of the type reported by Shantz and Steward (1955*a, b*).

Kinetin-IAA interactions in growth of cells. The requirement for both IAA and kinetin in the growth of excised pith tissue has been demonstrated. Detailed studies of cytological effects of kinetin in tobacco pith have been carried out by Drs. Patau and Das in cooperation with the writer. Summaries of counts of mitosis and of newly formed cells plotted as functions of concentration and length of kinetin treatments in the presence of IAA are shown in Text Figures 2*a* and *b* respectively. A diagram (Text Figure 3) illustrating the interaction of kinin and auxin (kinetin and IAA) in DNA† increase, mitosis and cytokinesis, has been prepared by Dr. Patau. It shows that some DNA formation may be induced by kinetin in the absence of added IAA, and vice versa that some mitoses may be induced (Naylor, Sander and Skoog, 1954), and also a few cell divisions may be induced by IAA in the absence of added kinetin, whereas no cell division or mitosis is found in the controls. These slight effects of the treatments with only one substance undoubtedly depend on the presence of small endogenous contents of the other. In general it can be stated that both substances are required for active DNA synthesis, mitosis and cell division to proceed continuously.

Kinetin-IAA interactions in organ formation. Perhaps we may think of these definite and rather quantitative effects of IAA and kinetin on cells as primary manifestations of their growth regulatory action. However this may be, the morphogenetic influences of the substances are numerous and "pliable," that is, subject to modification by a variety of factors and/or conditions. They are, nevertheless, consistently reproducible, and distinct to the visual observer to a degree that can

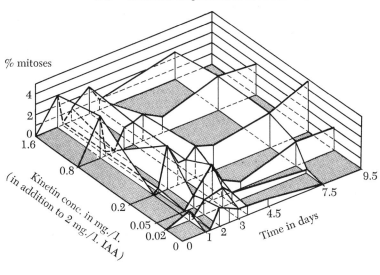

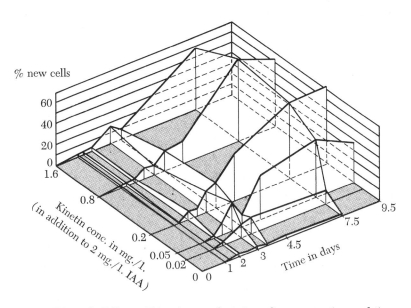

TEXT FIGURES 2a, b. Effect of kinetin as a function of concentration and time of treatment on: (a) the rate of cell division (percentage mitosis), and (b) the number of new cells formed in tobacco pith sections cultured on modified White's nutrient agar media with 2.0 mg/l. IAA added (Das, Patau and Skoog, 1956).

only be poorly reflected in black and white photographs, weights or dimensional measurements of various types.

(a) *Effects of concentration.* A most striking morphogenetic effect of kinetin is in the initiation and development of buds, as observed in tobacco callus or stem-tissue cultures (Plate 2). This effect is greatly dependent on the concentration and on the presence of other factors, especially the auxin level in the nutrient medium. The influence of a high phosphate level must also be noted. In Plate 3 is shown the effect of increasing kinetin concentrations on first generation subcultures of stem segments grown on modified White's medium (Miller and Skoog, 1953) with a constant 2 mg/l. level of IAA. Some growth, mainly cell enlargement and the formation of a few short roots, is seen to have occurred in controls. The effect of 0.02 mg/l. is mainly on undifferentiated callus growth, whereas that of 0.5 and 1.0 mg/l. is mainly on bud formation and development with a repression of root formation. Still higher concentrations of kinetin tend to inhibit growth under the conditions of this experiment, but are not very toxic, so that cultures with high kinetin levels actually will remain alive for months longer than the control or low-level kinetin cultures. The interaction of kinetin at two levels (0.2 and 1.0 mg/l.) with increasing concentrations of IAA from 0 to 3.0 mg/l. are compared with each other and with controls in Plate 4. Points to be noted are: (1) Very little growth occurred without addition of either kinetin or IAA. (2) In the presence of 0.2–3.0 mg/l. IAA these callus tissues subcultured from stem segments, as expected, underwent con-

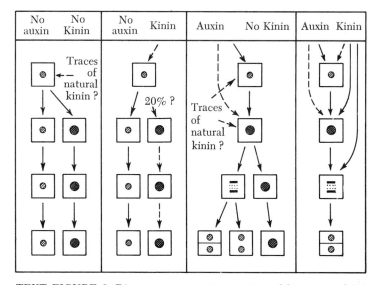

TEXT FIGURE 3. Diagram representing action of kinetin and IAA, separately and in combination, on DNA synthesis, mitosis and cell division in tobacco pith tissue (Patau and Das, unpublished).

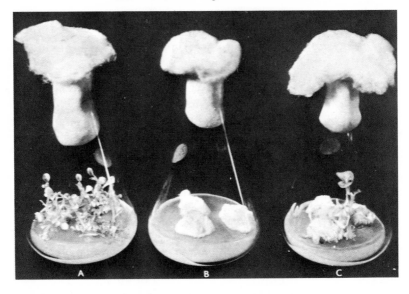

PLATE 2. Bud formation in tobacco callus. Callus (fifth subculture of tobacco stem) on modified White's medium. A. with kinetin 0.2 mg/l.; B. with kinetin 0.2 mg/l. plus IAA 2 mg/l.; C. with kinetin 0.2 mg/l., IAA 2 mg/l. and in addition KH_2PO_4 400 mg/l. Age of cultures, c. 45 days.

siderable enlargement associated with some cell division and root development from the cambial or phloem derivatives. (3) 0.2 mg/l. kinetin alone permitted sufficient growth to produce a bud or two per piece of tissue. (4) With increasing IAA concentrations growth increased, but bud formation was repressed by the higher IAA levels. (5) 1.0 mg/l. kinetin was more effective than was 0.2 mg/l. in promoting growth, especially bud development, but with increasing IAA concentration growth increased and again bud formation was gradually repressed in favour of callus growth. (6) The apparently greater increase in size of callus with high IAA levels and 0.2 mg/l. as compared with 1.0 mg/l. kinetin is misleading. It reflects "watery" tissues with a large proportion of loosely packed cells as compared with very firm tissues consisting of numerous small "meristematic" cells. (7) Finally, it should be mentioned that both kinetin levels used in this experiment were too high for promotion of root growth (cf. Plate 3).

III. DISCUSSION AND CONCLUSIONS

The evidence we have obtained points to a uniformity in growth-factor requirements and regulatory mechanisms for all types of growth. Definite parallelisms in these respects are found in cell elongation and cell division of tissues, in the initiation of roots and buds, and in the subsequent development of these organs. Interactions between IAA and

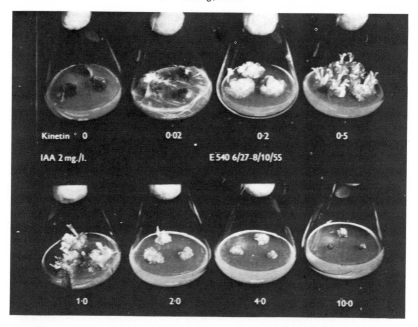

PLATE 3. Effect of kinetin concentration (in 0–10 mg/l. range) on growth and organ formation of tobacco callus cultured on modified White's nutrient agar with 2.0 mg/l. IAA added. Age of cultures, 44 days (Skoog *et al.*).

kinetin and between these and other factors appear to exert decisive influences in each case. Both types of chemical seem to be required for growth. Low levels of one with high levels of the other and vice versa lead to opposite morphological end-results. The same holds true in cuttings. For example, bean stems dipped into auxin solution and planted with their basal ends in water or nutrient solution will show increased root formation and decreased lateral bud development as compared with untreated controls. Cuttings dipped in a kinetin solution, on the other hand, will show enhanced bud development and no or markedly retarded development of adventitious roots. Thus, all the evidence reported here points to quantitative interaction rather than qualitative action of growth factors in the regulation of growth. This general conclusion is, of course, directly opposite to concepts of specific organ-forming substances — as advocated by Bouillenne (1950) or Gautheret (1950). It tends to minimize the significance of slight structural modifications found in plants or in cultured tissues, because these, even when consistently reproducible, often must reflect only slight differences in growth-factor contents. The results obtained also are sharply in conflict with the concept of "determination," i.e., irreversible loss in regenerative capacities of cells and tissues, in ontogeny.

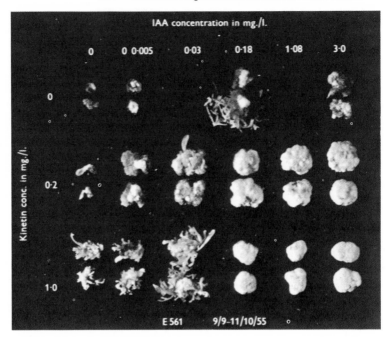

PLATE 4. Effect of increasing IAA concentration at different kinetin levels on the growth and organ formation of tobacco callus cultured on modified White's nutrient agar. Age of cultures, 62 days (Skoog *et al.*).

On the other hand, in drawing attention to the complexities and levels of chemical interactions in the regulation of growth, they suggest the futility of attempts to interpret growth phenomena on the basis of very precise computations of the interaction between only two factors in a multifactor system, as in the determinations of so-called auxin-anti-auxin competitions (cf. McRae, Foster and Bonner, 1953; Bonner and Foster, 1956). Even though they exist, as experimentally determined, they can have meaning only in a general sense. At the other extreme are schemes postulating interaction of fields or "gradients" which are too general or nonspecific to be meaningful, as, for example, Wardlaw's (1955) discussion based on Turing's (1952) proposal. Clearly actual control mechanisms must be too heterogeneous both in detailed structure and in location (dispersion) within the cells and tissues to be amenable to such treatments. In a recent discussion of our work, Thimann (1956) points to certain similarities in the structure of adenine, kinetin and IAA, as well as of biotin. It must be considered, however, that his structural formulae are purposely sketched in a suggestive manner with disregard for exact geometric relationships demanded by atomic considerations. We rather feel that the evidence we now have for the combined action of IAA and adenine or kinetin, or both, in processes varying from nucleic acid synthesis, cell division and cell elongation to the regulation of organ formation, would preclude an interpretation of the action of these substances merely on speculative considerations of competitive interaction between them.

As regards the pertinence of the present results to ontogeny, more work is needed. We do know that both kinins, of as yet unknown chemical nature, and auxins are present in leaf and stem tissues. It may be logically assumed that they participate in meristematic activity, differentiation and organ development in the intact plant in the same manner as in tissue cultures. It would appear therefore, that the results reported here go a long way towards answering the original question of the dual action of auxin on growth and in inhibition of buds. The exact chemical nature of the interaction of IAA and kinetin remains to be determined, but there can be little doubt that both are involved in nucleic acid metabolism, including nucleic acid synthesis. It is possible to visualize, therefore, an essentially nuclear mechanism of growth regulation which possesses recognized means for interaction with the cytoplasm and which also is considered to be represented rather directly in the synthesis of large molecular structural units of the cell walls.

We are approaching the stage, therefore, where sharp distinctions between stimuli, "energy-furnishing" metabolites and structural units are disappearing, as these can be seen to grade into each other in integrated biosynthetic systems which function in all types of growth, and which would account for the remarkable uniformity of the regulatory mechanisms in the different phases of growth and morphogenesis that we have observed. The present results suggest that numerous potential possibilities exist for the regulation of growth by chemical manipulations of the media at such different levels as 1 μg/l. hormone and 400 mg/l. inorganic phosphate. The reason for this must be that cellular constituents of all types, including growth factors, are so closely interlocked that a change in one affects many others. For the understanding of the detailed function or biological action of any one growth substance, therefore, we must also learn a great deal about many others.

SUMMARY

Approaches to studies of chemical regulation of growth are considered.

General results are presented of growth-factor investigations in plant tissue cultures, etc. These tend to show that quantitative interactions between growth factors, especially between IAA and kinetin (auxin and kinins) and between these and other factors, provide a common mechanism for the regulation of all types of growth investigated from cell enlargement to organ formation.

The bearing of these results on current concepts of plant morphogenesis is discussed.

REFERENCES AND NOTES

Much of the work covered in this report was supported in part by the Research Committee of the Graduate School with funds from the Alumni Research Foundation and by a Research Grant (Proj. BO-19 to F. Skoog) from the American Cancer Society upon recommendation of the Committee on Growth of the National Research Council. The authors are grateful to the graduate students and colleagues in the Department of Botany who have participated in this work, and especially to Prof. F. M. Strong and his students in the Department of Biochemistry for collaboration in the isolation and chemical investigations of cell-division factors.

* Slightly abridged.

† DNA measured spectrophotometrically on large numbers of individual, Feulgen-stained nuclei.

J. Bonner and R. J. Foster, in *The Chemistry and Mode of Action of Plant Growth Substances*, R. L. Wain and F. Wightman, Eds. (Butterworth's Scientific Pub., London, 1956), p. 295.

A. Bouillenne, *Année biol.* **54**, 597 (1950).

N. K. Das, K. Patau, F. Skoog, *Physiol. Plant.* **9**, 640 (1956).

R. J. Gautheret, *Année biol.* **54**, 719 (1950).

———, *Ann. Rev. Pl. Physiol.* **6**, 433 (1955).

H. Geissbühlerr, *Ber. schweiz. bot. Ges.* **63**, 27 (1953).

G. Haberlandt, *Beitr. allg. Bot.* **2**, 1 (1921).

R. W. Howell and F. Skoog, *Amer. J. Bot.* **42**, 356 (1955).

J. R. Jablonski and F. Skoog, *Physiol. Plant.* **7**, 16 (1954).

D. H. McRae, R. J. Foster, J. Bonner, *Plant Physiol.* **28**, 343 (1953).

C. O. Miller, *Proc. Soc. Exp. Biol., N.Y.*, **83**, 561 (1953).

———, *Plant Physiol.* **31**, 318 (1956).

——— and F. Skoog, *Amer. J. Bot.* **40**, 768 (1953).

———, F. Skoog, F. S. Okumura, M. H. von Saltza, F. M. Strong, *J. Amer. Chem. Soc.* **78**, 1375 (1956).

J. Naylor, G. Sander, F. Skoog, *Physiol. Plant.* **7**, 25 (1954).

F. S. Okumura, M. H. von Saltza, F. M. Strong, C. O. Miller, F. Skoog, 28th Meeting Amer. Chem. Soc., Minneapolis, Minn. (1955).

D. Paris and L. Duhamet, *Compt. Rend.* **236**, 1690 (1953).

E. M. Shantz and F. C. Steward, *J. Amer. Chem. Soc.* **77**, 6351 (1955a).

———, *Pl. Physiol. Suppl.* **30**, 35 (1955b).

C. G. Skinner and W. Shive, *J. Amer. Chem. Soc.* **77**, 6692 (1955).

F. Skoog, in *Dynamics of Growth Processes*, E. G. Boell, Ed. (Princeton Univ. Press, Princeton, 1954a), p. 148.

———, in *Abnormal and Pathological Growth, Brookhaven Symposia in Biol.*, 6 (BNL 258 [c-19]) (1954b).

——— and C. Tsui, *Amer. J. Bot.* **35**, 782 (1948).

———, in *Plant Growth Substances* (Univ. of Wisconsin Press, Madison, 1951), p. 263.

R. Snow, *New Phytol.* **34**, 347 (1935).

F. C. Steward and E. M. Shantz, *Année biol.* **30**, 139 (1954).

K. V. Thimann, *Amer. Nat.* **40**, 145 (1956).

J. G. Torrey, *Amer. J. Bot.* **37**, 257 (1950).

————, *Ann. Rev. Pl. Physiol.* **7**, 237 (1956).

K. Tryon, *Amer. J. Bot.* **42**, 604 (1955).

————, *Science,* **123**, 590 (1956).

A. M. Turing, *Proc. Roy. Soc. London* **B**, **237**, 37 (1952).

C. W. Wardlaw, *Embryogenesis in Plants* (Methuen, London, 1955).

F. W. Went, in *Plant Growth Substances,* F. Skoog, Ed. (Univ. of Wisconsin Press, Madison, 1951), p. 287.

D Morphogenesis

Garner, W. W., and H. A. Allard. 1920. Effect of the relative length of day and night and other factors of the environment on growth and reproduction in plants. *Jour. Agric. Res.* **18**, 553–606.

Čajlachjan, M. Ch. 1937. Concerning the hormonal nature of plant development processes. *Comptes Rend. (Doklady) de l'Acad. Sci. de l'USSR* **16**, 227–30.

Butler, W. L., K. H. Norris, H. W. Siegelman, and S. B. Hendricks. 1959. Detection, assay, and preliminary purification of the pigment controlling photoresponsive development of plants. *Proc. Nat. Acad. Sci. U.S.* **45**, 1703–1708.

Williams, Carroll M. 1947. Physiology of insect diapause. II. Interaction between the pupal brain and prothoracic glands in the metamorphosis of the giant silkworm, *Platysamia cecropia. Biol. Bull. Woods Hole* **93**, 89–98.

Gross, Jerome. 1964. Studies on the biology of connective tissues: Remodelling of collagen in metamorphosis. *Medicine* **43**, 291–303.

Effect of the Relative Length of Day and Night and Other Factors of the Environment on Growth and Reproduction in Plants*

W. W. Garner
H. A. Allard

Tobacco and Plant Nutrition Investigations, Bureau of Plant Industry, U.S. Department of Agriculture[1]

INTRODUCTION

The importance of the relationships existing between light and plant growth and development has been so long recognized and these relationships have been of so much interest to investigators that a very extensive literature on the subject has been developed. For present purposes it will not be necessary to attempt even a brief review of this literature, and only some of the leading features bearing upon the particular problems in hand need to be touched upon. For more extended discussions of the work in this field the monographs of MacDougal (*18*) and Wiesner (26) may be consulted. Three primary factors enter into the action of light upon plants — namely, (1) the intensity of the light, (2) the quality, that is, the wave length of the radiation, and (3) the duration of the exposure. Most phases of these three factors have been more or less extensively investigated. In the present investigation we are concerned chiefly with the general growth and development of plants and the reproductive processes as affected by the daily duration of the light exposure.

As regards intensity, it seems to be pretty well established that there is an optimum for growth in each species and that for

Reprinted from the *Journal of Agricultural Research* **18**, 553–606 (1920).

many species this optimum is less than the intensity of the full sunlight on a clear day. Within limits, reduction in light intensity tends to lengthen the main axis and branches and to increase the superficial area of the foliage of many species. Also, the thickness of the leaf lamina may be reduced, and there may be marked departures from the normal in internal structure, the tendency being toward a less compact structure. So far as is known, no important general relationships between differences in light intensity and reproductive processes have been experimentally demonstrated.

The comparative effects produced by different regions of the spectrum, including the ultraviolet, have been extensively investigated but with more or less conflicting results. The most extensive investigations on the subject, perhaps, have been made by Flammarion (8). It was found that there is abnormal elongation of the principal axis in several species under the influence of the red rays, while growth is markedly reduced under the green and especially under the blue rays. In some plants, however, such as corn, peas, and beans, growth is greatest in white light. Some plants blossomed considerably earlier in red light than in white. White light produced the greatest weight of dry matter. Leaves of Coleus developed decided differences in color patterns under differently colored lights. In subsequent work Flammarion has extended his studies to a large number of species.

The duration of the daily exposure to light needs to be considered in three separate phases — (1) continuous illumination throughout the 24-hour period, (2) continuous darkness throughout, leading to the phenomena of etiolation, and (3) illumination for any fractional portion of the 24-hour day. Under natural conditions continuous sunlight throughout the 24-hour period occurs, of course, only in very high latitudes. Schübeler (23) observed the behavior of several species transported from lower latitudes and grown in northern Scandinavia under continuous sunlight lasting for a period of two months. In the species under observation the vegetative period was shortened and the seeds produced were larger than the normal. It is stated, also, that there was an increased formation of aromatic and flavoring constituents. Another method of securing continuous illumination consists in the use of artificial light for illumination or in the supplementing of normal daylight with artificial light, though, of course, the quality and the intensity from the two sources will not ordinarily be the same. Using electric light alone, of an intensity one-third that of sunlight, Bonnier (6) observed a marked increase in chlorophyll formation which extended inwardly to unusual depths. He found also incomplete differentiation of the tissues, recalling, in this respect, the effects of continued darkness. In some instances the color of blossoms was deepened.

Etiolation, resulting from exposure to continuous darkness, has been the subject of much study. In this connection special mention should be made of the work of MacDougal (18) covering a very large number of species. This author also presents a comprehensive survey of previous work on the subject. In most instances stems, and frequently leaves, exhibited negative geotropism in the absence of light. In all species investigated etiolated tissues show a lesser degree of differentiation than the normal. In this connection MacDougal points out that the differences exhibited between etiolated specimens and normal plants demonstrate the fact that growth, or increase in size, and development, or differentiation, are distinct processes capable of separation. For present purposes perhaps his most important observation is that in no plant investigated had the stamens and pistils attained functional maturity.

The effects of differences in the length of the daylight period, the subject of the present study, have not been so extensively investigated as most other phases of light action. Obviously the problem may be approached in any one of four ways: by comparing the behavior of plants when propagated in different latitudes, by growing plants at different seasons of the year in the same latitude, by supplementing the daylight period with artificial light, and by preventing light from reaching the plant for a portion of the normal daylight period. In the records of attempts to grow various plants in different parts of the world there is undoubtedly a great deal of available data bearing on the present problem; but apparently no systematic effort has been made to utilize this material, the reason probably being that the importance of the relative length of day in affecting plant processes, and, in particular, reproduction, has not been appreciated. Bailey (3, 4, 5) carried out an extensive series of tests in which daylight illumination was supplemented by the electric arc light applied for different portions of the night. The addition of the artificial light induced blossoming and seed formation in spinach. The additional light also favored the growth of lettuce. Rane (20), using the incandescent filament electric light, and Corbett (7), employing incandescent gas light, observed that certain flowering plants and some vegetables blossomed somewhat earlier when the normal daylight illumination was supplemented with artificial light. In most of these tests the artificial light was applied for the entire night, but apparently the results so far as concerns reproduction were essentially the same as when the plants were darkened for a portion of the night. Tournois (24, 25) has reported the results of an interesting experiment with hemp (*Cannabis sativa* L.) and a species of hops (*Humulus japonicus* Sieb. and Zucc.) in which these plants were exposed to sunlight only from 8 A.M. to 2 P.M. daily. It had been shown by Girou de Buzareingues (10) as early as 1831 that when planted in the late winter or very early spring months the hemp plant first develops in the spring a number of abnormal sterile blossoms in the leaf axils and later produces normal flowers at the regular blossoming period. Following up this fact Tournois concludes from the above-mentioned experiment that the abnormal blossoming period is induced by the short length of day prevailing in the early spring months.

In a few words, previous work on light action clearly indicates that permanent exclusion of light effectually prevents completion of the blossoming and seed-forming processes, while in certain cases lengthening the normal daily period of illumination by the use of artificial light or by propagation in far northern latitudes hastens the approach of the blossoming period, and, in the case of two species, shortening the daily exposure to light induces the formation of precocious blossoms. That the relative length of the day is really a dominating factor in plant reproduction processes, as is demonstrated in the present paper, seems not to have been suspected by previous workers in this field.

PRELIMINARY OBSERVATIONS

In 1906 there were observed in a strain of Maryland Narrowleaf tobacco (*Nicotiana tabacum*, L.), which is a very old variety, several plants which grew to an extraordinary height and produced an abnormally large number of leaves. As these plants showed no signs of blossoming with the advent of cold weather, some of them were transplanted from the field to the greenhouse and the stalks of others were cut off and the stumps replanted in the greenhouse. These roots soon developed new shoots which blossomed and produced seed, as did also the plants which had been transferred in their entirety. This very interesting giant tobacco, commonly known as Maryland Mammoth, which normally continues to grow till cold weather in the latitude of Washington, D.C., without blossoming, proved to be a very valuable new type for commercial purposes, but the above-mentioned procedure has been the only method by which seed could be obtained. The type bred true from the outset, and no matter how small the seed plant the progeny have always shown the giant type of growth when propagated under favorable summer conditions. It may be remarked at this point that inheritance of gigantism[2] in this tobacco has been studied by one of the present writers (2) and it has been shown that this character acts as a simple Mendelian recessive.

On one occasion it was observed that seedings of the Mammoth transplanted to 8-inch pots in late winter blossomed in early spring after reaching a height of some 3 feet and developed an excellent crop of seed. From this it was at first concluded that growing the plant under conditions of partial starvation would induce blossoming, but this idea proved to be erroneous. Repeated attempts during the summer months to force blossoming by subjecting the plant to conditions which would permit only limited growth were futile. On the other hand, it was found that seedlings grown in the greenhouse during the winter months invariably blossomed without regard to the size of the pot containing the seedling or the extent to which the plant was stunted by unfavorable nutrition conditions. The seedlings behaved, therefore, like the summer-grown giant plants which were transferred to the greenhouse late in the fall. Finally, it was observed that the shoots which were constantly developing from the transplanted roots of giant plants transferred to the greenhouse blossomed freely during the winter months, but as early spring advanced blossoming soon ceased and the younger shoots once more developed giant stalks. Obviously, then, the time of year in which the Mammoth tobacco develops determines whether the growth is of the giant character. During the summer months the plants may attain a height of 10 to 15 feet or more and produce many times the normal number of leaves without blossoming, while during the winter months blossoming invariably occurs before the plants attain a height of 5 feet. Naturally it became of interest from both a practical and a scientific standpoint to determine the factor of the environment responsible for the remarkable winter effect in forcing blossoming. It may be added just here that gigantism also has been observed in several distinct varieties of tobacco other than the Maryland — namely, in Sumatra, Cuban, and Connecticut Havana.

Again, in following out an investigation on the relation of the nutrition conditions to the quantity of oil formed in the seeds of such plants as cotton, peanuts, and soybeans, the present writers (9) had occasion to investigate the significance of the observation made by Mooers (19), that successive plantings of certain varieties of soybeans (*Soja max* [L.] Piper) made through the summer months, show a decided tendency to blossom at approximately the same date regardless of the date of planting. In other words, the later the planting, the shorter is the period of growth up to the time of blossoming. In the course of the investigation on oil formation it became desirable to study the possible effects of temperature differences on the process. Since it is much simpler and cheaper to maintain temperature differences during the winter by the use of heat than during the summer by means of refrigeration, it was planned to make some tests with soybeans during the winter. It was soon found, however, that the plants began to develop blossoms before they had made anything like a normal growth, and the few blossoms produced were cleistogamous, so that it became necessary to abandon the plan of conducting the tests in question during the winter months. As in the case with the Mammoth tobacco, the time of year in which the plants are grown exerts a very profound influence on growth and reproduction in the soybean.

In seeking a solution of the problem as to why the behavior of these plants is radically different from the normal during the fall and winter months one naturally thinks of light and temperature as possible factors. It was observed, however, that both the Mammoth tobacco and the soybeans still showed the abnormal behavior in the winter even when the temperature in the greenhouse was kept quite as high as prevails out of doors during the summer months. This observation seemed to dispose of temperature as a possible factor of importance in the "winter effect." It is clear that the quantity of solar radiation received by plants is less in winter than in summer, for both the number of hours of sunshine per day and the intensity of the light are reduced during the winter months. The quality of the light also is affected, since the angle of elevation of the sun's path during the winter is less than during the summer and the selective absorptive action of the atmosphere comes into play. It happened that in the investigation on oil formation in seeds a number of experiments had been made with soybeans to determine the effect of light intensity on this process and, incidentally, it was observed that in no case was the date of blossoming materially affected by the intensity of the light. It had been found, also, that partial shading was without decided effect on the blossoming of the Mammoth tobacco. In view of these experiences it hardly seemed likely that the other primary factor controlling the maximum amount of radiation received by the plant — namely, the length of the daily exposure — could be responsible for the effects in question. Nevertheless, the simple expedient of shortening artificially by a few hours the length of the daily exposure to the sun by use of a dark chamber was tried, and some very striking results were obtained, as detailed in the following paragraphs.

PLAN OF THE EXPERIMENTS

The first experiments with the use of the dark chamber were begun in July, 1918. A small, ventilated, dark chamber with a door which could be tightly closed was placed in the field. The soybeans used in the tests were grown in wooden boxes 10 inches wide, 10 inches deep, and 3 feet long. These containers have been extensively used in growing soybeans and other small plants under controlled conditions, and it has been found that normal plants are easily obtained in this way. The dark chamber and the type of box used for growing soybeans and similar plants are shown in Plate 64, A.* Larger plants like tobacco have been grown in large galvanized iron buckets or, in some cases, in ordinary flower pots. When the test plants have attained the desired stage of development the procedure has been to place them in the dark chamber at the selected hour in the afternoon each day. The plants were left in the dark chamber till the hour decided upon in the following morning, when they were again placed in the sunlight. This procedure was followed each day till the test was completed. Appropriate control plants were left in the open throughout the test in each case. By this method the number of hours of exposure to sunlight during the 24-hour period could be reduced as far as desired.

In the preliminary tests of 1918 no special means were provided for moving the boxes and pots containing the plants in and out of the dark chamber. In the spring of the present year a much larger dark house was constructed, and suitable facilities were installed for easily moving the test plants in or out of the house as often as desired. The dark house consisted of a rectangular frame structure 30 feet by 18 feet and 6 feet in height to the eaves and 9 feet to the ridgepole. All crevices by which light could enter were covered, tight-fitting doors were provided, and the interior was painted black. Means were provided at the bottom and top of the house for free circulation of air without the admission of light. A series of four steel tracks, each entering through a separate door, was provided; and on these tracks were mounted a number of trucks carrying the test plants in their containers. This equipment proved very satisfactory. A general view of the dark house, the trucks, and the test plants is shown in Plate 64, B.*

It has been rather generally assumed that the pronounced changes in plant activities which come on with the approach of fall are due in some way to the lower mean daily temperatures or the wider daily range in temperature caused by cool nights. It seemed desirable, therefore, to compare the temperatures inside and outside the dark house, and for this purpose thermographs were installed. It was found that there were only slight differences in temperature. The temperature inside the dark house tended to run 2° to 3° F higher than the temperature outside, particularly at night. Hence, any responses on the part of the plants resembling those appearing in the fall of the year could not be attributed to lower temperatures. To guard further against possible temperature effects, as soon as the above-mentioned temperature difference was discovered all doors of the dark house were opened as darkness came on each day.

In the various tests the length of the exposure to light was varied from a minimum of 5 hours per day to a maximum of 12 hours, 7 hours and 12 hours being the exposures chiefly used. For the shortest exposure the plants were placed in the dark house at 3 o'clock P.M. and returned to the light at 10 A.M.; for the 7-hour exposure the plants were darkened at 4 P.M. and returned to the light at 9 A.M.; and for the 12-hour exposure they were in the dark house from 6 P.M. till 6 A.M. A further modification in exposure consisted in placing the plants in the dark house at 10 A.M. and returning them to the light at 2 P.M. In most instances the daily treatment began with the germination of the seed or in the earlier stages of growth and continued until maturity, but in some cases the plants were permanently restored to the open as soon as blossoming occurred, and in other cases the artificial shortening of the day was not begun until after blossoming had occurred. To facilitate discussion it will be convenient to use the expressions "long day" as meaning exposure to light for more than 12 hours and "short day" as referring to an exposure of 12 hours or less. The term "length of day" as used in this paper refers to the duration of the illumination period for each 24-hour interval.

As a part of the present investigation a series of plantings of soybeans was made in the field at intervals of approximately three days throughout the season, in order that the effects produced by different dates of planting might be compared with those produced by artificially shortening the length of the daily exposure to light.

BEHAVIOR OF THE PLANTS TESTED

The initial experiment was made in the summer of 1918, and in this instance a box containing the Peking variety of soybeans in blossom and three pots containing Mammoth tobacco plants which had been growing for several weeks were first placed in the dark chamber at 4 P.M. on July 10 and removed therefrom at 9 A.M. the following morning. This treatment was continued each day till the seeds of the beans and tobacco were mature. All subsequent experiments were made during the year 1919. Details of the tests for both years follow.

TOBACCO (NICOTIANA TABACUM AND N. RUSTICA L.)

(a) NICOTIANA TABACUM;[3] MARYLAND MAMMOTH, giant type:

(1) Exposed to light from 10 A.M. to 3 P.M. Observations on 14 test plants and 10 controls. Planted March 6, transplanted to 6-inch pots May 10, and placed in dark house May 14. First blossoms appeared July 8 to August 14 on test plants and in last week of October on controls. Average height of test plants 14 to 16 inches and that of controls 3 to 5 inches.

(2) Exposed to light from 9 A.M. to 4 P.M. Observations on 7 test plants and 10 controls. Planted March 6, transplanted to 6-inch pots May 10, and placed in dark house May 14. First blossoms appeared July 18 to August 1 on test plants and in last week of October on controls. Average height of test plants 12 to 14 inches and that of controls 5 to 6 inches.

(2a) Exposed to light from 9 A.M. to 4 P.M. Observations on 8 test plants and 8 controls. Planted January 8, transplanted to 8-inch pots May 3, and placed in dark house May 14. First blossoms appeared July 5 to 25 on test plants and October 1 to 25 on controls. See Plate 70.

(2b) Exposed to light from 9 A.M. to 4 P.M. Observations on three test plants and four controls. Planted April 14, transplanted in steam-sterilized soil in 12-quart iron pails and placed in dark house June 10. First blossoms appeared August 1 to 7 on test plants and August 30 to September 8 on controls. Average height of test plants 37 inches and that of controls 39 inches.

(3) Exposed to light from 6 A.M. to 6 P.M. Observations on 6 test plants and 3 controls. Planted April 14 and transplanted to 12-quart iron pails containing steam-sterilized soil and placed in dark house June 11. First blossoms appeared August 26 to September 4 on test plants and September 3 to 20 on controls. Average height of test plants 48 inches and that of controls 49 inches. See Plates 71 and 72, A.*

(b) N. TABACUM; STEWART 70-LEAF CUBAN,[3] giant type:

(1) Exposed to light from 9 A.M. to 4 P.M. Observations on 6 test plants and 5 controls. Planted April 14 and transplanted in steam-sterilized soil in 12-quart iron pails and placed in dark house June 10. First blos-

PLATE 70.
A. Maryland Mammoth tobacco in 8-inch pots
   exposed to light from 9 A.M. to 4 P.M. daily.
   Seed pods full-grown when photographed
   August 15, 1919.
B. Control series of Maryland Mammoth plants
   kept out-of-doors. No signs of flowering when
   photographed August 15.

soms appeared August 16 to September 2 on test plants and September 24 to October 10 on controls. Average height of test plants 53 to 69 inches and that of controls 73 to 84 inches.

(c) N. TABACUM; CONNECTICUT BROADLEAF:[3]

(1) Exposed to light from 9 A.M. to 4 P.M. Observations on 11 test plants and 10 controls. Planted April 14 and transplanted to 14-quart iron pails and placed in dark house June 5. First blossoms appeared July 18 to 24 on test plants and July 17 to 22 on controls. Average height of test plants 38 inches and that of controls 34 inches. Average number of nodes on test plants 36 and same number on controls.

(1a) Exposed to light from 9 A.M. to 4 P.M. Observations on 8 test plants and 6 controls. Planted April 5 and transplanted to 14-quart iron pails and placed in dark house May 28. First blossoms appeared July 13 to 20 on test plants and July 7 to 15 on controls. Average height of test plants 37 inches and that of controls 40 inches.

(d) N. RUSTICA:

(1) Exposed to light from 9 A.M. to 4 P.M. Observations on 5 test plants and 3 controls. Planted April 14, transplanted to 14-quart iron pails, and 5 plants placed in dark house on June 2. Test plants blossomed July 5 to 28 and controls July 1 to 12.

LENGTH OF DAILY LIGHT EXPOSURE IN RELATION TO SEXUAL REPRODUCTION

While the rate of growth of the species tested was markedly affected by change in the length of the daily illumination period, the effects on blossoming and fruiting are particularly interesting and important. The experiments with soybeans included four varieties which range from early to very late in maturing under normal conditions when grown in the latitude of Washington, D.C. Thus, for plantings in the field extending through the month of May the average number of days from germination to blossoming was approximately 27, 56, 70, and 105, respectively, for the Mandarin, Peking, Tokyo, and Biloxi, the last-named showing no open blossoms till early September. Table 3 brings out several important facts regarding the effects of reduced light exposure on these four varieties.

Coming to tobacco, the contrast in behavior of the Connecticut Broadleaf and the Maryland Mammoth varieties is very striking. Sexual reproduction in the Connecticut Broadleaf is not materially affected by changes in length of day within the seasonal range for the latitude of Washington or southward. On the other hand, the Maryland Mammoth, which is presumably a mutation from a very old variety of Maryland tobacco and appears to be a typical example of gigantism, cannot be forced into blossoming during the summer months by any method now known except artificial shortening of the duration of the daily exposure to light, while the character of gigantism is completely suppressed when the plant is grown during the short days of winter. A glance at Table 4 shows that shortening the daily light exposure has not materially affected the Connecticut Broadleaf but has been effective in shortening the vegetative period of the Maryland Mammoth. The Cuban type of Mammoth was affected like the Maryland type, but it appears that the former has a somewhat longer vegetative period than the latter under similar conditions. The Maryland type blossoms readily under the influence of a 12-hour light exposure; but there is a suggestion that a time factor is operative here, for the plants seem not to blossom so promptly as when under the 7-hour exposure. It seems probable also that the Cuban Mammoth will blossom under a 12-hour exposure to light. The observation has been made by Lodewijks (*17*) that a giant type of Sumatra tobacco — grown under the influence of the 12-hour equatorial day — which may reach the extreme height of 24 feet, either does not blossom at all or forms only a few flowers and seeds. Gigantism in tobacco disappears when the plant is brought under the influence of short days such as prevail in the temperate zone during the winter months. *Nicotiana rustica,* so far as tested, behaves like the Connecticut Broadleaf.

TABLE 4

Length of the Vegetative Period of Tobacco as Affected by the Length of the Daily Exposure to Light.

Length of exposure	*Connecticut Broadleaf*		*Maryland Mammoth*		*Stewart 70-Leaf Cuban*	
	Date of transfer to dark house	Length of vegetative period	Date of transfer to dark house	Length of vegetative period	Date of transfer to dark house	Length of vegetative period
		Days		Days		Days
10 A.M. to 3 P.M., 5 hours.	. . . .		May 14	55 to 61	. . . .	
9 A.M. to 4 P.M., 7 hours.	June 5	43 to 49	. . do . .	61 to 78	. . . .	
Full daylight, 12 to 15 hours.	Controls	42 to 47	Controls	152 to 160	. . . .	
9 A.M. to 4 P.M., 7 hours.	. . . .		May 14	52 to 72	. . . .	
Full daylight, 12 to 15 hours.	. . . .		Controls[a]	140 to 164	. . . .	
9 A.M. to 4 P.M., 7 hours.	May 28	46 to 53	June 10	52 to 59	June 10	67 to 84
Full daylight, 12 to 15 hours.	Controls	36 to 44	Controls	84 to 101	Controls	81 to 90
Daylight to 10 A.M. and 2 P.M. till dark, 11 to 8½ hours.	. . . .					
6 A.M. to 6 P.M., 12 hours.	. . . .		June 11	76 to 85	. . . .	
Full daylight, 12 to 15 hours.	. . . .		Controls	84 to 101	. . . .	

[a] *These controls and the test plants having a vegetative period of 52 to 72 days were in 8-inch pots.*

LENGTH OF DAY AS A FACTOR IN
THE NATURAL DISTRIBUTION
OF PLANTS

In an intelligent understanding of the natural distribution of plants over a particular area, those factors which are favorable or unfavorable to growth and successful reproduction for each species must be given consideration. Heretofore temperature, water, and light intensity relations have been considered the chief external limiting factors governing the distribution or range of plants. In the light of the observations and experimental results presented in this paper it seems probable that an additional factor, the relative length of the days and nights during the growing period, must also be recognized as among those causes underlying the northward or southward distribution of plants.[4] It is evident that the equatorial regions of the earth alone enjoy equal days and nights throughout the entire year. Provided the water relations are favorable, the warm temperatures in these regions favor a continuous growing season for plants. Passing northward from the equatorial regions into higher latitudes, temperatures promoting active vegetative growth and development are restricted to a summer period which, other conditions being equal, becomes progressively shorter as the polar regions are approached. Coincident with these changes from lower to higher latitudes, the summers are characterized by lengthening periods of daylight and the winters by decreasing periods of daylight. We may now consider how these different day and night relations operating during the summer growing period will exercise more or less control upon the northward or southward distribution of certain plants.

It is evident that a plant cannot persist in a given region or extend its range in any direction unless it finds conditions not only favorable for vegetative activity but also for some form of successful reproduction. For present purposes only sexual or seed reproduction need be considered. The experiments above described have indicated that for certain plants — for example, ragweed and the aster — the reproductive or flowering phase of development in some way depends upon a stimulus afforded by the shortening of the days and the consequent lengthening of the nights as the summer solstice is passed. It remains to consider more specifically the bearing these facts may have when plants characterized by this type of behavior are subjected to the daylight relations of different latitudes. In the vicinity of Washington, D.C., the ragweeds regularly shed their first pollen about the middle of August. It may be considered that the earliest flowering plants bloom about this date each season because they react to a length of day somewhat less than that of the longest day, which is about 15 hours in this latitude. In other words, as soon as the decreasing length of day falls somewhat below 15 hours, a condition which obtains about July 1, the period of purely vegetative activity is checked, and the flowering phase of development is initiated.

Should the seeds of such plants now be carried as far as northern Maine into a latitude of 46° to 47°, these plants would not experience a length of day falling below 15 hours in length, for which it is assumed they are best suited, until about August 1. In this latitude, then, provided other conditions did not intrude, flowering would be delayed until about August 1, and the chances of successfully maturing seed before killing frosts intervened would be greatly lessened. If the seed were carried still farther north, the plants might not blossom at all, owing to the fact that even the shortest days of the summer growing period would exceed those to which they were best suited in their normal habitat. Although in such instances these failures naturally would have been explained in the past on the basis of unfavorable temperature relations alone, it is obvious that length of day, primarily, is the limiting factor which has retarded the reproductive period so that unfavorable temperature relations have intervened to prevent the ripening of seed.

Although the Arctic summers are very short, plants have become successfully established under such conditions, largely by the development of specialized perennial types, which find the extremely long days favorable both to vegetative growth and to flower production. Although it has been usually considered that the purely Arctic forms are confined to Arctic conditions because of certain temperature requirements, etc., it is possible that length of day, hitherto overlooked as a factor in plant distribution, may have much to do with their restricted range apart from other factors of the environment.

In tropical regions it is probable that the success of many native plants is more or less closely dependent upon the conditions of equal or nearly equal days and nights which prevail there during the entire year. The varieties of bean coming from Peru and Bolivia appear to be of this type. It is evident that such plants, whose flowering conditions depend more or less closely upon a length of day little if at all exceeding 12 hours, cannot attain the flowering stage attended by successful seed production in higher latitudes, at least during the summer season, which would necessarily be characterized by days in excess of 12 hours. It is indicated by the beans in question, however, that some plants of this class may grow and attain successful seed production under day lengths less than 12 hours. This being the case, such plants could at least extend their range beyond the Tropics insofar as the temperature conditions of the winter months in these latitudes were favorable to growth and reproduction.

In any study of the phenological aspects of different species of plants the fact stands out that certain plants bloom at definite seasons of the year. This is quite as marked in subtropical regions as in more northern regions having a definite summer growing season. In this connection it is probable that the relative lengths of the days and nights are of particular significance in many instances. The behavior of the composite *Mikania scandens*, as observed under specially controlled conditions and under winter conditions in the greenhouse, may be more critically considered in relation to its normal blooming season throughout its range. This plant normally blooms from late July to middle or late September, indicating that blossoming becomes more or less inhibited as the autumnal equinox is passed in late September and the length of the day falls below 12 hours. In the greenhouse at Washington the short days of the winter, ranging around 9 to 10 hours in length, have completely inhibited the flowering phase of development of this plant. The shorter 7-hour daily exposures to light under controlled conditions have produced identical results. Thus it appears that the normal flowering period of *Mikania scandens* even in the warmer portions of its range should not occur much later in the season than the period when the days are not less than 12 hours in length. This seems to be the case in Florida, where the blooming season of *Mikania* is confined to August and September, as it is in much more northern portions of its range. Plants of this type, attaining their best development under daylight lengths of approximately 12 hours, should also find a more or less congenial environment under truly tropical conditions where the days are never much less than 12 hours in length. It is probable that in the Tropics, however, many plants of this type would not only become perennial in their aerial portions, but would also have a more or less continuous flowering period.

Since it has been shown that the stature of some plants increases in proportion to the length of the day to which the plants are exposed under experimental conditions, this factor should be expected to have some influence upon the stature of such plants in their normal habitat. In general, exceptional stature would be attained in those regions in which a long day period allowed the plants to attain their maximum vegetative expression before the shorter days intervened to initiate the reproductive period. This condition should hold true not only for different latitudes where a plant has an extensive northward and southward range but for different sowings in the same locality at successively later dates during the season. It is a matter of common observation that the rankest growing individuals among such weeds as the ragweed, pigweed (Amaranthus), lamb's quarters (Chenopodium), cocklebur (Xanthium), beggar-ticks (Bidens), other conditions being equal, are those which germinated earliest in the season, and consequently were afforded the longest favorable period of vegetative activity preceding the final flowering period. It is also a matter of common observation that all these weeds, when germinating very late in the summer and coming at once under the influence of the stimulus of the shortening days, blossom when very small, often at a height of only a few inches.

Many species of plants have an extensive northward and southward distribution. In these instances it may be that such species are capable of reacting successfully to a wide range of different lengths of day, or it is possible that the apparent adjustment to such a wide range of conditions may depend upon slightly different physiological requirements of different types which have been developed as a result of natural selections. It yet remains to be seen whether those individuals of a given species which grow successfully in high latitudes have the same physiological requirements with respect to length of day as those growing quite as successfully near the equator. In any study of the behavior of plants introduced from other regions, with a view to determining certain economic qualities, it is evident that the factor of length of day must be taken into consideration as a matter likely to have great significance.

RESULTS OBTAINED WITH ARTIFICIAL
LIGHT USED TO INCREASE THE
LENGTH OF THE DAILY
ILLUMINATION PERIOD DURING THE
SHORT DAYS OF WINTER

These results are of particular significance, since increasing the duration of the illumination period of the short winter day by the use of electric light of comparatively low intensity has consistently resulted in initiating or inhibiting the reproductive or the vegetative phases of development, depending upon whether the plants employed normally require long or short days for these forms of expression. In these experiments a greenhouse 50 feet long, 20 feet wide, and 12 feet high to the ridge, with side walls of concrete 5 feet high to the eaves, was provided with 34 tungsten filament incandescent lights, each rated at 32 candlepower, evenly distributed beneath the glass roof. As a control, a similar greenhouse without artificial light was used. The long axis of these houses was on a north and south line. The temperature was approximately the same in the two greenhouses, ranging at night around 60° to 65° F and 75° to 80° during the day. The unlighted greenhouse, however, tended to run two to three degrees higher than the illuminated house. Beginning on November 1 the electric lights were switched on at 4:30 P.M. and turned off at 12.30 A.M., this procedure being followed throughout the course of the experiments. Supplementing the natural length of the winter days with this 8-hour period of artificial illumination has given about 18 hours of continuous daily illumination, approaching in length the summer days of southern Alaska. Under these conditions the following results have been obtained:

Seedlings of the Maryland Mammoth variety of tobacco were transplanted to 12-quart iron pails on November 10, on which date they were placed in the control and the lighted houses. The control plants, six in number, exhibited the typical behavior of winter-grown Maryland Mammoth plants, all blossoming during the period from December 31 to January 8. The plants in the lighted house, six in number, behaved as typical summer-grown mammoths, becoming very compact, stout and leafy, with no indications of blossoming on February 12. On this date these plants had already produced many more leaves than the control plants.

It will be evident that these data dealing with an artificially length-ened illumination period obtained by means of the electric light greatly strengthen the results of the experiments secured during the previous summer by artificially shortening the natural period of illumination through the use of dark houses. The results with the Maryland Mam-moth variety of tobacco, the several soybean varieties in question, and the radish are of special significance since they were obtained by meth-ods the direct converse of those used during the summer. Although the intensity of the electric light was undoubtedly far below that of normal sunlight, it was sufficient to initiate or to suppress the reproductive and vegetative activities of these three species as did the long days of the summer time. With respect to the ever-blooming behavior of certain of the plants under study, the results obtained indicate that this behavior is likely to follow when an approximately constant daily illumination period of a duration favorable to both growth and reproduction is main-tained for a sufficient length of time. It thus seems possible that the comparatively uniform length of day prevailing in the Tropics accounts for the particular abundance of ever-bloomers in that region.

IS THE RESPONSE TO DIFFERENCES IN THE LENGTH OF DAY A PRINCIPLE OF GENERAL APPLICABILITY IN BIOLOGY?

Experience has abundantly demonstrated the fact that the biologist who attempts to draw sweeping generalizations regarding responses of plants or animals as a whole to conditions of the environment is in seri-ous danger of going astray, even though his observations be based on the behavior of relatively large numbers of species. With this fact clearly in mind, the following suggestions are put forward tentatively but as pos-sibly being of sufficient interest to justify careful consideration on the part of biologists especially concerned in the fields touched upon. It has been clearly brought out in this paper that for a number of plant species the appropriate length of day acts, not merely as an accelerative, but rather as an initiative influence in bringing into expression the plant's potential capacity for sexual reproduction. Perhaps, as an equally satis-factory way of expressing the fact, it may be said that the length of the day exercises a truly determinative influence on plant growth as be-tween the purely vegetative and the (sexually) reproductive forms of development. The response to length of day may be expected to hold for other species, although it would be premature at present to assert that all higher plants will be found to respond to this factor.

One is naturally inclined to inquire whether, also, the length of day is a controlling factor in sexual reproduction among the lower forms of plant life. The observed behavior of some of these lower forms certainly sug-gests that they come under the influence of the seasonal range in length of day. A single instance will suffice to illustrate the parallelism existing between the vegetative and the reproductive periods of activity, on the one hand, and the periodical change in the length of the day, on the other. Reference is made to the work of Lewis (*14*), in which it is shown that in certain species of red Algae there is a definite seasonal periodicity in the appearance of sexual and asexual forms. In brief, the July growth of these species consists primarily of tetrasporic or asexual individuals, while through August the growth is characterized by a predominance of sexual plants produced from the tetraspores of the July crop of plants. The carpospores of autumn become sporelings which persist through the winter and give rise to the tetrasporic plants of the early summer period. Should it be true that lower plants respond to differences in length of day as do some of the higher species it may be expected that various relationships between annual and perennial forms, differences in sensibility to relatively long and short days, and other facts which have been shown to apply to these higher species would likewise hold true for lower organisms. It is possible, even, that the seasonal activities of some of the parasitic microorganisms are the result of response to changes in day length.

As to animal life nothing definite can be said, but it may be found eventually that the animal organism is capable of responding to the stimulus of certain day lengths. It has occurred to the writers that possibly the migration of birds furnishes an interesting illustration of this response. Direct response to a stimulus of this character would seem to be more nearly in line with modern teachings of biology than are theories which make it necessary to assume the operation of instinct or volition in some form as explaining the phenomena in question.

CONCLUSION

The results of the experiments which have been presented in this paper seem to make it plain that of the various factors of the environment which affect plant life the length of the day is unique in its action on sexual reproduction. Except under such extreme ranges as would be totally destructive or at least highly injurious to the general well-being of the plant, the result of differences in temperature, water supply, and light intensity, so far as concerns sexual reproduction, appears to be, at most, merely an accelerating or a retarding effect, as the case may be, while the seasonal length of day may induce definite expression, initiating the reproductive processes or inhibiting them, depending on whether this length of day happens to be favorable or unfavorable to the particular species. In broad terms, this action of the length of day may be tentatively formulated in the following principle: Sexual reproduction can be attained by the plant only when it is exposed to a specifically favorable length of day (the requirements in this particular varying widely with the species and variety), and exposure to a length of day unfavorable to reproduction but favorable to growth tends to produce gigantism or indefinite continuation of vegetative development, while exposure to a length of day favorable alike to sexual reproduction and to vegetative development extends the period of sexual reproduction and tends to induce the "ever-bearing" type of fruiting.

The term *photoperiod* is suggested to designate the favorable length of day for each organism, and *photoperiodism* is suggested to designate the response of organism to the relative length of day and night.

SUMMARY

(1) The relative length of the day is a factor of the first importance in the growth and development of plants, particularly with respect to sexual reproduction.

(2) In a number of species studied it has been found that normally the plant can attain the flowering and fruiting stages only when the length of day falls within certain limits, and, consequently, these stages of development ordinarily are reached only during certain seasons of the year. In this particular, some species and varieties respond to relatively long days, while others respond to short days, and still others are capable of responding to all lengths of the day which prevail in the latitude of Washington where the tests were made.

(3) In the absence of the favorable length of day for bringing into expression the reproductive processes in certain species, vegetative development may continue more or less indefinitely, thus leading to the phenomenon of gigantism. On the other hand, under the influence of a suitable length of day, precocious flowering and fruiting may be induced. Thus, certain varieties or species may act as early or late maturing, depending simply on the length of day to which they happen to be exposed.

(4) Several species, when exposed to a length of day distinctly favorable to both growth and sexual reproduction, have shown a tendency to assume the "ever-blooming" or "ever-bearing" type of development — that is, the two processes of growth and reproduction have tended to proceed hand in hand for an indefinite period.

(5) The relationships existing between annuals, biennials, and perennials, as such, are dependent in large measure on responses to the prevailing seasonal range in length of day. In many species the annual cycle of events is governed primarily by the seasonal change in length of day, and the retarding or more or less injurious and destructive effects of winter temperatures are largely incidental rather than fundamental. Hence, by artificial regulation of the length of the daily exposure to light it has been found that in certain species the normal yearly cycle of the plant's activities can be greatly shortened in point of time, or, on the other hand, it may be lengthened almost indefinitely. In certain cases, annuals may complete two cycles of alternate vegetative and reproductive activity in a single season under the influence of a suitable length of the daily exposure to light. Similarly, under certain light exposures some annuals behave like nonflowering perennials.

(6) In all species thus far studied, the rate of growth is directly proportional to the length of the daily exposure to light.

(7) Although the length of the daily exposure to light may exert a controlling influence on the attainment of the reproductive stage, experiments reported in this paper indicate that light intensity, within the range from full normal sunlight to a third or a fourth of the normal, and even much less, is not a factor of importance. It follows that the total quantity of solar radiation received by the plant daily during the summer season, within the range above indicated, is of little importance directly so far as concerns the attainment of the flowering stage.

(8) In extensive tests with soybeans, variations in the water supply ranging from optimum to a condition of drought sufficient to induce temporary wilting daily and to cause severe stunting of the plants were entirely without effect on the date of flowering, although in some cases drought seemed to hasten somewhat the final maturation of the seed. Similarly, differences in light intensity, in combination with differences in water supply, failed to change the date of flowering in soybeans.

(9) The seasonal range in the length of the day is an important factor in the natural distribution of plants.

(10) The interrelationships between the length of day and the prevailing temperatures of the winter season largely control successful reproduction in many species and their ability to survive in given regions.

(11) The relation between the length of the day and the time of flowering becomes of great importance in crop yields in many instances and in such cases brings to the forefront the necessity for seeding at the proper time.

REFERENCES AND NOTES

* Abridged.

[1] The authors [W. W. Garner, Physiologist in charge, and H. A. Allard, Physiologist] desire to acknowledge their indebtedness to Prof. C. V. Piper, in charge of Forage Crop Investigations, Bureau of Plant Industry, for helpful suggestions, to Mr. W. J. Morse, of the office of Forage Crop Investigations, Bureau of Plant Industry, for seed of certain varieties of soybeans and information as to the characteristics of these varieties, to Dr. D. N. Shoemaker, of the Office of Horticultural and Pomological Investigations, Bureau of Plant Industry, for similar assistance as to certain varieties of ordinary beans, and to Prof. H. H. Kimball, of the Weather Bureau, United States Department of Agriculture, for important data relating to the shading effects of nettings of different mesh used in these investigations.

[2] Throughout this paper the term "gigantism" is used to signify a tendency toward more or less indefinite vegetative activity manifested by plants under certain favorable environmental conditions. Though an inherited characteristic, it may come into expression only under definite conditions of environment; and the present investigation seems to make it clear that the length of the daily light exposure is the controlling factor.

[3] Horticultural variety.

[4] In this connection the tables showing the time of sunrise and sunset at 10-day intervals through the year for various latitudes in North America, as given in *Smithsonian Contributions to Knowledge*, **21**, 114–19 (1876), will be found very convenient for reference.

1. Cleveland Abbe, A First Report on the Relations between Climates and Crops, *U.S. Dept. Agr. Weather Bur. Bul.* 36 (1905), 386 pp. Catalogue of periodicals and authors referred to . . . pp. 364–75.

2. H. A. Allard, Gigantism in *Nicotiana Tabacum* and Its Alternative Inheritance, in *Amer. Nat.* **53**, no. 626, 218–33 (1919). Literature cited, p. 233.

3. L. H. Bailey, Some Preliminary Studies of the Influence of the Electric Arc Light upon Greenhouse Plants, *N.Y. Cornell Agr. Exp. Sta. Bul.* **30**, 83–122 (1891), 13 fig., 2 pl.

4. _____, Second Report upon Electrohorticulture, *N.Y. Cornell Agr. Exp. Sta. Bul.* **42**, 133–46 (1892), illus.

5. _____, Greenhouse Notes for 1892–93. I. Third Report upon Electrohorticulture, *N.Y. Cornell Agr. Exp. Sta. Bul.* **55**, 147–57 (1893), 2 pl.

6. Gaston Bonnier, Influence de la Lumière Électrique Continue sur la Forme et la Structure des Plantes, in *Rev. Gen. Bot.*, t. 7, no. 78, 241–57 (1895); no. 79, 289–306; no. 80, 332–42; no. 82, 409–19. pl. 6–15.

7. L. C. Corbett, A Study of the Effect of Incandescent Gas Light on Plant Growth, *W. Va. Agr. Exp. Sta. Bul.* **62**, 77–110 (1899), pl. 1–9.

8. Camille Flammarion, Physical and Meteorological Researches, Principally on Solar Rays, Made at the Station of Agricultural Climatology at the Observatory of Juvisy, in *Exp. Sta. Rec.* **10**, no. 2, 103–14 (1898?), 4 fig., 2 col. pl.

9. W. W. Garner, H. A. Allard, C. L. Foubert, Oil Content of Seeds as Affected by the Nutrition of the Plant, in *Jour. Agr. Research* **3**, no. 3, 227–49 (1914). Literature cited, p. 249.

10. Ch. Girou de Buzareingues, Suite des Expériences sur la Génération des Plantes, in *Ann. Sci. Nat.* t. 24, 138–47 (1831).

11. H. Hoffman, Thermische Vegetationsconstanten; Sonnen- und Schattentemperaturen, in *Ztschr. Österr. Gesell. Met.*, Bd. 17, 121–31 (1882).

12. _____, Phänologische Studien, in *Met. Ztschr., Jahrg. 3 (Ztschr. Österr. Gesell. Met., Bd.* **21**), 113–20 (1886), pl. 6.

13. C. F. Kinman and T. B. McClelland, Experiments on the Supposed Deterioration of Varieties of Vegetables in Porto Rico, with Suggestions for Seed Preservation, *Porto Rico Agr. Exp. Sta. Bul.* **20** (1916), 30 pp., tab., diagr.

14. I. F. Lewis, The Seasonal Life Cycle of Some Red Algae at Woods Hole, in *Plant World* **17**, no. 2, 31–35 (1914).

15. Carl Linsser, Die Periodischen Erscheinungen des Pflanzenlebens in Ihrem Verhaltniss zu den Wärmeerscheinungen, in *Mém. Acad. Imp. Sci. St. Petersb.*, s. 7, t. 11, no. 7 (1867), 44 pp.

16. _____, Untersuchungen über die Periodischen Lebenserscheinungen der Pflanzen. Zweite Abhandlung, in *Mém. Acad. Imp. Sci. St. Petersb.*, s. 7, t. 13, no. 8 (1869), 87 pp.

17. J. A. Lodewijks, Jr., Erblichkeitsversuche mit Tabak, in *Ztschr. Induk Abstam. u. Vereb.*, Bd. 5, Heft 2/3, pp. 139–72 (1911); Heft 4/5, pp. 285–323, illus. Literaturverzeichnis, pp. 171–72, 322–23.

18. Daniel Trembly MacDougal, The Influence of Light and Darkness Upon Growth and Development, *Mem. N.Y. Bot. Gard.* **2** (1903), 319 pp., illus.

19. Charles A. Mooers, The Soy Bean. A Comparison with the Cowpea, *Tenn. Agr. Exp. Sta. Bul.* **82**, 75–104 (1908), illus.

20. William F. Rane, Electrohorticulture with the Incandescent Lamp, *W. Va. Agr. Exp. Sta. Bul.* 37 (1894), 27 pp., illus.

21. R. A. F. de Reaumur, Observations du Thermometre, Faites à Paris Pendant l'Année M.DCCXXXV. Comparées avec Celles qui ont Été Faites sous la Ligne, à l'Isle de France, à Alger, et en Quelques-unes de nos Isles de l'Amérique, in *Hist. Acad. Roy. Sci. [Paris], Mém. Math. & Phys., ann.* 1735, pp. 545–76 (1738).

22. Howard S. Reed, Certain Relationships Between the Flowers and Fruits of the Lemon, in *Jour. Agr. Research* 17, no. 4, 153–65 (1919), 1 fig.

23. Schübeler, The Effects of Uninterrupted Sunlight on Plants (Abstract), in *Nature* 21, 311–12 (1880), Original article (Studier over Klimatets Indflydelse paa Plantelivet) in *Naturen* Aarg. 3, no. 6, 81–89; no. 8, 113–23 (1879), illus.

24. J. Tournois, Anomalies Florales du Houblon Japonais et Chanvre Déterminées par des Semis Hâtifs, in *Compt. Rend. Acad. Sci.* [Paris], t. 153, no. 21, 1017–1020 (1911).

25. ――――, Influence de la Lumiére sur la Floraison du Houblon Japonais et du Chanvre, in *Compt. Rend. Acad. Sci.* [Paris], t. 155, no. 4, 297–300 (1912).

26. J. Wiesner, Der Lichtgenuss der Pflanzen . . . vii, Leipzig (1907), 322 pp., illus.

Concerning the Hormonal Nature of Plant Development Processes

M. Ch. Čajlachjan

The blossoming and fruit bearing of plants is bound with physiological processes proceeding in the vegetative tissues long before the formation of buds and flowers begin. The inception of these processes depends on the surrounding conditions under which the plant is reared. The works of Garner and Allard (1, 2) have shown how powerful is the influence yielded by the duration of the daylight illumination on the formative processes, the reaction of the plant to this factor being termed photoperiodism.

Determination of the processes which form the basis of the phenomenon of photoperiodism should also give a reply to the questions linked with the onset of flowering and fruit bearing of the plant, i.e., its sexual development. This has induced us to raise the problem of investigating the general mechanism of the photoperiodic reaction. The succession in which these problems are to be solved appeared to us as follows:

1. Ascertainment of the limit of influence of duration of daylight illumination in time (age of plant).

2. Ascertainment of the bounds of the influence of this factor in space (area of perception).

3. Ascertainment of the nature of the processes which arise in the vegetative tissues at the moment photoperiodical influence is first applied.

Beginning from 1932 we conducted the

From *Comptes Rendus (Doklady) de l'Académie des Sciences de l'USSR* **16**, 227–30 (1937).

study of these questions in the Institute of Plant Physiology of the Academy of Sciences of the USSR.

First experiments in the investigation of the part played by the leaves and growing points during photoperiodic reaction perception were conducted by us in Puskin (formerly Detskoe Selo) at the Department of Plant Physiology of the All Union Institute of Plant Industry. In 1933 these experiments as well as several others were conducted in Leningrad on the Kameni Ostrov at the greenhouse of the Chair of Agrobotanics of the Institute of Spinning Cultures. Experiments of the determination the mechanism of photoperiodic reaction in 1934 were conducted in the hothouse of the Institute of Plant Physiology in Leningrad. In connection with the removal of the Academy of Sciences to Moscow, all this work was transferred to this city in 1935 and 1936, where a hothouse, greenhouse, and a special-photoperiodic hut for the study of plant photoperiodism was erected on the territory of the Institute.

Various plants were taken as objects for investigation, mainly plants of extreme types in their nature of photoperiodic reaction. The greater part of our experiments were conducted on *Chrysanthemum indicum* and *Perillo nankinensis*.

The results of this experimental work, conducted over a period of five years, have been partly published in Doklady of the Academy of Sciences of the USSR in 1933–1937 (3–9). Certain general conclusions may now be drawn regarding this work, which, in brief, are as follows:

1. Beginning with the appearance of the first green leaf, subject to the presence of the corresponding complex of conditions, the plant, under any age, becomes perceptible to the influence of the light (photoperiodic) factor accelerating sexual development. Prior to the appearance of the first green leaf the germinating seed is not perceptible to this influence.

2. Influence of the light factor, causing the sexual process or accelerating its onset is strictly localized in separate parts of the plants. This localization depends on the presence, within the limits of influence of the factor, of sections of the plant embracing both leaves and shoots with growing points.

3. Processes caused by change of duration of daylight illumination and leading to sex maturity of the plant (flowering and fruit formation) proceed in the leaf tissues. Formative processes proceeding in the points (zones) of growth, represent secondary changes determined by the functional activity of the leaves. The light factor influence received by the leaves is transferred to the growth points by material carriers moving from the leaves along the stalk and shaping the formation of shoots in the direction of sexual development. The transfer of this influence proceeds likewise under condition of a substantial distance between the leaves and growth points.

4. The processes of sexual development of the plant (flowering and

fruit bearing) arise and proceed in the vegetative tissues independently of the rate of growth of the plant and are specific in their nature. Flowering of the plant is determined neither by accumulation of constructive substances nor by shifting in regard to organic matter (carbohydrates) towards mineral (nitrogenous) compounds, as may be understood according to the theory of Klebs. Neither is it dependent upon changes in concentration of growth hormones — auxines, determined according to Vent's method.

5. Just as the regulative functions in the growth processes belong to the growth hormones, the auxines, similarly, in the processes of development does this role belong to a special hormone of flowering — the flower-forming hormone. Flowering of the plant and formation of seeds sets in as the result of the formation in the leaves and transfer to the growth points of a sufficient quantity of flower-forming hormone. It is quite possible that flowering of the plant arises as a result of activity of several flowering hormones which jointly determine this complicated and multiform process.

6. Arising in the leaves, the flowering hormone moves towards the points of growth in all possible directions: up, down or horizontally. The phenomenon of polarity is not applicable to the movement and distribution of the flowering hormone. The basic condition under which this movement arises is the presence of the system: leaves — growth points. Velocity of movement of the flowering hormone from the tip of the plant to the base or vice versa is the same (vide Figs. 1 and 2).

7. Movement of the flowering hormone downwards, from the tip of the plant to the base, in the stalk proceeds along the bark. No movement of the hormone proceeds along the wood. Girdling of plants as a means of accelerating fruit bearing of perennials, has as its basis not only accumulation of organic substances, carbohydrates, due to cessation of their drainage but also the increase of concentration of flowering hormone retained by girdling.

8. Upon transplantation of parts of the plant, the flowering hormone, together with the nutritive substances moves from the leaves of the stock to the growth points of the scion. This movement proceeds both in cases where hormone accumulation in the stock is caused after transplantation of a vegetative grafting and where a sufficient quantity of hormone is accumulated in the stock prior to grafting. Upon the transfer of the flowering hormone from the stock to the scion all the leaves should be left on the stock and all shoots with growth points should be stripped from it.

By this method of transplantation may be obtained accelerated flowering of perennial and annual plants not flowering under the given natural conditions.

9. The flowering hormone is not specific in its action (for individual kindred species), and possesses a general nature for different plants.

FIGURE 1. Flowering of chrysanthemum shoots in connection with the influence of a shortened 10-hour day on the leaves irrespective of their position on the plant. The leaves are covered with a light-proof hood. (Photographed October 11, 1936.)

FIGURE 2. Same as Figure 1. Hood removed. Control plants in which the leaves were exposed to a long day (natural and, beginning from September 10, plus supplementary electrical illumination) possess vegetative shoots without buds and flowers. (Photographed October 11, 1936.)

The flowering hormone is not specific for long and short day plants but possesses a general nature for both one and the other. Thus, the fact that some plants flower and bear fruit quicker (or only) under a long day and others under a short day is explained not by the presence of several, or, at least two types of hormone, but by the ability of various plants to form one and the same hormone of flowering under definite conditions of light.

10. Substances with special functions of retarding or delaying sexual development in the plant are not formed. Photoperiodic after-effect or induction represents a process of accumulation of flowering hormone immediately beginning its regulative influence, directing the plastic substances to formation of flowers. It would therefore be more correct to name this phenomenon photoperiodic charge or photoperiodic accumulation.

11. Inception of the flowering hormone in the leaves does not as yet predetermine the onset of sexual processes; a definite quantitative accumulation is first necessary in the leaves and then in the growth points for formation of the new organ — the flower.

Conversion of the fruit shoots into vegetative and vice versa proceeds as a result of inception of new growth points in the shoots which develop either in the fruit shoots in the event of a sufficient quantity of flowering hormone accumulating in their tissues or in the vegetative shoots if the flow of flowering hormone ceases.

12. Flowering hormone causes not only formation of flowers as sexual organs but also the subsequent processes leading to seed formation. The flowering hormone is therefore the sexual hormone of the plant. The sexual hormone in bisexual monoecious plants causes formation and functional activity of both male and female elements of the bisexual flowers. The formation in monosexual plants of male flowers probably depends on the male sexual hormone, and the formation of female flowers on the female sexual hormone.

The difference in the general structure and in individual aspects between the male and female plants, change of their sex, existence of juvenile forms, aging and "rejuvenation" of plants may be explained by the regulative activity of plant sexual hormones.

13. In reflecting the main function of the flowering hormone, clearly that of formation of flowers, we can term it for brevity's sake "florigen," meaning "flower-former."

14. Florigen occupies a special place in the regulative endocrine plant system. Its comparison with auxin (or rather with the established auxin group) shows that the basic regulative function, condition of formation, locality of formation and nature of distribution in the plant clearly distinguishes the hormone of flowering — florigen from the growth hormones — auxins.

Communicated by A. A. Richter, Member of the Academy, July 9, 1937

REFERENCES

1. W. W. Garner and H. A. Allard, *Journ. of Agricult. Research* **18**, 553–606 (1920).
2. _____, *ibid.* **23**, 871–920 (1923).
3. M. Ch. Čajlachjan, *Comptes Rend. (Doklady) de l'Acad. Sci. de L'USSR* **6**, 306–14 (1933).
4. _____, *ibid.* **I**, 1, 37–39 (1934).
5. _____, and Alexandrovskaja, *ibid.* **II**, 2, 161–66 (1935).
6. _____, *ibid.* **I**, 2, 85–89 (1936).
7. _____, *ibid.* **III**, 9, 443–47 (1936).
8. _____, *ibid.* **IV**, 2, 77–81 (1936).
9. _____ and Jarkovaja, *ibid.* **XV**, 4, 215–18 (1937).

Detection, Assay, and Preliminary Purification of the Pigment Controlling Photoresponsive Development of Plants

W. L. Butler
K. H. Norris
H. W. Siegelman
S. B. Hendricks

Agricultural Marketing Service and Agricultural Research Service, U.S. Department of Agriculture

Responses of plant materials to radiation indicate that flowering and many other aspects of development are controlled by a reversible photoreaction (1, 2) involving two forms of a pigment, with action maxima near 660 and 735 mμ. The photoreversible pigment can readily be changed from one to the other form, as indicated by response of the plant to irradiation in the region of the appropriate action maximum. Because the nature of the enzymatic action involved is still unknown, it appeared that direct observation of the pigment in the living material and an assay for its isolation would have to be based on spectrophotometric methods. The pigment should show a change in absorption at 655 and 735 mμ following conversion by radiation.

The location of the pigment and its concentration in specific cells are evidenced by the photoinduced formation of anthocyanin, which depends upon energy transfer from both forms of the excited pigment (3). The concentration based on a molar absorptivity of 1×10^5 is estimated to be the order of 10^{-6} molar in the most effective cells and probably about 10^{-7} molar in the average tissue (4). A spectrophotometer suitable for detecting this low concentration of the pigment in tissue must measure absorption of radiation with high sensitivity in dense light-scattering

Reprinted from *Proceedings of the National Academy of Sciences* 45, 1703–1708 (1959), by permission of Warren L. Butler and the National Academy of Sciences.

material. Such measurements cannot be made with commercial instruments.

Instrumentation. The presence of the photoreversible pigment in intact tissue has been demonstrated with a recording, single-beam spectrophotometer. This spectrophotometer (5) employs an end-window multiplier-type phototube placed directly behind the sample to collect a large fraction of the transmitted light. The sample is illuminated by monochromatic light from the exit slit of a double, prism monochromator. Spectral measurements can be made on light-scattering samples having optical densities between 0 and 6, with a sensitivity as high as 0.1 for full scale deflection. The noise level is equivalent to an optical density change of 0.002 for samples having an optical density less than 4.

Since this is a single-beam instrument the recorded curve includes the spectral response of the instrument in addition to the absorption characteristics of the sample. The system response is sufficiently reproducible that valid difference spectra can be obtained by subtracting one recorded curve from another. When the spectral curve is very steep in the region of interest, an electrical compensation can be applied to alter the slope of the curve. This is achieved with a potentiometer geared to the wavelength drum which supplies an additional signal to the Y-axis. The compensation merely alters the system response to make it easier to compute difference spectra.

A more useful instrument for assay of the pigment is one which measures directly the optical density difference between two fixed wavelengths. Such an instrument, which is a double beam, bichromatic spectrophotometer similar in principle to one developed by Chance (6), is shown in Figure 1. The close juxtaposition of the end-window, multiplier-type phototube (P) and the sample allows dense light-scattering samples to be used. The two monochromatic beams are obtained with wedge interference filters F_1 and F_2. The spectral purity of the beams is improved with auxiliary filters f_1 and f_2. The rotating chopper blades Ch_1 and Ch_2 cause the sample to be illuminated alternately with the two beams through the diffusing disk d. The phototube is synchronized with the chopper blades so that the measuring circuit records the optical-density difference $(O.D._{\lambda 1} - O.D._{\lambda 2})$. This instrument can be operated at an optical-density sensitivity as high as 0.05 for full-scale deflection, with a noise level of 0.0005.

The radiation source to change the state of the pigment was a focused beam from a 75 watt internal-reflection projection lamp with appropriate filters. The "red" source was a band in the region of 600 to 700 mμ and the "far-red" source in the region >700.

Detection of the Pigment in Living Plants. The first tissue selected for examination was cotyledons of turnip seedlings (*Brassica rapa* var. white globe purple top) grown in the dark in the presence of chloramphenicol. This selection was based on the marked capacity of such tissue to form anthocyanin in light (7) and on the low content of proto-

FIGURE 1. A differential spectrophotometer suitable for assay of the reversible pigment in living tissue or solution.

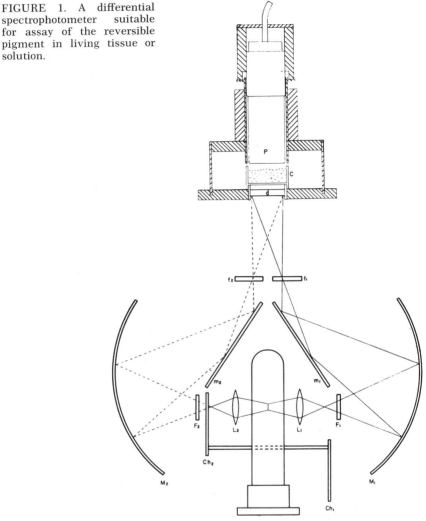

chlorophyll and chlorophyll which interfere with observations in the region of 670 mμ. The cotyledons were loosely pressed into the sample holder to a depth of about 1.5 cm and irradiated for about a minute with red radiation. This radiation converted any protochlorophyll present to chlorophyll and the pigment to the form with its absorption maximum near 735 mμ (later referred to as P_{735}). The curve of the optical densities of this tissue versus wavelength was measured in the 570 to 850 mμ region. The pigment was then converted to the form with the absorption maximum near 655 mμ (later referred to as P$_{655}$) by irradiation with far-red radiation for about a minute, and the optical density curve of the tissue was recorded again in the 570 and 850 mμ region.

The pigment was clearly evident by the optical density changes. Far-red radiation caused the optical density to decrease in the far-red region of the spectrum with a maximal change at 735 mμ and to increase in the red region with a maximal change at 655 mμ. Red radiation had the opposite effect.

A preliminary survey of etiolated parts of several seedling plants was then made and the shoots of 3-day-old maize seedlings were found to be particularly responsive. The shoots were cut and loosely pressed into a sample holder. A record from the spectrophotometer for a 1.5 cm thick sample of this material after irradiation with red and far-red radiation is shown in Figure 2. The difference spectrum is also plotted. It is evident that P$_{735}$ has an absorption maximum at 735 mμ and P$_{655}$ has an absorption maximum at 655 mμ. The reversibility between P$_{655}$ and P$_{735}$ by the action of red and far-red light can be repeatedly demonstrated. These results are in complete agreement with numerous action spectra (8) as also is the absorption in the region of 600 to 650 mμ.

The chlorophyll absorption near 672 mμ in Figure 2 is the result of the conversion of protochlorophyll by the initial irradiation with the red source. For a short period after the initial conversion, absorption in the red region of the spectrum changes because of a shift of the newly formed chlorophyll with an absorption maximum at about 680 mμ to a form with an absorption maximum at about 670 mμ (9). Subsequent shifts of the chlorophyll peaks are sufficiently slow as not to interfere with the assay for the photoreversible pigment. No resynthesis of protochlorophyll is evident in maize seedlings for about 2 hours after the initial irradiation. Thereafter, the assay for the pigment is complicated by the synthesis of protochlorophyll and its conversion to chlorophyll by red irradiation.

A sample of maize shoots examined on the differential spectrophotometer gave a $\Delta(\Delta\text{O.D.}) = (\text{O.D.}_{655} - \text{O.D.}_{735})$ far-red irradiated $- (\text{O.D.}_{655} - \text{O.D.}_{735})$ red irradiated $= 0.2$. The concentration of the pigment and the sensitivity of the instrument were such that the distribution of the pigment along a single shoot could be determined by limiting the sample to a 5 mm segment. Values of $\Delta(\Delta\text{O.D.})$ of 0.01 were observed with the coleoptile and 0.005 with the mesocotyl. Leaves of the maize seedlings were not responsive.

It was immediately evident from a preliminary survey of several tissues that the reversible pigment occurs at the maximum observed levels in shoots of several grasses irrespective of anthocyanin formation. Seemingly, the better guide is the responsiveness to etiolation of the shoots of gramineous plants which is displayed by the lengthening of internodes beneath the soil. Maize was selected as a suitable source for the pigment because the seed are readily available, the shoots are

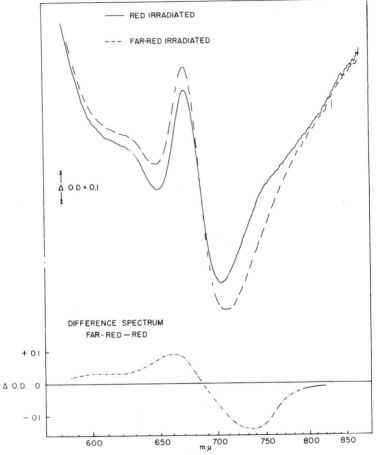

FIGURE 2. Recorded optical density curves from maize shoots in the 580 to 850 mμ region after red and far-red irradiations. The difference spectrum is shown.

large, and the pigment response is as great as with any tissue surveyed.

Separation of the Pigment. Initial stages of pigment purification were effected by straightforward methods of protein chemistry using the Δ(ΔO.D.) values for assay.

A 450 gram lot of 3-day-old seedling maize shoots grown in darkness at 27° of variety US-13 was run in a blender for 2 minutes with 450 ml of 0.1 M Na$_4$P$_2$O$_7$ buffer (pH 8.4) containing 0.01 M ascorbate and 0.01 M cysteine. The blended material was passed through cheesecloth and the filtrate was then centrifuged at 40,000 × g for 20 minutes. The supernatant was centrifuged at 140,000 × g for 120 minutes and the resulting supernatant was brought to 0.33 saturation with (NH$_4$)$_2$SO$_4$.

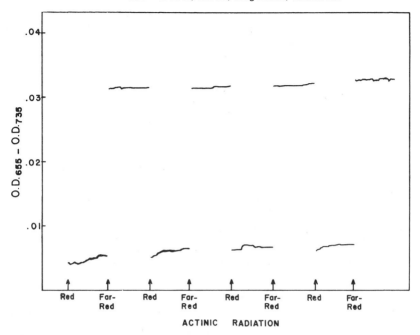

FIGURE 3. Photoreversible response to red and far-red radiation of a solution obtained from maize shoots.

The precipitate was stirred for 15 minutes. It was then removed and redissolved in 0.25 of the original volume of solution. All operations were performed at 2°. Results from one of five runs are shown in Table 1. Protein values in this table were determined by the biuret method. The precision of the $\Delta(\Delta O.D)$ values was $< 0.0005/cm$.

The pigment was retained upon dialysis at 2° against buffer at pH 8.4. The photoreversibility was retained for a period of at least two weeks upon holding solutions at $-15°$. It was lost upon heating to 50°.

TABLE 1

Purification from 450 Gm of Dark-grown Shoots of Seedling Maize for the Pigment Controlling Photoresponsive Development of Plants.

Fraction	Volume ml	Protein gm	$\Delta(\Delta OD)$ /cm	Purification factor
40,000 × g supernatant	590	6.25	0.004	1.0*
140,000 × g supernatant	550	3.85	0.004	1.6
$(NH_4)_2(SO_4)$ 0.0 to 0.33 saturation	135	3.02	0.012	6.0

Subject to some error from change in optical path-length by scattering.

A solution of the pigment gave the response shown in Figure 3 on the differential spectrophotometer. The reversibility of the pigment is also illustrated. In fact, it is necessary to lower the intensities of the analyzing light beams by about 100-fold, relative to the arrangement used for higher optical densities of unseparated plant material to prevent the beams from driving the reaction. This stage of purification brings the assay to the threshold of usual laboratory procedures. The presence of the pigment in a clear solution of the 0.33 $(NH_4)_2SO_4$ saturated precipitate has been detected by means of $\Delta(\Delta O.D.)$ values obtained from the four appropriate measurements on conventional spectrophotometers.

Discussion. Although many aspects of the nature of the pigment effective for control by light of plant development were found during the last seven years, attempts to separate it in several laboratories were unsuccessful and were usually left undescribed. This work supplies three needed elements for further progress: A source of the pigment, a method of assay, and a system for separation. There would seem to be no essential barrier to finding the nature of the enzymatic action of the pigment, P_{735}, which constitutes the limiting pacemaker (*10*) or "bottleneck" of control evident in plant development and to elaborating physiological and biochemical aspects of its action.

Summary. The photoreversible pigment controlling many aspects of plant development was observed in living tissue by direct spectrophotometry. The pigment was separated from the tissue by usual methods of protein chemistry using differential spectrophotometry for assay.

Communicated by S. B. Hendricks, October 1, 1959

REFERENCES

1. H. A. Borthwick, S. B. Hendricks, M. W. Parker, E. H. Toole, V. K. Toole, these *Proceedings* 38, 662–66 (1952).
2. H. A. Borthwick, S. B. Hendricks, M. W. Parker, these *Proceedings* 38, 929–34 (1952).
3. S. B. Hendricks and H. A. Borthwick, these *Proceedings* 45, 344–49 (1959).
4. S. B. Hendricks, H. A. Borthwick, R. J. Downs, these *Proceedings* 42, 19–25 (1956).
5. W. L. Butler and K. H. Norris, *Arch. Biochem. Biophys.,* in press.
6. B. Chance, *Rev. Sci. Instru.* 22, 634–38 (1951).
7. H. W. Siegelman and S. B. Hendricks, *Plant Physiol.* 32, 393–98 (1957).
8. S. B. Hendricks and H. A. Borthwick in *Aspects of Synthesis and Order in Growth,* D. Rudnick, Ed. (Princeton Univ. Press, Princeton, 1955), pp. 149–69.
9. K. Shibata, *J. Biochem.* (Japan) 44, 147–73 (1957).
10. H. A. Krebs and H. L. Kornberg, *Ergeb. der Physiologie* 49, 212–98 (1957).

Physiology of Insect Diapause. II. Interaction Between the Pupal Brain and Prothoracic Glands in the Metamorphosis of the Giant Silkworm, *Platysamia cecropia*

Carroll M. Williams[*]

The Biological Laboratories, Harvard University

In the Cecropia silkworm the progress of metamorphosis is interrupted as soon as the pupa is formed. There then intervenes a prolonged period of pupal diapause characterized by cessation of growth and differentiation. The mechanism that converts this cellular dormancy of diapause into the intense activity of adult formation was examined in a previous investigation performed on several species of giant silkworms (Williams, 1946b). For these species it was evident that diapause is under the control of the insect's brain. This control consists in a dependency of adult development on the action of a factor arising from the brain; the brain, in turn, is rendered competent to release this factor by exposure to low temperatures. It is the purpose of the present report to describe in greater detail the nature of the activating mechanism.

MATERIALS AND METHODS

The present communication is based on a total of 282 experiments performed, for the most part, on pupae of the giant silkworm, *Platysamia cecropia*. In a few experiments pupae of related genera were studied, including *Telea polyphemus*,

Reprinted from *The Biological Bulletin* 93, 89–98 (1947), by permission of the author and the Marine Biological Laboratory (Woods Hole), publisher.

Callosamia promethea, and *Samia walkeri.* The management of this array of animals was essentially identical to that described previously (Williams, 1946b).

DIRECT OR INDIRECT
ACTION OF THE BRAIN?

If the brain is removed from a diapausing pupa, the resulting insect never develops further and persists until death in permanent diapause — a matter of two years in some individuals. Yet at any time during this period adult development can be evoked by implanting into the brainless pupa a brain obtained from a previously chilled pupa.

It was a rational assumption that the development factor from the implanted brain had some direct action on the host tissues whereby the latter were converted from dormancy to activity. Yet the possibility remained that the brain's action might be indirect rather than direct, in a sense familiar to endocrinologists, as, for example, in the action of certain of the pituitary hormones on the uterus. Experiments have therefore been performed to test these two possibilities.

To this end techniques have been developed for subdividing individual pupae into fragments. In my experience division of these stout animals by means of ligatures has not met with success. Nor did gross slicing of the pupae into parts, as practiced by Crampton (1899), Hirschler (1903, 1904), and Hachlow (1931), produce viable preparations. A simple, successful technique that was ultimately developed will be described briefly.

ISOLATION OF PUPAL FRAGMENTS

The pupa, under continuous carbon dioxide anesthesia (Williams, 1946a), is placed on its side and the abdominal cuticle plus underlying hypodermis incised around the circumference of the abdomen at the level of the tips of the wingflaps. The incision is confined to the thin intersegmental membrane. Further maneuvers are designed to separate the abdomen from the anterior fragment without rupturing the midgut.[1] The intersegmental muscle masses, the heart, and the nerve cord are, in turn, cut through. The fat body and hindgut are then transected and the attachments of tracheae swept away from the walls of the midgut. The midgut plus nearly all of the Malpighian tubules may now be placed in the anterior fragment. Or by further dissection the midgut may be removed from the anterior fragment and discarded.

The cut surface of each of the two fragments is then sealed by melted paraffin to a circular, plastic cover slip which is provided with a centrally placed hole. Through the hole insect Ringer's is added to displace all air and the hole is finally plugged with melted paraffin.

It may be noted that these isolated abdomens (Fig. 3) consisted, in reality, of the terminal six abdominal segments, the anterior four abdominal segments being carried away with the anterior end (Fig. 1).

Transections at other levels were occasionally accomplished, but the one described proved to be most favorable. In certain instances abdomens were transected a second time to yield viable pairs of abdominal segments sandwiched between plastic slips.

The inner surface of the plastic slips is rapidly coated by a thin, transparent tissue formed by anastomoses developed between blood cells and, within about two weeks, by the outgrowth of epithelium and of tracheoles. At any time, however, one can operate inside the insect fragment by removing the paraffin plug from the centrally placed hole.

Of the entire series of isolated pupal parts, approximately two-thirds died within the first ten days after preparation. Death was invariably preceded by a darkening of the blood, a reaction which in itself seems to be toxic. The remaining preparations survived for considerable lengths of time, as indicated by the beating of the heart and by spontaneous movements of the abdominal segments. Isolated abdomens remained alive at 25°C for up to eight months. Anterior ends survived for not more than two or three months, however, unless Ringer's solution was occasionally added to compensate for loss of water by evaporation.

BRAIN IMPLANTATIONS
INTO PUPAL FRAGMENTS

Brainless diapausing pupae were transected at the level of the wing-tips to obtain ten pairs of viable anterior and posterior halves. Into each of these subdivisions a chilled Cecropia brain was then implanted (Figs. 1 and 3). Each anterior fragment proceeded to develop normally into the corresponding anterior end of a lively adult moth, the cut surface being closed by scaleless, regenerate, "chitinized" epithelium (Fig. 2). The isolated abdomens, to the contrary, remained undeveloped after brain implantation, although they continued to live for an average of three months.

With slight variations in technique these findings have been confirmed during the past three years on a total of 60 additional viable preparations. As many as six chilled brains have been implanted into a single abdomen without inducing development, even though some of these abdomens survived as long as eight months thereafter.

It is therefore apparent that anterior and posterior fragments respond differently to brain implantation. This difference in response might be explained if the anterior fragment possessed a second developmental center that was lacking in the posterior fragment. To test this possibility the level of transection was varied.

TRANSECTIONS OF PUPAE
AT VARIOUS LEVELS

Brainless, diapausing pupae were transected at various levels and the developmental capacity of the posterior fragments tested by implanting a chilled brain. The results of these experiments confirmed the findings

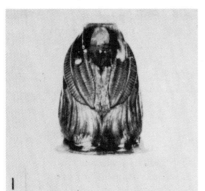

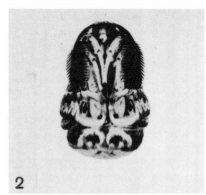

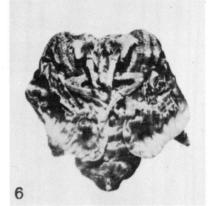

(Approximately life size)

of previous investigators that a "differentiation center" was present in the region of the thorax of lepidopterous pupae (Hachlow, 1931; Bodenstein, 1938; Bounhiol, 1938). Thus, abdomens in continuity with a pupal thorax invariably developed when a chilled brain was implanted. In contrast, similar treatment failed to evoke development of abdomens separated from the entire thorax. The critical level seemed to lie in the region of the mesothorax, for, after transection at this point, brain implantation induced development only after a long latent period of about six months (Figs. 5 and 6).

GRAFTING EXPERIMENTS
ON ISOLATED ABDOMENS

The importance of this anterior differentiation center was further revealed in experiments in which isolated abdomens were grafted to brainless, diapausing pupae (Figs. 7, 9, and 11) or to the anterior fragment of brainless, diapausing pupae (Fig. 12). In such combinations, the host and the graft grew together to establish tissue continuity, but did not develop further. This continuity was developed even when plastic tubes, as long as 3 cm, were interposed between the two parts (Figs. 11 and 12).

Now, when a brain from a chilled Cecropia pupa was implanted into either host or graft, diapause was terminated and the entire preparation developed into the fully formed, corresponding parts of the adult (Figs. 8 and 10).

IMPLANTATION OF
PROTHORACIC GLANDS

The evidence, up to this point, indicates that adult development after pupal diapause requires a factor from the brain plus some additional factor from the thorax. An extensive series of experiments was then performed in which a chilled brain plus various thoracic organs were implanted into isolated abdomens.

PLATE 1.

FIGURE 1. Anterior fragment of a brainless, diapausing pupa.
FIGURE 2. Fragment in Figure 1, after adult formation. Development was evoked by implanting a previously chilled brain.
FIGURE 3. Posterior fragment of a diapausing pupa.
FIGURE 4. Fragment in Figure 3, after adult formation. Development was evoked by implanting a previously chilled brain plus two pairs of diapausing prothoracic glands.
FIGURE 5. Posterior fragment of a diapausing pupa, showing critical level of section that includes the meso- and metathorax.
FIGURE 6. Fragment in Figure 5, after adult formation. Development was evoked by implanting a previously chilled brain. Note the complete development of those parts of the antennae, legs, and wings that were present in the fragment.

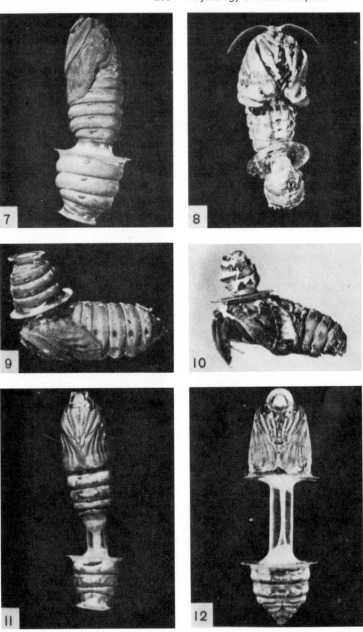

(Approximately life size)

This search was vastly aided by the publication of Fukuda's paper in 1941. In this communication Fukuda describes an endocrine activity of the "prothoracic glands" in evoking development of ligatured pupal abdomens of the commercial silkworm, *Bombyx mori*.

The great significance of the prothoracic glands was confirmed. Thus, isolated abdomens of diapausing Cecropia pupae developed readily when provided with a chilled brain plus two pairs of prothoracic glands.[2] The pupal cuticle became crisp and was delaminated and the abdomens appeared as the lively, corresponding segments of the adult, the cut surface being closed by scaleless, regenerate, "chitinized" epithelium (Fig. 4). Development wás complete externally and internally and, in the case of female abdomens, the eggs were matured. Similarly, abdomens isolated from chilled pupae after return to room temperature required both a chilled brain and prothoracic glands for the initiation of adult development.

In these experiments it was found that the prothoracic glands as well as the brain show a lack of species — or genus — specificity, for both of these organs remain effective when interchanged between *Platysamia cecropia* and *Telea polyphemus*.

In contrast to the results of Fukuda (1941), who studied a species without pupal diapause, no development of isolated abdomens occurred when prothoracic glands were implanted in the absence of a chilled brain.

FURTHER EXPERIMENTS ON
ISOLATED PUPAL ABDOMENS

From a series of six isolated abdomens of diapausing Cecropia pupae there were further removed the gonads, the entire digestive tract, the

---

PLATE 2.

FIGURE 7. Posterior fragment of a diapausing pupa joined directly to the tip of a brainless, diapausing pupa.

FIGURE 8. Preparation in Figure 7, after adult formation of host and graft. Development was evoked by implanting a previously chilled brain into the host. Note the regenerate tissue passing through the hole in the plastic slip to connect the two parts.

FIGURE 9. Posterior fragment of a diapausing pupa joined directly to the thoracic tergum of a brainless, diapausing pupa.

FIGURE 10. Preparation in Figure 9, after adult formation of host and graft. Development was evoked by implanting a previously chilled brain into the tip of the graft.

FIGURE 11. Posterior fragment of a diapausing pupa joined to a brainless, diapausing pupa by means of a short, square, plastic tube. Note the tube of regenerate tissue traversing the plastic tube's lumen. In order to follow the onset and progress of development, plastic windows have been placed at each end of the preparation.

FIGURE 12. Posterior fragment of a diapausing pupa joined to an anterior fragment of a brainless, diapausing pupa by means of a long, plastic tube. Note the tube of regenerate tissue within the plastic tube.

Malpighian tubules (with the exception of a few loose fragments), and the entire central nervous system, including the residual chain of five ganglia and connectives. Three of these preparations survived, the heart continuing to beat. After the implantation of a chilled brain plus prothoracic glands, two of the abdomens developed into flaccid, but fully mature adult abdomens.

DISCUSSION

It is evident from these experiments that the termination of pupal diapause requires a minimum of two factors, one from the brain and the other from the prothoracic glands. The easiest way to render these organs functional is to expose the diapausing pupa to low temperatures and then return it to room temperature. As has been shown previously, the effectiveness of chilling in terminating dormancy can be explained in terms of an action of low temperature on the brain, whereby the latter is made competent to release its developmental factor (Williams, 1946b). Manifestly, the prothoracic glands do not require similar exposure to cold, for they are promptly activated when a chilled brain is implanted into a diapausing pupa.

From these observations it may be concluded that the brain exerts a controlling action on the prothoracic glands. Subsequent experiments have confirmed this hypothesis consistently. Thus to induce the development of isolated pupal abdomens, it is necessary that the implanted brain be obtained from a previously chilled pupa. This is not the case in regard to the implants of prothoracic glands, for these organs are equally effective when obtained from diapausing pupae. The functional failure of the prothoracic glands at the outset of diapause seems therefore to result from a primary failure of the brain in releasing its factor.

The mechanism that terminates diapause must ultimately supply the dormant tissues with something necessary for cellular growth and differentiation. In respect to this process the experimental results may be interpreted from two points of view. On the one hand, the brain factor may be conceived as having sole action on the prothoracic glands and the prothoracic gland factor, in turn, as having specific effect on the tissues of the body in general. On the other hand, the tissues may require interaction with both factors, the first factor serving to condition the tissues for reaction with the second.

Although the evidence at hand does not suffice to exclude either interpretation,[3] it seems likely that the factor from the prothoracic glands has ultimate action on the dormant tissues to convert them to activity. Thus, we have noted previously that adult formation becomes independent of brain action as soon as the earliest sign of adult development is evident (Williams, 1946b). However, for some days thereafter, the animal continues to require further function of its prothoracic glands, for if the abdomen is isolated during this period, it ceases to develop. When tested in this fashion, adult development shows a dependency on the protho-

FIGURE 13. Diagrammatic interpretation of experimental results when a chilled brain is implanted into the tip of the graft in preparations such as Figure 11. Development begins first in the anterior end of the pupa, containing the prothoracic glands. For explanation, see text.

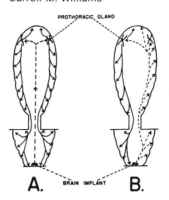

racic glands until a critical stage, signalled by the initiation of eye pigmentation.

Further evidence favoring the view that the factor from prothoracic glands has ultimate action on the tissues has been derived from the experiments, described above, in which isolated abdomens were grafted to brainless, diapausing pupae (Figs. 7 and 9). When development was evoked by implanting a chilled brain *into the tip of the graft,* the brainless pupa, containing the prothoracic glands, was observed to initiate development one day in advance of the abdomen, containing the brain. This difference in time can be magnified to three days or longer by interposing a plastic tube between host and graft (Fig. 11). In such preparations the final organ to initiate development was the imaginal disc of the graft's genitalia, notwithstanding the fact that this lay alongside the implanted brain that had touched off the whole process.

In terms of this type of preparation we may finally summarize our present information diagrammatically, as indicated in Figure 13. In Figure 13*a,* the brain factor is viewed as activating the prothoracic glands and the prothoracic glands as activating the tissues. In Figure 13*b,* the brain factor is conceived to act on all the bodily tissues to prepare them for final reaction with the factor from the prothoracic glands. In either case, the brain is the organ of primary control, but this control, at least in part, is exercised by an indirect mechanism.

SUMMARY

1. The mechanism that initiates adult development after pupal diapause has been studied in a total of 282 experiments, supplementary to those reported previously.

2. Brainless, diapausing pupae were divided transversely and the developmental capacities of anterior and posterior fragments tested and compared.

3. Implantation of a previously chilled brain sufficed to terminate the dormancy of anterior fragments.

4. Isolated abdomens, to the contrary, remained undeveloped after brain implantation. Yet such abdomens, even without implantation, could be induced to develop by grafting them to developing anterior fragments. Manifestly, the abdomens required for development an additional factor normally produced in the anterior end of the pupa.

5. By transections at various levels the source of this additional factor was found to be the thorax.

6. A testing of various thoracic organs revealed the effectiveness of the "prothoracic glands." Thus, implantation of a chilled brain plus prothoracic glands induced the complete adult development of isolated abdomens. In this effect the prothoracic glands as well as the brain showed a lack of species — or genus — specificity.

7. The termination of diapause requires in these species the action of a minimum of two factors, one arising from the brain and the other from the prothoracic glands. The brain factor is necessary for the activation of the prothoracic glands.

8. The factor from the prothoracic glands, most probably, has ultimate action on the tissues in terminating diapause.

9. The brain is the organ of primary control over diapause in the species studied, but this control, at least in part, is exercised by an indirect mechanism.

REFERENCES AND NOTES

[*] The assistance of the Society of Fellows, Harvard University, and the Lalor Foundation, Wilmington, Delaware, is gratefully acknowledged.

[1] Rupture of the midgut floods the body cavity with a dark green fluid that contains a good deal of particulate matter and shows a broad, dense absorption band centering at 670 mμ. The fluid is apparently non-toxic, but the particulate matter is frequently drawn into the cut end of the heart. Within the heart it then acts as embolus to occlude the aorta at its narrowest portion just behind the brain. Such animals usually fail to survive.

[2] Due to the numerous ramifications of the pupal prothoracic glands in the pro- and mesothorax, it was usually impossible to remove these organs in their entirety. For this reason two pairs were usually implanted into each isolated abdomen. This proved to be an important detail, for a single pair of the incomplete glands did not generally suffice to produce development after brain implantation. For a description of the prothoracic glands in *Platysamia cecropia* see Williams, 1948.

[3] Since this paper went to press, proof has been obtained of the validity of the first interpretation (see Fig. 13a).

D. Bodenstein, Untersuchungen zum Metamorphoseproblem. II. Entwicklungs-relationen in verschmolzenen Puppenteilen, *Arch. f. Entwmech. d. Organ.* **137**, 636–60 (1938).

J. Bounhiol, Recherches expérimentales sur le déterminisme de la métamorphose chez les Lépidoptéres, *Bull. Biol. de France et de Belgique, suppl.* **24**, 1–199 (1938).

H. E. Crampton, An experimental study upon Lepidoptera, *Arch. f. Entwmech. d. Organ.* **9**, 293–318 (1899).

S. Fukuda, Role of the prothoracic gland in differentiation of the imaginal characters in the silkworm pupa, *Annot. Zool. Japan.* **20**, 9–13 (1941).

V. Hachlow, Zur Entwicklungsmechanik der Schmetterlinge, *Arch. f. Entwmech. d. Organ.* **125**, 26–49 (1931).

J. Hirschler, Studien über Regenerationsvorgänge bei Lepidopterenpuppen, *Anat. Anz.* **23**, 612–27 (1903).

————, Weitere Regenerationsstudien an Lepidopterenpuppen (Regeneration des vorderen Körperendes), *Anat. Anz.* **25**, 417–35 (1904).

C. M. Williams, Continuous anesthesia for insects, *Science* **103**, 57 (1946a).

————, Physiology of insect diapause: The role of the brain in the production and termination of pupal dormancy in the giant silkworm, *Platysamia cecropia, Biol. Bull.* **90**, 234–43 (1946b).

————, Structure and function of the prothoracic gland in the metamorphosis of the Cecropia silkworm (1948), in preparation.

Studies on the Biology of Connective Tissues: Remodelling of Collagen in Metamorphosis*

Jerome Gross

Because of the rapid increase in our knowledge concerning collagen (*6, 7, 8, 9, 10, 16, 20, 22*), it has been possible in the last few years to explore in a more pointed and knowledgeable way several experimental diseases involving this protein, and the processes of normal remodelling of connective tissues during growth and development. Thus, we are gradually coming back to the whole animal with the advantage of fundamental knowledge at several levels and with more firmly based ideas as to how the tissue components are manipulated *in vivo*.

Amphibian metamorphosis, a process in which radical remodelling of connective tissues occurs under the influence of a hormone, currently commands our major interest. Since collagen is a very good subject for study of processes of organization of tissue structure and because the phenomena of regeneration and remodelling are so dramatic and controllable in amphibia, we have attempted to examine simultaneously the morphology, biosynthetic process and resorption mechanism during thyroxin induced metamorphosis. These studies represent the combined efforts of Drs. C. Lapiere, Y. Nagai, G. Usuku, M. Tanzer, Miss A. Bruschi, and myself.

The bullfrog tadpole, obtainable in large numbers throughout the year, remains in the larval stage for about two and one-half

Reprinted from *Medicine* 43, 291–303 (1964), by permission of the author and the publisher. Copyright © 1964, The Williams & Wilkins Company (Baltimore, Md. 21202, U.S.A.).

years before undergoing spontaneous metamorphosis. This process is under control of the thyroid gland — see review by Frieden (3). The back skin, which thickens in the transition from tadpole to frog, and the tail fin which is rapidly resorbed, furnish two contrasting tissues basically similar in composition but different in reactivity to thyroxin. The gross changes observed in a thyroxin treated bullfrog tadpole after nine days are seen in Figure 1.

The histology of the tail fin of resting and thyroxin treated tadpoles is illustrated in the following series of phase and electron micrographs of epon embedded tissues (Usuku and Gross, to be reported in detail elsewhere). Figure 2 shows the general organization of a cross section of the resting tail fin as seen in the phase microscope. The epidermal cells appear on each side of the fin overlaying the basement lamella, a densely packed collagen layer, the equivalent of dermis. Underneath the basement lamella is seen a nearly unicellular layer of mesenchymal cells of several types. The central core of the fin is gelatinous, containing transverse fibers and a scattering of large mesenchymal cells and capillaries.

In Figure 3a we see an enlargement of a phase micrograph of the normal basement lamella, revealing its dense packing. In contrast, a similar region of tail fin from an animal exposed to thyroxin for 10 days (Fig.

FIGURE 1. Resting tadpole *Rana catesbiana;* above, tadpole after nine days' treatment with thyroxin. From Lapiere and Gross (15).

Inches

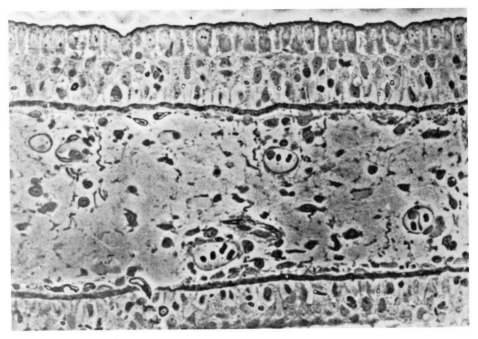

FIGURE 2. Phase micrograph of thin section of epon embedded osmium fixed resting tadpole tail fin. Note compact basement lamella underlying epidermis (magnification, × 350).

3b) shows marked loosening of the structure and cellular invasion. The detailed structure of the basement lamella as revealed by electron microscopy has been described by Weiss and Ferris (24), Kemp (13, 14), Salpeter and Singer (20) and Edds and Sweeney (1) among others. The last named investigators have also analyzed the content of the basement lamella as a function of age of the larvae (1).

The organization of collagen fibrils in the lamella of the dorsal tail fin of R. catesbiana, the bullfrog tadpole, is shown in Figure 4. In other species such as R. pipiens, the orthogonal array of alternating layers is more perfect. There are very few cell processes in the collagen layer and the packing of fibrils is quite dense. In thyroxin treated tissue, on the other hand (Fig. 5), the whole structure is loosened and there are many cell processes and even whole cells lying within the lamella. In many regions not shown here these invading mesenchymal cells have engulfed large numbers of fibrils. Weiss and Ferris (24) and Kemp (14) had described earlier the invasion of the basement lamella by mesenchymal cells.

The organization of the basement lamella in the tadpole is identical with that of nearly all aquatic vertebrates. During metamorphosis a

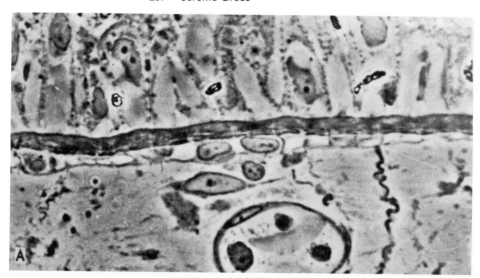

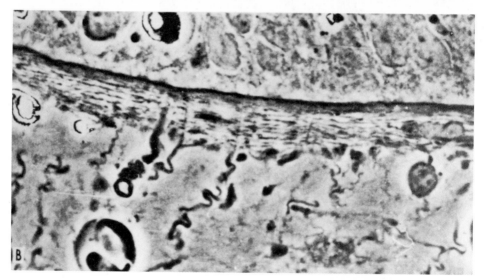

FIGURE 3.
(*a*) Phase micrographs of basement lamella region of tail fin of resting tadpole. Note mesenchymal cells lying beneath the lamella but not within it (magnification, × 1,000).
(*b*) Tailfin basement lamella of tadpole treated 6 days with thyroxin. Note fraying of collagen layers and cellular invasion.

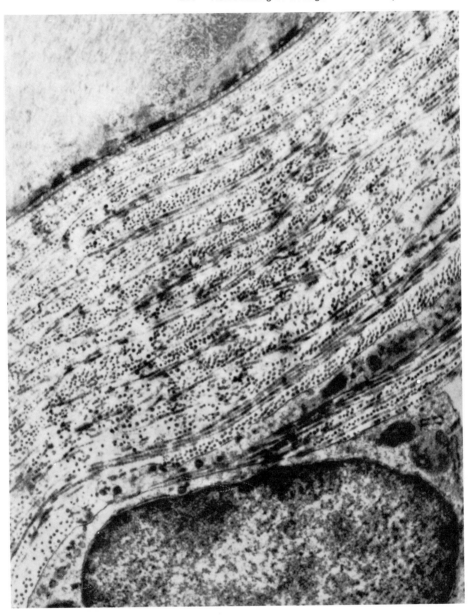

FIGURE 4. Electron micrograph of thin section of tail fin of resting tadpole. The edge of an epidermal cell is seen at the top and a portion of mesenchymal cell at the bottom. The collagen is arranged in compacted layers at right angles to each other. Note the absence of cell processes within the lamella.

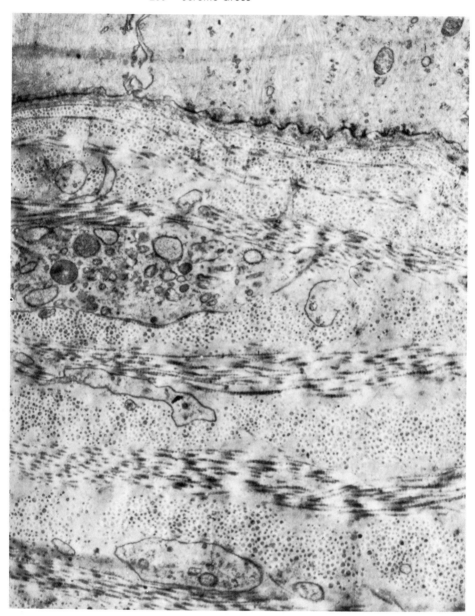

FIGURE 5. Tail fin after nine days of thyroxin treatment. Note extensive loosening of the collagenous layers, the spaces devoid of fibrils, and the mesenchymal
cell processes within the lamella.

new dermis is laid down in the back skin of the frog-to-be which now has the more random weave characteristic of terrestrial animals (*14*).

Within 4 days after immersing the tadpole in 0.0001 *M* thyroxin there is a rapid loss of water from the tail fins causing a twofold increase in percent of dry weight (Table 1). Resorption of the tail fin then proceeds at a rapid rate of speed.

In Table 2 we have recorded the changes in amount of total collagen in the two tissues and also the distribution between the several soluble fractions and the insoluble residue. There is clearly a considerable difference in the total content and also in the distribution between the two tissues. The back skin contains considerably more collagen than tail fin, the largest amount being represented by insoluble fibrils. The tail fin is unusual in having a nearly equal distribution of collagen among neutral extractable, acid soluble and insoluble fractions. In metamorphosis there is a further shift from insoluble to the soluble fractions in both tissues but more pronounced in the tail fin.

Preliminary studies have been made in an effort to detect any differences between the collagen of back skin and tail fin. The denaturation temperatures of the acid extractable fractions from back skin, tail fin and adult bullfrog skin are essentially identical. Examination of the molecular size and shape and amino acid composition are in progress.

Net loss or increase in amount of tissue components is dependent upon the balance between synthesis and degradation. The resorptive

TABLE 1

Composition of Tail Fin and Back Skin in Thyroxin-treated and Non-treated Tadpoles.*

	Tail fin		Back skin	
	Control	Treated	Control	Treated
No. fins and back skins	40	40	40	40
Wet weight (mg) per organ	473	107	354	256
Percent dry weight	5.7	10.0	7.7	10.5
	Mg/gm wet tissue		Mg/gm wet tissue	
Collagen	10.5	21.7	45.8	56.5
Free proline	0.07	0.16	0.14	0.16
Proline (noncollagen protein)*	0.20	0.21	0.37	0.44
DNA	1.5	2.7	0.63	0.77
	Mg per fin		Mg per back skin	
Collagen	4.9	2.3	16.2	14.5
Free proline	0.03	0.02	0.05	0.04
Proline (noncollagen protein)†	0.09	0.02	0.13	0.11
DNA	0.7	0.3	0.22	0.20

* *Six days with 6×10^{-7} M thyroxin in the water.*
From Lapiere and Gross (15).
   † *Fraction of extracted noncollagenous protein not precipitated by dialysis against water.*

TABLE 2

Collagen (Hydroxyproline) Fractions in Tissues
of Thyroxin-treated and Non-treated Tadpoles.[1]

	Wet weight per organ (gm)	*Av. total hydroxyproline (μmoles per fin or back skin)*			
		Neutral extract (1 M NaCl)	*Acid extract (0.1 M acetic acid)*	*Insoluble*	*Total*
Control tail fin	0.47	0.73 (31.5%)	1.00 (42.8%)	0.59 (25.7%)	2.32 (100%)
Thyroxin tail fin	0.11	0.46 (42.8%)	0.43 (39.8%)	0.19 (17.4%)	1.08 (100%)
Control back skin	0.35	0.29 (3.5%)	2.52 (30.2%)	5.53 (66.3%)	8.34 (100%)
Thyroxin back skin	0.26	0.36 (5.4%)	3.02 (44.6%)	3.38 (50%)	6.77 (100%)

[1] *Average values for 140 whole fins and 140 back
skins pooled and analyzed in 7 groups. From Lapiere
and Gross (15).*

process must be carried out in such a way that the organ remains
functional until it disappears; thus, it is not likely that the tissue fabric
will be randomly disorganized. The synthetic process was examined
by classical isotope incorporation studies. H[3]-labeled proline was injected intraperitoneally into groups of non-treated tadpoles and others
exposed to 0.0001 M thyroxin for 6 days. At short time intervals up to
30 hours post injection back skin and tail fin were dissected quantitatively from small groups of animals and the minced tissues extracted
three times in cold 1 M saline followed by three extractions in 0.1 M
acetic acid. Specific radioactivity of hydroxyproline from hydrolysates of
the isolated collagen, including the insoluble residue, were analyzed as
described elsewhere (23). Figures 6 and 7 illustrate the changes in total
radioactivity per organ and specific activity of the hydroxyproline
extracted from the total collagen. It is evident that the total radioactivity
in the tail fin from metamorphosing animals is substantially less than
that in the normals. However, if the data are corrected for the net loss
in collagen due to increased resorption, the rate of incorporation of total
radioactivity is essentially identical with the control except for the last
time point. This fact is more evident in the specific activities shown in
Figure 7. In the case of back skin, however, there is an increased rate
and extent of incorporation manifested both in total counts per organ
and in specific activity. Thus, there would appear to be no change in
rate of synthesis of collagen in the resorbing tail tissue, but there is
clearly an increase in the back skin. When one examines the distribution
of amino acid between the neutral, acid extractable and insoluble
collagen (Figs. 8 and 9) several unusual features become evident.

FIGURE 6. Total radioactivity of hydroxyproline isolated from collagen of the entire tail fin and back skin of control and thyroxin treated tadpoles. From Lapiere and Gross (*15*).

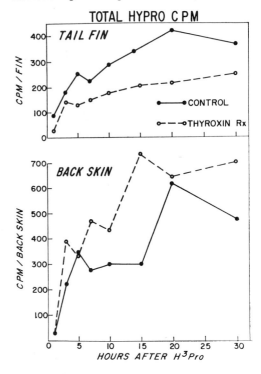

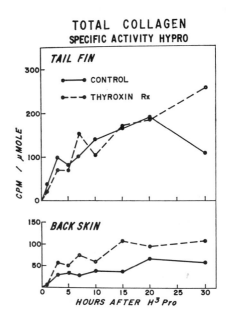

FIGURE 7. Specific activity of hydroxyproline from total collagen of tail fin and back skin in experiment reported in Figure 6. From Lapiere and Gross (*15*).

(Only specific activities are shown here. Total activities per organ are reported in a recent publication [15]). Within the limits of the time intervals used, it would appear that labeled proline is incorporated as rapidly into the insoluble collagen fraction as it is into the neutral extractable. This has been evident in all of our studies. It would suggest that the transformation of newly synthesized molecules to insoluble fibrils takes place at an extremely rapid rate, faster than we can detect by our relatively crude methods. The alternative is that both fractions derive from a common precursor. It is not likely that collagen is made as an insoluble fibril at the synthesizing site. The second unusual feature of the data is the fact that the least radioactive fraction is acid extractable. Harkness *et al.* (9) and Jackson (*11, 12*) were able to show in rodents that the neutral extractable fraction is labeled first and most extensively, the acid extractable next and the insoluble fraction least. This appears not to be the case in the tadpole. These observations suggest that at least in this species the acid extractable fraction is a derivative of the insoluble fibrils, and possibly is on the pathway to degradation rather than on the synthetic route.

The most striking and illuminating difference between normal and metamorphosing animals is that the specific activity of the insoluble collagen rises considerably above that of the neutral extractable in the resorbing tissues. This occurs in the face of a diminishing total amount of insoluble collagen. We conclude that there is a preferential degradation of the old, cold fibrils of the preexisting collagen framework, the newly laid down "hot" fibrils being spared. This makes sense if one were to suppose that during the process of resorption a new temporary collagen framework is being deposited and with time becomes susceptible to degradation. In this manner the animal would maintain a continuously functional although rapidly changing and diminishing extracellular scaffolding. One may guess at the possible mechanisms used. From the morphologic studies it would appear that the collagen fibers in the lower part of the basement lamella are attacked first leaving relatively intact the fibrillar mat underlying the epithelium. It could be that this outer layer is the newly deposited framework whereas the deeper layers are older. An alternative explanation might invoke the presence of more ground substance surrounding the newly formed fibrils thereby affording some protection against attack. With the passage of time the perifibrillar ground substance might be removed leaving the fibrils more accessible. These ideas are useful only insofar as they are subject to experiment.

The rapid resorption of collagen in the post partum uterus, in growing bone, in certain types of osteolytic tumors and in resorbing amphibian tissues has stimulated active exploration for tissue "collagenases" in a number of laboratories. To date tissue extraction with a variety of media has uniformly failed to reveal the presence of an enzyme capable of degrading native collagen at physiologic pH and temperature. The fruitless search has led some to postulate that collagen is resorbed in a

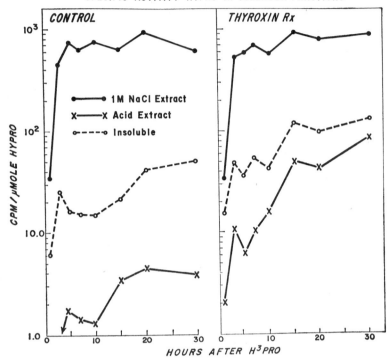

FIGURE 8. Specific activity of hydroxyproline of three collagen fractions isolated from back skin. From Lapiere and Gross (15).

two-stage process, first denaturation, then attack by cathepsins. A second suggestion based on evidence for a collagenolytic factor in tissue extracts which acts at acid pH, *ca.* 3.5 to 4 (2, 26) proposes that a local increase in acidity around the collagen fibrils destined for resorption makes them susceptible to these recently described proteases. Of course, both suppositions are within the realm of possibility; however, there is no evidence that native mammalian collagen in fibril form will denature at temperatures below 52°C. Urea, guanidine, and thiocyanate in concentrations above 2 *M* will denature *dissolved* collagen at body temperature. No one has yet found a collagen denaturing agent active at physiologic concentrations, temperatures and hydrogen ion concentrations. It is also very unlikely that any appreciable amounts of collagen exist in the dispersed form in the tissues at any one time (if there were it would be conceivable that in this state, at physiologic pH, it might undergo slow denaturation). While it is also conceivable that tissue pH might drop as low as 4 in localized regions there is no evidence as yet for such

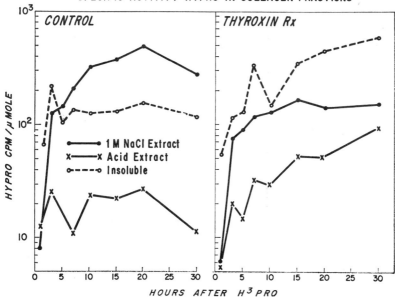

FIGURE 9. Specific activity of hydroxyproline of three collagen fractions isolated from tail fins. From Lapiere and Gross (*15*).

conditions except perhaps in peptic ulcers. It seemed to us that there must be animal collagenolytic enzymes operating at neutral pH. We (5, 15) have suggested possible reasons why collagenolytic activity has not been found in tissue extracts. It seems highly unlikely that any appreciable amount of free, active collagenase would be present in the tissues at any one time since it would result in indiscriminate destruction of the collagen framework. Such an enzyme would probably be present in extremely small amounts at any one time and probably be under very direct control of the cells. Second, we know from the work of Gallop *et al.* (4) that bacterial collagenase binds tightly to the fibers until they are degraded; then the enzyme is released to act elsewhere. Thus, a simple tissue extraction might fail to release a collagenase from the tissue collagen. With these thoughts in mind we cultured tissues, capable of resorbing their collagen on reconstituted native collagen gels *in vitro* for periods up to 3 to 5 days (5). If a collagenolytic enzyme were to be produced in small amounts, it should accumulate with time in the culture medium and manifest itself by lysing the foreign collagenous substrate, releasing increasing amounts of collagen degradation products. We used calf skin and guinea pig skin collagen, reconstituted in small tissue culture chambers to form an opalescent gel of collagen fibrils at neutral pH and body temperature in amphibian Tyrode solution. Such collagen gels were not appreciably attacked by any of the commonly known proteolytic enzymes at high concentrations but were susceptible to bacterial collagenase in extremely small amounts. Within 24 to 48 hours of incubation at 37°, cultures of tadpole tail fin, gill and gut exhibited clear-cut lysis of the collagen substrate. The lysing cultures shown in Figure 10 are rat uterus and are identical with the picture presented by tadpole tissue cultures. The pH of the amphibian culture medium remained between 7.4 and 8.0 and more than 50 percent of the degraded collagen was dialyzable (5). Bacterial contamination was ruled out by examination in aerobic and anaerobic culture and by direct observation of the media in the phase microscope. Tadpoles had been previously sterilized by immersion in penicillin-streptomycin and Chloramphenicol[R] for 24 hours prior to use. Collagenolytic activity was clearly reduced in those cultures which did become contaminated.

FIGURE 10. Six cultures of rat uterus on reconstituted calf skin collagen gels showing the dark areas of lysis in the opalescent collagen substrate. The identical pictures are presented by cultures of tadpole skin, gut, and gills.

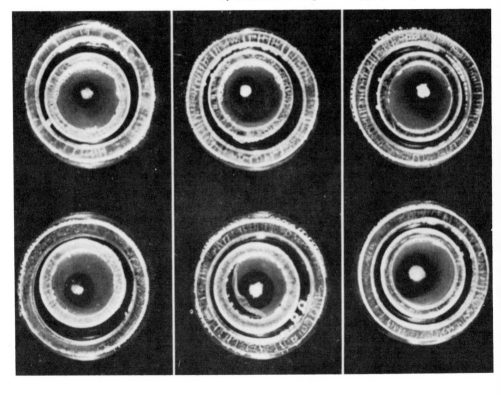

Using C^{14} labeled collagen from guinea pig skin we could show a linear relationship between area of lysis and solubilized radioactive collagen fragments.

It is unlikely that the enzyme activity is stored within the cells in lysosomes awaiting release through autolysis, since frozen-thawed tissue exhibited no collagenase activity, and also the presence of one μg of puromycin, an inhibitor of protein synthesis, per ml of culture media prevented lysis of the substrate. It thus appears that the collagenolytic enzyme is being synthesized continuously in small amounts and can be detected in culture since it accumulates over an extended period of time, attaining levels which are measurable in terms of break- down of the collagen substrate.

Examination of different tissues of the tadpole including tail fin, back skin, gill, gut, muscle, notachord, kidney, gonads, heart, liver, and spleen revealed collagenolytic activity only in the first four. These are the collagen-containing tissues which undergo massive resorption or re- modelling during metamorphosis.

Tail fin tissues from tadpoles treated with thyroxin for six days ex- hibited a two- to fourfold increase in rate of accumulation of colla- genolytic activity in cultures incubated at 28°. Since there is at least a twofold increase in percent dry weight in the metamorphosing tail fin, there is the distinct possibility that the modest increase in collagenoly- tic activity may be ascribed to increasing concentrations of cells rather than to increasing enzyme output per cell. However, the question re- mains unsettled at this time.

By cultivating a large amount of tadpole tissues cut into thin strips, on filter paper discs in petri dishes containing sterile amphibian Tyrode solution we (18) have succeeded in obtaining the collagenolytic enzyme in crude form in the culture medium after several days of incubation. The remaining tissue which has undergone considerable digestion is removed by centrifugation, the breakdown products dialyzed away, and the solution lyophilized. The culture medium from the back skin and tail fin of 400 large bullfrog tadpoles provide us with about 1 gm crude powder containing the enzyme. Incubation of calf skin collagen at 20° in the presence of the dissolved crude powder degrades collagen to fragments of which as much as 80 percent are dialyzable. A large pro- portion of the protein has been degraded to amino acids as well as pep- tides of various sizes. Sephadex gel filtration followed by ammonium sulfate precipitation, then starch block electrophoresis and finally elution from a DEAE-cellulose column resulted in a 300-fold purifica- tion of collagenolytic enzyme (19). This final product contains very little caseinolytic activity. It is reversibly inhibited by EDTA in low concentrations and irreversibly inactivated by cysteine and by heating to 60° for 10 minutes. It is not affected by diisopropylfluorophosphate. Its optimal pH range is from 8 to 9 with no activity below pH 6.5.

The viscosity of the reaction mixture of purified tadpole collagenase

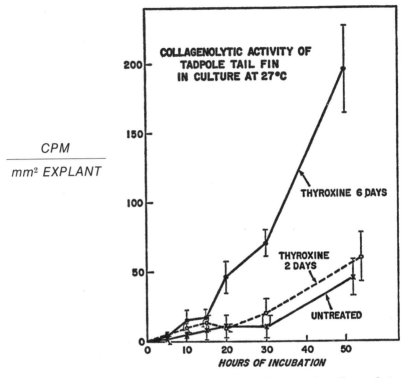

FIGURE 11. Accumulation of collagenolytic activity in tadpole tail fin cultures measured by release of radioactivity from C¹⁴ glycine labeled guinea pig skin collagen. Tissues from tail fins of tadpoles treated with thyroxin for 6 days, 2 days and untreated controls. From Lapiere and Gross (15).

with dissolved calf skin collagen at neutral pH reveals a fall to about 50 percent of the initial viscosity after which there is no further change. At the same time there is no alteration in optical rotation. These observations indicate that the enzyme cuts across the rod-shaped collagen molecule breaking it into a few long fragments without disrupting the helical conformation of the polypeptide chains. Analysis for N- and C-terminal amino acids in the reaction mixture has indicated the appearance of C-terminal glycine only and N-terminal isoleucine, the amounts indicating very few breaks across the three polypeptide chains (19). The site of action of this enzyme is quite different from that of the collagenase from *Clostridium histolyticum*. In this latter system only N-terminal glycine is liberated while any of the other amino acids can be C-terminal. Also bacterial collagenase attacks the collagen molecule much more extensively, breaking it into small fragments which lose their helical conformation — see Mandl (*16*) for review. Because of the extreme structural specificity of its attack on native collagen the tadpole enzyme will be valuable as a tool in further elucidating the structure of this molecule. It also gives one hope of finding other animal collagenases with different highly localized substrate specificities. We have found collagenolytic activity in cultures of rat and human endometrium (in the pre and post partum rat uterus) and in metaphyseal bone from parathyroid treated and untreated young rats. In the latter, Walker, Lapiere and Gross (*25*) have observed a five- to tenfold increase in lytic activity of metaphyseal tissue from parathyroid treated rats over that of controls. We have not yet succeeded in accumulating these enzymes in mass culture as we have with amphibian tissues.

If we had to guess at the mechanism whereby thyroxin triggers the resorption of collagen in the metamorphosing tadpole tail the picture might look somewhat as follows: The thyroid hormone causes a shift in water from the central gelatinous core of the fin into the basement lamella resulting in a separation of collagen layers. Alternatively, a hyaluronidase-like enzyme breaks down the ground substance of the lamella. Loosening of the structure permits the underlying mesenchymal cells to invade, thereby bringing the collagenolytic enzyme, which appears at the cell surfaces, into direct contact with the fibrils. Thus, it is a question of the cells carrying the enzyme to the substrate. These cells may even become phagocytic for the fibrils attacked by the enzyme. Perhaps the collagenolytic enzyme is being produced continuously and exported slowly through the cell surface in very small amounts at any one time. Dilution in the extracellular fluid and perhaps inactivation by extracellular substances may prevent an attack on fibrils at any distance from the cells. Perhaps the normal turnover of the collagen of the basement lamella is restricted to that layer of fibrils immediately adjacent to the mesenchymal cells underlying the compact lamella in the resting state. These conjectures are worth making at this point, since they are subject to experimental confirmation.

Although the work I have described has not been deliberately aimed in the direction of human disease, I would hope that, in time, it becomes relevant. It reflects in large measure, Dr. Bauer's philosophy, concretely expressed, when he established the basic science laboratories of the Robert W. Lovett Memorial Group. He believed in the intrinsic worth of fundamental knowledge, and also had solid faith in the idea that our understanding of human disease must of necessity grow as a result of such knowledge. Both these articles of faith have been firmly implanted in the members of his group.

REFERENCES AND NOTES

* This is Publication No. 361 of the Robert W. Lovett Memorial Group for the Study of Diseases Causing Deformities, Massachusetts General Hospital, Boston, Mass. 02114. These investigations were supported by Public Health Service

Research Grants AM 03564-04 and AM 05142-03, and National Science Foundation Grants G 10270 and 24307, and The Eli Lilly & Co.
From the Biology Laboratory of the Robert W. Lovett Memorial Group for the Study of Diseases Causing Deformities, Department of Medicine, Harvard Medical School at the Massachusetts General Hospital, Boston, Mass.

1. M. V. Edds, Jr., and P. R. Sweeny, Chemical and morphological differentiation of the basement lamella, in *Synthesis of Molecular and Cellular Structure*, D. Rudnick, Ed. (Ronald Press, New York, 1961), p. 111.

2. D. M. Franklin and C. H. Wynn, The degradation of acid-soluble collagen by rat-liver preparations, *Biochem J.* **85**, 276 (1961).

3. E. Frieden, Biochemical adaptation and anuran metamorphosis, *Amer. Zoologist* **1**, 115 (1961).

4. P. M. Gallop, S. Seifter, E. Meilman, Studies on collagen. I. The partial purification, assay and mode of activation of bacterial collagenase, *J. Biol. Chem.* **277**, 891 (1957).

5. J. Gross and C. M. Lapiere, Collagenolytic activity in amphibian tissues: A tissue culture assay, *Proc. Nat. Acad. Sci. U.S.* **48**, 1014 (1962).

6. J. Gross, C. M. Lapiere, M. L. Tanzer, Organization and disorganization of extra-cellular substances: The collagen system, in *Cytodifferentiation and Macromolecular Synthesis,* M. Locke, Ed. (Academic Press, New York, 1963), p. 175.

7. J. Gross, Collagen, *Scien. Amer.* **204**, 120 (1961).

8. _____, Comparative biochemistry of collagen, in *Comparative Biochemistry, A Comprehensive Treatise,* M. Florkin and H. S. Mason, Eds. (Academic Press, New York, 1963), p. 307.

9. R. D. Harkness, A. M. Marko, H. N. Muir, A. Neuberger, The metabolism of collagen and other proteins of the skins of rabbits, *Biochem. J.* **56**, 558 (1954).

10. W. F. Harrington and P. H. von Hippel, The structure of collagen and gelatin, in *Advances in Protein Chemistry,* C. B. Anfinsen, Jr., K. Bailey, M. L. Anson, J. T. Edsall, Eds. (Academic Press, New York, 1961), p. 1.

11. D. S. Jackson, Connective tissue growth stimulated by carrageenin. I. The formation and removal of collagen, *Biochem. J.* **65**, 277 (1957).

12. _____ and J. P. Bentley, On the significance of the extractable collagens, *J. Biophys. Biochem. Cytol.* **7**, 37 (1960).

13. N. E. Kemp, Development of the basement lamella of larval anuran skin during metamorphosis, *Develop. Biol.* **1**, 459 (1959).

14. _____, Replacement of the larval basement lamella by adult-type basement membrane in anuran skin during metamorphosis, *Develop. Biol.* **3**, 391 (1961).

15. C. M. Lapiere and J. Gross, Animal collagenase and collagen metabolism, in *Mechanisms of Hard Tissue Destruction,* R. Sognnaes, Ed., Publication No. 75, Amer. Assoc. Advancement of Science, Washington, D.C. (1963), p. 663.

16. I. Mandl, Collagenase and elastase, in *Advances in Enzymology,* F. F. Nord, Ed. (Interscience, New York, 1959), XXIII, 174.

17. *Collagen Currents,* E. Martin, Ed., Vols. 1–4 (Ethicon Co., Somerville, N. J.).

18. Y. Nagai, C. M. Lapiere, J. Gross, Isolation and partial characterization of an animal collagenolytic enzyme, *Fed. Proc.* **22**, 648 (1963).

19. Y. Nagai, C. M. Lapiere, J. Gross, Purification and characterization of amphibian collagenolytic enzyme, *6th Intern. Cong. Biochem.,* in press.

20. *Collagen,* N. Ramanathan, Ed. (Interscience, New York, 1962).

21. M. M. Salpeter and M. Singer, Differentiation of the submicroscopic adepidermal membrane during limb regeneration in adult Triturus, including a note on the use of the term basement membrane, *Anat. Rec.* **136**, 27 (1960).

22. *Recent Advances in Gelatin and Glue Research,* G. Stainsby, Ed. (Pergamon Press, New York, 1958).

23. M. L. Tanzer and J. Gross, Collagen metabolism in normal and lathyritic chick, *J. Exp. Med.* **119**, 235 (1964).

24. P. Weiss and W. Ferris, Electron microscopic study of the texture of larval amphibian skin, *Proc. Nat. Acad. Sci. U.S.* **40**, 307 (1954).

25. D. C. Walker, C. M. Lapiere, J. Gross, A collagenolytic factor in rat bone promoted by parathyroid extract, *Biochem. Biophys. Res. Comm.,* in press.

26. J. F. Woessner, Catabolism of collagen and non collagen protein in the rat uterus during post partum involution, *Biochem. J.* **83**, 304 (1962).

E Molecular basis of developmental control

Beermann, W. 1963. Cytological aspects of information transfer in cellular differentiation. *Amer. Zool.* 3, 23–32.

Varner, J. E., and G. Ram Chandra. 1964. Hormonal control of enzyme synthesis in barley endosperm. *Proc. Nat. Acad. Sci. U.S.* **52**, 100–106.

Cytological Aspects of Information Transfer in Cellular Differentiation

W. Beermann

Max-Planck-Institut
für Biologie,
Tübingen, Germany

The embryonic development of higher, multicellular organisms, especially animals, offers some of the most striking examples of cellular specialization. The diverse forms and functions of cells, all of which by virtue of their common descent from the zygote must contain identical sets of genes, demonstrate that, at least in the higher organisms, very effective control mechanisms exist which must be capable of activating some of the genetic potencies of the cell and of suppressing others. More specifically, since the structural as well as the functional character of a cell will ultimately depend on its protein composition, differentiation may be described as a controlled process whereby cells of identical genetic constitution develop different protein patterns. This view has some obvious implications from the point of view of biochemical genetics. Since we know that the structural information for the synthesis of proteins is laid down in a coded form in the nucleotide sequences of the informational DNA units of the genome (the classical "genes") we are led to postulate the existence of a mechanism which reads the genetic information differentially in different types of cells. In looking for mechanisms which, on the basis of a given genotype, would bring about the development of

Reprinted from *American Zoologist* 3, 23–32 (1963), by permission of the author and the American Society of Zoologists.

313

different protein patterns, several possibilities may be envisaged. The transfer of information from the DNA of the gene to the protein involves two main steps: first, the transcription of the nucleotide sequences of the DNA into nucleotide sequences of RNA molecules (synthesis of "messengers") and, secondly, the transcription of the nucleotide sequences of the RNA messengers into the amino acid sequences of the protein. The first of these processes, messenger synthesis, would have to take place at the site of the genes themselves. The second could take place anywhere in the cell, most probably at the site of the ribosomes in the cytoplasm. With respect to the regulation and control of these processes, we are therefore left with several possibilities. One could take the extreme stand of those embryologists who, in the past, tended to ignore entirely the nucleus and the Mendelian factors in assuming that there is no differentiation at the level of the chromosomes, or, in modern terms, that all genes are producing messenger molecules at the same rate all the time. Under these circumstances a change in the pattern of protein synthesis can only be produced by a specific inhibition or activation of specific messengers, or by a differential self-reproduction of some species of messenger molecules. Both types of control would meet with certain *a priori* limitations from the theoretical standpoint, that is, they could only be effective to a limited extent. The drastic changes accompanying the actual differentiation of cells seem to require a direct involvement of the genes in the control mechanism such that the initial production of the messengers can be regulated. The well known results of Jacob and Monod (1961) show that this type of gene regulation is actually realized in bacteria. In the course of our own work on dipteran giant chromosomes we have collected data of a quite different nature which, however, lend further support to the hypothesis of differential gene control as outlined above.

VISIBLE DIFFERENTIATION OF
GIANT POLYTENE
CHROMOSOMES IN INTERPHASE

Giant interphase chromosomes occur in the highly differentiated giant cells of dipteran larval and imaginal tissues. They attain a length of at least 10 times, and a cross section of up to 10,000 times that of normal univalent interphase chromosomes. According to the generally accepted views of Koltzoff (1934), Bauer (1935), and Bridges (1935), these chromosomes are to be considered as being "polytene," i.e., multivalent in a cable-like fashion, as a result of progressive replication of the chromatids without mitotic splitting. The most conspicuous feature of the polytene chromosomes is their banding pattern which, according to the concept of polyteny, reflects the ultimate chromomeric organization of the mitotic chromosomes of the individual. In other words, it is commonly taken for granted that the "phenotype" of the giant chromosomes — in most instances salivary gland chromosomes — is directly representative of the underlying genetic organization of the constituent strands and is not subject to phenotypic variation. However, if one actually studies the banding pattern of homologous chromosomes in different tissues of the same individual it is quite obvious that the statement of constancy needs further specification. Although it is not true that the pattern varies in the sense of actual variations in the number, the distance, and the arrangement of the bands relative to each other, specific differences can be observed with respect to the fine structure of individual bands in different tissues. The same band may appear as a sharply defined disc of considerable density and DNA concentration or it may have the appearance of a "puff." Sometimes the puffing may be rather inconspicuous, with the locus in question still forming a band-like coherent structure of only slightly changed texture and dimensions. In other cases a single band may be blown up into a huge ball-like, diffusely staining structure, called a Balbiani-ring (Fig. 1). From our investigations on *Chironomus,* where polytene chromosomes in four different tissues may be studied on a comparative basis, one elementary fact emerged quite early (cf. Beermann, 1956, 1959): The variations in the puffing behavior of the bands are not random but strictly correlated to cellular differentiation. Different tissues are characterized by different puffing patterns in their chromosomes, and developmental changes are always paralleled by characteristic changes in the puffing pattern as well. The statement is therefore justified that cellular differentiation regularly involves chromosomal differentiation, at least on the morphological level. Before we go on from here to discuss the possible physiological meaning of the observed chromosomal differentiation, the process of puffing as such needs

FIGURE 1. One of the three large puffs ("Balbiani's rings") of the 4th chromosome characteristic for all salivary gland nuclei of *Chironomus tentans* and *Chironomus pallidivittatus.* Three different stages of puffing are shown (magnification, approximately 1000).

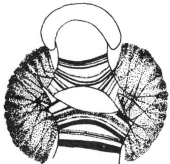

to be defined in terms of chromosome fine structure and chemistry. The unchanged chromomere, i.e., the ultimate unit composing each band, may be considered as a tightly folded-up portion of the constituent DNA-histone fiber of the chromatid. Puffing in terms of the single chromomere would mean the unfolding, or uncoiling, of the DNA-histone fiber into a long, loop-like thread. This has actually been observed to be so in the case of Balbiani's rings, both by light and by electron microscopy (Beermann and Bahr, 1954). The cytochemistry of puffing strengthens the structural interpretation. The intensity of the Feulgen reaction diminishes as the puffing of a band increases. The diffuse, peripheral regions of large puffs no longer show any visible Feulgen reaction. This would be expected on the basis of a progressive unfolding of the DNA which is equivalent to a structural dilution. On the other hand, cytochemistry shows the presence in large amounts of non-histone proteins in the puffs. The role of these proteins in the formation of puffs, i.e., in the unfolding of the chromomeric DNA fiber, may be a decisive one but has not yet been elucidated. All puffs contain RNA, but it is doubtful whether RNA plays any structural role at all. As will be seen presently, the RNA of the puffs seems to be exclusively concerned with genic activity.

On cytochemical as well as structural criteria, about 10% of all the bands appear to be in a more or less puffed condition in each tissue but, as has been already pointed out, as a rule these are not the same bands, the puffing pattern being specifically different from tissue to tissue and from stage to stage. Even the size attained by any one puff is usually quite characteristic for the cell type studied, the most outstanding example being Balbiani's rings which are characteristic for the polytene chromosomes of the salivary glands in all Chironomids. It has actually been demonstrated that puffing is a completely reversible phenomenon and does not involve any permanent change in the structure of the chromosome. Mention should be made, however, of an exceptional situation found in some puffs of polytene chromosomes of *Sciarid* flies. Here, in a few loci, puffing is always accompanied by the accumulation of large amounts of DNA (Rudkin and Corlette, 1957). If, as it seems, extra replications of the constituent chromomeres are involved, this may indeed lead to an irreversible structural and functional change of the locus.

PUFFING PATTERNS AS
PATTERNS OF GENIC ACTIVITY,
IN TERMS OF
RNA SYNTHESIS

A priori, there is little doubt that the chromosomal differentiation observed in polytene chromosomes is primarily a functional phenomenon. A fruitful working hypothesis may be based on the assumption that puffing is an expression of, or the actual mechanism which causes enhanced genic activity whatever this may mean in precise biochemical terms. For, if we consider the puffs to be activated gene loci, then the observed differentiation with respect to puffing patterns would be equivalent to differentiation with respect to patterns of genic activity — in other words, it is exactly what one would expect if differential gene activation occurred in embryonic development. This interpretation implies that those loci which are puffed in any one tissue, or stage of development, contain genetic information which is of special importance to the cells under consideration. One should expect, for instance, that the bands forming the giant puffs of the Balbiani ring type in the salivary glands contain genes which specifically control the structure or the function of the salivary glands, the more so since the same bands are not found in a puffed condition in other tissues of the *Chironomus* larva. Before we furnish direct genetic proof for this hypothesis, let us see what general physiological arguments we can adduce in favor of an interpretation of puffing in terms of genic activity.

On account of their large size, the polytene chromosomes lend themselves to autoradiographic studies. If radioactive (tritium-labeled) precursors of the nucleic acids or of the proteins are injected into *Chironomus* larvae, and if after a short incubation period the salivary glands are dissected, fixed, and squashed, then covered with autoradiographic stripping film, the following results are obtained. Tritiated thymidine is exclusively incorporated into the DNA during the endomitotic replication of the chromosomes. On the average only 2 out of 50 cells are found in the replication phase, the chromosomes of all other cells remaining unlabeled. The pattern of labeling in the case of thymidine exactly reflects the pattern of banding as demonstrated by the Feulgen reaction. The results are radically different if tritiated uridine, a precursor of RNA, is injected. Fifteen minutes after injection, appreciable amounts of labelled RNA are found in all nuclei of the salivary glands, whereas little or none is found in the cytoplasm. Within the nucleus the labeled RNA shows a highly characteristic distribution: it is almost exclusively located in the puffed regions of the chromosomes and in the nucleolus. The radioactivity of these regions increases when longer incubation times are used, but the topography remains essentially unchanged. With longer incubation times the cytoplasmic RNA will also become labeled, indicating a transfer of labeled RNA from the nucleus, that is, from the puffed chromosome regions and from the nucleolus to the cytoplasm. Such a transfer is also indicated by the fact that the amount of label in the puffs cannot be increased indefinitely by prolongation of the incubation period. A maximal value is very soon reached (after 2 hours) while the activity of the cytoplasm still increases over the next 12 hours. The relationship is, however, not entirely clear because most of the cytoplasmic RNA label could also be derived not from the puffs but from the nucleolus. That non-nucleolar RNA from the nucleus is actually transported into the cytoplasm can only be inferred from an independent study of lethal embryos lacking the nucleolus-organizing regions (Beermann, 1960).

The incorporation studies with tritiated uridine show that puffs are active centers of chromosomal RNA synthesis. Since, in addition to RNA, large amounts of μ protein always occur in the puffed regions, one might expect to find a similar situation with respect to protein synthesis or turnover in the puffs. However, there is no indication of a rapid and strictly localized incorporation of tritiated amino acids into the chromosomes or the nucleolus of *Chironomus* salivary gland nuclei. In fact, the autoradiograph of a salivary gland cell one hour after injection of tritiated leucine looks almost like a negative of a uridine autoradiograph; no label in the nucleus and heavy incorporation in the cytoplasm. Although these observations by no means exclude nuclear and chromosomal protein synthesis as a possibility, they seem to rule out protein synthesis as a major function of the puffed chromosome regions. We are therefore left with the conclusion that the activity of the puffed chromosome regions consists entirely in the synthesis of RNA; in other words, the puffing pattern of the polytene chromosomes represents the pattern of RNA synthesis along the chromosomes. Are we justified in considering this type of a chromosomal activity pattern as being equivalent to a pattern of "genic activity" in the sense of a differential reading of the genetic information? In a very general sense this question can be answered in the affirmative since, as is well known from modern biochemical studies on protein synthesis, RNA molecules play a central role in the transfer of information from the DNA to the protein, as "messengers" or "templates" and, in the case of the so-called soluble RNA, as specific vehicles for the amino acids to direct them into their correct position on the templates. However, in order to prove the point directly, one would have to characterize the RNA produced in the puffs chemically and demonstrate that it actually plays one or the other decisive role in protein synthesis. A first attempt to characterize the RNA of the puffs of *Chironomus* polytene chromosomes has been made in collaboration with Dr. Edström from Gothenburg, Sweden.

The largest puffs (the Balbiani rings) of the salivary gland chromosomes of *Chironomus tentans* are very suitably located in the short fourth chromosome which can easily be isolated with glass needles from the nuclei of formalin-fixed glands. These chromosomes are collected, individually placed on coverslips, and left to dry. They can then be cut into three pieces, each containing one of the three giant Balbiani-ring puffs. The RNA from a number of homologous pieces, i.e., RNA which practically represents the specific RNA of one single puff, is extracted by repeated RNAase digestion and then subjected to a microanalytic procedure involving hydrolysis in micropipettes, electrophoresis on a rayon fiber of 25 μ diameter, and UV microphotometry of the fractions separated on the fiber (cf. Edström, 1960). The sensitivity of the method is about 10^{-10} g RNA per analysis. This quantity roughly corresponds to 50 Balbiani rings, or 5 nucleoli, or half the cytoplasm of one salivary gland cell in *Chironomus*. The method leads to a characterization of the cellular RNA fractions in terms of their base ratios (adenine + uracil + cytosine + guanine = 100%). The results are shown in Table 1.

The information gained from base ratios is, of course, limited. Base ratios do not tell us anything about the size of the RNA molecules analyzed, nor do they reflect their nucleotide sequence. In our case, we cannot even decide whether we are dealing with pure RNA fractions; our fractions might be mixtures of several molecular species. Therefore, the observed similarity between the nucleolar and the cytoplasmic RNA's might be spurious although it agrees nicely with the idea that the structural ribosomal RNA in the cytoplasm is of nucleolar origin. However, if large, significant differences in the base composition are consistently found between the nucleolar and the cytoplasmic RNA's on the one hand, and the chromosomal and puff RNA's on the other, the idea of one being the precursor of the other becomes less likely. More specifically, our data speak against the possibility that the RNA produced at the puffs is collected in the nucleolus and/or is stored in the cytoplasm in the form of ribosomal stationary RNA. It could, however, represent a short-lived messenger type of RNA, or, perhaps, soluble transfer RNA, or a mixture of both. If we consider this chromosomal RNA as a direct copy of the chromosomal DNA, the specific way in which it differs in its base composition from the other RNA fractions becomes highly significant. The DNA molecules are generally known to be double-stranded, with the base composition of one strand complementary to the other, so that the ratios thymine/adenine and cytosine/guanine both equal 1. If both strands of the DNA molecules in the puffs were copied by the RNA at the same rate, then, obviously, one should obtain a mixture of two types of single-stranded RNA molecules complementary to each other, with an overall base composition where uracil/adenine and cytosine/guanine again both equal 1. But this type

TABLE 1

Base Composition of the RNA Extracted from Different Components of *Chironomus* Salivary Gland Cells, as Molar Proportions in Percent of the Sum.
(*From Edström and Beermann, 1962.*)

	Adenine	Guanine	Cytosine	Uracil	A/U	G + C%	n
Chromosome 1	29.4 ± 0.5	19.8 ± 1.0	27.7 ± 0.8	23.1 ± 0.6	1.27	47.5	4
Chromosome 4							
proximal (BR 1)	35.7 ± 0.6	20.6 ± 1.7	23.2 ± 1.2	20.8 ± 0.8	1.72	43.8	5
median (BR 2)	38.0 ± 0.6	20.5 ± 0.6	24.5 ± 0.6	17.1 ± 0.6	2.22	45.0	6
distal (BR 3)	31.2 ± 2.2	22.0 ± 2.0	26.4 ± 1.9	20.2 ± 1.4	1.54	48.4	3
Nucleolus	30.6 ± 0.8	20.1 ± 0.5	22.1 ± 0.6	27.1 ± 0.6	1.13	42.2	13
Cytoplasm	29.4 ± 0.4	22.9 ± 0.3	22.1 ± 0.4	25.7 ± 0.3	1.14	45.0	7
A/G ratio for DNA							
Chromosome 1	37.8	12.2				24.4	
Chromosome 4	35.9	14.1				28.2	

of symmetry is approached only in the nucleolar and the cytoplasmic RNA fractions. The chromosomal RNA fractions are extremely asymmetric, with A/U more than 2 in the case of the Balbiani rings, and with large deviations from 1 also in the ratio G/C, especially in chromosome 1. It should be pointed out that RNA fractions of such an extreme asymmetry have never been detected before. If, as is very likely, we are dealing with copies of the chromosomal DNA we are faced with the following possibilities: (1) The DNA in the puffs may be effectively single-stranded so that only one type of RNA molecule is produced; this single-strandedness could have either a structural or a functional (enzymatic) basis. (2) The two complementary types of RNA copies are both actually formed, but one of the two is immediately removed from the site of synthesis, either by enzymatic destruction or by rapid transport mechanisms. In any case it would appear that either the production or the selection of only one, and a specific one, of the two possible RNA copies of the genic DNA is a necessary prerequisite for an unambiguous information transfer mechanism. Our data, then, support the hypothesis that the RNA of the puffs is either the messenger itself or its complementary counterpart, the "anti-messenger." This conclusion, in turn, once more strengthens our original view that the puffing pattern of the polytene chromosomes is an expression of differential gene activation.

GENETIC CHARACTERIZATION OF A SPECIFIC PUFFED REGION IN SALIVARY GLAND CHROMOSOMES

In *Chironomus* the salivary glands continuously produce a mucopolysaccharide secretion which hardens under water and enables the larvae to build from mud particles the tubes in which they live and feed. The protein moiety of the secretion rapidly incorporates radioactive amino acids. The rate of synthesis of the secretion protein must be high as compared to the rates of synthesis of any other cellular proteins. If there is any quantitative relationship between the rate of messenger production and the rate of protein synthesis at all, one should expect the locus, or loci, containing the information for the synthesis of secretion protein to be especially, and exclusively, active in the salivary glands. As judged by their giant size and their synthetic activity with respect to RNA, the Balbiani rings of the salivary gland chromosomes seem to represent such loci. The bands forming Balbiani rings are always few in number (2–5), and those forming Balbiani rings in the salivary glands never seem to form a puff in any other tissue. Moreover, whenever one lobe of the gland differs from the others in the composition of the secretion which it produces — as is the rule in Chironomid salivary glands — this differentiation on the level of cellular function is invariably accompanied by a differentiation on the chromosomal level, with respect to the pattern of bands forming Balbiani rings. This differentiation is often mutually exclusive so that different bands are transformed into Balbiani rings in different regions of the gland. In other instances the cells of the gland may all share two or three Balbiani rings, but specialized regions of the gland may have chromosomes with additional Balbiani rings of their own. If the general views outlined above are correct, a lobe-specific Balbiani ring would furnish the genetic information necessary for the production of a lobe-specific component of the secretion. Any change, genetic or other, which would prevent a lobe-specific Balbiani ring from being developed should, on our hypothesis, lead to the loss of a lobe-specific secretion component. We have been able to verify this correlation by cytogenetic methods (Beermann, 1961).

In *Chironomus pallidivittatus* and in many other *Chironomus* species a small specialized sector of the larval salivary gland, usually consisting of four cells, produces a secretion which, in contrast to the clear secretion of the major part of the gland, is granular in character. However, in *Chironomus tentans*, the closest relative of *C. pallidivittatus,* the granular component is not present in the secretion of the special cells. This difference between the two species does not seem to be due to a loss of structural differentiation in the salivary glands of *C. tentans,* since the special cells in the latter maintain the same fine structural details which characterize them in *C. pallidivittatus,* e.g., a cytoplasmic secretion zone of the brush border type which is not found in the normal gland cells of both species. The difference between the two species, then, must be due to the loss of a specific synthetic function from the special cells of *C. tentans.* The chromosomal situation is exactly what one would expect: In both species there are three Balbiani rings which are shared by all the cells of the glands, all in the small 4th chromosome, as mentioned earlier. In *C. pallidivittatus,* where the special cells regularly produce secretion granules, the small 4th chromosome always shows an additional Balbiani ring close to its centromeric end (Fig. 2). In *C. tentans,* on the other hand, there is no lobe-specific Balbiani ring so that, concomitant with the loss of the major, and distinctive, function of the special cells the only major distinguishing character on the chromosomal level is also lost. We may formulate the hypothesis, therefore, that the genetic information necessary for the production of the secretion granules is entirely or partially located in the band which forms the lobe-specific Balbiani ring in *C. pallidivittatus,* and that the transfer of this information to the cellular synthetic sites depends on the actual formation of the Balbiani ring in question. These postulates can be put to test by classical gene localization techniques. *C. tentans* and *C. pallidivittatus* produce fertile hybrids, and their chromosomes are marked by a number of species-specific rearrangements, mainly inversions, which prevent crossing-over in most chromosome regions. It was found that the "mutant character" in question, namely, the inability to produce secretion granules, is recessive,

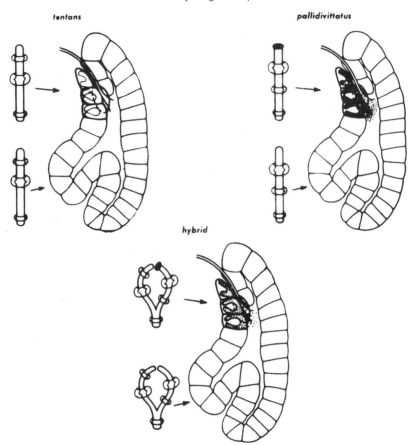

FIGURE 2. The pattern of Balbiani rings in the two functionally different portions of the salivary gland in *Chironomus tentans, pallidivittatus,* and their hybrid. See text for further details.

and that it is inherited as a simple Mendelian factor whose pattern of inheritance closely follows the inheritance of the 4th chromosome of *C. tentans.* Its location within the 4th chromosome was determined by crossing-over tests and found to coincide with the location of the lobe-specific Balbiani ring. In heterozygotes, the two allelic segments behave visibly differently so that the allelic segments originally furnished by *C. pallidivittatus* form the Balbiani ring whereas the homologous segment furnished by *C. tentans* fails to do so in the same nucleus. This permits a parallel scoring of crossovers both on the chromosomal level and on the level of the phenotype, always with identical results. Moreover, some exceptional cases have been observed in these hybridization experiments where the formation of the lobe-specific Balbiani ring was suppressed by modifying genetic factors. In all these instances a parallel decrease was observed in the amount of secretion granules in the special lobe of the salivary glands.

Apart from demonstrating that our interpretation of the puffing phenomenon is basically correct, these results also illustrate another general point, namely, the possibility of purely "operational" mutations as opposed to informational ones. No visible deficiency is present at the locus of the mutant which distinguishes *C. tentans* from *C. pallidivittatus*. Thus, it is conceivable that the mutation did not involve the informational content of the locus at all but only its operational properties. These might be determined by a special segment immediately adjacent to the informational one, just as the operation of bacterial genes is controlled via a special "operator" site (Jacob and Monod, 1961). At any rate, since we know now that puffing is an operational phenomenon, we are in a position to use this phenomenon to define operational units or "operons" in polytene chromosomes. The question may then be raised whether or not the units thus defined always coincide with the units defined by other means, morphological as well as genetic ones. We will probably have to revise the statement that a puff as a rule represents only a single band which in turn could be considered as an informational unit. A combined study of position effects and puffing may throw further light on this problem.

THE INDUCTION AND CONTROL OF PUFFING

The existence of different activity patterns of the genes in different types of cells and in different stages of development must be due to the action of specific triggering and controlling factors in development. Unfortunately, the mechanism of puff formation as such is at present a complete mystery. When a puff is formed, the most conspicuous change from a chemical standpoint is the incorporation of large amounts of nonbasic proteins, presumably in an organized fashion. The same protein must be incorporated also whenever chromosomal replication occurs in a place where a puff is already present. With radioactive precursors, however, we have not been able to find evidence for a substantial net synthesis of protein, nor for that matter, for any kind of turnover during puff formation or puff growth. Probably the proteins are made elsewhere in the cells and become subsequently attached to the site of puff formation. The properties of this protein are not known in detail, nor do we know whether the protein is the same in all puffs. An attractive hypothesis would be that the protein represents RNA polymerase. As regards RNA, we have seen earlier that the bulk of the RNA in the puffs seems to be involved in information transfer but we can by no means exclude the presence in puffs of small amounts of RNA with an "inductive" function.

In the present state of ignorance about the puffing mechanism, the search for inducing or controlling agents is largely determined by the view that agents known to be effective as inducers in animal development might act via the activation of genes. This idea is generally supported by the fact that unspecific physical and chemical factors which are able to bring about specific changes in development, such as temperature or ionic strength of the medium, can also evoke specific responses in the puffing pattern of the chromosomes (Becker, 1959; Ritossa, 1962; personal communication). A much better clue to the understanding of the puffing mechanism should, of course, be derivable from the use of biological agents such as the hormones, which are known to be extremely specific both in their action and their chemical structure. In insects the molting process is initiated and can be experimentally induced by the molting hormone, "ecdysone," a product of the prothoracic glands. This hormone has been highly purified, but not yet chemically identified by Karlson (1956); there are indications that it is a cholesterol derivative. Clever (1961) in our laboratory has found that the injection of minimal doses of this hormone into *Chironomus* larvae leads within 30 minutes to the formation of a puff at a specific site in chromosome 1, and 30 minutes later to the formation of another puff in chromosome 4. The hormone, as judged by the puffing reaction, is active in concentrations as low as 10^{-7} μg/mg larval weight in the case of the first puff, and 10^{-6} μg/mg in the case of the second puff. These values are equivalent to a few hundred molecules per single chromatid in each nucleus. After molting has been induced, the first puff stays on until after the molting process is completed — as it should, since ecdysone is constantly present in the hemolymph during the molting period, owing to an induction of hormone production in the animals themselves. The second puff, however, invariably regresses after 2 days, a process which must be due to the action of a specific "repressor." The formation of the two primary puffs is followed, in normal development as well as in the experiments, by a chain of secondary puffing reactions, the amplitude of which does not, however, depend on the hormone concentration as it does in the case of the primary puffs. These data indicate that the hormone acts as a direct inducer of activity in two loci, an activity which in its turn triggers off the whole chain of secondary events which may include the production of several new enzymes. That the primary puffs probably only act as recipients for the developmental signal is further indicated by the fact that they are formed not only in the salivary glands but also in the Malpighian tubules and probably in all tissues. Jacob and Monod (1961) think that inducers, or repressors, of gene activity exert their function as co-factors by forming a molecular complex with an internal "apo-repressor," thereby changing its stereochemical affinity to the "operator" in the operon involved. It is possible that the hormone in our case is just such an "effector."

The fact that, in the case of the ecdysone, a hormone has been found to act as a specific inducer of puffing at a specific site of the chromosomes does not, of course, justify generalization in one way or the other. Neither must all hormones of necessity act as gene inducers, nor can the majority of substances that act in gene regulation be considered as hormones. On the contrary, the very fact that cellular differentiation can take place in a multicellular organism shows that most of the specific inducers or repressors of gene activities must remain limited in their effects to the cell in which they are produced. It is the search for these substances that may, in the future, prove to be the most illuminating approach to the problem of cellular differentiation.

REFERENCES

H. Bauer, Der Aufbau der Chromosomen aus den Speicheldrüsen von Chironomus Thummi Kiefer (Untersuchungen an den Riesenchromosomen der Dipteren I), Z. *Zellforsch.* **23**, 280–313 (1935).

H. J. Becker, Die Puffs der Speicheldrüsen-chromosomen *von Drosophila melanogaster*. 1. Mitteilung. Beobachtungen zum Verhalten des Puffmusters im Normalstamm und bei zwei Mutanten. *giant* und *giant-lethal-larvae, Chromosoma (Berlin)* **10**, 654–78 (1959).

W. Beermann, Nuclear differentiation and functional morphology of chromosomes. *Cold Spring Harbor Symp. Quant. Biol.* **21**, 217–32 (1956).

——, Chromosomal differentiation in insects, in D. Rudnick, Ed., *Developmental Cytology* (Ronald Press, New York, 1959), pp. 83–103.

——, Der Nukleolus als lebenswichtiger Bestandteil des Zellkerns, *Chromosoma (Berlin)* **11**, 263–96 (1960).

——, Ein Balbiani-Ring als Locus einer Speicheldrüsen-Mutation, *Chromosoma (Berlin)* **12**, 1–25 (1961).

—— and G. F. Bahr, The submicroscopic structure of the Balbiani-ring, *Exptl. Cell. Research* **6**, 195–201 (1954).

C. B. Bridges, The structure of salivary chromosomes and the relation of the banding to the genes, *Amer. Naturalist* **69**, 59 (1935).

U. Clever, Genaktivitäten in den Riesenchromosomen *von Chironomus tentans* und ihre Beziehungen zur Entwicklung. 1. Genaktivierung durch Ecdyson, *Chromosoma (Berlin)* **12**, 607–75 (1961).

J. E. Edstrom, Extraction, hydrolysis, and electrophoretic analysis of ribonucleic acid from microscopic tissue units (microphoresis), *J. Biophys. Biochem. Cytol.* **8**, 39–46 (1960).

—— and W. Beermann, The base composition of nucleic acids in chromosomes, puffs, nucleoli, and cytoplasm of *Chironomus* salivary gland cells, *J. Cell. Biol.* **14**, 371–79 (1962).

F. Jacob and J. Monod, Genetic regulatory mechanisms in the synthesis of proteins, *J. Mol. Biol.* **3**, 318–56 (1961).

P. Karlson, Chemische Untersuchungen über die Metamorphose-hormone der Insekten, *Ann. Sci. nat. Zool.* **11**, 125–37 (1956).

N. K. Koltzoff, The structure of the chromosomes in the salivary glands of *Drosophila, Science* **80**, 312–13 (1934).

G. T. Rudkin and S. L. Corlette, Disproportionate synthesis of DNA in a polytene chromosome region, *Proc. Nat. Acad. Sci. U.S.* **43**, 964–68 (1957).

Hormonal Control of Enzyme Synthesis in Barley Endosperm*

J. E. Varner
G. Ram Chandra

RIAS, Baltimore

The activities of several enzymes of isolated barley endosperm increase markedly in response to added gibberellic acid (1–6). In the normal, intact germinating seed, evocation of these same enzymatic activities in the endosperm is caused by the embryo which is known to produce gibberellic acid (7, 8). We have, in the present case then, an example of hormonally regulated enzymatic activity and one with which it is particularly convenient to work since the principle enzyme involved is α-amylase. We shall show below that the gibberellic acid-dependent increase in α-amylase activity in barley endosperm is due to *de novo* synthesis of the enzyme. Thus, when isolated barley endosperm is treated with gibberellic acid in the presence of C^{14}-labeled amino acids and the α-amylase subsequently isolated, it is found to contain label.

We shall further show that the α-amylase produced in response to application of gibberellic acid is identical with that synthesized by the normally germinating seedling. Finally, we shall show that the gibberellic acid-induced synthesis of α-amylase is suppressed in the presence of actinomycin D, and that the effect of gibberellic acid is therefore upon the expression of the genetic information which controls α-amylase production.

Reprinted from *Proceedings of the National Academy of Sciences* 52, 100–106 (1964), by permission of J. E. Varner and the National Academy of Sciences.

Materials and Methods. Dry barley seeds (*Hordeum vulgare*, var. Himalaya) were cut in half along their equatorial axes and the embryo halves discarded. The endosperm halves were soaked in 1% sodium hypochlorite for 15–20 minutes, rinsed in sterile distilled water, and transferred aseptically to sterile moist sand contained in Petri dishes. After incubation for 3 days at 17–23°, ten half-seeds were transferred to an aseptic 25-ml Erlenmeyer flask containing 2.0 ml of 0.001 M sodium acetate buffer (pH 4.8) and the appropriate treatment solution. Such flasks were shaken at top speed at 25° on a Dubnoff metabolic shaker during the incubation period. The medium was then poured off, and the half-seeds were rinsed once with 3.0 ml distilled water. They were next ground in a mortar with sand and 5.0 ml 0.001 M acetate buffer (pH 4.8). The homogenate was then centrifuged at 1000 × g. The resultant supernatant (extract) and the incubation medium were next assayed separately for α-amylase activity by the method of Shuster and Gifford (9). The assay was calibrated by use of crystalline α-amylase prepared according to Schwimmer and Balls (10).

Labeled, gibberellic acid-induced α-amylase for fingerprinting was prepared as follows: twenty preincubated half-seeds were aseptically transferred to an aseptic 25-ml Erlenmeyer flask which contained 1.0 ml of 0.001 M acetate buffer (pH 4.8), 10^{-6} M gibberellic acid, and 20 μc of L-threonine-C^{14}. After 24 hours' incubation at 25°, the medium contained 400 μg of α-amylase. The medium was poured off, and the half-seeds were rinsed twice with 1.0-ml portions of water. Authentic carrier α-amylase (4.5 mg) was added to the combined medium and washings.

Calcium chloride was added to a final concentration of 0.003 M and the solution adjusted to pH 7.0. The solution was then heated at 70° for 20 minutes, centrifuged, and the precipitate discarded. Carrier L-threonine (0.01 M) was added and enough absolute alcohol added to make the solution 40% with respect to ethanol. After 10 minutes the solution was centrifuged and the precipitate discarded. Glycogen (0.2 ml of a 1.6% solution [11]) was added and after 10 minutes the precipitate recovered by centrifugation. The glycogen-α-amylase precipitate was washed once with 2.0 ml of 40% ethanol and taken up in 1.0 ml of H$_2$O. The solution of the glycogen-α-amylase complex was incubated at 25° for 1 hour to digest the glycogen then dialyzed overnight against 0.01 M L-threonine.

The labeled α-amylase preparation was heated to 95° for 5 minutes and ammonium carbonate added to a final concentration of 0.01 M, and incubated at 20° for 18 hours with 20 μg of trypsin. After freeze-drying and sublimation of the ammonium carbonate, the hydrolysate was separated into its component peptides by chromatography and electrophoresis (14).

The α-amylase is produced by the aleurone layer of the seed. Dissection of half-seeds into aleurone layers (plus testa-pericarp) and starchy endosperm was performed after the 3-day preincubation period.

Labeled amino acids (L-threonine-u-C^{14} and L-phenylalanine-u-C^{14}) were purchased from the New England Nuclear Corporation, Boston. The actinomycin D was a gift from Dr. Clement A. Stone of the Merck Institute for Therapeutic Research, West Point, Pa. The 5-bromouracil, 6-azaguanine, and 8-azaadenine were purchased from California Corporation for Biochemical Research, Bethesda, Md.

Crystalline trypsin was obtained from the Worthington Biochemical Corporation, Freehold, N.J.

The rabbit liver glycogen was purchased from Nutritional Biochemicals, Cleveland, Ohio, and further purified as described by Loyter and Schramm (11). Barley malt α-amylase for use as standard and carrier was purified and crystallized by the method of Loyter and Schramm (11) and of Schwimmer and Balls (10). The two methods yielded α-amylase of identical specific (enzymatic) activities. The incorporation of labeled amino acids into protein was determined by addition to the extract of 10% trichloroacetic acid containing 0.01 M carrier amino acid. The precipitate was filtered on a membrane filter (Schleicher and Shuell, B-6) and washed with 10% trichloroacetic acid. Radioactivity was measured with a Nuclear-Chicago gas-flow (D-47) detector.

Results. The time course of the development of α-amylase activity in half-seeds and in isolated aleurone layers in response to added gibberellic acid is given in Figure 1. There is a lag period of 9–15 hours after addition of gibberellic acid before the maximum rate of production of α-amylase is attained. Production of the enzyme ceases suddenly about 33 hours after addition of the hormone. The bulk of the α-amylase produced is released into the medium surrounding the tissue. Although isolated aleurone layers do not produce as much α-amylase as intact half-seeds, we believe that this is a matter of nutrition. The addition of phosphate ions, calcium ions, magnesium ions and glucose, and amino acids increases the quantity of α-amylase produced by isolated aleurone layers.

It is clear that the aleurone cells are able to incorporate labeled amino acids into protein in the absence of added gibberellic acid (Table 1). This fact, together with the knowledge that there is no increase in respiration preceding or paralleling α-amylase formation (*12*), and that there is no qualitative change in the pattern of $P^{32}O_4$ incorporation into acid-soluble compounds (*12*) following the addition of gibberellic acid, allows us to conclude that the energy apparatus and the materials for protein synthesis are at hand before the addition of gibberellic acid. It is, therefore, the function of gibberellic acid to influence the synthesis of certain specific proteins. A further examination of Table 1 shows that the total label of amino acid incorporated into protein decreased in half-seeds incubated with gibberellic acid. This is the result of a gibberellic acid-dependent increase in proteolytic activity (*13*) which causes the release within the tissue of relatively large quantities of free amino

FIGURE 1. Time course for the development of α-amylase activity in half-seeds and in isolated aleurone layers. The fresh weight of ten half-aleurone layers (plus testa-pericarp) is 168 mg. The gibberellic acid (10^{-6} M) was added at 0 time.

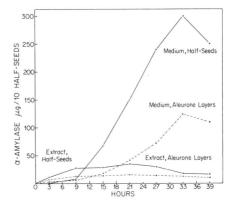

acids (4). The increase in level of free amino acids in turn dilutes out the label added and makes it impossible to determine readily the amount of protein synthesized in the gibberellic acid-treated half-seeds. Inhibitors of protein synthesis prevent the gibberellic acid-induced increase in proteolytic activity (12). It is, therefore, likely that the protease is also produced by *de novo* synthesis. For the present discussion, it is sufficient to observe (Table 1) the marked difference in the distribution of the labeled protein between medium and extract in the gibberellic acid-treated and -untreated half-seeds, and the rough parallel between the release of α-amylase into the medium and the release of labeled proteins into the medium. In the absence of gibberellic acid, about 5 percent of the newly synthesized, i.e., labeled, protein is released into the medium during a 30-hour incubation period. In the presence of gibberellic acid, about 50 percent of the newly synthesized protein is released into the medium.

The physical properties of the labeled proteins formed undergo a dramatic qualitative transformation in the presence of gibberellic acid (Table 1). Of the proteins labeled in the absence of gibberellic acid, about 75 percent are precipitated by heating to 70° for 20 minutes. Only 0–40 percent of the labeled proteins released into the medium in the presence of GA are thus precipitated (Table 1). Addition of carrier extract to the labeled medium does not carry down any more of the labeled proteins during the heating of the medium, nor does the medium stabilize the labeled proteins in the extract. It is, of course, well known that α-amylase is heat-stable. So also is the endo-β-glucanase which increases as does α-amylase in response to added gibberellic acid (4). The α-amylase recovered by the ethanol-glycogen procedure (11) contains about 12 percent of the total counts incorporated into protein and about 35 percent

TABLE 1

L-Phenylalanine-C[14] Incorporation into Protein *in vivo.*

Hours		Minus Gibberellic Acid			Plus Gibberellic Acid		
		Radio-activity, in protein, cpm	% Labeled protein precipitated by heating	α-Amylase, μg	Radio-activity, in protein, cpm	% Labeled protein precipitated by heating	α-Amylase, μg
10	Medium	16	0	3	41	0	19
	Extract	640	74	<20	480	79	28
20	Medium	92	2	7	287	37	276
	Extract	2200	75	<20	588	74	31
30	Medium	176	23	12	480	40	440
	Extract	2760	75	<20	465	76	15

Each flask contained ten half-seeds, 10^{-3} M acetate buffer, and 1.0 μc of L-phenylalanine-C[14]. The counts shown were for 0.10-ml aliquots of a total of 5.0 ml.

TABLE 2

Physical Properties of Labeled Proteins.

Fraction	Radioactivity, cpm	Heat-precipitable, percent
Extract	34,000	80
Medium	29,200	15
Ethanol PPT	7,000	0
Glycogen S.F.	8,000	0
α-Amylase	8,000	0

The numbers shown indicate the total number of counts incorporated into protein during incubation of ten half-seeds in acetate buffer, 10^{-6} M gibberellic acid, and 1 μc of L-leucine-C^{14}. The ethanol precipitate, glycogen supernatant fraction, and α-amylase fraction refer to the fractions produced during the purification procedure (11).

of the heat-stable labeled proteins (Table 2). Thus, α-amylase accounts for a large fraction of the total protein synthesis triggered by gibberellic acid.

Labeled leucine, alanine, proline, and threonine were all shown, in separate experiments, to be incorporated into the purified α-amylase. Each of these labeled samples of α-amylase was digested with trypsin and "fingerprinted"(14). Of a total of 31 ninhydrin spots, 20 were labeled with proline, 26 with alanine, 30 with leucine, and 25 with threonine. Only 2 of the 31 ninhydrin spots contained none of the above labeled amino acids. The fingerprint obtained with labeled threonine is shown in Figure 2. We experienced some difficulty in obtaining complete digestion of the α-amylase with trypsin. The rate of digestion is slow and variable. This is probably due to the presence of limit dextrins and traces of calcium ions which may serve to protect the α-amylase against tryptic attack. It appears from the information of Figure 2 as well as from the similar fingerprints of α-amylase labeled with other amino acids that the entire α-amylase molecule is synthesized in response to the addition of gibberellic acid.

We turn next to the question of how gibberellic acid causes the production of α-amylase. It could, in principle, be through derepression of the previously repressed gene for α-amylase synthesis with consequent production of appropriate messenger RNA. We approach this problem by finding out whether inhibitors of RNA synthesis inhibit the gibberellic acid-dependent synthesis of α-amylase.

Of the RNA synthesis inhibitors used, 5-bromouracil, 8-azaadenine, and actinomycin D caused some inhibition of α-amylase formation (Table 3). Application of 100 μg/ml of actinomycin D completely inhibits the formation of α-amylase (Table 3), although 10 μg/ml is almost without effect. We suspect that actinomycin D is partially destroyed by

FIGURE 2. Autoradiograph of a fingerprint of α-amylase obtained by tryptic digestion of threonine-C^{14} labeled α-amylase. The solid lines show the position of ninhydrin-positive spots which coincide with the exposed spot on the film. The dotted lines are ninhydrin-positive spots which were not labeled.

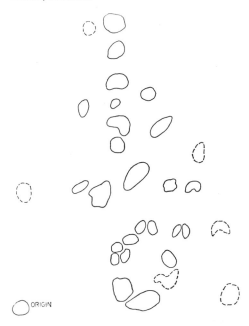

ORIGIN

the proteases of barley because addition of 10^{-3} M potassium bromate (which inhibits the protease action without preventing α-amylase synthesis) (12) to the medium together with gibberellic acid and actinomycin D increases the inhibition caused by 10–50 μg/ml of actinomycin D. Evidence that actinomycin D, even at these high concentrations, is, in fact, selective is shown in Table 4. In the presence of gibberellic acid and actinomycin D, the small amount of α-amylase formed and the distribution of labeled proteins are characteristic of the untreated aleurone layers. However, actinomycin D has little effect on the rate of the gibberellic acid-independent incorporation of labeled phenylalanine into proteins. The obvious and most attractive conclusion is that the labeled heat-stable proteins synthesized and released into the medium after the addition of gibberellic acid require DNA-dependent synthesis of RNA. That incorporation which occurs without added gibberellic acid could use messenger RNA formed during the pre-incubation period or perhaps even during the maturation of the developing seed.

The formation of α-amylase by the isolated aleurone layers is sensitive to actinomycin D only during the first few hours after addition of gibberellic acid (Table 5). Actinomycin D added 7 hours after the addition of gibberellic acid has little effect. However, p-fluorophenylalanine added at this time is still effective. These results are consistent with the postulate that the addition of gibberellic acid causes the formation of a specific messenger RNA which directs the *de novo* synthesis of α-

TABLE 3

The Effect of RNA Synthesis Inhibitors on α-Amylase Formation by Isolated Aleurone Layers.

Treatment	Extract	α-Amylase, μg Medium	Total
−GA	9.4	5.8	15.2
Control	12	53	65
5-Bromouracil	10	26	36
6-Azaguanine	14	43	57
8-Azaadenine	10	33	43
Actinomycin D	10	4.3	14.3

For each sample, ten half-aleurone layers were incubated with buffer, 10^{-6} M gibberellic acid, and 10^{-4} M inhibitor — except the actinomycin D which was 100 μg/ml — for 30 hours at 25°.

TABLE 4

Amino Acid Incorporation in vivo by Aleurone Layers.

Treatment GA	Act D	Radioactivity Extract	Medium	α-Amylase, μg Extract	Medium
−	−	72,600	18,900	22	11
+	−	21,300	25,500	12	55
−	+	69,900	12,700	4	0.5
+	+	74,000	18,000	26	12

The numbers shown indicate total c/m incorporated into protein during a 30-hour incubation of ten half-aleurone layers with buffer, 1 μc L-phenylalanine-C^{14}, 10^{-6} M gibberellic acid, and 100 μg/ml actinomycin D where indicated.

amylase. Within a few hours after the addition of gibberellic acid, the quantity of messenger RNA is no longer rate-limiting in α-amylase synthesis. From this time on, the formation of α-amylase would not be susceptible to inhibition by actinomycin D but would, of course, still be susceptible to protein synthesis inhibitors.

Discussion. Simple dissection experiments have shown that only the aleurone layer cells are capable of respiration and amino acid incorporation (6). The QO_2 ($μl \cdot O_2 \cdot hr^{-1} \cdot 100$ mg fresh wt^{-1}) for the aleurone layers at 25° is 15–30. The aleurone layers consist of a single cell type derived from the triple fusion nucleus. Aside from the possibility that a layer of living cells surrounding the dead starchy endosperm may provide protection against attack by microorganisms, the only obvious function of the aleurone cells is to produce and secrete hydrolytic enzymes

TABLE 5

Time Course of Sensitivity to Inhibitors.

Conditions	α-Amylase, μg
−GA	13
+GA	66
+GA + Act D	24
+GA + Act D (after 7 hr.)	55
+GA + pFφ Ala	12
+GA + pFφ Ala (after 7 hr.)	12

For each sample, ten half-aleurone layers were incubated with buffer, and 10^{-6} M gibberellic acid added at the beginning of the incubation. The actinomycin D (100 μg/ml) and p-fluorophenylalanine (10^{-3} M) were added either at the same time as the gibberellic acid or after 7 hours.

for the digestion of the reserves of the dead starchy endosperm cells. It is a delightful nicety that the key to these reserves is kept by the embryo — the only tissue capable of growth.

The simplest possible way to explain the data in this paper is to postulate that gibberellic acid exerts its control at the level of the gene to bring about the synthesis of messenger RNA's specific for the proteins being synthesized. It appears that this hypothesis can be checked experimentally by the techniques developed for assessing those DNA sites available in chromatin for transcription into messenger RNA by RNA polymerase (*15*).

Summary. The development of α-amylase activity by isolated aleurone layers of barley endosperm is completely dependent upon added gibberellic acid and is a result of the *de novo* synthesis of the α-amylase molecule. The synthesis of α-amylase and of other heat-stable proteins is prevented by actinomycin D. It is therefore postulated that gibberellic acid controls the synthesis of α-amylase and of other heat-stable proteins in aleurone cells by causing the production of specific messenger RNA's.

Communicated by James Bonner, May 4, 1964

REFERENCES AND NOTES

The authors gratefully acknowledge the technical assistance of Miss Nancy Joseph and Miss Anne Wiley. We wish to thank Dr. H. Yomo for supplying translations of his papers, and Professor R. A. Nilan for supplying the Himalaya variety of barley.

* This research was supported by research contract AT (30-1) — 3232 with the Atomic Energy Commission.

1. H. Yomo and H. Iinuma, *Agri. Biol. Chem. (Tokyo)* **26**, 201 (1962).
2. L. Paleg, *Plant Physiol.* **36**, 829 (1961).

3. A. M. MacLeod and A. S. Millar, *J. Inst. Brewing*, **68**, 322 (1962).

4. D. E. Briggs, *J. Inst. Brewing* **69**, 13 (1963).

5. J. E. Varner and G. Schidlovsky, in *Proceedings of the International Seed Protein Conference,* New Orleans, USDA (1963).

6. J. E. Varner, *Plant Physiol.* **39**, 413 (1964).

7. H. Yomo, *Hakko Kyokaishi* **18**, 603 (1960).

8. L. G. Paleg, *Plant Physiol.* **35**, 902 (1960).

9. L. Shuster and R. H. Gifford, *Arch. Biochem. Biophys.* **96**, 534 (1962).

10. S. Schwimmer and A. K. Balls, *J. Biol. Chem.* **179**, 1063 (1949).

11. A. Loyter and M. Schramm, *Biochim. et Biophys. Acta* **65**, 200 (1962).

12. G. Ram Chandra and J. E. Varner, unpublished.

13. H. Yomo, *Hakko Kyokaishi* **19**, 284 (1961); *Chem. Abstracts* **57**, 11544 (1961).

14. A. M. Katz, W. J. Dreyer, C. B. Anfinsen, *J. Biol. Chem.* **234**, 2897 (1959).

15. J. Bonner, R. C. Huang, R. O. Gilden, these *Proceedings* **50**, 793 (1963).

SECTION THREE   Evolution of Organisms

Charles Darwin presented a large amount
of evidence that evolution was a reality,
but his greatest contribution lay in presenting the hypothesis that natural selection was the process accounting for this
fact. Natural selection is now defined in
Mendelian terms and can actually be
measured in certain populations. There are
situations where the relationships between taxonomic groups can be ascertained, and the steps in the evolution of
the respective taxa can be traced. The
student of evolution is constantly looking for populations where he can observe
"evolution in action," because it is from
such model populations that most of our
information about natural selection has
been obtained. The papers in this section
deal with cases where the origin of new
taxa can be observed or experimentally
produced, and with the role played by
certain adaptations in fitting the organisms to the environment. The first group
of papers describes past or present evolution in populations, the second group
discusses some of the mechanisms controlling these observable changes, and the
last group is concerned with interactions
between the population and the environment.

The seed for Darwin's theory was
planted during the five-year world voyage
of the HMS "Beagle," and it was his
visit to the Galapagos Islands that really
started him thinking on the subject.

335

Islands have been favorite haunts of biologists ever since. Darwin was fascinated with the finches which differed slightly from island to island in the Galapagos, but which were plainly related to finches on the South American mainland. The tortoises and plants also showed a great variation from island to island. Localized forms of life are called endemics, and on islands an unusually high percentage of the organisms are endemics. It is also common on islands for organisms occupying different ecological niches to be closely related. Darwin's finches, for example, resemble many other unrelated kinds of birds such as warblers and woodpeckers. The original group, or groups, of mainland finches which colonized the Galapagos had a landscape full of unused habitats and no competitors. The colonizer finches adapted to these habitats over the years, and there are now many different kinds of finches. This phenomenon is called adaptive radiation, and the Galapagos Islands are famous for their endemic organisms which exhibit this trait.

Even more splendid examples of adaptive radiation, however, are found in the Hawaiian Islands. These islands are young geologically, and they are farther away from continental land masses than just about any other group of islands. These circumstances make them a showcase for the evolution of isolated populations. This is illustrated by that singular group of birds, the Hawaiian honeycreepers, which provide the topic of Dean Amadon's paper.* They are one of the best examples we have of what can happen over a relatively short space of time to a taxonomic group faced with a great variety of unexploited ecological niches. Organisms which make their living in a similar way tend to look and act alike even though they may be quite unrelated. A Galapagos finch which looks like a Hawaiian honeycreeper is an example of this phenomenon, called convergent evolution.

The next two papers by George S. Myers* and by Richard F. Johnston and Robert K. Selander* describe situations where very rapid speciation can be observed. Islands are not necessarily bits of land surrounded by water. Any isolated environment is an island from an evolutionary standpoint, and lakes are a particularly good example. The fish of Lake Lanao in the Philippine Islands provide two significant lessons: their evolution can be measured in thousands of years rather than millions, and has resulted in the formation of taxonomic categories higher than species. Man has shifted plants and animals all around the world to suit his fancy, and while many of these efforts have had disastrous consequences, they have on occasion provided excellent opportunities for the student of evolution. At first glance the ubiquitous house sparrow seems an unlikely candidate for speciation studies, but Johnston and Selander have shown otherwise. Accurate information is available on the dates the house sparrow was introduced into North America and

* An asterisk indicates that the paper is included in this section.

the Hawaiian Islands, and the dates of its unwelcome arrival in various parts of the continent are also known. In the hundred years it has been in these new environments, there has been adaptive radiation in the sparrow population. This study also shows that rapid speciation can occur in large populations on continental land masses as well as in small populations on islands.

A basic component of the criticism directed at Darwin was the fear that man would be placed among the products of natural selection. We no longer hesitate to relate man to apes, but the nature of the time, place, and manner of his diversion from the other primates is not completely clear. Recent years have seen a tremendous increase in our knowledge of man's origins, and discoveries of human fossils in Africa have provided the impetus for this quickened pace. The present status of our information about man's early evolution is provided by Phillip V. Tobias* in his analysis of the African discoveries.

Man is placed within a single species, but the genus *Homo* has not always had such a paucity of species, and we can only conclude that man's wanderlust and ability to communicate has negated any tendency towards reproductive isolation. Even though the concept of race is too muddled to argue about here, it cannot be denied that there are significant variations in the species *Homo sapiens*. Whether those differences are altogether the result of genotypic differences is not easily settled. It is simple to score the degree of skin pigmentation, and the genotypic basis for this variation is universally accepted, but differences in body build and such characteristics as whether Eskimos or Australian bushmen are more inured to cold than Madison Avenue executives are more difficult to place on a firm genetic basis. This question of difference in geographical groupings of humans is discussed by Eugène Schreider,* and he concludes that real differences exist and have adaptive value with respect to particular environments. If people who live in cold climates have a subcutaneous layer of fat not possessed by people in more temperate climates, we can discuss the adaptive value of the fat layer with some measure of confidence. There are many features of the human phenotype, however, whose adaptive significance is by no means obvious. We feel a certain compulsion to assign adaptive significance to just about every feature of organisms we notice, and a great deal of nonsense has been written as a result. The reasons given for pigmentation of human skin is a case in point. Harold F. Blum* discusses such points in his essay on human skin color. You might want to return to this paper after reading the one by W. Farnsworth Loomis* in the next group.

Man has evolved, and it is frequently asked if he is still evolving and if this evolution is taking any direction. It would be surprising if man was not changing, but it is difficult at any single point in time to decide this about any organism. A more difficult task is identifying trends and predicting future results. It is frequently stated that natural selection is no longer relevant to man's condition because cultural evolution has made him his own master. The development of the human brain has perhaps made man the first organism to escape his environment, but that development has also led to an infinite capacity for self-delusion.

Biologists have been studying evolution since Darwin, but it is only within the last twenty-five years that natural selection has been critically analyzed in natural populations. One of the first of these studies was made by Th. Dobzhansky* on the fruitfly, *Drosophila*. His studies on this organism have continued to the present, and they provide population genetics with some of its solidest foundations. A new environment, whether produced by an ice age, continuous clouds of pesticides, or repeated injections of streptomycin, always reveals genetic variation in a population. This variation permits some organisms to survive in the new environment. Do these new variations result from mutations induced by the changed environment, or is the new environment merely selecting for preexisting genotypes? It was important to learn the answer because this would tell a great deal about how natural selection works. The Lederbergs* developed an elegant technique permitting them to identify parent bacterial colonies from which streptomycin-resistant clones were established. The new environment containing the toxic drug was actually selecting for previously existing resistant cells. Among other things, their work increases our understanding of how difficult it is to eradicate our competitors. As a result of our modifying their environments with poisons, we are selecting for resistant varieties of microbes, insects, and rodents.

The population geneticist defines natural selection as anything promoting a shift in the gene frequency of a population. H. B. D. Kettlewell's study* of moth populations in England provides a most dramatic example of how natural selection works. The moth *Biston betularia* has gray and black forms which occur in certain frequencies in the population. In the nonindustrial parts of Britain the gray form predominates, while in the sooty industrial regions the populations are almost entirely black. It is known that the black form did not appear in large numbers until industry was widespread. The explanation for this shift in gene frequency is quite simple. These moths spend the day on tree trunks, and in the "clean" parts of Britain the tree trunks have lichens growing on them. The mottled gray moths blend in so well with the mottled gray tree trunks it is difficult for birds to find and eat them; the black form, on the other hand, is conspicuous. The reverse is true in the industrialized regions where the tree trunks are sooty and no lichens grow: the black forms have perfect camouflage, while the gray forms are conspicuous. Kettlewell put this explanation to experimental test by releasing the black and light forms in the two kinds of environment. He recaptured the released moths after a period and found that the predominant color form was consistent with the above explanation. He watched birds prey on the moths in the different environments, and in both cases the conspicuous color form was eaten in the greater number. The shift in gene frequency in this moth population is due to the selective predation of one color form. Adaptations permitting organisms to escape predation by blending with their environment are widespread in nature and are referred to as cryptic mimicry.

The papers of A. C. Allison* and W. F. Loomis* return us to the discussion about the difficulty of assigning adaptive significance to traits of organisms in general and of humans in particular. Allison has studied sickle-cell anemia, which is a hereditary blood disease found in certain parts of the world. Individuals homozygous for this trait do not live long, but heterozygous individuals are found in large numbers. One wonders why some populations have such a high frequency of an obviously deleterious gene. Correlations have been made between the occurrence of sickle-cell anemia and the prevalence of malaria in the area. There is good evidence that the individuals heterozygous for sickle-cells are more resistant to malaria than individuals with normal blood cells. The sickle-cell trait is rapidly selected against in populations not faced with selection by malaria.

The adaptive value of human skin was the subject of a previous paper, and Loomis presents convincing evidence that skin color is selected on the basis of vitamin-D synthesis. These last two papers are fine examples of the fact that information from all branches of biology and biochemistry eventually form grist for the evolutionist's mill.

The primary driving force for evolution is natural selection, but new taxa can arise in other ways as well. Hybridization is one such way, and there are examples of new kinds of organisms being produced directly by hybridization. This form of promoting change in populations has been important in some plant groups, but it is not considered to be a main-line event. The neo-Darwinian definition of evolution is that it consists of a change in the gene frequency of a population. In small populations this can happen as sort of a statistical long shot in the results of genetic recombination. This influence of chance in changing gene frequency is called genetic drift and Paul A. Moody's paper* explains how it can be analyzed.

The whole biosphere is very much like an organism. It is difficult to take one part of it and study it in isolation because all parts are completely integrated with the whole. Just as any single organ did not evolve independently of other organs, so one population or taxa did not evolve independently of other living things. This fact is seen clearly in the regulation of population size. Any factor which alters the size of one population will make its effect known on other populations. A stable environment will possess populations of organisms which have established a certain numerical equilibrium. It can even be argued that behavior patterns which result in a certain population regulation would have adaptive value and would be selected. The last three papers provide insights about how population levels are regulated. Quantitative population studies are a relatively new subject in biology, and the youth and complexity of this subject make it a focal point for controversy. There is, however, no controversy in the universal feeling that this subject is rapidly becoming one of the most important and exciting in all biology. Perhaps studies in this area will finally convince the human animal that it too has evolved in harmony with the total environment, and that its future is dim unless it learns to coexist with that environment.

SUGGESTIONS FOR FURTHER READING

Darwin, Charles. 1958. *The Voyage of the Beagle*. Bantam Books, New York.

———. 1962. *The Origin of Species*. Collier, New York.

Davis, D. E. 1966. *Integral Animal Behavior*. Macmillan, New York.

De Beer, Sir Gavin. 1965. *Charles Darwin, A Scientific Biography*. Doubleday, Garden City, N.Y.

Dobzhansky, Th. 1963. *Evolution, Genetics, and Man*. John Wiley & Sons, New York.

Ehrlich, Paul R., Richard W. Holm, and Peter H. Raven. 1969. *Papers on Evolution*. Little, Brown, Boston.

Eiseley, Loren. 1958. *Darwin's Century*. Doubleday, Garden City, N.Y.

Grant, Verne. 1963. *The Origin of Adaptations*. Columbia University Press, New York.

Hardin, Garrett. 1959. *Nature and Man's Fate*. Mentor Books, New York.

Huxley, Julian. 1953. *Evolution in Action*. Harper & Row, New York.

Lack, David. 1961. *Darwin's Finches*. Harper & Bros., New York.

Lorenz, Konrad. 1965. *Evolution and Modification of Behavior*. University of Chicago Press, Chicago.

Mayr, Ernst. 1966. *Animal Species and Evolution*. Belknap Press, Cambridge, Mass.

Ornduff, Robert. 1967. *Papers on Plant Systematics*. Little, Brown, Boston.

Simpson, George G. 1949. *The Meaning of Evolution*. Yale University Press, New Haven.

Spiess, Eliot B. 1962. *Papers on Animal Population Genetics*. Little, Brown, Boston.

Stebbins, G. L. 1966. *Processes of Organic Evolution*. Prentice-Hall, Englewood Cliffs, N.J.

A Differentiation
of populations

Amadon, Dean. 1947. Ecology and the evolution of some Hawaiian birds. *Evolution* 1, 63–68.

Myers, George Sprague. 1960. The endemic fish fauna of Lake Lanao, and the evolution of higher taxonomic categories. *Evolution* 14, 323–33.

Johnston, Richard F., and Robert K. Selander. 1964. House sparrows: Rapid evolution of races in North America. *Science* 144, 548–50.

Tobias, Phillip V. 1965. Early man in East Africa. *Science* 149, 22–33.

Schreider, Eugène. 1964. Ecological rules, body-heat regulation, and human evolution. *Evolution* 18, 1–9.

Blum, Harold F. 1961. Does the melanin pigment of human skin have adaptive value? An essay in human ecology and the evolution of race. *Quart. Rev. Biol.* 36, 50–63.

Ecology and the Evolution of Some Hawaiian Birds

Dean Amadon

The American Museum
of Natural History

The land animals and plants of isolated archipelagos have evolved from a few straggling colonists which crossed wide expanses of ocean by occasional accidents of dispersal. Many groups numerous on continents are entirely absent, thus leaving ecological niches vacant and setting the stage for rapid adaptive radiation. One example of adaptive radiation in birds is the Geospizidae or Galapagos finches, which Darwin studied. Even more remarkable in this respect are the Hawaiian honeycreepers (Drepaniidae). During fifteen months in the Hawaiian Islands I studied these birds in the field and in the collection of the Bishop Museum, Honolulu. Some of the conclusions reached below are foreshadowed in the work of Dr. R. C. L. Perkins (1903, 1913), the greatest authority on the Hawaiian fauna. The present paper analyzes some examples of adaptive modification among Hawaiian birds and suggests that competition between related sympatric species with similar ecological requirements has been a major cause of such modifications.

PHAEORNIS

The thrush family (Turdidae) is represented in Hawaii by one endemic genus, *Phaeornis*, containing two species. One species, *P. obscurus,* was represented by a different subspecies on each of the islands except Maui, where the genus is absent (some of the subspecies are now extinct). The other species, *P. palmeri,*

Reprinted from *Evolution* 1, 63–68 (1947), by permission of the author and publisher.

occurs only on Kauai, the most isolated island of the group (Fig. 1). Presumably the first *Phaeornis* stock to reach Kauai was so isolated that differentiation to the specific level resulted, giving rise to *palmeri*. Later the widespread *P. obscurus* again colonized Kauai successfully. Such speciation by double invasion on suitably located islands is common in birds (Mayr, 1942: 173). On the other Hawaiian islands, which are less isolated, we may assume that stragglers of the thrush have wandered from island to island frequently enough to keep differentiation below the specific level.

Phaeornis obscurus feeds on berries and fruits but sometimes takes insects. *Phaeornis palmeri* is chiefly insectivorous. Perkins (1903: 377) found in the stomachs of specimens of this species ". . . the large hard weevils of the genus *Rhyncogonus,* and these unquestionably form a large part of their food. Spiders and caterpillars are also eaten, and the insectivorous habits of the species are strongly contrasted with the berry-eating propensity of the other members of the genus [i.e., the races of *obscurus*]. . . . Owing however to their totally different habits there is little or no competition between the two forms, as at present constituted." Since the five races of *obscurus* do not differ, so far as known, in habits, it is probable that the different habits of *palmeri* were accentuated by competition with a congeneric species after the second colonization of Kauai by *Phaeornis*.

FIGURE 1. Map of Hawaiian Islands. Distances between islands in kilometers; areas of islands in square kilometers.

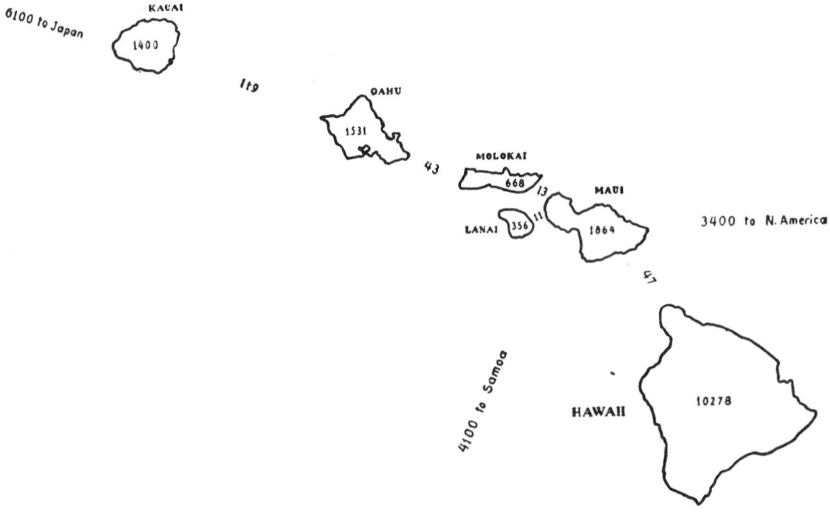

Lack (1944) in a summary of information on ecology and speciation in birds points out that when two species with similar requirements meet in the same area those individuals which differ most in feeding habits (or in structures concerned with feeding such as the bill) will have a selective advantage. This differential selection will tend to draw the two species apart, especially where suitable empty ecological niches exist. Some slight difference in requirements must exist at the time two such species first overlap since ecologists consider it virtually impossible that two species with identical requirements (if such ever evolve) could exist together for any length of time.

In *Phaeornis* the morphological differences between the two forms occurring on Kauai are not known to be adaptive. One is considerably smaller than the other, a common difference between pairs of very similar (sibling) species which is probably adaptive (Lack).

ADAPTIVE EVOLUTION
IN THE DREPANIIDAE

The following examples are from the family Drepaniidae. The bills of most of the species mentioned are shown in Figure 2.

LOXOPS

The genus *Loxops* contains two closely related species, *L. virens* and *L. parva*. They are often placed in a separate genus *Chlorodrepanis*. As in the thrushes, one of these species (*virens*) is found throughout the islands while the other, which was apparently derived from it, is restricted to Kauai. *L. virens* searches for insects among foliage; it also uses its short decurved bill to extract nectar and small insects from flowers; occasionally it digs away bits of loose bark with its bill. The Kauai subspecies (*L. virens stejnegeri*) has a noticeably heavier bill and digs more in bark and moss while seeking insects. Munro (1944: 100) wrote of it: "I noted particularly in skinning that the muscles on the back of its head were more strongly developed than in the other Kauai birds and its skull more heavily built. This development was evidently occasioned by its habit of digging in the bark of trees to a greater extent than any of the other Kauai birds; or other *amakihis* [i.e., other races of *virens*]." *L. parva*, on the other hand, is a tiny bird with a small, almost straight bill. Munro (1944: 104) wrote of it: "It usually gathers its insect food among the twigs and leaves but sometimes in the loose bark. It is very fond of visiting the koa [*Acacia koa*] flowers."

In *Loxops* the two Kauai forms have both changed somewhat, as compared with the more generalized races of the ancestral species occurring on the other islands. In *stejnegeri*, at least, the changed feeding habits are correlated with adaptive changes in the bill. Thus we may, with more confidence than in *Phaeornis*, suggest that modification of the Kauai forms has resulted from interspecific competition following overlap in range.

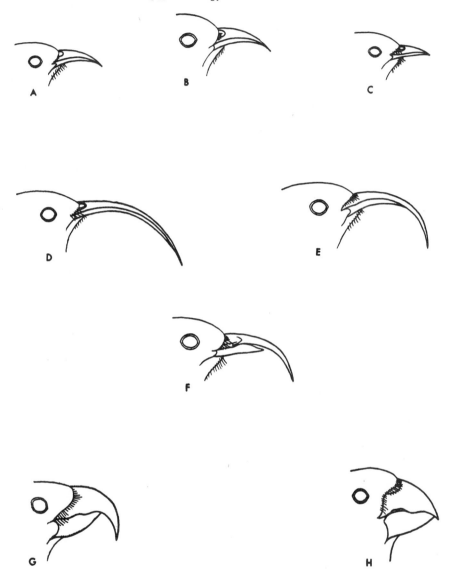

FIGURE 2. Bills of (A) *Loxops virens chloris*; (B) *Loxops virens stejnegeri*; (C) *Loxops parva*; (D) *Hemignathus o. obscurus*; (E) *Hemignathus lucidus hanapepe*; (F) *Hemignathus (lucidus) wilsoni*; (G) *Pseudonestor xanthophrys*; (H) *Psittirostra kona*. From drawings by F. W. Frowhawk in "Avifauna of Laysan and the Hawaiian Possessions" by Walter Rothschild (London, 1893–1900).

HEMIGNATHUS

The genus *Hemignathus* contains two species groups (superspecies). Their geographical distribution is shown in Table 1.

TABLE 1

	Hemignathus obscurus	Hemignathus lucidus
Kauai	H. (obscurus) procerus	H. lucidus hanapepe
Oahu	H. obscurus ellisianus	H. l. lucidus
Molokai	(lacking)	(lacking)
Maui	(lacking)	H. lucidus affinis
Lanai	H. obscurus lanaiensis	(lacking)
Hawaii	H. o. obscurus	H. (lucidus) wilsoni

H. obscurus is related to *Loxops virens* but is larger and has a much longer, more decurved bill and a relatively shorter tail. Its representative on Kauai *(procerus)* has a huge bill and is best treated as a distinct species. All members of the *obscurus* group, with the doubtful exception of *procerus,* are extinct. *Hemignathus obscurus* fed on insects which it sought by hitching along the trunks or larger limbs of trees as would a creeper or woodpecker, meanwhile probing in crevices in the bark with its bill in search of prey. At times it would tap or pry away a loose bit of bark with its thin, delicate bill. It also probed in flowers for nectar and insects and in the deep leaf axils of the climbing pandanus *(Freycinetia)* for insects.

In *H. lucidus* (all three races of which are probably extinct) the upper mandible is like that of *obscurus* but the lower is much shortened and thickened producing a unique bill. This species like *obscurus* crept along the trunks of trees in search of insects. It used its heavier lower mandible to pry or chip off bits of bark; the tapping of its bill when so doing was sometimes audible (Perkins, 1903: 428). The bill of *lucidus* was not well adapted to probing for nectar and this species rarely visited flowers.

In *H. wilsoni,* the geographical representative of the *lucidus* group on Hawaii, the lower mandible has become straight, heavy and like a chisel. It was always commoner than any race of *lucidus* and still occurs in fair numbers. Munro (1944: 119) wrote of it: "All its muscles are well developed, especially those of the head and neck, and its skull is exceptionally thick. The head is larger than that of the Kauai species [*H. lucidus hanapepe*] and we had difficulty in getting the skin over it. The mandible seems to extend further back than in most birds. I believe this has been brought about by its habit of using the lower mandible as a woodpecker does its bill. It uses great energy in beating at the bark and wood, breaking off pieces and dropping them. . . . It drives the lower mandible with considerable force into the crevices of the bark, the mouth kept open, the tapping noise being plainly heard at a distance. . . . When it gets the lower mandible inserted it uses it as a lever. . . . The pieces which break off it takes with both mandibles and throws off,

sweeping the long upper one into the crevices opened on the branch."
Perkins (1903: 428) adds: "Not infrequently it lays hold of a project-
ing piece of bark or the stump of some small broken branch, and shaking
its head from side to side, and pulling in all directions, endeavours to
tear it down. If unsuccessful in the attempt, it will alternate this treatment with a shower of blows from its gaping bill." Unlike its congeners,
H. wilsoni never visits flowers for nectar.

The difference in the bills of *Hemignathus obscurus* and *H. wilsoni* is
greater than that existing within the limits of many families of birds,
much less within a single genus. Yet in other respects these two species
are very similar, indicating close relationship, which is further shown
by the intermediate species, *H. lucidus*. We may assume that the modification of the bill in *Hemignathus* has been rapid. Further evidence
on this point is given by geology. The latest authority (Stearns, 1946)
suggests that the Hawaiian Islands are of Pliocene and later age.
Assuming it was mid-Pliocene before the islands were forest-clad and
suitable for birds, about five million years would be available for the
evolution of the Drepaniidae. Speciation within *Hemignathus,* one of
the specialized later genera of the family, occupied, we may be sure,
only a small portion of this time.

Thus in *Hemignathus* a rapid divergence in feeding habits and correlated structure of the bill has occurred. One species, *lucidus,* is intermediate and appears ill adapted for either the old or new habits. The
three races of *lucidus* were uncommon and local and the total population of each may have been only a few hundred. This further suggests
that the species was relatively unsuccessful. *H. wilsoni* was commoner
and more generally distributed ecologically and since it occurred on the
large island of Hawaii, its total population was probably several thousand. *H. o. obscurus* of Hawaii was originally as common as *wilsoni* or
more so, suggesting that it too was well adapted to its particular ecological niche. All forms of *Hemignathus* are strictly limited to the
forests, and doubtless individuals were blown or carried from island
to island only very rarely and accidentally. It is unlikely that the population of one island was subdivided into partially isolated colonies, unless
temporarily on the larger islands by lava flows.

The rapid divergent evolution believed to have occurred in *Hemignathus* seems to represent what Simpson (1944: 206) has called quantum evolution, i.e., "the relatively rapid shift of a biotic population
in disequilibrium to an equilibrium distinctly unlike an ancestral condition." While there is some objection to this use of the word "quantum,"
the type of evolution in question is real and of great importance, since
it is often involved in the major transformations that give rise to families
and other higher taxonomic categories. In quantum evolution preadaptation, selection, and sometimes nonadaptive genetic change, all play a
part. The most plausible genetic basis for such evolution differs with the
importance assigned to each of these factors (Simpson, 1944; Wright,

1945); probably the role of each varies under different circumstances. It seems likely that *Hemignathus obscurus* and *H. lucidus* were originally geographical representatives of a single species and quite similar morphologically at the time they were first brought into competition by secondary overlap in range. Selection then began and led to increasing divergence in feeding habits and bill structure, just as in the two Kauai species of *Loxops* but more pronounced. Perhaps the overlap in range occurred first on Hawaii, since *wilsoni* of that island is the most modified species. In *Hemignathus*, therefore, preadaptation and nonadaptive change may have been relatively unimportant and selection (in the presence of empty ecological niches) of great significance. If such were the case, it is not essential to postulate a number of very small, partially isolated populations, as considered necessary by Wright (1945) if both selection and nonadaptive genetic drift are to be simultaneously effective.

The changes in the bill of *Hemignathus* illustrate the transformation of a specialized structure. The result, as seen in *H. wilsoni,* is somewhat grotesque but appears effective and may be further perfected. Equally peculiar bills occur in a few continental birds of wide distribution (and hence successful) such as crossbills *(Loxia)*, skimmers *(Rynchops)*, or certain parrots. The evolutionary modification of a specialized structure, though rare, may be of great importance occasionally (Amadon, 1943).

Transformation of the bill has occurred at least four times in the Drepaniidae, although *Hemignathus* is the only genus in which the intermediate form still existed. In the peculiar *Pseudonestor xanthophrys* of Maui both the upper and lower mandibles are very heavy. Its bill is used to crush dead twigs of the koa tree thus exposing larvae of cerambycid beetles. *Pseudonestor* is closely allied to *Hemignathus;* perhaps these two came into competition at a time when they were more similar, leading to divergence. In the five species of the genus *Psittirostra* the bills are, to varying degrees, finch-like. The genus probably evolved from a less specialized ancestor, similar to *Loxops virens.* The extreme of this genus is *Psittirostra kona* which cracked hard seeds in its huge bill. The little known *Ciridops* also evolved a finch-like bill.

SUMMARY

The Hawaiian honeycreepers (Drepaniidae) are an excellent example of rapid adaptive radiation occurring in recent geological periods in a favorable environment having many vacant ecological niches. In the genus *Hemignathus* three species, one of them intermediate and apparently ill adapted, represent stages in a rapid ecological shift in habits and correlated morphological structures of the type Simpson has called quantum evolution. Such evolution, though important, occurs rarely or locally and is comparatively rapid, so that direct evidence, fossil or recent, is scanty. *Hemignathus* provides perhaps the only known contemporary example among birds and even here some of the species involved are extinct. Simpler examples of divergence in the Hawaiian genera *Phaeornis* and *Loxops* suggest that much of the impetus for such change comes from competition between similar species.

Received January 28, 1947

REFERENCES AND NOTES

I am indebted to Drs. Ernst Mayr, John A. Moore and Bobb Schaeffer for valuable suggestions.

Dean Amadon, Specialization and evolution, *Amer. Nat.* **77**, 133–41 (1943).

David Lack, Ecological aspects of species formation in passerine birds, *Ibis* **86**, 260–86 (1944).

Ernst Mayr, *Systematics and the Origin of Species* (Columbia Univ. Press, New York, 1942).

George C. Munro, *Birds of Hawaii* (Tongg Publishing Co., Honolulu, 1944).

R. C. L. Perkins, *Fauna Hawaiiensis,* Vol. 1, pt. 4, Vertebrata; Vol. 1, pt. 6, Introductory essay on the fauna (Cambridge Univ. Press, Cambridge, 1903, 1913).

George Gaylord Simpson, *Tempo and Mode in Evolution* (Columbia Univ. Press, New York, 1945).

Harold T. Stearns, Geology of the Hawaiian Islands, Bull. 8, Terr. Hawaii, Div. Hydrography, 1946.

Sewall Wright, Tempo and mode in evolution: A critical review, *Ecology* **26**, 415–19 (1945).

The Endemic Fish Fauna of Lake Lanao, and the Evolution of Higher Taxonomic Categories[1]

George Sprague Myers

Stanford University

INTRODUCTION

The present paper is concerned only incidentally with speciation. Its purpose is to point out some striking but neglected features of lake-fish evolution that illustrate the rapid origin of genera and still higher categories going on at the present time. I have selected the Lanao fishes as an example for several reasons. First, I have examined the fishes myself. Second, the Lanao fishes are in a recognizable stage of what has been called "explosive" evolution. Third, the age of the lake can be determined geologically, and its relative youth cannot be in serious dispute. Fourth, the remarkable zoogeographical situation of Lanao and of Mindanao Island excludes any reasonable possibility that more than one still existing species could have given rise to the 18 endemic species and four endemic genera now inhabiting the lake. The endemic Lanao fish fauna is without parallel, so far as known, in demonstrating explosive specific and generic evolution from a known and still existing ancestral species.

I am deeply indebted to my long-time friend and colleague, Dr. Albert W. Herre, discoverer and describer of the Lanao fish fauna, for many discussions regarding Lake Lanao and its fishes, extending through a period of 30 years. The late

Reprinted from *Evolution* 14, 323–33 (1960), by permission of the author and publisher.

Professor Bailey Willis of Stanford, well known for his geological researches on four continents, did me the honor of employing his extensive
firsthand knowledge of Philippine geology to prepare the brief geological
account of Lake Lanao quoted below. Finally I must present my best
thanks to my present graduate student, Mr. Angel Alcala, Instructor
in Zoology at Silliman University, Dumaguete, Oriental Negros, for
making further collections of Lanao fishes for Stanford. Mr. Alcala was
working under National Science Foundation Grant G4381, made to
Dr. Walter C. Brown for herpetological research in the Philippines.

THE LAKE

Lake Lanao lies at an altitude of approximately 2,100 feet in the midst
of a volcanic area in central Mindanao, the largest island of the southern
Philippines. Its exact area is in dispute, Herre giving it 375 square
kilometers and others as many as 900. The late Professor Bailey Willis,
who had given much attention to Philippine geology, as well as to that
of the African Rift Valley and its lakes, investigated what was known
of the geological history of Lake Lanao and prepared the following
statement for me:

"The island of Mindanao has risen from the ocean gradually and
unequally since the Miocene. It now consists of plateaus, hill country,
swamps, and volcanoes. The streams were initially small and isolated
from each other. The headwaters were, and are, generally swift and the
lower courses estuarine.

"A north-central region was built up by basalt flows to a plateau, on
which a small system of rivers developed. Some of them flowed southwesterly to Illana Bay, others northwesterly to Iligan Bay. The divide
between them ranged from southwest to northeast.

"Volcanoes were built up across the southwesterly flowing streams
and they were dammed. Their headwaters gathered in the basin thus
formed until they overflowed a low pass in the divide at Camp Keithly
and discharged into Iligan Bay on the north coast.

"The impounded waters constitute Lake Lanao. The basin is probably
shallow, 200 to 300 feet, perhaps, where deepest. The outlet at Camp
Keithly plunges over a fall into a short canyon, indicating an age of
10,000 years, more or less. The principal tributaries to the lake enter
from the southeast, from young but dormant volcanoes, and may at
times have brought in quantities of ash."

While I have no specific reason to doubt Dr. Willis's estimate of the
age of Lake Lanao, 10,000 years seems to be a very short time for the
evolution of the Lanao fish fauna. When I brought up this question,
Dr. Willis replied that the length of the canyon worn by the Agus River
indicated a very brief erosional period. The possibility remains that
more than one volcanic damming has been involved in the history of
Lake Lanao, but the relative youth of the lake cannot be seriously
doubted. The geology of the Lanao Plateau obviously needs more . . .
investigation.

THE FISHES

Dr. A. W. Herre collected fourteen species of the Lanao fishes and described them formally in 1924, without mentioning the peculiar evolutionary features concerned. Before the publication of his 1924 paper, he had prepared an account of the zoogeography of Philippine freshwater fishes, in which he implicitly recognized the autochthonous nature of the Lanao fish fauna. However, this distributional paper was not published until considerably later (Herre, 1928). Dr. Herre visited the lake upon later occasions, adding two more species in 1926 and two in 1932.

After Dr. Herre joined the Stanford Museum staff in 1928, I urged upon him the value of preparing an account of the evolutionary features of the Lanao fauna. This resulted in the proposal of a new genus for one remarkable Lanao species (Herre and Myers, 1931) and, finally, in Herre's well-known paper of 1933. Since that time, nothing of importance has been published on these fishes save for Dr. Brooks' review of 1950.

This history is important because of the destruction of Herre's earlier material when the Bureau of Science was dynamited and its collections totally destroyed by Japanese troops in February, 1945, during the battle of Manila. The only sizable collection of Lanao fishes presently available is that in the Natural History Museum of Stanford University. This consists of a few specimens obtained by exchange from the Bureau of Science before World War II; the excellent collection made by Dr. Herre in 1931, including the types of two of his species; and a small collection made at my request in 1959 by Mr. Alcala. Two of the endemic genera (*Mandibularca* and *Spratellicypris*) and the majority of the species are represented. The only other collection of Lanao fishes known to exist in any museum is a small one obtained in 1908 by Dr. Hugh M. Smith and Dr. Paul Bartsch, and now in the U.S. National Museum. This collection was not reported upon *in extenso* until long after Herre's work was completed (Fowler, 1941). I am unable to accept some of Fowler's identifications and have not considered them in the present paper. Two of Herre's endemic genera (*Cephalakompsus* and *Ospatulus*) are known only from the destroyed types.

I have examined the Stanford collection and have had much unpublished information from Dr. Herre. Despite the unavailability of several of the described species, I am convinced that most if not all of the species described by Herre are distinct, some of them remarkably so. Unfortunately, little ecological information is on record. Most of the collections obtained from the lake have been purchased from the native fishermen. The lake is extensively fished, and some of the endemic forms are highly prized as foodfishes by the local Moros.

The endemic forms are all members of the Cyprinidae, the largest family of primary freshwater fishes. The large species flock consists of 13 known species of the genus Dr. Herre called *Barbodes,* better called

Puntius (see Weber and de Beaufort, 1916) but in my opinion not easily distinguished from the widespread genus *Barbus* (Myers, 1960). Five more species are placed in four genera, *Spratellicypris* (1), *Mandibularca* (1), *Ospatulus* (2), and *Cephalakompsus* (1), all of them obviously immediately derived from stocks of *Barbus* within the lake. Other still undescribed species are probably present in the lake. Two non-endemic predators are present, *Channa striata*, perhaps introduced by man, and one diadromus eel (*Anguilla celebesensis*). Eels of this group are known to be able to ascend rapids and waterfalls impassable to other fishes. The North American black bass (*Micropterus salmoides*), a voracious predator, is said to have been introduced in recent years.[2]

DERIVATION OF THE MINDANAO CYPRINIDAE

Herre (1928 and 1933) has outlined some of the distributional history of the Philippine Cyprinidae, and I have published a general study of the zoogeography of the freshwater fishes of the region (Myers, 1951). The essential facts are as follows:

Central and southern Borneo teems with Cyprinidae, but the cyprinid fauna of North Borneo is relatively depauperate. Cyprinids have entered the Philippines from North Borneo in two widely different directions, through the Palawan-Calamianes chain to Mindoro, and through the Sulu chain to Mindanao. Cyprinids got no farther. The family is absent in the rest of the Philippines, and in Celebes. The Palawan-Mindoro cyprinids do not concern us here.

That Cyprinidae reached Mindanao via a sweepstakes route, across a series of saltwater gaps, is unlikely. My own studies (Myers, 1938, 1949, 1951) indicate that freshwater fishes are less likely to cross such gaps, especially a series of them, than any terrestrial animals, although they must have done so (probably only once, across a very narrow barrier) at Lombok Strait (Myers, 1951). The Lombok crossing, if not by the hand of man, was almost certainly by means of a local cyclone (Darlington, 1938; Myers, 1951), for the saltwater gap at Lombok Strait, although probably broader now than in the Pleistocene, cannot have been bridged very recently (see Bruun and Kiilerich, 1957). Nor is it likely that hurricane (typhoon) winds could have aided the fishes invading Mindanao. The typhoon tracks shown by Dickerson (1928: 40) are all westerly in direction. Finally, freshwater fishes are not well adapted to raft-dispersal across seas!

The obvious conclusion is that freshwater fishes entered Mindanao across a dry-land filter bridge, through the Sulu chain. Just what lowering of sea level occurred there during the Pleistocene, or what elevations or depressions of the Sulu chain may have occurred, is not known. The region is a volcanic, unstable one.

That few or no remains of the cyprinid migration are to be found today on the islands of the Sulu Archipelago is not too surprising. Dr. Herre fished the largest island, Jolo. He found the streams small and without Cyprinidae, but believes that relatively recent volcanic activity has wiped out the freshwater fishes of the island (Herre, 1928).

Quite clearly, then, North Borneo itself, together with the Sulu Archipelago, acted as a filter bridge to limit the access of freshwater fishes to Mindanao. Only three genera of Cyprinidae reached Mindanao (*Barbus, Rasbora,* and *Nematabramis*) and these three are still the dominant cyprinid genera in the streams of North Borneo. Probably only one species of each genus reached Mindanao.

The cyprinid fauna of Mindanao Island outside the Lanao Plateau is very small. There is a single endemic *Rasbora (R. philippina)* confined to the western part of the island and closely related to a North Borneo species (Brittan, 1954: 127–131). There are two species of *Nematabramis (N. alestes* and *N. verecundus),* very closely allied to each other and to the species of North Borneo (Herre, 1953). Finally, there are four nominal species of *Barbus* (or *Puntius*). *Barbus binotatus* is widespread in Mindanao, and, according to Herre (1953: 123), has been erroneously reported from Lake Lanao by Fowler. *Barbus montanoi* is a doubtful form known only from the type from the Agusan River drainage, eastern Mindanao. *Barbus quinquemaculatus* from the Zamboanga Peninsula is probably a geographical subspecies of *B. binotatus*. *Barbus cataractae* (see Fowler, 1941: 797), also from the Zamboanga Peninsula, is probably a localized variant of *B. binotatus*. After examining the evidence, I suspect that there are really only three well-established cyprinid species in Mindanao outside the Lanao Plateau, one *Rasbora,* one *Nematabramis,* and one *Barbus,* each possibly represented on the island by several subspecies.

NATURE OF THE LANAO FISH FAUNA

Barbus binotatus is the commonest, most widespread, and probably the most variable cyprinid of Sundaland (see Weber and de Beaufort, 1916). It ranges from Siam to Singapore, and throughout Sumatra, Java, and Borneo. It is one of the three cyprinids that have been able to cross Wallace's Line at Lombok Strait; the others are forms of *Rasbora* (Brittan, 1954). *Barbus binotatus* exists in most or all of the lowland streams of Mindanao. It exhibits innumerable local races throughout its range.

With no other large endemic lake fish fauna is it possible with such certainty to identify the ancestral species. Lake Lanao was clearly formed rather rapidly, by volcanic action. The ill defined races of *Barbus binotatus* surrounding the Lanao Plateau form the only local source of invasions. Multiple invasions by dissimilar species of *Barbus* or other cyprinid genera are ruled out, unless one wishes to postulate a series of aerial invasions from Borneo, which dropped fishes only on the Lanao Plateau without colonizing the remainder of Mindanao!

Nor are any cyprinids known from Borneo or elsewhere which parallel or are similar to the strange Lanao genera *Mandibularca* and *Spratellicypris*. The same may be true of the genera *Cephalakompsus* and *Ospatulus*, but the types and only known specimens of these two genera were destroyed in Manila.

We are thus forced to the conclusion that *Barbus binotatus* alone gave rise to at least 18 species on the Lanao Plateau, including four new genera. All of the species that I have examined give evidence of derivation from *Barbus binotatus* or at least a close relative. Two or three of the species are only slightly differentiated from *binotatus* and occur both in the lake and its tributary streams. The most distinctive species are known only from the lake itself. *Mandibularca* occurs only in highly turbulent water at the outlet. One or two of the species are said by local fishermen to inhabit only the deeper waters of the lake, while others are found only in the shallow *Potamogeton* beds. *Barbus binotatus* is not known to occur on the plateau, nor are any of the lake species known from below María Cristina Falls, 65 meters in height, in the Agus River which drains the lake.

THE SUPRALIMITAL SPECIALIZATIONS

In 1936, in connection with a report on fishes from Lake Tanganyika, I briefly pointed out (perhaps for the first time) some of the general features of fish evolution in large lakes throughout the world — the African lakes, Titicaca, Baikal, and Lanao. Brooks (1950) has reviewed the subject of speciation in ancient lakes, including Lanao, but Lanao is not an ancient lake, geologically speaking, and the particular features I wish again to stress are neither limited to ancient lakes nor recognized by Brooks.

In Lake Lanao, the peculiar but quite different lower jaw modifications evolved in the genera *Mandibularca* and *Spratellicypris* (and probably in *Ospatulus* as well) are approached nowhere else in the very large family Cyprinidae, which is generally distributed throughout Eurasia, Africa, and North America, and exhibits many remarkable specializations. In other words, the jaw modifications of some Lanao cyprinids transcend the familial limits of all the 1,500 to 2,000 non-Lanao cyprinid species in the world. For want of a better term I am calling these supralimital specializations.

That peculiar supralimital specializations are not confined to Lanao, but are a common and general feature of the evolution of endemic fish faunas in large lakes, is easily demonstrated. The remarkable scaleless cyprinid *Sawbwa* of the Inlé Lake in Burma (Annandale, 1918), the highly modified species of *Orestias* in Titicaca, the extraordinarily modified cichlid genera of Nyasa and Tanganyika, and many of the cottoids of Lake Baikal, all transcend, in one way or another (often strongly and in many characteristics) the limits of specialization of the large, widespread, and varied families to which they belong.

One illustration will suffice. The Percomorphi form the largest order of bony fishes, containing nine thousand species or more. Within the order, many families are defined by relatively few characteristics, of which dentition is often of considerable importance. The freshwater percomorphs of the family Cichlidae form a large family of perhaps 700 species, distributed throughout Africa, Syria, Madagascar, southern India, and tropical America. Their dental characteristics are generally rather uniform, the modifications usually of small degree. Yet in some of the endemic cichlid genera of Lake Tanganyika, the dental modifications (especially the great, double pointed, heavy-based teeth of *Perissodus* and the utterly strange leaf-like teeth of *Plecodus*) far transcend the limits of dental modification not only of the family Cichlidae, but also of the order Percomorphi and of the entire class of bony fishes. Nothing remotely like them exists. Nor are dental characters the only ones involved. Specializations of the pelvic fins for bottom living (genera *Asprotilapia, Enantiopus*), which elsewhere are considered to be taxonomically of great importance, occur. Indeed, some of the Nyasa and especially the Tanganyika cichlids have come to resemble closely such diverse percomorph families as the Blenniidae (*Telmatochromis*), Girellidae (*Tropheus*), and certain European Percidae (*Asprotilapia*), representing a radiative divergence, and convergence towards different families, entirely unknown elsewhere in the entire gigantic order Percomorphi.

Both *Perissodus* and *Plecodus,* as well as certain other African lake cichlids, might easily be held to represent monotypic families, as has indeed been done with the Comephoridae and (by some) the Cottocomephoridae of Lake Baikal. The late Dr. David Starr Jordan, when shown the jaw of the Lanao genus *Mandibularca*, remarked that a family might well be set up for this genus alone. While I cannot quite agree with this opinion, Jordan's remark is indicative of the situation.

It may be noted that supralimital specializations in fishes are not confined to lake faunas. Any specialization peculiar to one species or genus is, in a sense, a supralimital specialization. However, the general or perhaps the invariable occurrence of extreme and unique specializations in the fishes of lakes that have existed long enough to have produced considerable endemic fish faunas, is notable. Still more notable is the fact that species possessing striking supralimital specializations form a much higher percentage of older lake faunas than they do of stream faunas in general.

The reason for this seems obvious. Most freshwater fishes inhabit streams and are adapted to life in running water. When lakes are formed, only species already adapted to the slow moving, quiet backwaters are able to take immediate and full advantage of an extensive stillwater environment. This extensive new environment usually provides many biotopes not represented in streams, and, in addition, geographical barriers (especially in larger lakes) which may either be present originally or develop with the evolution of the lake itself. The inability of biologists, who are terrestrial animals, to envision these subaquatic facts has greatly hindered studies of fish evolution in lakes.

STAGES OF LAKE FISH EVOLUTION

It is possible to point out sequential steps in the evolution of lake fish faunas, using different existing large lakes as examples; it seems worthwhile to do so. I have specifically refrained from any attempt to evaluate the probably numerous instances in which a relatively small or recent lake has obviously permitted the evolution of one or a few species, sometimes of diverse groups. One such lake is Lake Waccamaw in North Carolina (Hubbs and Raney, 1946). Another is Bear Lake, on the Utah-Idaho boundary, in which three distinct coregonids have evolved (Snyder, 1919). The coregonids have been especially prone to apparent endemism in northern glacial and alpine lakes, but doubt as to the real distinctiveness of many such forms in Postglacial lakes has often been expressed.

In the North American Great Lakes, which have become generally available to fishes only since the geologically recent retreat of glaciation, the coregonids of the "lake herring" (*Leucichthys*) type have experienced a burst of evolution, but many of the endemic species and races are still difficult to separate (Koelz, 1929), if indeed they are really distinct. The fauna is still too young to show anything very definite in the way of supralimital specializations, but the development of species flocks of coregonids is evident. Except for the "lake herrings," no other group of fishes so well preadapted to very cold, still water was present, and this one gained ascendancy.

A similar situation, but probably of greater age because of the greater distinctiveness of the species, is seen in the athernids (*Chirostoma*) of Lake Chapala and other lakes in Mexico (Regan, 1906–1908; Jordan and Hubbs, 1919; Alvarez, 1950) and the cichlids (Meek, 1907; Regan, 1906–1908) of Lakes Nicaragua and Managua. Supralimital specializations among the Cyprinodontidae are clearly foreshadowed in the dwarf, deep-bodied species of *Orestias* in Lake Titicaca (Tchernavin, 1944), which are unlike any of the non-Titicaca *Orestias*.

A clearly more advanced stage is represented by Lake Lanao, in which a single ancestral species of cyprinid has given rise to a species flock, five members of which have become so distinct as to be referable to four endemic genera. Their supralimital specializations have been mentioned above. The excellent work of Mr. Greenwood on the Cichlidae of Lake Victoria shows that the Victoria cichlids are in a state more or less comparable to that of the Lanao cyprinids, although evolution is proceeding on a far grander scale. The species flocks are much larger and there are four distinctive endemic genera (Greenwood, 1956, 1959), but the ancestral types are either lost or unidentifiable. However, as in Lanao, endemics of families other than the dominant one are absent.

A much older stage is represented by the fishes of Lake Nyasa, which Brooks (1950: 135) estimates to be approximately 500,000 years old. Fryer (1959: 264) gives evidence pointing to greater age. As in all other large Central African lakes, the cichlids (Trewavas, 1935; Fryer, 1959) are dominant. They present the greatest of all known species flocks among lake fishes — over 100 species of the widespread genus *Haplochromis*. In addition, there are over 70 cichlid species belonging to 20 endemic genera, several of which exhibit remarkable supralimital specializations. However, fishes of other families have entered the lake and established endemic species, but only one endemic genus (Worthington, 1933; Jackson, 1959). Most large lakes are drained by physiographic evolution before they attain any age such as that of Nyasa, and it alone remains to represent the evolutionary stage of its fish fauna. The same is true of the two still older lake fish faunas, those of Tanganyika and Baikal.

Lake Tanganyika is at least 1,500,000 years old and may be even older (Brooks, 1950: 148). Its fish fauna (Poll, 1946; 1953) indicates a much later evolutionary stage than that of Nyasa, this being especially notable because of the comparable size and geographical proximity of these two immense Rift Valley lakes. The cichlids are still dominant; they are fewer in number of species than in Nyasa, but the vast majority belong to endemic Tanganyika genera. The only group that could be called a "species flock" is formed by the 19 species of *Lamprologus,* a genus also represented in the Congo.[3] Several of the endemic genera, as has already been noted, are morphologically worthy of familial or subfamilial groupings, and several have come to resemble quite different families of Percomorphi. In non-cichlid fishes, Tanganyika has had time to develop, in addition to a number of endemic species belonging to non-endemic genera, two endemic genera of Clupeidae, two of Bagridae, two of Clariidae, one of Cyprinodontidae (representing a distinctive subfamily; Myers, 1936) and one (*Luciolates*) of Centropomidae (Worthington and Ricardo, 1937; Poll, 1953). Evolution of some of these must have been accomplished in the face of strong competition by the entrenched Cichlidae.

Lake Baikal is the oldest of all, perhaps as much as 75,000,000 years old; its southern basin is Paleocene or possibly even late Cretaceous in age. However, the present lake basin was enlarged and deepened as late as the Pleistocene (Brooks, 1950: 33), and it is doubtful that even the most distinctive Baikal fishes arose prior to the Mid-tertiary. The Cottidae and their derivatives are dominant in Baikal; species of no other fish families are endemic to the lake (Taliev, 1955). The absence of non-cottoid endemics is notable; it is probably due to the poverty of the Siberian fish fauna. The 26 endemic cottoid species belong to nine endemic genera, eight referred by Taliev to two endemic subfamilies of the Cottidae and one genus with two species to the endemic family Comephoridae.

Other lake fish faunas might be fitted into the sequence, but this seems unnecessary.[4]

In all the larger endemic lake-fish faunas, from the youngest to the very oldest, a single family group, preadapted over other stream fishes for lake life, has gained dominance over all others and has retained it. This accounts for my former belief (Myers, 1936) that access to lakes dominated by a single fish family must have been restricted. Access was restricted in Lake Lanao, but probably this has only rarely been true in other lakes. Moreover, in all except the youngest lake fish faunas, supralimitally specialized forms are evident and continue to become more striking until some of them, in the older lakes, could be or are accepted by taxonomists as distinct families.

One other important point should be made. The greater richness in genera and species of the older lake fish faunas, insofar as the dominant family is concerned, compared to the fluviatile fauna of the same family in the same region, is always striking. The Lanao cyprinid fauna dwarfs the cyprinid fauna of Mindanao outside the lake. More than half the African species and far more than half the African genera of the large family Cichlidae are endemics in the lakes of East Central Africa. The greater part of the North American forms of *Leucichthys* are lake endemics. Probably the same is true of Mexican atherinids of the genus *Chirostoma*. The forms of *Orestias* in Lake Titicaca are more numerous than those in the rest of the Andean Altiplano. The cottoid genera of Baikal comprise over three-fourths of the known genera of freshwater cottoids in the world.

ISOLATED ENDEMICS

Whether the strange little mastacembelid-like *Chaudhuria caudata* (Annandale, 1918) of the Inlé Lake, sole representative of the family Chaudhuriidae, and the possibly even stranger *Indostomus paradoxus* (Prashad and Mukerji, 1929) of the Indawygi Lake, sole representative of the family Indostomidae, are to be considered as vastly modified relics of autochthonous lake-fish families, is unknown. If so, they would be the ultimate examples of lake-fish specialization, but neither species has any known close relatives, and both may be mere survivors of once widely distributed families. The two genera and three known species of the strange family Adrianichthyidae, from Lake Posso and Lake Lindu in Celebes (see Weber and de Beaufort, 1922), which are undoubtedly derivatives of the family Cyprinodontidae, likewise have no known close relatives by which to judge their exact origin. I would suspect them to be derivatives of the subfamily Oryziatinae, members of which are still widely distributed in fresh waters from India and Japan to Timor, and which have given rise, in India, to the remarkable fish *Horaichthys*. Isolated lake-fish endemics are not too rare, often in lakes in which fishes of another family have become dominant, but the endemic nature of the genus or higher category represented by them is sometimes in doubt. . . . Perhaps some of these isolated endemics are relics of previous cycles of lake-fish evolution in the same basins, cycles which were terminated by great changes in the basin itself.

NEW AREAS,
NEW GROUPS

What has happened, in the normal course of evolution, when one or more representative of an animal group not hitherto represented in the fauna has suddenly gained access to a large area replete with numerous available and unoccupied biotopes, seems to be clear. If the invaders are unable to withstand the competition of the older fauna, they disappear. If they can overcome competition, or especially if there is little or none, rapid or tachytelic evolution occurs, evolution that was impossible in their old home, where better balanced ecological conditions and a balanced fauna held evolutionary divergence more tightly in check. New genera, often utterly unlike their ancestors in one or more striking characteristics, appear with great rapidity. The rapid proliferation of proboscideans, and their development of supralimital specializations after their invasion of America, is a case in point.

The same sort of evolution has happened time and again when island groups were colonized. The supralimital bill specializations of the Galápagos finches, and (whatever their ancestors may have been) especially those of the drepanidid birds in Hawaii, are well known instances. Island evolution of this kind, like lake-fish evolution, is often striking, because the original colonizers found abundant biotopes totally unoccupied when they arrived.

However, the situation differs somewhat in lakes. The colonizers and founders of evolutionary dynasties in lakes must contend not only with the same types of problems that confront island or continent colonizers. In addition, they must face the change from a flowing to a still-water environment, and, in many instances, problems of depth, pressure, and salinity, perhaps new or inimical to them. In fact, it seems possible that gradually increasing salinity in a closed lake basin might eventually check the evolution of some freshwater fish groups very severely (Myers, 1938; 1949).

The tachytelic evolution of lake fishes, in part at least representing quantum evolution in Simpson's sense, seems to point out in a really striking way how genera, families, or even higher categories of different animal groups have evolved. If they could get out of their lakes and use their supralimital specializations in other lakes or in streams, as some undoubtedly have done in the past, many existing lake fishes could easily become the founders of large and flourishing new groups at new adaptive levels. Terrestrial groups are not usually as limited in their ability to escape their ranges as are lake animals. As Simpson has so ably pointed out, the tachytelic evolution of new superior groups has seldom left a fossil record because of the speed with which events progressed, and, we may add, because of the probable localization of those events.

It seems probable that events of the sort I have been discussing account for the almost unbelievably rich fauna of characid fishes of the greatest of all rivers, the Amazon. In its present form the Amazon is not an old river. In its lower course it is probably a reversed river; its old structural basin plunges westward. Its Peruvian reaches formed a great lake in relatively recent geological times, and the immense but fluctuating lakes that now line its lower course comprise one of the largest areas of ponded fresh water now existing on earth.

Finally, we cannot forbear to mention the largest of all bodies of still, quiet water, the deep seas. The supralimital specializations exhibited by the highly modified deep-sea descendants of invaders from more turbulent shallow waters have long been the wonder of all zoologists.

It follows that opportunity — the absence of well-adapted competing groups — is extremely important as a factor in the evolution of higher categories. The importance of such a conclusion in relation to the early, rapid evolution of the main animal phyla is obvious.

SUMMARY

1. The endemic fish fauna of Lake Lanao, all belonging to the family Cyprinidae, consisting of a species flock of 13 species and five species referred to four endemic genera, has evolved in a relatively short time, possibly as little as 10,000 years.

2. The distributional facts permit the identification, beyond reasonable doubt, of the single, still-existing, ancestral species that gave rise to the entire endemic fish fauna.

3. Certain specializations of the endemic Lanao genera are paralleled or approached by no others in the large, widespread family Cyprinidae; because they transcend the morphological limits of all non-Lanao cyprinids, these are termed supralimital specializations.

4. Supralimital specializations are shown to be very characteristic if not invariable features of all large, older, endemic lake-fish faunas; some are so distinctive as to provide characters worthy of family rank.

5. The stages of endemic lake-fish evolution are illustrated by examples, the youngest being the American Great Lakes, the oldest Lake Baikal.

6. A single preadapted fish family represented in the surrounding fluviatile fish fauna assumes dominance in the evolution of large endemic lake-fish faunas.

7. The evolution of lake-fish faunas is compared to that of island faunas, and to the evolution of any groups newly admitted to extensive areas where competition is light or absent, and shown to be essentially similar in the relatively rapid production of supralimitally specialized forms.

8. The latter are often capable of becoming the founders of new genera, families, or perhaps even higher categories, at new adaptive levels. They have unquestionably already done so in the older lake-fish faunas, where certain endemic Tanganyika and Baikal genera are worthy of subfamilial or familial rank.

9. It is suggested that the origin of the excessively rich characid fauna of the Amazon River, and of the striking forms and groups of deep-sea fishes, has been due to similar tachytelic or quantum evolution.

10. It follows that opportunity for rapid radiative evolution is of very great importance in the evolution of higher categories, and that such opportunity still may occur from time to time through geological changes.

Received January 25, 1960

REFERENCES AND NOTES

[1] Abstract published in *Proc. XVth Internat. Congr. Zool.* 151–52 (1959).

[2] It is difficult to see why such an introduction should have been considered. Ecologically, and as a measure for increasing food production, it is clearly unsound. Scientifically, in view of the unique nature of the endemic Lanao fish fauna, it becomes a crime!

[3] The interesting possibility presents itself that Lamprologus is an autochthonous Tanganyika genus which has colonized the Congo basin.

[4] Some other lakes, with the families to which the dominant endemics belong, are: Lake Biwa, Japan (Cyprinidae); the Celebes lakes (Atherinidae, usually); various Mexican lakes (Atherinidae); the African lakes George, Albert, etc. (Cichlidae); various Central Asiatic lakes, such as Lop Nor, Koko Nor, etc. (Cyprinidae or Cobitidae); Utah Lake (Catostomidae).

J. Alvarez, Claves para la determinacion de especies en los peces de las aguas continentales Mexicanas, Secretaria de Marina, Dirreción General de Pesca e Industrias Conexas (Mexico, 1950), 136 pp.

N. Annandale, Fauna of the Inle Lake. Rec. Ind. Mus. **14**, (1918), 214 pp., 26 pls.

M. L. Brittan, A revision of the Indo-Malayan fresh-water fish genus *Rasbora, Inst. Sci. Tech. (Manila), Monograph* 3 (1954), 224 pp., 3 maps.

J. L. Brooks, Speciation in ancient lakes, *Quart. Rev. Biol.* **25**, 30–60, 131–76 (1950).

A. Bruun and A. Kiilerich, Bathymetrical features of the Bali-Lombok Strait, *Marine Research in Indonesia* 3, 1–6 (1957).

P. J. Darlington, The origin of the fauna of the Greater Antilles, with discussion of dispersal of animals over water and through the air, *Quart. Rev. Biol.* **13**, 274–300 (1938).

R. E. Dickerson and others, Distribution of life in the Philippines, *Bureau Sci. (Manila), Monograph* 21 (1928), 322 pp., 42 pls.

H. W. Fowler, Fishes of the groups Elasmobranchi ... Ostariophysi obtained by the ... Albatross ... chiefly in the Philippine Islands, *U.S. Nat. Mus. Bull.* **100** (13) (1941), 879 pp.

G. Fryer, The trophic interrelationships and ecology of some littoral communities of Lake Nyasa with especial reference to the fishes, and a discussion of the evolution of a group of rock-frequenting Cichlidae, *Proc. Zool. Soc. London* **132**, 153–281 (1959), 2 pls.

P. H. Greenwood, The monotypic genera of cichlid fishes in Lake Victoria, *Bull. Brit. Mus. (Nat. Hist.)* 3, 295–333 (1956).

———, Evolution and speciation in the *Haplochromis* (Pisces, Cichlidae) of Lake Victoria, *Proc. XVth Int. Congr. Zool. London* (1959), pp. 147–50.

A. W. Herre, The Philippine Cyprinidae, *Philippine J. Sci.* 24, 249–307 (1924), 2 pls.

———, Two fishes from Lake Lanao, *Philippine J. Sci.* 29, 499–502 (1926), 2 pls.

———, True fresh-water fishes of the Philippines, in Dickerson, 1928 (which see), 242–47. [This paper was written previous to the publication of Herre's 1924 paper, and some of the fish names do not agree with those of the 1924 paper.]

———, Five new Philippine fishes, *Copeia* 1932, 139–42 (1932).

———, The fishes of Lake Lanao: A problem in evolution, *Amer. Nat.* 68, 154–62 (1933).

———, Check list of Philippine fishes, *U.S. Fish and Wildlife Service, Research Report* 20 (1953), 977 pp.

——— and G. S. Myers, Fishes from southeastern China and Hainan, *Lingnan Sci. J.* 10, 233–54 (1931).

C. L. Hubbs and E. C. Raney, The endemic fish fauna of Lake Waccamaw, North Carolina, *Misc. Publ. Mus. Zool. Univ. Michigan* 65 (1946), 30 pp.

P. N. B. Jackson, Revision of the clarid catfishes of Nyasaland, with a description of a new genus and seven new species, *Proc. Zool. Soc. London* 132, 109–28 (1959).

D. S. Jordan and C. L. Hubbs, Studies in ichthyology: A monographic review of the family of Atherinidae or silversides, *Leland Stanford Jr. Univ. Publ. Univ. Ser.* (1919), 87 pp., 12 pls.

W. Koelz, Coregonid fishes of the Great Lakes, *Bull. U.S. Bur. Fisher.* 27 (2), 297–643 (1929).

S. E. Meek, Synopsis of the fishes of the Great Lakes of Nicaragua, *Field Columbian Museum, Zool. Ser.* 7 (4), 97–132 (1907).

G. S. Myers, Report on the fishes collected by H. C. Raven in Lake Tanganyika in 1920, *Proc. U.S. Nat. Mus.* 84, 1–15 (1936), 1 pl.

———, Fresh-water fishes and West Indian zoogeography, *Ann. Rep. Smithsonian Inst.* 1937, 339–64 (1938), 3 pls.

———, Salt-tolerance of fresh-water fish groups in relation to zoogeographical problems, *Bijdr. Dierk.* 28, 315–22 (1949).

———, Fresh-water fishes and East Indian zoogeography, *Stanford Ichth. Bull.* 4, 11–21 (1951).

———, Preface to any future classification of the fishes of the genus Barbus, *Stanford Ichth. Bull.* 7 (4) (1960), in press.

M. Poll, Revision de la faune ichthyologique de Lac Tanganika, *Ann. Musée du Congo Belge, zool.* 4 (1), 145–364 (1946), 3 pls., map.

———, Poissons non Cichlidae, *Explor. Hydrobiol. Lac Tanganika (1946–1947), Result. Scientif.* 3 (5A) (1953), 251 pp., 11 pls.

B. Prashad and D. D. Mukerji, The fish of the Indawygi Lake and the streams of the Myitkyina District (Upper Burma), *Rec. Ind. Mus.* 31, 161–223 (1929), pls. 7–10.

C. T. Regan, *Biologia Centrali-Americana. Pisces* (London, 1906–1908), xxxiv + 203 pp., 26 pls.

G. G. Simpson, *The Major Features of Evolution* (New York, 1953), xx + 434 pp.

J. O. Snyder, Three new whitefishes from Bear Lake, Idaho and Utah, *Bull. Bur. Fisher.* 36, 1–9 (1919).

D. E. Taliev, Bitschki-podkamenschtschiki Baikala (*Cottoidei*) (Akademiia Nauk U.S.S.R., Moskva, 1955), 603 pp.

V. Tchernavin, A revision of the subfamily Orestiinae, *Proc. Zool. Soc. London* **114**, 140–233 (1944).

E. Trewavas, A synopsis of the cichlid fishes of Lake Nyasa, *Ann. Mag. Nat. Hist.* **16** (10), 65–118 (1935).

M. Weber and L. F. de Beaufort, *The Fishes of the Indo-Australian Archipelago,* Vol. 3 (Leiden, 1916), xiv + 455 pp.

———, *ibid.* (Leiden, 1922), 4, xiv + 410 pp.

E. B. Worthington, The fishes of Lake Nyasa (other than Cichlidae), *Proc. Zool. Soc. London* **1933**, 285–316 (1933).

——— and C. K. Ricardo, The fish of Lake Tanganyika (other than Cichlidae), *Proc. Zool. Soc. London* **1936**, 1061–1112 (1937).

House Sparrows: Rapid Evolution of Races in North America

Richard F. Johnston[*]
Robert K. Selander[†]

A number of workers have attempted to demonstrate evolutionary changes in the house (English) sparrow (*Passer domesticus*) in North America since its introduction from England and Germany in 1852 (*1*). Several early studies based on small samples of specimens produced results (*2*) which were negative or statistically unreliable. In an investigation which has been widely cited (*3*) as evidence for slow rates of evolution of avian races, Lack (*4*) found no unequivocal evidence of divergence in bill and wing dimensions of the North American and Hawaiian populations from the Old World stock. However, Calhoun (*5*), using larger samples and employing refined methods of analysis, was able to show that average wing length in populations of the eastern and central United States increased slightly more than 1 mm between the time of introduction and 1930. He also demonstrated geographic variation in average length of wing, femur, and humerus correlated with regional differences in duration and severity of freezing temperatures in the United States. Recently, the possibility that New World populations exhibit regional color differences has been suggested by Keve (*6*).

To assess the full extent of variation in characters of color and size, series of 100 to 250 specimens of house sparrows

Reprinted from *Science* 144, 548–50 (May 1, 1964), by permission of Richard F. Johnston and *Science*. Copyright 1964 by the American Association for the Advancement of Science.

FIGURE 1. Map of North America showing distribution of house sparrow (shaded area) and localities where specimens were taken (dots).

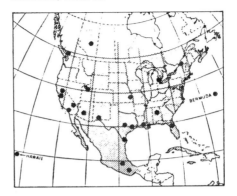

in fresh plumage were taken by us in October and November, 1962 and 1963, at various localities in North America and in the Hawaiian Islands, Bermuda, England, and Germany (Fig. 1). This extensive material clearly demonstrates the existence of pervasive geographic variation in a large number of characters in the North American and Hawaiian populations. Each New World population sampled has differentiated to greater or lesser degree from any other and from the Old World stock. Preparation and analysis of this material is still in process, but the preliminary findings presented here provide a general indication of the surprising extent to which selection has produced morphologic differentiation in a small number of generations. We have not as yet undertaken studies of the developmental basis of the morphologic characters of the house sparrow populations, but, in view of extensive evidence for comparable racial characters in other species of birds and in mammals (7), we are safe in assuming that the geographically variable characters of color, pattern, size, and body proportions are in fact genetically controlled and are either directly adaptive in themselves or represent selectively neutral or weakly nonadaptive correlates of other adaptive characters.

In analyzing individual and geographic variation in color, as well as in size, we have found it useful to segregate our specimens into adult and first-year age groups, since many of the characters studied exhibit significantly different means and variances in the two age groups.

In general, geographic variation is more pronounced in characters of color than in those of size. Specimens from northern and Pacific coastal localities and from the Valley of Mexico (Mexico City) are darkly pigmented, and those from Vancouver, British Columbia, are especially dark. Sparrows from collecting stations in the arid southwestern United States from southern California east to southern and central Texas are relatively pale in color, with extremes of pallor being achieved in samples from Death Valley, California, and Phoenix, Arizona. Samples from Salt Lake City, Utah, Lawrence, Kansas, and other localities in North America can be categorized broadly as intermediate in color. Specimens from Zachary, Louisiana, and Oaxaca City, Mexico, have a conspicuous yellow wash on the posterior under parts which is absent or only weakly indicated in birds from other North American localities.

Geographic variation in color of the breast in female house sparrows from Honolulu, Hawaii, and several localities in North America is shown in Figure 2, which presents spectral reflectance curves (8) for five specimens from each locality.

The overall geographic pattern of color variation in North American house sparrows conforms with Gloger's ecogeographic rule, which relates color to regional variation in temperature and humidity (9). Students of geographic variation in warm-blooded vertebrates a priori expect native North American species to be darker along the northwestern coast and paler in the arid southwest. The fact that house sparrows manifest this pattern of variation is evidence for the selective action of the same environmental factors that are assumed to be significant for native species.

Sparrows from Oahu, Hawaiian Islands, are very distinctive in color, being unlike specimens from English, German, and North American localities. They are characterized by a reduced value of the dark markings of the plumage, a general absence of fine streaks on the under parts, and an overall rufous-buff color which is especially intense on the breast and flanks. The legs and feet tend strongly to be pale buff in color rather than dark brown as in continental birds. The unusually strong differentiation of the sparrows of the Hawaiian Islands is not surprising in view of their geographic isolation and the fact that they have had an evolutionary history apart from North American populations. Sparrows were introduced to the islands in 1870 or 1871 from a New Zealand stock, which in turn had been brought to New Zealand from England in the years 1866–1868 (10).

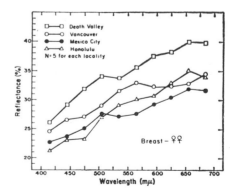

FIGURE 2. Spectral reflectance curves for the breast of female house sparrows from Honolulu, Hawaii, and several North American localities.

We emphasize the fact that geographic variation in color in New World house sparrows does not consist merely of subtle average differences among the samples, with broadly overlapping ranges of variation. On the contrary, in many cases the color differences between samples are both marked and consistent, permitting 100 percent separation of specimens from the two localities. For example, we have observed no overlap in color of the pileum (top of the head) in females between samples from Oakland, California, and Progreso, Texas, or between those from Death Valley, California, and Vancouver, British Columbia. Again, specimens of either sex from the Hawaiian Islands and any of the North American localities are consistently separable on the basis of color.

Geographic variation occurs as regularly in size as in color, and for the most part parallels trends which are generally characteristic of indigenous species. The pattern of variation in size is largely clinal: in the United States and Canada the largest individuals are from the more northerly localities sampled, the smallest are from the desert southwest, and birds from other stations are of intermediate sizes. Some indication of the degree of geographic variation in wing length in North America is provided by data for adult males of three popula-

FIGURE 3. Individual and geographic variation in wing length in adult male house sparrows from three localities. Vertical line: mean; horizontal line: observed range; solid rectangle: 2 standard errors on either side of mean; open rectangle: one standard deviation on either side of mean.

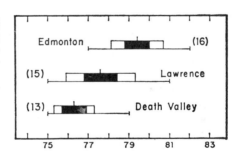

FIGURE 4. Individual and geographic variation in bill length (from nostril) in adult male house sparrows from four localities. See Figure 3 for an explanation of the graph.

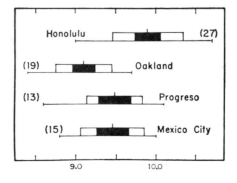

tions shown in Figure 3. Variation in bill length in four representative populations is shown in Figure 4. Note that the bill averages longer in the sample from Honolulu than in the continental populations. This was previously suggested by Lack's data (4), which had been considered equivocal because of uncertainties concerning seasonal variation in his material (11).

For reasons not important to the exposition here, wing length in house sparrows tends to vary independently of body size. Body weight is a good index of size, provided weights are taken from specimens having similar relative amounts of body fat, a character known to vary seasonally with the gonadal condition of the individual (12). Our samples are strictly comparable, since all were taken when the birds had just completed the annual molt and were in the same condition gonadally and physiologically; all specimens show uniformly moderate degrees of subcutaneous lipid deposition.

In Figure 5, mean body weights of adult males from 17 localities in North America are plotted against isophanes of the localities. Isophanes are calculated from latitude, longitude, and altitude of the localities and hence reflect gross climatic features (13). For localities north of southern Texas a simple relationship is evident, and a straight line fitted to the points by the method of least squares has the equation $Y = 24.1 + 0.12X$. The regression coefficient is highly significant (99.9 percent confidence interval = 0.02 to 0.21), and 93 percent of the variability is attributable to the linear regression effect. The observed relationship, which was predictable on the basis of Calhoun's geographically more restricted study (5) of linear dimensions, exemplifies the ecogeographic rule of Bergmann, which describes adaptive trends in body size as they relate to problems of heat flow and temperature regulation (9). Birds of larger body size occur at localities having high isophane numbers, reflecting boreal climates with severe winter cold; and those of smaller body size are from stations with low isophane numbers, reflecting mild or austral climates, occasionally with severe summer heat. A similar relationship between body size and climate is found in many native species of birds.

South of latitude 28°N in North America, other selective factors tend to override the effects of selection for body size as described by Bergmann's ecogeographic rule. Although mean body weight in the sample from Oaxaca City does not fall far from an expected position along the regression line based on data from samples taken in the United States and Canada, birds from Mexico City are surprisingly light in weight and those from Progreso, Texas, are unexpectedly heavy. That these differences reflect real variation in body size and not merely nongenetic variation in level of fat deposition is indicated not only by examination of the fat condition of the specimens but also by data on the length of the tarsus, which in house sparrows is closely correlated with body weight.

Current taxonomic practice gives formal nomenclatural recognition,

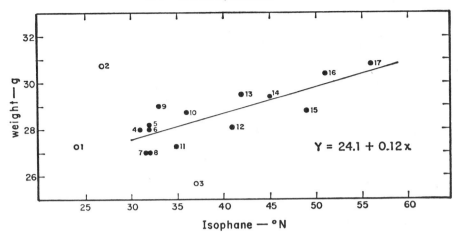

FIGURE 5. Mean body weights of adult male house sparrows plotted against isophanes (see text for explanation). Localities: 1, Oaxaca City, Mexico; 2, Progreso, Tex.; 3, Mexico City, Mexico; 4, Houston, Tex.; 5, Los Angeles, Calif.; 6, Austin, Tex.; 7, Death Valley, Calif.; 8, Phoenix, Ariz.; 9, Baton Rouge, La.; 10, Sacramento, Calif.; 11, Oakland, Calif.; 12, Las Cruces, N.M.; 13, Lawrence, Kan.; 14, Vancouver, B.C.; 15, Salt Lake City, Utah; 16, Montreal, Quebec; 17, Edmonton, Alberta. The regression line is based on data from localities 4 to 17.

at the subspecific level, to morphologically definable geographic segments of species populations. And it is obvious that the levels of differentiation achieved by the introduced house sparrow in the Hawaiian Islands and in a number of areas in North America are fully equivalent to those shown by many polytypic native species. Although application of subspecific trinomials to certain New World populations of sparrows would be fully warranted, we are not convinced that nomenclatural stasis is desirable for a patently dynamic system. Nomenclatural considerations aside, the evolutionary implications of our findings are apparent. Current estimates of the minimum time normally required for the evolution of races in birds range upward from about 4000 years (*14*), and nowhere is there a suggestion that such conspicuous and consistent patterns of adaptive evolutionary response to environments as we have found in New World house sparrows are to be expected within a period covering not more than 111 generations. Actually, much of the differentiation in North American populations must have occurred in the present century, since sparrows did not reach Mexico City until 1933 (*15*), and they were not present in Death Valley before 1914, or in Vancouver before 1900. Our findings are consistent with recent evidence of evolutionary changes in some other groups of animals, including mammals and insects (*16*), within historical times. Clearly, our thinking must not exclude the possibility of animals attaining to extremely rapid rates of evolution at the racial level.

ABSTRACT

Conspicuous adaptive differentiation in color and size has occurred in the house sparrow (*Passer domesticus*) in North America and the Hawaiian Islands since its introduction in the middle of the 19th century. Patterns of geographic variation in North America parallel those shown by native polytypic species, in conformity with Gloger's and Bergmann's ecogeographic rules. Racial differentiation of house sparrow populations may require no more than 50 years.

January 27, 1964

REFERENCES AND NOTES

* Museum of Natural History, University of Kansas.

† Department of Zoology, University of Texas.

1. W. B. Barrows, *U.S. Dept. Agr. Div. Econ. Ornithol. Mammal. Bull.* 1 (1889); L. Wing, *Auk* 60, 74 (1943).

2. C. W. Townsend and J. Hardy, *Auk* 26, 78 (1909); J. C. Phillips, *ibid.* 32, 51 (1915); J. Grinnell, *Am. Naturalist* 53, 468 (1919); _____, *Proc. Calif. Acad. Sci.* 13, 43 (1923).

3. E. Mayr, *Systematics and the Origin of Species* (Columbia Univ. Press, New York, 1942), p. 60; J. Huxley, *Evolution: The Modern Synthesis* (Harper, New York, 1943), p. 519; B. Rensch, *Evolution above the Species Level* (Columbia Univ. Press, New York, 1960), p. 91.

4. D. Lack, *Condor* 42, 239 (1940).

5. J. B. Calhoun, *Am. Naturalist* 81, 203 (1947).

6. A. Keve, *Proc. XII Intern. Ornithol. Congr., Helsinki,* pp. 376–95 (1960).

7. L. R. Dice and P. M. Blossom, *Carnegie Inst. Wash. Publ.* 485, 1 (1937); W. F. Blair, *Contrib. Lab. Vert. Biol.* 25, 1 (1944); _____, *ibid.* 36, 1 (1947); F. B. Sumner, *Bibliog. Genetica* 9, 1 (1932); J. Huxley, *Evolution: The Modern Synthesis* (Harper, New York, 1943), p. 433.

8. Reflection was measured with a Bausch and Lomb Spectronic 20 colorimeter equipped with a color analyzer reflectance attachment. Readings were taken at 30-mμ intervals and a magnesium carbonate block was used as a standard of 100-percent reflectance. See R. K. Selander, R. F. Johnston, T. H. Hamilton, *Condor,* in press, for further explanation.

9. C. L. Gloger, *Das Abändern der Vögel durch Einfluss des Klimas* (Breslau, 1833); C. Bergmann, *Gött. Stud.* 1, 595 (1847); B. Rensch, *Arch. Naturgesch N. F.* 7, 364 (1938); _____, *ibid.* 8, 89 (1939); E. Mayr, *Evolution* 10, 105 (1956); T. H. Hamilton, *ibid.* 15, 180 (1961).

10. D. Summers-Smith, *The House Sparrow* (Collins, London, 1963), p. 182.

11. J. Davis, *Condor* 56, 142 (1954).

12. R. K. Selander and R. F. Johnston, unpublished.

13. A. D. Hopkins, *U.S. Dept. Agr. Misc. Publ.* 280 (1938).

14. R. E. Moreau, *Ibis* (ser. 12) 6, 229 (1930); E. Mayr, *Animal Species and Evolution* (Harvard Univ. Press, Cambridge, 1963), p. 579.

15. H. O. Wagner, Z. *Tierpsychol.* 16, 584 (1959).

16. E. H. Ashton and S. Zuckerman, *Proc. Roy. Soc. London, Ser. B* 137, 212 (1950); E. C. Zimmerman, *Evolution* 13, 137 (1960); E. O. Wilson and W. L.

Brown, Jr., *ibid.* **12**, 211 (1958); R. M. Lockley, *Nature* **145**, 767 (1940); J. N. Kennedy, *Bull. Brit. Ornithol. Club* **33**, 33 (1913); F. C. Evans and H. G. Vevers, *J. Animal Ecol.* **7**, 290 (1938); Th. Dobzhansky, *Evolution* **12**, 385 (1958); _____, *ibid.* **17**, 333 (1963); E. B. Ford, *Cold Spring Harbor Symp. Quant. Biol.* **20**, 230 (1955); P. M. Sheppard, *Advan. Genet.* **10**, 165 (1961); H. B. D. Kettlewell, *Heredity* **10**, 287 (1956).
17. Supported by NSF grants GB 240 and GB 1739.

Early Man in East Africa

RECENT EXCAVATIONS IN OLDUVAI GORGE, TANZANIA, HAVE LAID BARE A NEW CHAPTER IN HUMAN EVOLUTION

Phillip V. Tobias[*]

*Department of Anatomy,
University of the Witwatersrand*

Olduvai Gorge in Northern Tanganyika (Republic of Tanzania) has in recent years thrown a flood of light on an early chapter in the evolution of man. Between 1955 and 1963, L. S. B. Leakey, M. D. Leakey, and their sons and helpers uncovered fossil bones representing no fewer than 14 individuals from various levels in the Olduvai strata (*1*). Although detailed descriptions are yet to be published (*2*), it is clear that earlier and lower mid-Pleistocene deposits of East Africa contain the remains of at least two different kinds of fossil hominids (that is, members of the Hominidae, the family of man). The first group of fossils fits comfortably into a well-defined category, the australopithecines, which have long been recognized as a partially hominized group, that is, a group possessing some characteristics like those of *Homo*. The second assemblage has proved most difficult to place in any existing category. After exploring every other possibility, we have been forced to attribute this second group of fossils to a new and lowly species of *Homo*, namely *Homo habilis*: this species represents a more markedly hominized lineage than the australopithecines and comprises a hitherto-unrecognized and even unsuspected transitional or intermediate form of early man (*3*).

Reprinted from *Science* 149, 22–33 (July 2, 1965), by permission of the author and *Science*. Copyright 1965 by the American Association for the Advancement of Science.

In this article I consider the history and some of the characteristics of the new fossils, as well as their cultural and evolutionary position, and propose modifications to some existing schemes of hominid phylogeny in the light of these new discoveries.

THE OLDUVAI SEQUENCE

Before I review the new discoveries in detail, it may be useful to describe briefly the Olduvai stratigraphic succession (Fig. 1).

FIGURE 1. Schematic representation of the lower half of the Olduvai sequence, showing the approximate vertical positions of hominid fossils (numerals enclosed in squares). The potassium-argon dates are indicated near the left margin (m = million years).

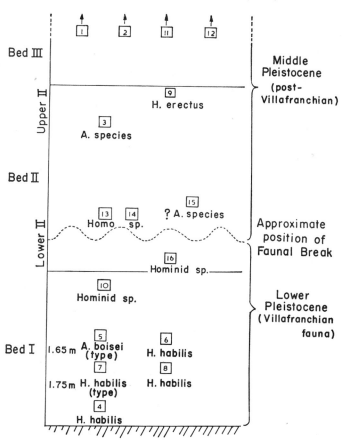

Olduvai Gorge has been cut by river action through a deep succession of old sediments, tuffs, and lavas. From the exposed strata, a remarkable series of fossils and implements has been recovered, ranging in age from Lower to Upper Pleistocene.

The strata exposed in the walls of Olduvai Gorge were divided by Hans Reck into five beds, numbered I to V, from the lowest upwards. This classification was adopted and the limits of the beds were more precisely defined by Leakey and, more recently, by Hay (4). It should be stressed, however, that these beds are not absolute stratigraphic units corresponding to sharp divisions in the Pleistocene sequence of events. Rather they are conveniently mappable units. Thus, as Hay has pointed out, two different marker beds have in various parts of the Gorge been regarded as the top of Bed I. Again, while Reck defined the base of Bed I as the basalt flows, Hay has preferred to include within Bed I the tuffs beneath the basalt. Hay thus regards the basalt flows as a constituent of Bed I in the eastern part of the Gorge.

Further, the newer analyses of fauna made by Leakey and his collaborators (5) tend to relate the fauna of the lower part of Bed II to that of Bed I and to interpret both as belonging to a final Villafranchian faunal stage. On the other hand, the fauna of the middle and upper part of Bed II is considered post-Villafranchian and so to be associated with that of Beds III and IV. The complex of Middle and Upper II, III, and IV comprises a mid-Pleistocene stratigraphic sequence.

In this presentation, the subdivision into five beds will be used to provide a background against which to consider the hominid remains.

Potassium-argon dates are available for several levels within Bed I. The span of time represented by these Beds is suggested by ages 1.75 and 1.65 million years for two levels in the lower half of Bed I. In a word, the chapters of human evolution which are dealt with here cover the period from about 2 million to about half a million years ago.

THE AUSTRALOPITHECINE CHAPTER

Exactly 40 years have elapsed since R. A. Dart published a description of a new kind of higher primate which had been recovered from a limestone fissure at Taung in South Africa (6). This discovery was one of the most remarkable, perhaps the most important, in the history of paleoanthropology. Earlier discoveries of fossilized human ancestors had shown unequivocally human affinities: this is true of the Neanderthal group and even of the earlier and morphologically more primitive Java ape-man, *Homo erectus* (or *Pithecanthropus*, as he has been called until fairly recently). But the Taung specimen differed from the others in being so much smaller-brained, bigger-toothed, and in other respects morphologically more archaic, that its precise affinities remained a cause for dispute for decades. Initially, Dart claimed no more than that it was an ape with a number of features suggesting hominization, that is, an advance in a general human direction. He therefore

TABLE 1

Dates of Discovery of Australopithecine Fossils.

1924	Taung (S. Afr.)
1936–1949	Sterkfontein Type Site (S. Afr.)
1938–1954	Kromdraai (S. Afr.)
1939	Garusi (E. Afr.)
1947–1961	Makapansgat (S. Afr.)
1948–1952	Swartkrans (S. Afr.)
1955–1959	Olduvai (E. Afr.)
1957–1958	Sterkfontein Extension Site (S. Afr.)
1964	Peninj, Lake Natron (E. Afr.)

called it *Australopithecus africanus* — simply the "southern ape of Africa."

With the wisdom of hindsight, we are today able to recognize in Dart's fossil the first real proof of the animal origins of man, the first concrete fossil evidence that Darwin's theory of the origin of species by small modifying steps and gradations from other preexisting species is applicable to man. For here was an apelike creature which showed in its anatomical makeup a greater number of resemblances to hominids than are shown by any of the existing manlike apes of Africa or Asia.

It took time, as well as the discovery of many new specimens of *Australopithecus* (Table 1), the patient study of their anatomical features, and a closer look at the living great apes, to reach the now widely accepted conclusion that the australopithecines were an early branch of the Hominidae, the family of man, rather than of the Pongidae, the family of the apes. No fewer than eight sites in Africa have yielded australopithecine fossils (Fig. 2).

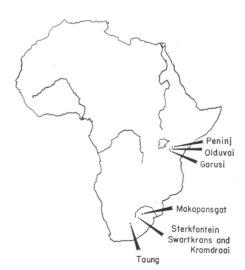

FIGURE 2. The African sites which have yielded fossilized remains of *Australopithecus,* popularly known as ape-men, near-men, or half-men. The three northern sites are in the Republic of Tanzania; the five southern sites are in the Republic of South Africa.

TABLE 2

Number of Australopithecine Teeth from Various Sites Available for Study.

Taung	24
Sterkfontein	162
Kromdraai	39
Swartkrans (35)	311
Makapansgat	55
Garusi	2
Peninj (Natron)	16
Olduvai (7)	16
Total	621

Most of the African australopithecines belong to deposits which have been classified, on comparative faunal evidence, as Lower Pleistocene. At least three sites have provided evidence that the australopithecines survived in Africa into the Middle Pleistocene — namely Swartkrans and Kromdraai in the Transvaal and Peninj (Natron) in Tanganyika.

Of all early hominid groups, the Australopithecinae are the best represented in our fossil storehouses. From the South African sites alone, no fewer than 315 australopithecine entries have been prepared for the forthcoming new edition of the *International Catalogue of Fossil Man*: some comprise a single isolated tooth, some an almost complete cranium. If we accept that all the isolated teeth from Swartkrans and Sterkfontein do indeed belong to australopithecines, the total number of australopithecine teeth now available is over 600 (Table 2). The figure for Olduvai includes only the 16 maxillary teeth of the type specimen of *A. boisei* (7), although others may need to be added to this total on further study. Juvenile and adult specimens are known, as well as male and female. Apart from age and sex variations, more than one kind of australopithecine is represented; the diversity is such that some would classify them as different genera, while others have lumped them into one genus (*Australopithecus*) with several subgenera; yet others would see them as simply different species of a single genus.

Whatever the proper classification, there is an abundance of evidence bearing on the anatomical structure and variation, the behavioral (or cultural) characteristics, and the ecological, geographical, and temporal background of the australopithecines. These lines of evidence concur in demonstrating that at least some of the known australopithecines, or of slightly earlier creatures of very similar aspect, fulfill the morphological requirements for a hypothetical human ancestor.

EAST AFRICAN AUSTRALOPITHECINES

Australopithecines have been found at three East African sites, Garusi (1939), Olduvai (1955, 1959, and ?1963), and Peninj (1964), all situated in northern Tanganyika.

The first specimen was found by Kohl-Larsen at Garusi in 1939. It comprises a fragment of upper jawbone containing both premolars. In 1943 Kohl-Larsen stated that his specimen resembled *Australopithecus* (8), but Weinert later reclassified it as an African species of *Meganthropus* (9). However, Robinson (10) has shown convincingly that the premolars fall within the range for the South African *Australopithecus* from Sterkfontein. This is the smaller-toothed *Australopithecus* which is usually classified today as *A. africanus*. As yet, the Garusi specimen is the only evidence we have suggesting the presence in East Africa of the gracile *africanus* species of australopithecine. The other East African australopithecines are of the larger-toothed *boisei* or *robustus* species.

The most important East African australopithecine is the specimen originally called by Leakey *Zinjanthropus boisei* (11) and now reclassified by Leakey, Tobias, and Napier as a species of the genus *Australopithecus*, namely *A. boisei* (3). For the time being the name *Zinjanthropus* is being retained to designate a subgenus within the genus *Australopithecus*. The specimen comprises a very complete cranium, including all 16 upper teeth; the wisdom teeth or third molars were still in process of erupting, suggesting that the individual was in his late teens at the time of death. A brief preliminary description has been given by Leaky (1, 11). Tobias (12) has placed on record the cranial capacity as 530 cubic centimeters; that is, the specimen's brain was no larger than that of the small-toothed *A. africanus* child from Taung. A detailed monograph on *A. boisei* will appear as part of a series of volumes on Olduvai Gorge by Leakey and his collaborators (2). It may be mentioned here that *A. boisei* is the biggest-toothed and most robust of all the australopithecines, exceeding in most dental dimensions even the largest-toothed of the crassident *A. robustus* group from Swartkrans in the Transvaal (Fig. 3).

It is probable that more large-toothed australopithecines are present in the Olduvai deposits. Three adult teeth, found at the site MNK II, in the lower middle part of Bed II, are for the most part of australopithecine form, shape, and dimensions (Fig. 1, hominid 15). According to Leakey (5), this part of Bed II is characterized by a post-Villafranchian fauna; it is early mid-Pleistocene. These teeth were referred to by Leakey and Leakey (1), but no attempt has yet been made to identify them specifically. Other australopithecine remains may well be present in Bed II, including the very large molar discovered in 1955, high in Bed II (13). Detailed studies of all these specimens are under way, and it will be some years before the complete series of full reports is published.

The third site in East Africa to yield an australopithecine is Peninj, on the west side of Lake Natron, about 80 kilometers northeast of Olduvai Gorge. Here, in January 1964, one of Leakey's assistants, Kamoya Kimeu, a member of the expedition led by Richard Leakey and Glynn Isaac, discovered a nearly complete and superbly preserved

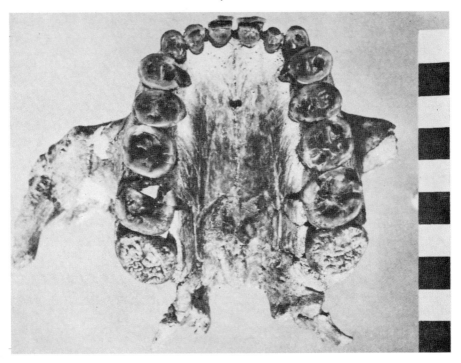

FIGURE 3. The teeth and palate of the large-toothed hominid, *Australopithecus* (*Zinjanthropus*) *boisei,* from Bed I, Olduvai Gorge.

mandible of a large-toothed australopithecine (*1*). According to Leakey's provisional identification of the fauna from this new site, it is of early mid-Pleistocene age and thus much later than the original *A. boisei* from Olduvai. It would seem to be equivalent in age to the upper part of Bed II, or even to the overlying Beds III and IV, in the Olduvai sequence. Despite this age difference, it is of interest to note that the mandibular dental arcade fits that of the maxilla of the Olduvai *A. boisei* almost perfectly and may be provisionally identified as a mandible of *A. boisei* (Fig. 4). Although age comparisons between East and South Africa are fraught with difficulties, it would seem likely that the Peninj australopithecine is comparable in age with those of Swartkrans and Kromdraai. The three sites give evidence that the large-toothed australopithecines survived in Africa well into the mid-Pleistocene (Table 3).

FIGURE 4. Two views of the lower jawbone and teeth of a large-toothed australopithecine from Peninj, next to Lake Natron, some 80 km northeast of Olduvai Gorge. The very small front teeth (incisors and canines) and very large cheek teeth (premolars and molars) characteristic of the robust australopithecine are well shown. This mandible represents a Middle Pleistocene survivor of the African australopithecines, probably a late member of the Olduvai species, *A. boisei.*

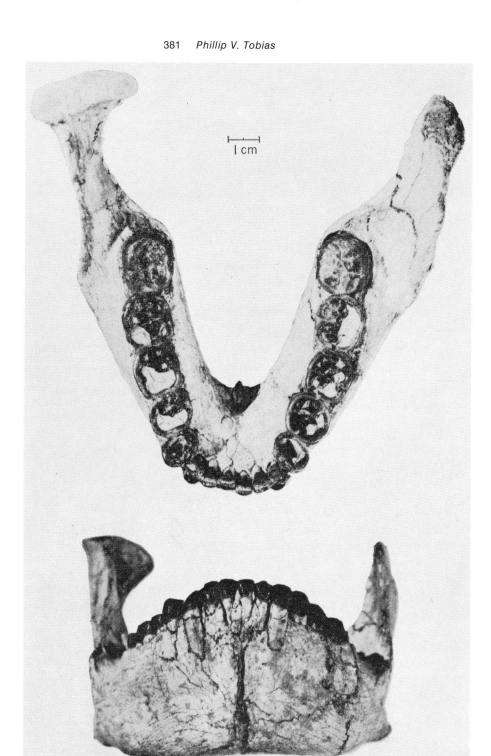

TABLE 3

Chronological and Geographical Distribution of Australopithecines. The Relative Chronological Positions of the East and South African Sites Are Uncertain, as Indicated by the Question Marks. Whereas Potassium-argon Dates Are Available for Olduvai, None Is Available for South African Sites. Comparisons of Fauna Are Valuable Among the Sites Within Each Major Geographical Zone, as Exemplified by Forthcoming New Analyses of Fauna from South African Sites by H. B. S. Cooke and from East African Sites by L. S. B. Leakey. Since Comparisons Between Fauna from the East and South African Sites Are Somewhat Vitiated by the Large Distance and Ecological Differences Between the Areas, This Scheme Must Be Regarded as Highly Provisional.

	South Africa	East Africa
	Kromdraai	?Olduvai II (Upper)
		?Peninj (Natron)
	Swartkrans	?Olduvai II (Middle)
MIDDLE PLEISTOCENE	?Sterkfontein	
LOWER PLEISTOCENE	Extension Site	?Olduvai II (Lower)
		?Garusi
	Makapansgat	
	Sterkfontein	
	Type Site	
	Taung	
		Olduvai I

UNLIKELY CLAIMANTS FOR AUSTRALOPITHECINE STATUS

At least one other fossil from Africa has been claimed to be australopithecine, namely an incomplete cranium discovered in northern Chad and described by Coppens as an australopithecine (14). In 1963, we invited Coppens to visit South Africa and study the original australopithecine material. As a result of his study, Coppens has reached the same conclusion as Leakey and I reached independently, namely that the Chad fragment represented a more advanced hominid than *Australopithecus*. It may belong to the new species, *Homo habilis,* or even to the more advanced *Homo erectus*. The original diagnosis of the Chad fauna as very early Villafranchian is likewise being revised by Coppens; the site is apparently late Villafranchian. Unfortunately, the extremely weathered and distorted state of the Chad specimen may preclude exact comparison with other hominine remains, but it is possible that further hominid material and stone tools may yet be discovered in the area.

The possibility has been raised that the teeth and cranial fragments found outside Africa, at Ubeidiya on the Jordan River in Israel, may have belonged to an australopithecine (15). From a preliminary study of the scanty human remnants, generously placed at my disposal by M. Stekelis, these remains are highly likely to have belonged to *Homo* rather than to *Australopithecus,* although it may be impossible, without the discovery of further material, to attribute them to a particular species of *Homo.*

From Java has come another form of early hominid known as *Meganthropus palaeojavanicus,* of which three or possibly four mandibular fragments were found in the Djetis Beds dated to the beginning of the Middle Pleistocene (16). Robinson has suggested that this Javanese *Meganthropus* is simply an australopithecine (10). However, from a recent reexamination of the originals of *Meganthropus* I and II in comparison with original material from Africa, von Koenigswald and I concluded that, while *Meganthropus palaeojavanicus* has some strong resemblances to australopithecines, it shows several features in which it is somewhat advanced beyond the australopithecine grade (17). In this sense, it stands in the same relation to *Australopithecus* as does *Homo habilis* in Africa, except that *Homo habilis* has departed further from *Australopithecus* in some respects.

Another group of Asian fossils has been thought to possess australopithecine status, namely a group of isolated teeth from China attributed by von Koenigswald to *Hemanthropus peii* (18). Simons has suggested that these teeth are australopithecine (19). It is not impossible, however, that they may represent a more advanced hominid, such as *Homo habilis*; but it may be impossible to resolve the problem of their status until more specimens are recovered, including teeth in a mandible or cranium (17). The position of some claimants to australopithecine status is summarized in Table 4.

In sum, the case for the existence of an australopithecine stage in Asia remains unproven; the only convincing australopithecine sites remain the eight East and South African sites listed in Table 1.

THE GAP BETWEEN
AUSTRALOPITHECUS AND HOMO

Although *Australopithecus* fulfills the morphological requirements for an ancestor of man, there remains a substantial gap between the australopithecines and the most lowly representative of the hominines hitherto recognized (that is, *Homo erectus,* formerly called *Pithecanthropus, Sinanthropus, Atlanthropus,* and so on). The size of this morphological gap may best be illustrated by reference to three parameters which have shown most marked change during the process of hominization in the Pleistocene: brain size, tooth size, and tooth shape. Unfortunately, we cannot use the evidence of hand and foot bones, since we have insufficient evidence bearing on these features in *Australo-*

TABLE 4

Some Fossil Hominids Which Have Been Claimed to Be Australopithecines.

Nature of specimen	Original designation	Revised attribution	Latest interpretation
Swartkrans			
1 mandible, 1 mandibular fragment, and 1 radial fragment	*Telanthropus capensis*	Australopithecine (Dart, Le Gros Clark)	*Pithecanthropus* (Simonetta), *Homo erectus* (Robinson)
Chad			
Craniofacial fragment	Australopithecine	*Homo* sp.	*Homo* sp. (unpublished)
Ubeidiya			
2 teeth and 4 cranial fragments	Hominid	?Australopithecine	*Homo* sp. (unpublished)
Sangiran (Djetis Beds)			
3 mandibular fragments	*Meganthropus palaeojavanicus*	Australopithecine (Robinson)	More advanced than African Australopithecine (?*Homo* sp.) (Tobias and von Koenigswald)
China			
Isolated teeth	*Hemanthropus peii* (originally *Hemianthropus peii*)	Australopithecine (Simons)	Status not clear (?*Homo habilis*)

pithecus and in *Homo erectus*. On the other hand, good samples of braincases and endocranial casts exist for both of these groups.

From seven australopithecine crania it has been possible to make fair estimates of cranial capacity. One of these crania is the Olduvai type specimen of *A. boisei* and six are of small-toothed South African specimens. They include the child from Taung, whose estimated capacity is 500 to 520 cm³; when allowance was made for probable changes with growth, his adult capacity was estimated by various workers (12) as 570, 600, and 624 cm³, bigger, in fact, than any australopithecine capacity actually measured. Selecting the median value (600 cm³), we obtain an australopithecine range of 435 to 600 cm³ and a mean of 508 cm³. The range for nine *Homo erectus* crania, including 1000 cm³ for Olduvai hominid 9 (20), is 775 to 1225 cm³ with a mean of 978 cm³. The cranial capacity of the smallest-brained *H. erectus* was originally estimated by von Koenigswald as 750 cm³; an earlier estimate by

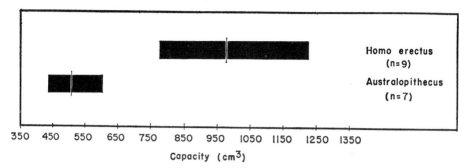

Capacity (cm³)

FIGURE 5. The ranges and means of cranial capacity in two early hominids, *Australopithecus* (including both small- and large-toothed forms) and *Homo erectus* (formerly known as *Pithecanthropus*). The largest estimated australopithecine capacity is 600 cm³ and the smallest of *Homo erectus* 775 cm³.

Weidenreich (*21*), subsequently disavowed by him, was 850 cm³, while Boule and Vallois give 815 cm³ (*22*). Most workers have accepted Weidenreich's final estimate of 775 cm³. These variations, however, reinforce an impression I gained recently when, through the courtesy of D. Hooijer and G. H. R. von Koenigswald, I examined the original Javanese crania: there is a need for reassessment of the capacities of the several Javanese crania of *Homo erectus* (*23*).

Figure 5 represents the ranges and the gap between the presently accepted estimates of cranial capacity for *Australopithecus* and *H. erectus*. There is an interval of 175 cm³ between the capacities of the largest-brained australopithecine and the smallest-brained *H. erectus*. However, this difference is rather meaningless unless we consider the estimated body size of the two forms. Jerison has analyzed brain size (to which cranial capacity is an approximation) into two independent components, one of which is determined by body size and the other of which is associated with improved adaptive capacities (*24*). Given certain assumptions, it has further been possible to estimate the number of cortical nerve cells in the brain as a whole, as well as in each of the two components. The number of "excess" nerve cells — that is, of cells over and above those which can be accounted for by body size — may then be taken as a measure of the real advancement in brain volume, irrespective of body size.

The following are estimates of the numbers of excess nerve cells based partly on Jerison's estimates and partly on my own (*25*):

African great apes	3.4 to 3.6 billion
Australopithecines	4.0 to 5.0 billion
Homo erectus	5.8 to 8.4 billion
Homo sapiens	8.4 to 8.9 billion

If our estimates are correct, there is a bigger gap between *Australopithecus* and *H. erectus* than between the apes and the australopithecines or between *H. erectus* and *H. sapiens*. If, instead of comparing ranges, we compare the mid-values for the groups, we obtain values of 3.5, 4.5, 7.1, and 8.65 billion for the four groups, respectively. Clearly, there is a greater distance between *Australopithecus* and *H. erectus* than between any other two consecutive groups.

To compare dental features of the two groups, it is necessary to point out that on the basis of tooth size, the australopithecines fall into two more or less well-defined subgroups. The first — represented by the fossils from Taung, Sterkfontein, Makapansgat, and Garusi — has somewhat smaller cheek teeth (premolars and molars), but somewhat larger anterior teeth (incisors and canines); this group is called *Australopithecus africanus*. The second — represented by the australopithecine fossils from Swartkrans, Kromdraai, Olduvai, and Peninj (Natron) — has larger cheek teeth and smaller front teeth; this group comprises *A. robustus* and *A. boisei* in the most recent classifications.

Figure 6 demonstrates the ranges of tooth sizes for *A. africanus* and *H. erectus*. Once more the extent of the morphological distance between the Australopithecinae and *H. erectus* is apparent. The differences

FIGURE 6. Crown areas of the maxillary (left) and mandibular (right) teeth of *A. africanus* (the australopithecine from Taung, Sterkfontein, Makapansgat, and Garusi) compared with those of *H. erectus* from Africa, Asia, and Europe. Crown area is the product of the length and breadth of the crown of a tooth; values are in square millimeters.

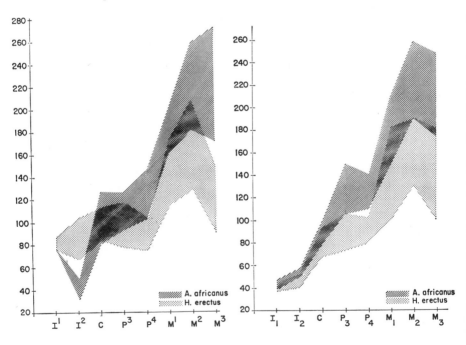

are more striking when *A. robustus* and *A. boisei* are compared with *H. erectus*.

Similarly, Figure 7 reflects variations in the shape and size of the teeth of *A. africanus* and *Homo erectus*. In a word, australopithecine cheek teeth are broader buccolingually, while hominine cheek teeth are narrower (but more elongate) from front to back.

On the basis of these three parameters, there is a clear and sizable gap between known australopithecines and *Homo erectus*. Until recently, it has apparently been tacitly assumed that *Australopithecus* graded more or less insensibly into *Homo erectus* in the manner postulated in general terms by Charles Darwin. It is therefore of no small interest to note that so large a gap exists, not only with respect to one parameter, brain size, but, in the same creatures, with respect to dental traits.

It is this gap that has been filled by *Homo habilis*, the newly discovered hominid which, with respect to the three parameters used to characterize the gap, as well as with respect to other morphological markers, lies in a largely intermediate position.

FIGURE 7. Buccolingual breadths (in millimeters) of the maxillary (left) and mandibular (right) teeth of *A. africanus* and *H. erectus*. The cheek teeth (from P3 to M3) of the australopithecines are characteristically broadened, as contrasted with those of the hominines, represented here by *Homo erectus*.

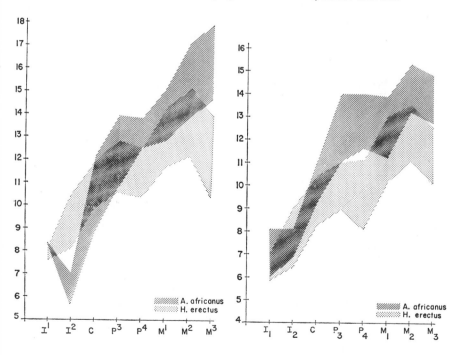

HOMO HABILIS: THE EARLY
PLEISTOCENE HOMININE

The family Hominidae may be divided into two subfamilies, the Austra-lopithecinae and the Homininae. The term "hominine" is the common or colloquial name connoting a member of the subfamily Homininae.

From at least four levels in Bed I and the lower (Villafranchian) and middle parts of Bed II in the Olduvai succession have come skeletal remains of another type of hominid (Fig. 1). This hominid differs widely from *A. boisei,* the large-toothed australopithecine found in the same beds. For instance, the teeth are appreciably smaller than those of *A. boisei.* While the sizes of the teeth of *A. boisei* in general fall above the top of the range for the South African australopithecines, the teeth of this second hominid, especially the premolars, fall at or below the lower end of the australopithecine range (23). Such wide divergence between the two hominids from the same site is far in excess of what can be attributed to sexual dimorphism: in any event, it is accompanied by divergences in shape, proportions, and detailed morphology of the teeth, in cranial shape and curvature, and in cranial capacity. Clearly the second batch of fossils represents another type of hominid. In almost all the departures of the second hominid from the australopithecine morphological pattern, it approaches more closely to the hominine pattern. In other words, the total pattern is more markedly hominized than that of *Australopithecus.* To the Bed I form characterized by these more hominized features we have given the name *Homo habilis.*

The formal naming of the species was announced by Leakey, Tobias, and Napier on 4 April 1964 (3). The generic name implies that this primitive hominid belonged to the genus *Homo,* while the specific name *habilis,* which was suggested by R. A. Dart, means "able, handy, men-tally skillful, vigorous," from the inferred ability of the man to make stone tools.

In accordance with international convention in the naming of new species, one set of remains was selected as the "type specimen" of *Homo habilis.* These were the remains of a juvenile (No. 7 in Fig. 1) whose bones — comprising a lower jaw with teeth, an upper molar tooth, the incomplete parietal bones of the cranial vault, and a set of hand bones — were found scattered on a single floor at the site FLK NNI in the Olduvai Gorge (Fig. 8). In the 3 years that elapsed between his discovery and his naming, he was known as "pre-Zinjanthropus" be-cause the living floor on which his bones were found lies some 35 cm *below* the living floor on which "Zinjanthropus" (or *A. boisei*) had been found. The youth of the individual represented was attested by the state of eruption of the teeth and by the signs of incomplete growth and ossification of the other bones, thus permitting the confident association of this group of bones as those of a single individual.

FIGURE 8. Left lateral view of the dental arcade and body of the mandible of the type specimen of the new Olduvai hominine, *Homo habilis*. In this juvenile specimen, only the first two molars have erupted. The "enamel line" on each tooth is clearly defined; areas of hypoplastic enamel are well shown on the canine tooth.

Apart from the type specimen, remains of four other individuals — three from Bed I (hominids 4, 6, and 8 in Fig. 1) and one from the middle part of Bed II (hominid 13) — were listed as "paratypes" of *Homo habilis*. Bones from two further individuals in the lower and middle parts of Bed II (hominids 14 and 16 in Fig. 1) were referred to the same species, but one of these only provisionally. All told, this batch of remains comprises some 40 teeth, two tolerably complete lower jawbones and a fragment of a third, parts of a pair of upper jawbones, varying portions of the braincases of four skulls, the hand bones of at least two individuals, foot bones, and a collarbone. In addition, two leg bones (tibia and fibula) *may* belong to *H. habilis,* but we cannot rule out the possibility that they belonged to an australopithecine.

The features which distinguish *H. habilis* remains from those of australopithecines and relate them rather to the more advanced Homininae include the capacity of the braincase, both absolutely and in relation to estimated body size, the size, proportions, and shape of the teeth, the shape and size of the jaws, and the curvature of the cranial bones. In addition, the postcranial bones help us to obtain a picture of the very hominine morphological pattern of *Homo habilis,* but they do not assist in the taxonomic problem of deciding whether, for instance, the hand of *H. habilis* was closer to that of *Australopithecus* or to that of the Homininae. This is because we do not know enough about the structure of the hand in either the australopithecines or *H. erectus.*

In all those parts for which we do possess adequate comparative material for both australopithecines and early hominines, most of the bones of *H. habilis* fall at the extreme or beyond the range of variation for the australopithecines.

One important example of the greater degree of hominization shown by *H. habilis* is provided by his cranial capacity. Although the cranial vault of the type specimen is incomplete, it has been possible to estimate the capacity of the intact vault (26). The estimates range from 643 to 724 cm³, with central values 674 and 681 cm³. This is some 80 cm³ more than the largest known capacity of *Australopithecus* and 95 cm³ smaller than the smallest known capacity of *H. erectus.*

When Jerison's formulae (24) are applied to the estimate of 680 cm³, the body size being estimated from the size of the foot bones, a value of 5.3 to 5.4 billion "excess nerve cells" is obtained. That is, the "intelligence" component of the brain of *H. habilis* has about 0.8 to 1.0 billion more neurons than that of the australopithecines, but about 1.7 to 1.8 billion fewer than that of *H. erectus* (25). Jerison's formulae thus provide striking confirmation of the evidence provided by absolute cranial capacity that *H. habilis* is a more advanced hominid than *Australopithecus* but not so advanced as *H. erectus.*

The parameter of tooth size has the same story to tell. Most of the teeth of *H. habilis* are smaller than those of most australopithecines. Thus, in 30 out of 38 comparisons, the absolute sizes of the *H. habilis* teeth lie at the extreme of the range for *Australopithecus* or outside the range.

Not only the size, but the shape of the teeth is distinctly different from that of *Australopithecus* (Fig. 9). Instead of possessing the great breadth characteristic of the teeth of the latter, the teeth of *H. habilis* are narrow and relatively elongated, this departure being found in 20 out of 30 comparisons with the australopithecine teeth. In this respect, the teeth of *H. habilis* resemble those of *H. erectus.*

In sum, *H. habilis* was a pygmy-sized hominid with a relatively large cranial capacity, reduced and narrow teeth, and a number of markedly hominine features in his limb bones. His total structural pattern was that of a creature appreciably more hominized than any of the large group of australopithecines of South and East Africa. The advanced features, moreover, were not those of an individual extreme variant, but characterized all the individuals represented over some considerable

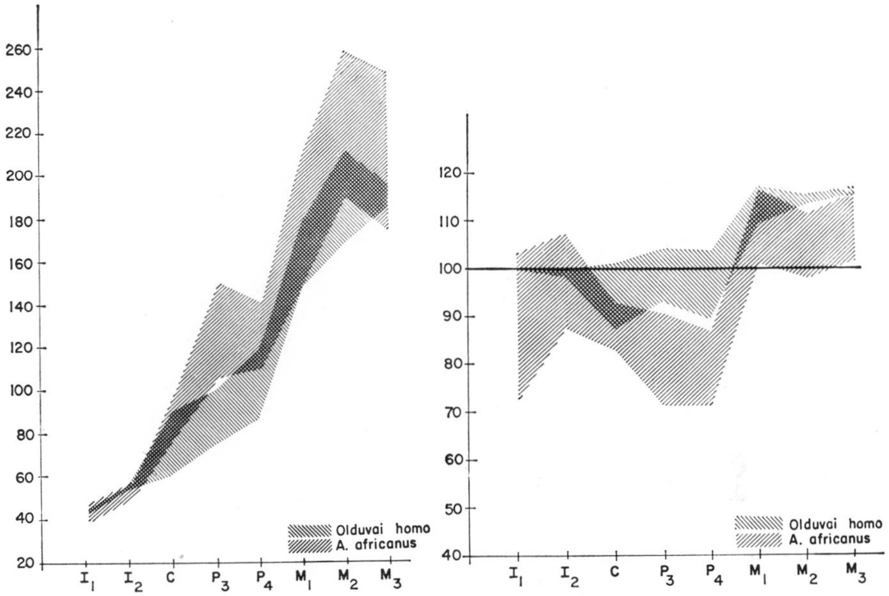

FIGURE 9. Ranges of size and shape of mandibular teeth in the *H. habilis* from Bed I and the hominine from lower Bed II compared with those of *Australopithecus africanus*. Left, crown areas (mm²). Right, the length of the tooth expressed as a percentage of the breadth. The cheek teeth (premolars and molars) of the hominines have higher indices because they are elongated and lack the characteristic australopithecine broadening of these teeth.

time. Clearly, this strain represents a distinct taxon intermediate between the most advanced *Australopithecus* and the most primitive *Homo*.

   Since the original description was published in April 1964, a detailed comparison has been made between the original specimens from Tanganyika and those from Java. As a result, G. H. R. von Koenigswald and I have concluded that in the Bed II paratype of *H. habilis* (which lived some 3/4 million years later than the type specimen), the hominizing trends have been carried still further; as a result, the jaws and teeth of the later specimen (Fig. 10) closely resemble those of *H. erectus* attributed to the early Middle Pleistocene Djetis Beds of Java (*17*). If these features represent sequential changes, we are virtually seeing here evolution in action, with subtle intergrades from one level of hominization to the next.

CULTURAL STATUS OF HOMO HABILIS

It is accepted that cultural or ethological evidence may be added to morphological evidence in assessing the taxonomic status of a group.

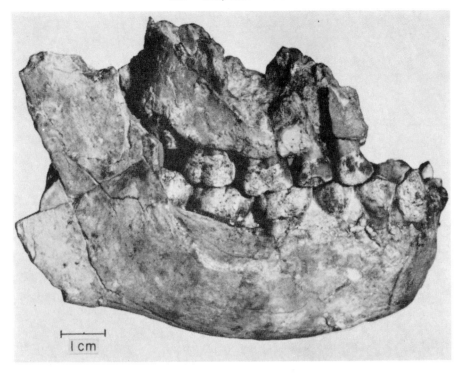

FIGURE 10. Part of the right maxilla (upper jawbone) and the mandible of the hominine (no. 13) from the lower part of Bed II, Olduvai Gorge. These jaws and teeth bear close comparison with those assigned to the Djetis Beds of Java (the Sangiran IV cranium and the Sangiran B mandible).

We may ask the question: Did *H. habilis* behave like an *Australopithecus* or like a *Homo*?

At each of the levels in Bed I where remains of *Homo habilis* have been found, primitive stone implements have been recovered. These artifacts are commonly made from pebbles or irregular fragments, and the cultural phase represented by the succession of stone industries constitutes the Oldowan Culture, formerly known as the Oldowan phase of the pre-Chelles-Acheul Culture. For long, the identity of the makers of the Oldowan Culture tools has been uncertain: some have maintained that the australopithecines were responsible, others have attributed the tools to early members of *Homo erectus* — but always on the basis of very indirect arguments. When in 1959 the cranium of the Olduvai australopithecine (*A. boisei*) was found on a living floor alongside Oldowan tools, at a time when no other adequate hominid remains were known to be associated with these tools, Leakey claimed that this australopithecine must have been the Oldowan toolmaker (*1*). This left a difficult problem: Why was the East African australopithecine associated with stone tools, whereas the Makapansgat australopithecine was associated with the bone, tooth, and horn tools described by Dart? Subsequently, however, remains of *H. habilis* were found on the same living floor as *A. boisei* and the tools. Furthermore, remains of *H. habilis* were found on the lower (earlier) living floors in Bed I, in each instance associated with Oldowan artifacts. While it is possible that both *A. boisei* and *H. habilis* made tools, it is probable that *H. habilis* was at least the more advanced toolmaker.

Furthermore, if we make a survey of all the evidence from South and East Africa, we see that *Australopithecus* alone has not yet been found with stone objects which are undoubtedly tools, except where advanced hominid remains were present as well (20, 25). Six out of 12 deposits have yielded australopithecine remains with no stone tools (27); four sites which have australopithecines and stone tools contain, in addition, indications of a more advanced hominid. The remaining two deposits contain only the more advanced hominid and stone tools. At no site where australopithecine remains are the only hominid remains present are there any stone implements; conversely, at every site which has yielded stone implements and associated hominid remains, these hominid remains include those of a more advanced hominid, whether or not australopithecine remains are present in addition. Furthermore, at every site which has yielded the more advanced hominid, stone tools are present.

It has tentatively been concluded from these associations that no unequivocal evidence exists that *Australopithecus* made Oldowan stone tools to a set and regular pattern and according to a developing cultural trend. On the other hand, it seems very probable that *H. habilis* was the maker of the Oldowan stone tools, while *H. erectus* made the later (Chelles-Acheul) implements.

Dart (28) has demonstrated that the australopithecines were capable of a wide range of cultural activities. It may, however, be argued that all of these activities fall into the categories which Napier (29) has classified as *ad hoc* tool-using, purposeful tool-using, tool-modifying for an immediate or even for a future purpose, and possibly even *ad hoc* tool-making. But it may be questioned whether these australopithecine activities constitute cultural tool-making — that is, whether they exhibit a set and regular complex of patterns which, moreover, show developmental trends with the passage of time.

If this interpretation is correct, ethological or cultural evidence could be added to the anatomical evidence which tends to ally *H. habilis* with the hominines rather than with the australopithecines.

One further probable manifestation of the culture of the early Olduvai hominids is a rough circle of loosely piled stones discovered on a living floor at DK I in the lower part of Bed I (3). It suggests a crude shelter or windbreak and is on the same level as that on which the earliest remains of *H. habilis* were found (MK I). *H. habilis* may have been responsible for this rude structure.

SIGNIFICANCE OF HOMO HABILIS

Both its structure and its place in time impart a unique significance to *Homo habilis*, while, culturally, it seems to provide us for the first time with a knowledge of the makers of the Oldowan Culture.

Structurally, *H. habilis* may be regarded as a most effective link between the Australopithecinae and the Homininae, between which, as has been mentioned, there is a larger gap than has hitherto been recognized. Its very intermediacy is underlined by the fact that some workers would regard the newly discovered form as the most advanced australopithecine and others as the most primitive hominine. Thus, even in the short time since the new fossils were discovered, various workers have believed that the habilines were simply another australopithecine (30), a new genus between *Australopithecus* and *Homo* (31), a new lowliest species of *Homo*, namely *H. habilis* (3), and even a new subspecies of *H. erectus*, namely *H. erectus habilis* (32). The position adopted by my colleagues and myself would seem to be a compromise between the extreme views on either side. Although argument on the exact taxonomic position may continue for some time, it seems that there is already fairly general agreement on this virtually uniquely linking position of *H. habilis*. Perhaps only *Meganthropus palaeojavanicus* of Sangiran, Java, lies in a similarly intermediate position between the Australopithecinae and the Homininae, albeit a little nearer to the australopithecines than is *H. habilis* (17).

Chronologically, the recognition of *H. habilis* means that a more hominized line of creatures was evolving alongside the somewhat less hominized australopithecines even in the Lower Pleistocene. Previously, the *H. erectus* remains of the Djetis Beds, agreed by most as belonging to the beginning of the mid-Pleistocene, represented the earliest recognized hominine. It was still possible then to claim that, if indeed the Homininae stemmed off from an australopithecine ancestral group, this lineage of *Homo* need not have arisen any earlier than the end of the Lower Pleistocene. It now seems clear that, if the habilines are in fact members of the Homininae, then hominines were already present in Africa, and perhaps in Asia, during at least the second half of the Lower Pleistocene. The departure of the hominine line from its presumed australopithecine ancestor must then have occurred as early as at least the Upper Pliocene or the first part of the Lower Pleistocene.

The early hominines must have been contemporaries of several diversified australopithecines — a megadont line (*A. boisei*), a macrodont line (*A. robustus*), and a mesodont line (*A. africanus*). In fact, at least in East Africa, and probably, too, in South Africa, *H. habilis* and *Australopithecus* spp. were sympatric and synchronic. More precisely,

Olduvai I provides us with early evidence of the sympatric coexistence of the largest-toothed australopithecine (*A. boisei*) and *H. habilis,* while Swartkrans gives us later evidence for the sympatric compresence of the large-toothed *A. robustus* and a more advanced hominine, *H. erectus* (*"Telanthropus"*). Doubtless, ecological differences permitted this situation to persist right through until the middle part of the mid-Pleistocene (Fig. 11).

BEARINGS ON HOMINID EVOLUTION

As a total morphological complex, *H. habilis* represents a more advanced grade of hominid organization than *Australopithecus*. Have the habilines arisen from the australopithecines? Since they are contemporary with *H. habilis,* the australopithecine populations represented by the actual fossils recovered to date are clearly too late — and possibly slightly too specialized — to have been on the actual human line, unless we are to postulate a polyphyletic origin of the Homininae at varying times from australopithecine stock. Morphologically, the gracile *A. africanus* is closest to *H. habilis* and seemingly least specialized. It would not be rash therefore to suggest that of the various australopithecines *A. africanus* has departed least from the common ancestor of *A. africanus* and *H. habilis.* On the other hand, the large-toothed, specialized *A. robustus* and *A. boisei* would seem to be far off the common *africanus-habilis* line. Two possible interpretations spring to mind:

(1) The Pliocene ancestral australopithecine was large-toothed and perhaps adapted to a vegetarian diet (33); *A. boisei* and *A. robustus* would then represent a conservative line which maintained these qualities right through into the Middle Pleistocene, while *A. africanus* developed different ecological requirements which, perhaps through a more carnivorous or, at least, omnivorous diet, led to a relaxation of selective pressures maintaining large teeth. The gracile *H. habilis* stemmed off from this smaller-toothed line of australopithecines and became selected for increasingly hominine features.

(2) The ancestral australopithecine was unspecialized, small-toothed, omnivorous. At some time in the Upper Pliocene, it diversified into macrodontic and megadontic lines (*A. robustus* and *A. boisei*), with specialized dentition, perhaps accompanying a specialized, essentially herbivorous diet. Another line remained little changed and unspecialized, eventually to dichotomize into a progressively more hominized line represented by *H. habilis* in Africa and perhaps *Meganthropus* in Asia and a more conservative residual line (*A. africanus*) which, because of ecological similarities to *H. habilis,* did not long outlast the emergence of this hominine.

Which of the two interpretations is correct, or whether other alternatives should be considered, only the direct evidence of Pliocene fossils will determine. Pending their discovery, I incline to favor the second view, on indirect lines of evidence to be presented elsewhere. That is,

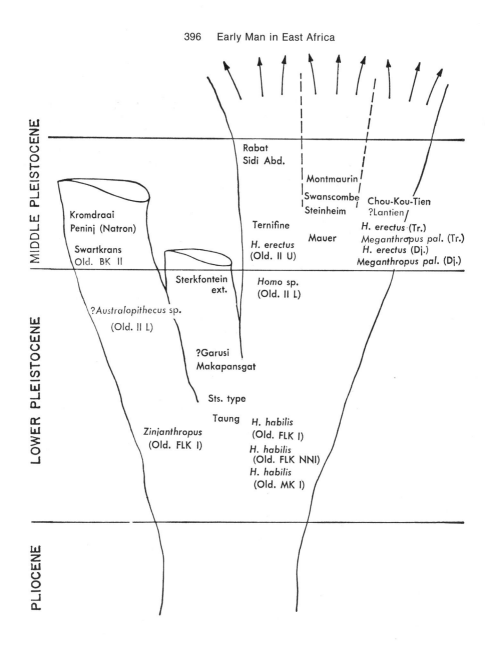

FIGURE 11. Schema of Lower and Middle Pleistocene hominids, showing the position in time and space of the most important specimens discovered to date. The left trunk of the tree represents the large-toothed australopithecine line; the middle trunk the small-toothed australopithecine line; and the right trunk the hominine line leading to modern man. *Sts.,* Sterkfontein; *Sidi Abd.,* Sidi Abderahman; *Old. II,* Olduvai Bed II; *U,* upper; *L.* lower; *Tr.,* Trinil Beds; *Dj.,* Djetis Beds.

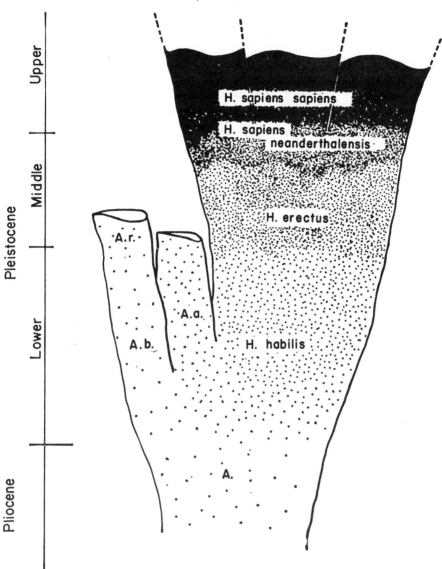

FIGURE 12. A provisional schema of hominid phylogeny from Upper Pliocene times to the Upper Pleistocene. Increasing intensity of shading represents increasing degrees of approach toward the structure and behavior of modern man. *A,* the hypothetical ancestral australopithecine; *A.b., Australopithecus (Zinjanthropus) boisei; A.r., Australopithecus robustus; A.a., Australopithecus africanus.* The schema indicates the synchronic coexistence of several different hominids in the Lower and Middle Pleistocene, the australopithecines surviving into the Middle Pleistocene alongside more advanced hominids of the genus *Homo.* This figure should be considered in conjunction with Figure 11.

I tend to regard the large teeth and supporting structures of A. *robustus* and A. *boisei* as secondary specializations, rather than as primitive or ancestral features which J. T. Robinson seems to believe (33).

Irrespective of which interpretation we adopt, it seems reasonable to infer that late in the Pliocene, or thereabouts, some populations of ancestral *Australopithecus*-like hominids moved forward to a further grade of hominization, thus generating the Homininae. We may tentatively conclude that H. *habilis* is on this direct hominine line. Such is the message of his morphology and his culture, while his position in space and time is compatible with this conclusion (34). As a Lower Pleistocene hominine, he bids fair to provide us with a population, one or more sections of which were ancestral to the mid-Pleistocene hominines (Fig. 12). Nothing in the structure or dating of the relevant fossils rules out the possibility that some populations of H. *habilis* underwent further hominizing changes by phyletic evolution late in the Lower Pleistocene, to attain the H. *erectus* grade of hominization.

Such a reconstruction permits us to recognize a series of grades of hominization, within which we may classify the available fossils. Despite wide variation within each grade — only a fraction of which is as yet known for most grades — we may recognize: (i) an australopithecine grade, represented convincingly only in South and East Africa; (ii) a habiline grade from Africa, perhaps corresponding to a meganthropine grade in Asia; (iii) an earlier H. *erectus* grade, represented in Africa possibly by remains from middle Bed II, Olduvai, and by *"Telanthropus"* from Swartkrans, and in Asia by the Djetis Beds hominines from Sangiran, Java; (iv) a later H. *erectus* grade, represented in Africa by "Chellean Man" from upper Bed II, Olduvai and by *"Atlanthropus"* of Northwest Africa; in Asia by the Trinil Beds and Chou-Kou-Tien hominines; and in Europe possibly by the remains of Mauer; (v) an earlier H. *sapiens* grade (Neanderthal) widely distributed in the Old World; and (vi) a later H. *sapiens* grade, ultimately worldwide in distribution. This sequence shows remarkable parallels between Africa and Asia from grade 2 onwards (17).

We see in conclusion that H. *habilis* has bridged the last remaining major gap in the Pleistocene part of the story of human evolution.

Summary. Recent discoveries of early Pleistocene hominids in East Africa have revealed a new stage in human evolution. The remains of *Homo habilis*, discovered by L. S. B. Leakey and his family, bridge the hiatus between the most advanced australopithecines and the most primitive hominines. The new species was bigger-brained and smaller-toothed than *Australopithecus,* the fossil apeman from South and East Africa. It is very probable that *Homo habilis* was, as his name implies, a "handyman," maker of the earliest stone culture, the Oldowan.

These primitive hominines were already in existence in the Lower Pleistocene, living alongside a variety of more conservative hominids, the australopithecines. The closeness of morphology between H. *habilis* and *Australopithecus africanus* points strongly to a common ancestry in the Upper Pliocene or the very beginning of the Pleistocene. The large-toothed *A. robustus* and *A. boisei* were already diverging by specialization from the postulated unspecialized ancestral australopithecine. The first hominines must thus have come into being by the beginning of the Pleistocene. Later, some populations of *H. habilis* seemingly underwent further hominizing changes to generate a new species, *Homo erectus,* bigger men with larger and more effective brains, smaller and more modern human teeth, probably more complete adjustment to upright stance and bipedal gait, a more precise manual grip, and an appreciably advanced material culture.

Homo habilis thus fills in the last remaining major gap in the Pleistocene story of human evolution.

REFERENCES AND NOTES

* The author is professor and head of the Department of Anatomy at the University of the Witwatersrand, Johannesburg, Republic of South Africa.

1. L. S. B. Leakey, *Nature* 184, 491 (1959); 189, 649 (1961); ⸻ and M. D. Leakey, *ibid.* 202, 5 (1964).

2. The skulls and teeth have been entrusted to me by Dr. Leakey for detailed study, while Drs. J. Napier, P. Davis, and M. Day of London are studying the other (postcranial) parts of the skeleton. Our detailed reports will appear in a new series of volumes on the Olduvai Gorge to be published by Cambridge University Press.

3. L. S. B. Leakey, P. V. Tobias, J. R. Napier, *Nature* 202, 7 (1964).

4. R. Hay, *Science* 139, 829 (1963).

5. L. S. B. Leakey, *Olduvai Gorge 1951–1961,* vol. 1, *A Preliminary Report on the Geology and Fauna* (Cambridge Univ. Press, Cambridge, 1965).

6. R. A. Dart, *Nature* 115, 195 (1925).

7. There are some 54 additional teeth from Olduvai. Some of them belong to *H. habilis*; some may be australopithecine; while others are as yet of unknown affinities.

8. L. Kohl-Larsen, *Auf den Spuren des Vormenschen* (Strecker and Schröder, Stuttgart, 1943).

9. H. Weinert, *Z. Morphol. Anthropol.* 42, 113 (1950); 43, 73 (1951).

10. J. T. Robinson, *Am. J. Phys. Anthropol.* 11, 1 (1953); 13, 429 (1955).

11. L. S. B. Leakey, *Nature* 186, 456 (1960).

12. P. V. Tobias, *ibid.* 197, 743 (1963).

13. L. S. B. Leakey, *ibid.* 181, 1099 (1958); J. T. Robinson, *ibid.* 185, 407 (1960); G. H. R. von Koenigswald, *Koninkl. Ned. Akad. Wetenschap. Proc. Ser. B* 63, 20 (1960); A. A. Dahlberg, *Nature* 188, 962 (1960).

14. Y. Coppens, *Compt. Rend.* 252, 3851 (1961); *Bull. Soc. Préhistorique Franc.* 58, 756 (1961); in *Problèmes Actuels de Paléontologie (Évolution des Vertébrés)* (Centre National de Recherche Scientifique, Paris, 1962), p. 455.

15. M. Stekelis, L. Picard, N. Schulman, G. Haas, *Bull. Res. Council Israel* 9G, 175 (1960).

16. F. Weidenreich, *Amer. Mus. Nat. Hist. Anthropol. Papers* 40, 1 (1945).

17. P. V. Tobias and G. H. R. von Koenigswald, *Nature* 204, 515 (1964).

18. G. H. R. von Koenigswald, *Koninkl. Ned. Akad. Wetenschap. Proc. Ser. B* **60**, 153 (1957).
19. E. L. Simons, *Science* **141**, 879 (1963).
20. P. V. Tobias, *Current Anthropol.*, in press.
21. F. Weidenreich, *Palaeontol. Sinica* n.s. **D10**, 1 (1943).
22. M. Boule and H. V. Vallois, *Fossil Men* (Thames and Hudson, London, 1957).
23. P. V. Tobias, "Festschrift on the 65th birthday of Juan Comas," in press.
24. H. J. Jerison, *Human Biol.* **35**, 263 (1963).
25. P. V. Tobias, in *Proc. 8th Intern. Congr. Anthropol. Ethnol. Sci., Moscow, August 1964,* in press.
26. P. V. Tobias, *Nature* **202**, 3 (1964).
27. Although cultural material and an australopithecine mandible are known from Peninj (Lake Natron), the implements are not associated with the mandible. I am indebted to Glynn Isaac for the information that excavation of the jaw site itself has yielded no cultural material. Scattered stone artifacts and two early Acheulian sites occur some distance from the mandible site. G. Isaac, *Quaternaria*, in press.
28. R. A. Dart, "The Osteodontokeratic Culture of *Australopithecus prometheus*," *Transvaal Museum Mem. 10* (1957).
29. J. R. Napier, in *Classification and Human Evolution*, S. L. Washburn, Ed. (Viking Fund, Chicago, 1963), p. 178.
30. W. E. Le Gros Clark, *Discovery* **25**, 49 (1964).
31. G. H. R. von Koenigswald, personal communication.
32. D. R. Hughes, *The Times,* London, 10 June 1964.
33. J. T. Robinson, in *Evolution und Hominisation*, G. Kurth, Ed. (G. Fischer, Stuttgart, 1962), p. 210; J. T. Robinson, *S. African Archaeol. Bull.* **19**, 3 (1964).
34. P. V. Tobias, in *Britannica Book of the Year, 1964* (Encyclopaedia Britannica, Chicago, in press).
35. As a second type of hominid (*Homo erectus* or *Telanthropus*) is known to be present in the Swartkrans deposit, the possibility cannot be excluded that some of the large numbers of isolated teeth from this deposit may *not* belong to the australopithecine.
36. I thank Dr. L. S. B. Leakey for entrusting the fossils to me for study; Prof. G. H. R. von Koenigswald and Dr. D. Hooijer for helpful cooperation; L. P. Morley, A. R. Hughes, Miss J. Soussi, and Mrs. R. W. Levine for technical assistance; the South African Council for Scientific and Industrial Research, the Boise Fund, the Wenner-Gren Foundation for Anthropological Research, Cambridge University, the University of the Witwatersrand, and the National Geographic Society for financial assistance.

Ecological Rules, Body-Heat Regulation, and Human Evolution

Eugène Schreider*

During the last ten years ecological rules related to body-heat regulation have been discussed by many authors.[1] It seems to me that their points of view can be summarized as follows:

Supporters of classical rules, named after Bergmann (1847) and Allen (1877), believe that variations in size and body-build of a homeotherm species, observed in different parts of its geographical range, must be considered as evolutionary adaptations to thermal environment. Zoologists are mostly concerned with size, while anthropologists usually put the stress on body-build.

An opposite view is held by some physiologists in whose opinion the actual existence of geographical gradients of this kind is doubtful, as there are many exceptions to the rule. Be that as it may, such gradients could not be explained by adaptive changes because the adaptation to thermal environment is achieved by physiological, rather than by anatomical means.

A third point of view has been expressed by some authors who do not seem to be generally concerned with ecological rules, but who emphatically deny their applicability to human species. In their opinion, man modifies his natural surroundings so efficiently that he escapes the pressure of climatic factors.

Reprinted from *Evolution* 18, 1–9 (1964), by permission of the author and publisher.

In my own opinion, these points of view should be revised critically, but sympathetically, as, in spite of conflicting conclusions, the evidence quoted in support of them is generally good.

THE EFFICIENCY OF
ARTIFICIAL MICROCLIMATES

Although the idea that man can modify his environment at will is largely correct, it leads to faulty interpretations if it is forgotten that far-reaching changes continue to take place even in our time, without the demands of the human organism being taken into account.

Regarding protection against extremes of temperature, the situation varies considerably according to the technique standards used, the materials available, and local customs. Wherever social distinctions are marked, it also differs according to economic resources. Even in modern houses, heating, for economic reasons, may be highly inadequate.

Tradition and routine may also impede changes desirable from the physiological point of view. The average temperature in most houses in the British Isles is markedly lower than in American dwellings. From the physiological viewpoint it is insufficient, so insufficient, in fact, that some doctors are of the opinion that in certain conditions it is responsible for perinatal mortality: "prevention which is of paramount importance because of high mortality, can be achieved only by safeguarding against a fall of room temperature" (Mann and Elliot, 1957).

The American microclimate is more satisfactory probably because the harder winter demands stricter precautions being taken. Negligence is more liable to occur in countries whose winter is reputedly mild. This explains why chilblains are more common in France and Italy than in Russia, Sweden, or Canada.

Improvements are possible only if knowledge and technical means permit. Numbers of Arctic populations have been unable to solve the problem of heating. The portable tent used by certain Siberian autochtons provided no effective protection against low temperatures (Bogoras, 1901, 1904–1909). A similar observation has been made about certain Canadian aboriginal tribes (Stefansson, 1943). The Eskimo igloo, with its "tropical" heat, should not be too exclusively singled out for quotation. The igloo is of relatively recent invention, and is not the only dwelling known to the Eskimos. In certain Eskimo huts, it may be cold (Birket-Smith, 1937).

Man, however, even with inferior material resources, but with a knowledge of fire going back to time immemorial, is capable of protecting himself with varying success against the cold. On the other hand, even with advanced techniques, he is generally defenseless against excesses of heat. Air conditioning is an extremely rare privilege, and the thermal environment in which, for instance, farm work is done, cannot be modified at will.

In damp tropical countries, as well as in deserts, the heat puts the organism to a severe test. Shade does not necessarily offer protection. In dry regions in Soviet Asia, the temperature in summer may reach 40° C inside the homes. In some regions of the Sahara, the heat is so hard to bear, even at night, that, for part of the year, the inhabitants of certain towns sleep on terraces, unless they leave their permanent dwellings for reed huts (Rochefort, 1957).

It is true that in certain hot and arid regions the nights, at least in winter, are very cold. It has sometimes even been thought that it is the cold, rather than the heat, to which the inhabitants must have adapted themselves. Now, whatever the level of civilization, man has to work in order to live, and his work is generally done before nightfall: *the daytime environment counts above all,* for this is the environment in which his active life is lived, with the main expenditure of energy and the highest calories production (Schreider, 1962).

In the lower latitudes, the daytime environment, unless moderated by altitude or other local peculiarities, is characterized by the intense heat which man, impelled by economic needs, cannot escape. However ingenious he may be, he cannot entirely withdraw from the climatic environment, particularly the heat. It is therefore impossible to dismiss the problem of selective pressure exercised by the thermal environment.

HUMAN ECOLOGICAL GRADIENTS

Let us now study the question whether gradients exist in man. A certain regularity in the geographical distribution of human characters was observed by the early naturalists. They noted, for example, that the inhabitants of cold mountainous regions are short but compact, whereas those of the neighboring lowlands with a damp, warm climate are more slender in form (Orbigny, 1839). Some authors judged it possible to group Eskimos and Fuegians in a single "hyperborean race," by basing their argument on the fact that all of them are of short and massive build.

Other similar generalizations have been made more recently, and they are on the whole correct. However, like the earlier conclusions, they are still based on impressions, rather than upon direct evidence, and, for want of quantitative data, propose one simple gradient for a given morphological "character," such as "body-build," without taking into account that the same biological result can be obtained, as we shall see, in different anatomical ways.

I have chosen a strictly biometrical approach to the problem. The first stage was the study of ten metric characters in eleven human populations, which permitted an approximate estimation of trunk volume and surface. It then appeared that the volume/surface ratio is very similar in groups as distinct as Parisian workmen and Somali nomads. It fluctuates around 0.5 liter per square decimeter, which leads one to believe that in spite of their obvious imperfection, estimated volume and surface reflect an anatomical fact. And, despite the small variation, the ratio appeared higher in European populations than in tropical populations.

If the body weight/estimated trunk surface ratio is found, closely related figures are still obtained, the European samples, however, forming one group (1.26–1.30 kg/dm²), and the tropical samples another (1.09–1.24 kg/dm²) (Schreider, 1950a, 1951a). These initial observations allow the assumption that a geographical gradient exists for the body weight/body surface ratio (W/S). In fact, it proved impossible to pursue the work along these lines, because human samples, for whom measurements are available allowing the estimation of the trunk volume and surface, are extremely rare. I therefore had to use the much greater number of samples for which each individual body height and weight was known; this allowed the calculation of the body surface, by means of a well-known formula: Surface area (cm²) = Weight in kg$^{0.425}$ Height in cm $^{0.725}$ 71.84 (Du Bois).

Published information so far relates to a hundred or so male samples, which represent all the main subdivisions of the human species, and about twenty female samples. For all these samples, the body height, the body weight, the body surface, and the body weight/body surface ratio are known, but in a fairly large number of cases, additional measurements are available, allowing the body structure to be estimated, which is highly important.

Figures now available confirm on the whole the geographical gradient of the W/S ratio, which tends to decrease in hot countries. They reveal, however, a more complex situation than had at first been thought, for they suggest that there is either an exception to the rule, or else that there is a plurality of distinct gradients for the various races.

As regards the European leucoderm group, no complication occurs. In Europe itself the ratio which can attain 39 kg/m² in Germany, more than 38 in northern Ireland and Finland and 37.9 in France, falls to 37.0 in Calabria and 37.4 in Sicily. It drops still further in North Africa (37.1–36.5), to 36 among the Arabs of the Yemen, and to 35.4 in a Berber population in the Sahara. The existence of the W/S ratio gradients in the white races has been moreover confirmed in the United States (Newman and Munro, 1955).

The only important exception to the W/S ratio gradient concerns the melanoderm (black) racial group. This exception is less important than one might believe at first sight, for although it is represented by almost twenty populations, it is limited geographically to neighboring tribes all grouped in the west of Africa (partly Mali and especially Haute Volta).

Beginning with this group of tribes whose W/S ratio fluctuates between 37.2 and 37.9 kg/m², the figures decrease towards the north, in the direction of the Sahara (36.5–36.8), towards the Atlantic coast (35.9–36.6), as well towards the interior of the African continent, where the average figures are in the region of 33.5–36.2. If this territorial unit of relatively high values did not exist, the conclusion might have been reached that there is one single gradient of the body weight/body surface ratio, with progressive decrease in figures from northern Europe to East Africa (32.8–36.3) and South Africa (33.9).

Several populations of Somalia, a country close to the hot desert, give averages ranging between 34 and 35. We do not know whether it is permissible to include these human groups in the Black gradient, as their anthropological status is uncertain. And we naturally have to put in a class apart the Bushmen (30.2), as well as the Congo Pygmies (31.4–31.5) who give low figures but cannot mingle with the racial groups of Black Africa.

It has not been possible to find documentary material concerning the Siberian or Central Asiatic populations. We know, however, that the inhabitants of hot Asiatic countries, whether Tonkinese or Southern Indians, give low averages, especially the latter (32.4–34.6). Low figures are also found for a small group of Autochtons in the Australian desert (35.6) and for the pygmy inhabitants of the Andaman Islands (32.4), the Philippines (31.4–31.9), and Malaya (30.91).

There is a distinct shortage of information about the aborigines of the New World. Nevertheless, the few figures available clearly suggest the existence of a gradient. The highest are found in cold climates, among the Mapuches in the Andes (39.2), the Eskimos of Greenland (38.0) and of Canada (39.1), and some distinctly lower values in Guatemala (36.9), Venezuela (35.6), and Mexico (34.9–36.4).

This undoubtedly tallies with the classical ecological rules, and provides a satisfactory biometric confirmation of them. But I have further attempted, by testing it on human populations, to verify the rule that in closely related homeotherm forms, protruding and exposed organs tend to become shorter as the average temperature of the habitat decreases (Allen, 1877). In order to carry out this verification, I found the ratio, to the body weight, of the total length of the limbs,* which, as was shown long ago in physiology, are "thermolytic" organs (Bernard, 1858, 1878). It then appeared that the limbs/weight ratio shows a definite increase in populations dwelling in hot climates, as Table 1 shows.

The collected results confirm, therefore, the generalization made over ten years ago, namely, that "in races or closely related homeotherm species, the relative value of the body surface, expressed as a ratio of the volume or the mass, increases in climates which, at least during part of the year, subject the thermolytic mechanisms to stress. The inverse tendency appears in climates which over-facilitate the elimination of heat" (Schreider, 1951a). This last sentence should, I think, be emphasized, since the idea that the heat stress alone plays a role has been erroneously ascribed to me. This, however, concerns the interpretation of the results, to which we shall have occasion to return later. For the

---

* Total length of limbs = [(acromion – dactylion) + symphysion height] × 2.

TABLE 1

Limb Length/Body Weight Ratios (cm/kg) for Adult Males (Schreider, 1957a and b and Unpublished Data).

| | Limbs/weight ratio | | Body height average |
	Average	SD	
73 Parisian workers	4.88	0.47	168.8
47 Finns	4.89	0.41	169.5
80 French soldiers	4.91	0.47	166.2
50 French students	4.94	0.43	174.6
300 British soldiers*	5.00	—	170.9
113 French soldiers	5.02	0.41	168.9
504 Ukrainians*	5.08	—	167.3
120 Sicilian soldiers	5.09	0.43	169.1
100 Tonkinese	5.37	0.36	159.9
82 Otomis (Mexico)	5.51	0.49	157.6
31 Arabs (Yemen)	5.63	0.47	162.2
18 Asheraf (Somalia)	5.64	0.56	170.9
119 Nhungues (Mozamb.)	5.66	0.52	167.9
123 Darod (Somalia)	5.74	0.54	172.2
119 Rahanoween (Somalia)	5.83	0.59	169.4
51 Gobaween (Somalia)	5.90	0.51	168.4
47 Dir (Somalia)	6.01	0.49	172.9
26 Antumba (Mozambique)	6.06	0.64	164.9
87 Hawyah (Somalia)	6.21	0.51	170.0
18 Korana (S. Africa)	6.21	0.58	159.8
35 Indians (Madras)	6.61	0.71	168.4
95 Aka Pygmies (Congo)	6.98	0.67	144.1
115 Basua Pygm. (Congo)	7.03	0.77	144.3

Calculated from published averages. All other figures calculated from individual measurements. Data concerning Finns and Madras Indians communicated by M. Pelosse (Paris) and Dr. Henrotte (Liège), respectively.

moment, the essential fact is the existence of gradients, namely anatomical changes whose parallelism with certain aspects of the environment it is hard to deny.

What, one may ask, are these anatomical changes? A number of anthropologists apparently consider that there is a correlative modification of stature and body-build, somewhat short stature and thickset, stocky figures typifying Arctic peoples, whereas inhabitants of the tropical belt tend to be characterized by tall stature combined with slenderness (Coon et al., 1950; Coon, 1955). The example, popularized by a number of publications (e.g., Barnett, 1961), is given, on the one hand, by the Eskimo, with its bulky shape, and on the other, by the tall, thin Nilotic. This conception is an oversimplification of the facts, and is utterly incompatible with the anthropometric data and the two gradients brought to light by my results.

In fact, if brachymorphic Eskimos give a high W/S ratio (38–39), the Otomi of Mexico, like other Indians of the tropical regions, are also brachymorphic, but show a much lower figure (W/S ratio = 34.9; stature = 157.6), which is close to that of the Darod of Somalia, leptomorphs of tall stature (W/S ratio = 35.1; stature = 172.2), whose anatomy is rather similar to that of Nilotics. There is no *exact* parallelism between the two gradients shown by my results, and the geographical distribution of weight, stature, or body-build. This is explained by the fact that the same result, like the reduction of the W/S ratio, is obtainable by different anatomical variations, namely, the diminution of all body dimensions, as in the case of the Otomi, and, to a more marked extent, the Pygmies; or by the considerable shortening of the trunk, accompanied by lengthening of limbs, as in the case of Somalis.

The opposition of the Eskimo and the Nilotic is, therefore, in some way fallacious and even from the didactic angle, it may lead to error. There exist in tropical regions brachymorphs of small size, with a low W/S ratio and a high limbs/weight ratio. The facts are such that there appears to be a convergence for the biologically important ratios in human groups which originally did not enjoy the same evolutionary opportunities. But, before we can accept this conclusion, we must be backed by a number of guarantees of certainty.

THE VALUE OF BASIC DATA

The first task is to find how much reliance can be placed in the figures which allowed the existence of the weight/surface and limbs/weight ratios to be shown. Some understandable initial reserve can be expressed on the account of the body surface having been estimated by using a formula in which weight is a factor. In connection with this, it is worth recalling that the first rough draft of a gradient was obtained in a totally different way, the trunk surface having been estimated from a set of anthropometrical measurements. The facts show that the weight/total surface ratio gives the same results as the weight/trunk surface ratio.

By way of a check, we have also worked out, separately for the two sexes, correlations between the weight/*surface calculated by the formula* ratio, and the weight/*surface measured by integrator* ratio: these correlations amount to 0.83 for adult males, and 0.84 for females (Schreider, 1951a). There is a sufficient degree of agreement, if it is borne in mind that we have only to compare the averages.

It is true that the formula used for obtaining the total surface was established on individuals of white race, so that some correction might be necessary before applying it to other human groups. No correction appears, however, to be needed for the Eskimos (Rodahl, 1952); and for the yellow races, if one is necessary, it is not an extensive one (Necheles and Loo, 1932). The formula seems to imply a relatively important error only in the case of African and Australian black races, because it does not take into account the considerable length of limbs which characterizes the two racial groups. But if this is the case, a corrected formula could only still further accentuate the geographical gradient of the W/S ratio (Newman, 1956).

Doubt can, however, be expressed about the value or the significance of a character such as weight. The question is important, but is directly related to the biological interpretation of the gradients, and they will be studied together.

THE BIOLOGICAL
MEANING OF GRADIENTS

In an interesting study confirming the geographical gradient of the W/S ratio in the United States, two American authors reach the conclusion that the cause of it is to be sought in the influence of the climate over food consumption, the latter being greater in regions where cold winters are experienced (Newman and Munro, 1955).

No one will question the influence of nutrition on body weight, and since this is the case, one is tempted to think that the low W/S ratio of populations living for the most part in underdeveloped countries is simply a reflection of their insufficient nutritional state. This explanation is too simple to be correct. Body weight's normal fluctuations are *loosely* correlated with calorie intake (Thomson *et al.*, 1961). And as far as I know, I did not take into account data concerning populations stricken by famine or abnormally overnourished.

Certain samples, indeed, benefited from unusually plentiful nourishment, but they are found in tropical countries, and are military series from former colonial armies, whose average weight is greater than that of civilians of the same origin. However, their W/S ratio generally does not reach temperate climate figures. Such is the case, notably, of certain Somali samples. This is also the case of our Tonkinese, who were studied while stationed in France. Inversely, French soldiers who had, on the average, lost some kilograms during the last war, gave a W/S ratio comparable to that of the French samples studied in less exceptional circumstances. Other similar cases could be quoted.

This may well appear strange should it be forgotten that, if nutrition influences body weight, it is not the sole determining factor. The situation becomes clearer if, instead of confining oneself exclusively to weight, one takes into account a set of anthropometric data. Fortunately this is possible in a number of cases. It is then observed that, in the populations under study, the *average man* is neither skeleton-like nor obese, whatever his weight. In fact, the average weight of a population is dependent primarily on its average dimensions and its morphology, which limit ponderal fluctuations.

The short trunk and very long limbs of the Nilotics, Somalis, and Australians (Abbie, 1957, 1958) can no more be explained by a particular nutritional status than can the structure of the trunk of European populations which, out of geometrical necessity, shows excessive volume in relation to its surface (Schreider, 1950a). Moreover, direct observation of some human groups showing a low W/S ratio or a "deficient" body weight leads one to state that their nutrition is sufficient (Schreider, 1953–1955; Roberts, 1960).

One of the main arguments against the purely nutritional interpretation of the weight/surface ratio differences resides in the fact that the W/S ratio gradient, which is so clearly defined in men, is *nonexistent in women,* who are nevertheless represented by about twenty populations (Schreider, 1950a, 1951a, and unpublished material). It is difficult to conceive that the men's diet should be insufficient, whereas the women of the same tribe may sometimes appear overnourished, for their averages, for both body weight and the W/S ratio, may even be above the male averages: such is the case of Andaman Islands aborigines and two populations of Somalia.[2]

It is, in short, impossible to suppose, when human groups whose dimensions and body structure are fairly well known, that the differences in their average body weight are due solely, or even essentially, to the nutritional regimen. Food may be a disturbing factor likely to invert the ranking of similar averages, without, however, perturbing the whole gradient.

The problem is somewhat different for irregularities appearing as true departures from the rule. Exceptions, in the case of certain animals, had been known for some time. They are partly explained by ecological adaptation, i.e., by the behavior characterizing the species. Moreover, various physiological mechanisms may reduce the role of the body mass in relation to its thermolytic surfaces. It is, nevertheless, equally certain that the importance of the W/S ratio is not to be dismissed in homeotherms as a whole, as seems to be the opinion of physiologists who deny all relationship between anatomical dimensions and structures, on the one hand, and climatic characteristics on the other. In polar bear, whose coat, when completely soaked with water, offers no protection, the heat is probably retained by peripheral vasoconstriction. However, "the polar bear is also a very large animal with large heat capacity and has a proportionately small surface" (Scholander *et al.,* 1950). If it is granted that the polar bear benefits from its very considerable mass compared to its relatively small surface, it is difficult to see why it should not be the case with other mammals, particularly with man.

As regards the human species, the problem is simplified, for man's hairy coating does not show physiologically important variations. Moreover, we have multiple proofs of the influence exercised by the W/S ratio over his thermal balance. In heat, individuals with a high ratio perspire more freely than others, but this is useless waste, since the excessive sweat drips away and is largely lost from a physiological point of view (Schreider, 1951b). On the other hand, we observe, in 120 French soldiers, that those who stand up to heat well include a high proportion of individuals having a W/S ratio lower than 36 kg/m², whereas this proportion is low in those who find it difficult to stand high temperatures. The difference between the two percentages is equal to 23.2% ± 6.4 and the probabilities are fewer than one in a thousand that this is due to mere chance. Again, by keeping men walking at a speed of 7 km/hour for 15 minutes on the treadmill, we find, despite the short test time, a positive correlation of 0.31 between the W/S ratio and the final temperature of the subjects.

Does the limbs/weight ratio, in its turn, play a part in thermoregulation? In heat, with an environmental temperature of 35°–36.9° C, the negative correlation between the body temperature and the ratio amounts to −0.38 ($P = 0.03$). Like the previous one, this correlation is not very marked, but there is no reason to suppose that it ought to have been more so; the anatomical conditions of thermoregulation are not the only determining cause of this. The plurality of cross-factors partly explains why, in physiology, correlations are generally low. If we neglected the low coefficients, we should run the risk of rejecting, one by one, all the factors which, taken together, ensure the physiological success of the species (Schreider, 1958, 1960).

SUMMARY

There are serious grounds for considering geographical gradients of biometrical characters such as the weight/surface ratio or limbs/weight ratio as true ecological gradients, linked in the course of evolution to climatic conditions and thermoregulation. We must not be deterred by the existence of exceptions. The sole important exception in man known at present is limited territorially to part of West Africa. It may be due to compensating physiological mechanisms, or be considered as the beginning of a gradient peculiar to African melanoderms: our present state of knowledge allows no clear choice to be made between these two hypotheses. Finally, it has to be borne in mind that certain exceptions might well be due to relatively recent migrations.

The most plausible hypothesis is that these ecological gradients are, in fact, the product of natural selection. Nutritional habits cannot explain the gradients even if they may influence them. The wide differences revealed by the figures do not admit of this interpretation: both gradients, like the average body mass of the populations, are linked in the first place to the very marked variations in average sizes and anatomical proportions which are largely, if not exclusively, hereditary. The outstanding fact is that, in similar climatic conditions, populations differing greatly in stature, weight, or other metric characters give closely related and sometimes identical figures for the weight/ surface or limbs/weight ratio. This can only be explained by a phenomenon of convergence which, in partly differing anatomical ways, but under similar environmental conditions, has led to biologically equivalent results.

Accepted May 1, 1963

REFERENCES AND NOTES

* Laboratoire d'Anthropologie Physique, École Pratique des Hautes Études; Laboratoire de Biométrie Humaine, Centre National de la Recherche Scientifique, Paris.

¹ Among the recent authors, entirely or partly favorable to ecological rules, the following should be quoted: Baker (1960), Bodenheimer (1957), Coon *et al.* (1950), Coon (1955), Garn (1958), Mayr (1956), Newman (1953), Rensch (1959), Salt (1952), and Snow (1954, 1958); the "rules" have been criticized mostly by Hensel (1959), Scholander (1955, 1956), Irving (1957), and Wilber (1957). A "synthetic" view, which is not inconsistent with the present writer's opinion, has been expressed by Hamilton (1961).

² The fact of women showing no gradient comparable with that of men may be explained by the fact that body-heat regulation in females has peculiarities not found in males (Hardy and Milhorat, 1939; Hardy, Milhorat, and Du Bois, 1941; Du Bois, Ebaugh, and Hardy, 1952). Account has also to be taken of the possible influence of sexual selection, which favors corpulent women (Baker, 1960).

A. A. Abbie, Metrical characters of a central Australian tribe, *Oceania* 27, 220–43 (1957).

———, Timing in human evolution, *Proc. Linn. Soc. N. S. Wales* 83 (2), 197–213 (1958).

J. A. Allen, The influence of physical conditions in the genesis of species, *Radical Review* 1, 108–40 (1877).

P. T. Baker, Climate, culture and evolution, *Human Biol.* 32, 3–16 (1960).

A. Barnett, *The Human Species* (Penguin Books, Harmondsworth, rev. ed., 1961).

C. Bergmann, Ueber die Verhaltnisse der Wärmeökonomie des Thiere zu ihrer Grösse, *Göttinger Studien* 3, 595–708 (1847).

Cl. Bernard, *Leçons sur les propriétés physiologiques et les altérations pathologiques des liquides de l'organisme*, Vol. 1 (Paris, 1859).

———, *Lecons sur les Phénomènes de la Vie Communs aux Animaux et aux Végétaux* (Paris, 1878).

K. Birket-Smith, *Moeurs et Coutumes des Esquimaux* (Payot, Paris, 1937).

F. S. Bodenheimer, *The ecology of mammals in arid zones* [Recherches sur la Zone Aride, Ecologie humaine et animale] (UNESCO, Paris, 1957), pp. 100–37.

W. C. Bogoraz, *Otcherk materialnovo byta olennikh Tchouktchei. Sbornik Muzeia po antropologhii i etnografii*, Vol. 2 (St. Petersbourg, 1901).

———, *The Chukchee. Memoires of the Jesup North Pacific Expedition,* Vol. 7 (Amer. Mus. Nat. Hist., New York, 1904–1909).

C. S. Coon, Some problems of human variability and natural selection in climate and culture, *Amer. Nat.* 89, 257–80 (1955).

———, S. M. Garn and J. B. Birdsell, *Races* (Thomas, Springfield, 1950).

E. F. du Bois, F. G. Ebaugh, J. D. Hardy, Basal heat production and elimination of thirteen women at temperatures from 22° C to 35° C, *J. Nutr.* 48, 257–93 (1952).

S. M. Garn, A comment on Wilber's "Origin of human types," *Human Biol.* 30, 338–40 (1958).

T. H. Hamilton, The adaptive significance of intraspecific trends of variation in wing length and body size among bird species, *Evolution* 15, 180–95 (1961).

J. D. Hardy and A. T. Milhorat, Basal heat loss and production in women at temperatures from 23° to 36° C, *Proc. Soc. Exp. Biol. Med.* 41, 9 (1939).

———, ———, E. F. du Bois, Basal metabolism and heat loss of young women at temperatures from 22° to 35° C, *J. Nutr.* 21, 383 (1941).

H. Hensel, Heat and cold, *Ann. Rev. Physiol.* 21, 91–116 (Palo Alto, 1959).

L. Irving, The usefulness of Scholander's views on adaptive insulation of animals, *Evolution* 11, 257–59 (1957).

T. P. Mann and R. I. K. Elliott, Neonatal cold injury, *Lancet* 272, 229–33 (1957).

E. Mayr, Geographical character gradients and climatic adaptation, *Evolution* 10, 105–108 (1956).

H. Necheles and T. C. Loo, Uber den Stoffwechsel der Chinesen. I. Die Körperober-flache. *Chinese J. Physiol.* 6, 129 (1932).

M. T. Newman, The application of ecological rules to the racial anthropology of the aboriginal New World, *Amer. Anthr.* (n.s.) 55, 311–27 (1953).

———, Adaptation of man to cold climates, *Evolution* 10, 101–104 (1956).

R. W. Newman and E. H. Munro, The relation of climate and body size in U.S. males, *Amer. J. Phys. Anthr.* 13, 1–17 (1955).

A. d'Orbigny, *L'homme américan,* Vol. 1 (Paris, 1839).

B. Rensch, *Evolution above the Species Level* (Methuen, London, 1959).

D. F. Roberts, Effects of race and climate on human growth as exemplified by studies on African children, in J. M. Tanner, *Human Growth* (Pergamon, London, 1960), pp. 59–72.

R. Rochefort, Les effets du milieu sur les communautés humaines des régions arides, adaptation de ces communautés aux conditions locales de milieu, in *Recherches sur la zone aride, VIII, Ecologie humaine et animale* (UNESCO, Paris, 1957), pp. 11–42.

K. Rodahl, The body surface area of Eskimos as determined by the linear and the height-weight formulas, *Amer. J. Phys. Anthr.* 10, 419–26 (1952).

G. W. Salt, The relation of metabolism to climate and distribution in three finches of the genus Carpodacus, *Ecol. Monogr.* 22, 122–52 (1952).

P. F. Scholander, Evolution of climatic adaptation in homeotherms, *Evolution* 9, 15–26 (1955).

———, Climatic rules, *Evolution* 10, 339–40 (1956).

———, R. Hock, V. Walters, L. Irving, Body insulation of some arctic and tropical mammals and birds, *Biol. Bull.* 99, 225–36 (1950).

E. Schreider, Les variations raciales et sexuelles du tronc humain, *L'Anthropologie* 54, 67–81, 228–61 ,1950a).

———, Geographical distribution of the body-weight/body-surface ratio, *Nature* 165, 286 (1950b).

———, Race, constitution, thermolyse, *Rev. Sci.* 89, 110–19 (1951a).

———, Anatomical factors of body-heat regulation, *Nature* 167, 823–25 (1951b).

———, Régulation thermique et évolution humaine, *Bull. Mem. Soc. Anthr. Paris* 4 (10), 138–48 (1953).

———, Recherches anthropologiques sur les Otomis de la région d'Ixmiquilpan (Mexique), *L'Anthropologie* **57**, 453–89; **59**, 253–96 (1953–1955).

———, Ecological rules and body-heat regulation in man, *Nature* **179**, 915–16 (1957a).

———, Gradients écologiques régulation thermique et différénciation humaine, *Biotypologie*, **18**, 168–83 (1957b).

———, Les régulations physiologiques. Essai de révision biométrique du probléme de l'homéostasie, *Biotypologie* **19**, 127–215 (1958).

———, *La biométrie* (Presses Univ. de France, Paris, 1960).

———, *Anthropologie physiologique et variations climatiques,* Natural Sci. Dept. Arid Zone Report (UNESCO, Paris, 1962, in press).

D. W. Snow, Trends in geographical variation in Palaearctic members of the genus Parus, *Evolution* **8**, 19–28 (1954).

———, Climate and geographical variation in birds, *New Biology* **25**, 64–84 (1958).

F. V. Stefansson, *The Friendly Arctic* (Macmillan, New York, 1943).

A. M. Thomson, W. Z. Billewicz, R. Passmore, The relation between calorie intake and body weight in man, *Lancet* **1**, 1027–1028 (1961).

C. G. Wilber, Physiological regulations and the origin of human types, *Human Biol.* **29**, 329–36 (1957).

Does the Melanin Pigment of Human Skin Have Adaptive Value?

AN ESSAY IN HUMAN ECOLOGY AND THE EVOLUTION OF RACE

Harold F. Blum

*Department of Biology, Princeton University**

Melanin pigment plays a predominant role in giving the brown and black color to the skin, which provides some of the most striking differences in outward appearance of human races. This would seem a very superficial difference, yet there has been attempt to find adaptive significance in the presence of the pigment itself. It is quite generally accepted, without qualification, that the pigment constitutes a protective barrier against injurious effects of sunlight. Reasoning on this basis, Negroes have been thought to be better adapted than white-skinned peoples to life in the tropics, and this has been attributed to natural selection. Charles Darwin himself made this suggestion, although he hedged it with characteristic caution. The argument has been expanded since, and the idea has come to be widely accepted. This is sometimes cited today as a definite example of natural selection in Man.

In Darwin's day very little was known about the effects of sunlight on the human body or their relation to the spectrum of sunlight, nor about the geographical distribution of sunlight; and although a good deal has been learned since, the knowledge does not seem to have been widely disseminated. There are still many things to be explained, but enough is known for a reasonably critical examination of various aspects of the above

Reprinted by permission of the author and *The Quarterly Review of Biology* **36**, 50–63 (1961).

thesis. When one attempts such an examination he cannot but be surprised that such far-reaching conclusions, based on such tenuous evidence, should have received so much credence.

MELANIN AND ITS POSITION
IN HUMAN SKIN

The term melanin is applied to a type of finely granular, dark-colored substances in skin, hair, and some other organs of animals. While there is basic similarity in chemical composition there is a good deal of variety among the types of melanins. The color, which ranges through various shades of brown to black, is strongly affected by scattering of light by the pigment particles. The latter factor makes it difficult to relate the color to chemical composition, because of the difficulty it introduces into the measurement of absorption spectra.

In human skin the melanin is normally contained in the *epidermis* — a thin outer layer ranging from about 0.07 to 1.2 millimeters in thickness. The relationship of the epidermis to other structures, and some approximate dimensions, are indicated in Figure 1 B. In discussing the optical properties of skin, which concerns us here, it may be necessary to oversimplify the details of structure, which are quite complex. To this end I shall treat the epidermis as composed of two layers; the *malpighian*, made of living cells; and exterior to this the *corneum,* a dead layer which is produced from the living malpighian. The optical properties of these two layers differ greatly, although it would be difficult to demonstrate a sharp boundary between them, either optically or biologically. The distinction is useful, however, because the corneum obviously serves as an efficient barrier to ultraviolet light, greatly diminishing the amount that reaches the viable cells of the malpighian. Beneath the epidermis is the dermis, where are found a variety of structures, including the hair follicles, sebaceous glands, and sweat glands. The most superficial blood vessels are located in the dermis just underneath the epidermis. The melanin is produced in specialized cells, the *melanocytes*; but passes into neighboring cells of the malpighian, and may be carried up into the corneum. For a discussion of the melanocytes and the general histology of the epidermis the reader is referred to the excellent review of Billingham and Silvers (1960). In the white races the corneum and upper part of the malpighian may be relatively free of melanin except after injury — including the action of ultraviolet light which results in the familiar suntan. Negro skin, on the other hand, not only contains more melanin, but this is more evenly distributed throughout the epidermis, including the corneum.

The distinction made here between "negro skin" and "white skin" is perforce somewhat arbitrary. With few exceptions neither optical nor histological studies specify exactly the race or origin of the subject; and one can only assume that these terms apply to some reasonably well distinguished extremes of pigmentation. There seems to have been little

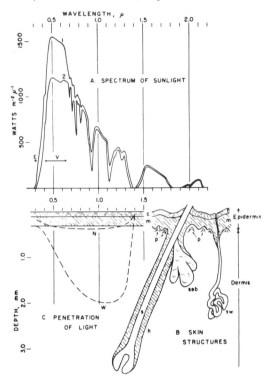

FIGURE 1.

A. Spectral Distribution of Sunlight at the Surface of the Earth (after Moon, 1941). Curve 1, with sun at zenith. Curve 2, with sun at 60° (four hours) from zenith. V, spectral limits of human vision. E, spectral limits (within sunlight) for sunburn, antirachitic action and cancer induction.

B. Diagrammatic Representation of Skin Structures. A schematized conception in which the dimensions should not be taken as generally representative, since the skin may vary widely in its thickness. c, corneum, i.e., horny layer of epidermis. m, malpighian layer of epidermis. sw, sweat gland. seb, sebaceous gland. p, the most superficial blood vessels, arterioles, capillaries, and venules. h, hair follicle. s, hair shaft.

C. Penetration of Light into Human Skin as a Function of Wavelength. The curves N and W indicate for Negro and White skin, respectively, *rough estimates* of depths at which radiation of the corresponding wavelengths is reduced to 5 percent of its incident value. There are insufficient data to make more than rough estimates, and these curves should be regarded as suggestive rather than in any way exact (see text). Curve W is based on Hardy and Muschenheim (1934, 1936), and on Kirby-Smith, Blum, and Grady (1942). Curve N is based on Hardy and Muschenheim (1934, 1936) and on Thompson (1955).

or no optical study of skins of intermediate color, beyond reflectance measurements, which are not very instructive in the present regard.

While the study of evolution of races is one of separation of genotypes, the role of natural selection in such a process must depend upon inter-relationships between phenotype and environment, and it is at this level that we find ourselves in the present discussion. Thus the mechanism of inheritance of the melanin of human skin need not enter directly here. This is fortunate because of the complicated nature of the problem, into which many facets of the phenotype may enter. For example, a matter of first importance is the penetration of light into the skin, and while one may measure this directly with some success the contributing factors might be very difficult to analyze. They include the absorption and light scattering properties of the various layers; and to what extent melanin is concerned in this must depend upon such factors as dispersion and distribution of the pigment, its chemical composition and spectral absorption, and the character of the other components. To disentangle the genetics pertinent to all these factors, some of which we do not understand at all clearly, would be a difficult matter indeed. For the recent status of genetic studies on melanin of mammal skin, the reader is again referred to Billingham and Silvers (1960).

SUNLIGHT AND ITS
PENETRATION INTO SKIN

Figure 1 A shows the spectral distribution of sunlight at the surface of the earth, when the sun is at two different angles; curve 1 for the sun at zenith, and curve 2, for the sun at 60° (four hours) from zenith. The lower wavelength limit (i.e., in the ultraviolet) is set at about 0.29 μ by absorption of the shorter wavelengths by ozone in the upper atmosphere. The serrated appearance in the infrared part of the spectrum is due principally to spectral absorption bands of water vapor. The human eye detects only a small part of this spectrum, as the line labelled V indicates — normally a range from about 0.4 μ to 0.65 μ. Thus the eye is a poor judge of total sunlight, and no judge at all of the ultraviolet or infrared parts. The very short wavelengths of sunlight are those which cause sunburn, that is, a range from the lower limit at 0.29 μ to about 0.32 μ, as indicated at E in the figure. This is a very tiny fraction of the total (less than 0.1%) under the maximal conditions represented by curve 1; and is reduced to a negligible amount when the sun moves a few hours from zenith, as indicated by curve 2. On the other hand, total sunlight varies much less with zenith angle, that is, with season, latitude, and time of day, as is easily seen by comparing curves 1 and 2 for the whole range of wavelengths.

In order to interpret the various physiological effects of sunlight on Man, it is necessary to have some idea of the extent of penetration of the different wavelengths into the skin. But this is not an easy matter to determine, and although a number of dependable measurements have been made for limited spectral regions these cannot be put together into more than a rough composite picture. Skin is made up of optically in-homogeneous layers, having different properties and varying in thick-ness and structure from one part of the body to another, and since different investigators have measured different samples of skin the re-sults cannot be fitted together accurately. Even with more complete measurements no universal values for skin transmission could be assigned which would apply to skin from all parts of the body. The curves drawn in Figure 1 C, which purport to show the depth of penetra-tion of 5 percent of the incident radiation, for negro skin (N) and for white skin (W), cannot therefore be accepted as more than rough esti-mates; but I think they will be useful and not misleading if they are employed only as approximate guides.

Referring to these curves, it is seen that the sunburning radiation (wavelengths shorter than 0.32μ) is nearly all absorbed in the epider-mis — it is here, then, that this radiation must have its effect. Penetra-tion increases toward longer wavelengths — reaching the superficial blood vessels and other structures of the epidermis — until a maximum depth is reached around 1.0μ in the infrared. The penetration then decreases rapidly as wavelength increases, there being little of impor-tance beyond 1.4μ, within the spectral range of sunlight. While some investigators have claimed greater transmission of some wavelengths in the visible and infrared, it seems clear that no portion of the radiation of sunlight penetrates in important amount below a few millimeters. General discussions often fail to recognize the great importance of dif-ferences in penetration of different spectral regions of sunlight, and that different regions have different physiological effects (e.g., Coon, Garn, and Birdsell, 1950).

Faulty measurements have led from time to time to misconceptions regarding the depth of penetration of sunlight into skin. Important errors may enter in two ways: (1) low measurements are obtained when scattering is neglected, this error being increased by drying out of the skin sample; (2) if care is not taken to minimize heating of the skin by absorbed radiation, or proper shielding is not provided, the measure-ments may indicate too great penetration. In preparing the curves in Figure 1C, the measurements of Hardy and Muschenheim (1934, 1936), of Kirby-Smith, Blum, and Grady (1942), and of Thomson (1955) have been relied upon. For a discussion and other references, see Blum (1945a).

The curves in Figure 1 C neglect the specific absorption bands of hemoglobin, carotenoids, and other substances. Hemoglobin in the superficial vessels absorbs the shorter wavelengths of the visible spec-trum quite strongly, so that light reflected back is predominantly red, this giving the ruddy tint to many complexions. The curves indicate that negro skin is less transparent in the visible spectrum than white skin, and this is no doubt due chiefly to the difference in melanin content. But negro skin also has a thicker corneum than white skin, an important factor with regard to sunburning radiation (see below).

PHYSIOLOGICAL EFFECTS OF
SUNLIGHT ON MAN, AND
FACTORS AFFECTING THEM

Sunlight has several physiological effects on Man, which may be separated into two general categories on the basis of the spectra involved: (1) the effect of adding the energy of sunlight to the heat load of the body; and (2) specific effects of those wavelengths that cause sunburn, which also, have carcinogenic and antirachitic action. The latter are classed together, not because of physiological similarity, but because they are produced by the same spectral region of sunlight, since this factor is of basic importance if we are to relate them to geographical distribution.

At least one other, minor, effect will be mentioned below, and there are certain pathological conditions brought about by parts of the solar spectrum (e.g., see Blum, 1941, 1950) which are so rare that they are of no interest in the present discussion. There are also diseases of domestic animals in which sunlight is the precipitating factor; but which, for physiological or dietetic reasons do not have their counterpart in Man (e.g., Blum, 1941; Clare, 1955).

THE SOLAR HEAT LOAD

In the standard resting state the human body produces a certain amount of heat by its own metabolism, which must be dissipated in some way. If the body becomes active this heat production increases, and in case of severe exercise may rise several fold above the resting condition. The human body has several means of getting rid of this heat load. The blood, heated internally, comes to the surface to pass through the vessels of the skin, and a certain amount of heat may be *conducted* to the surrounding air. The rate of dissipation is increased by movement of air over the skin, that is, *convection* is a factor. Another important means of dissipating heat is by *evaporation* of water from sweat at the surface of the skin. A factor less commonly recognized and more difficult to assess is the loss to cooler surroundings by *radiation.*

All bodies emit radiation according to their temperature and size. In the ordinary range of temperatures, all this radiation is in the infrared spectrum and hence invisible, although it may be detected through the sense organs of the skin as a sensation of coolness, warmth or, if intense, of pain (Oppel and Hardy, 1937a, b; Hardy and Oppel, 1937). The human body radiates to its surroundings and receives radiation from them; it may gain or lose in the exchange, for example, it gains heat from a hot radiator or loses heat to a block of ice, even though these objects are at some distance. But there is also a constant imperceptible or barely perceptible exchange with objects nearer the temperature of the body — indoors with the walls of the room, outdoors with hot soil or rocks or the cool foliage of plants. It is clear that the effective temperature of the environment, with respect to the human body, is a complex matter, and is not to be measured adequately in terms of the temperature and humidity of the ambient air alone.

Out-of-doors one may receive an important amount of heat from direct exposure to the sun; that is, the total spectrum of sunlight impinging upon the body adds a certain amount of heat load. On the other hand, the body may lose a considerable amount of heat by radiation to the clear sky, which is, effectively, at a lower temperature than the body, the amount of loss through this channel being largely determined by the quantity of water vapor in the atmosphere. This radiation to "space" may be an important factor in desert areas, where the atmospheric water vapor is low (see Blum, 1945b, for a consideration of various factors involved under desert conditions).

It is clear that the human body is constantly exchanging heat with its environment in a number of ways. Hence the amount of heat lost, and the means of losing it, must vary according to the particular environmental conditions, and some of these may be difficult to evaluate. The radiation factor is among the most difficult to assess because it involves both the geometry of the human body and that of the surroundings, since the amount of heat exchange by radiation must depend upon the profiles which the radiating masses present to each other (see Blum, 1945b). The heat dissipation is modified by clothing, which may prevent the conduction of heat away, and may absorb or reflect the incident radiation according to the wavelengths concerned. Thus, dissipation of the heat load — which is essential if the man is going to live — becomes quite a complicated matter, and one that can be treated only with reference to the particular complex of environmental conditions that may obtain.

If the conditions are such that the man cannot adequately dispose of his heat load the temperature of the body must rise, but there are no climatic conditions in the world inhabited by Man where death is likely to result directly from raising the body temperature — the body is not likely to be "cooked" by coagulation of its proteins. Even under maximum conditions, the energy of sunlight is not nearly sufficient to burn the skin by heating unless concentrated by means of a lens, sunburn being caused by ultraviolet light acting in a very different way. Contrary to common impression, there is no evidence that the brain may be unduly heated by exposure of the head to direct sunlight (see Aron, 1911).

A man may, however, suffer collapse due to circulatory failure under environmental conditions that lead to excessive water loss, as, for example, in desert climate, and sunlight may be a factor in this. If the intake of water is not sufficient to compensate for the loss by evaporation and through other channels, the blood volume may fall so low that the heart can no longer maintain sufficient blood flow. The resulting collapse may be sudden, although the condition of low blood volume has accumulated for hours. Being usually associated with high environmental

TABLE 1

Estimated Relative Absorption of Sunlight by
White and Negro Skin, Based on Heer (1952);
Values for Color Temperature 6000°C, Which Is
Approximately That of the Photosphere of the
Sun.

White		*Negro*	
untanned (inner forearm)	tanned (forehead)	untanned (inner forearm)	tanned (forehead)
1.00	1.16	1.36	1.46

temperature, such collapse has been called "heat stroke," or — since it
often occurs when the person is exposed to the sun — "sunstroke."
The factors contributing to the depletion of water may be complex. They
are most easily analyzed, perhaps, in the case of desert conditions where
the temperature of the air is above that of the body, so that loss of heat
by conduction and convection is virtually nil, and cooling must be accomplished almost entirely by evaporation of water from sweat. Such
conditions may be exaggerated by the solar heat load, coming both
directly from sunlight impinging on the body and also from reflection
and reradiation from heated surroundings. Walking under these conditions, a man may lose as much as one liter of water per hour, and if this
is not adequately replaced, the blood volume must be eventually reduced, with ultimate collapse (Adolph *et al.*, 1947).

Under such conditions the radiant energy absorbed from sunlight may
constitute a critical increment of heat load, and the man who can most
readily reduce this increment would have an advantage, and might
survive longest. In this case the man whose skin reflected more of this
load should be better off. Table 1 indicates that negro skin absorbs
roughly 30 percent more sunlight than white skin; but it is to be remembered that this figure applies to only a part of the total heat load.
Thus, if a Negro and a white-skinned man walked side by side, naked,
in direct sunlight, across a desert where the temperature of the air was
above that of the body, the Negro might be expected — other things
being equal — to collapse before the white man. But these particular
competitive conditions are not likely to be often met. If the bodies of
both men were similarly clothed or otherwise covered any advantage
would, of course, be largely lost.

It has been suggested that the melanin of the Negro, because it brings
about greater local heating of the skin, leads to more profuse sweating,
and that this is of advantage to him in the tropics. Thomson (1951)
has recently shown that sunburn tends to reduce sweating in white
skins to a greater degree than in negro skins, and this might conceivably
give the Negro a certain advantage in this regard. But while profuse
sweating may confer a somewhat greater degree of comfort under con-

ditions where water is rapidly evaporated, it could only increase the water loss, and this would seem to be the factor of real importance — a disadvantageous one — with regard to survival.

Taking all things into consideration, it seems necessary to assume that the possession of a dark skin should be a disadvantage to the Negro, as regards heat load and life in hot desert areas, but that the disadvantage is not a very great one, and probably of little importance under his usual conditions of life. It would seem that, if anything, his melanin pigment might be of some, although limited, advantage to the Negro in a cooler climate where it was important to conserve rather than to lose heat.

EFFECTS OF ULTRAVIOLET LIGHT

We now come to consider some other effects of sunlight in which melanin may also play a role. These are: (1) *sunburn*, a phenomenon with which everyone is acquainted; (2) *carcinogenesis*, i.e., the induction of cancer of the skin; and (3) *antirachitic action*, the prevention of rickets, a disease of bone. All three effects are caused only by wavelengths shorter than about 0.32 μ, which, as we have seen, constitutes a very tiny fraction of sunlight. The fact that all three effects have the same long wavelength limit does not mean, however, that all are closely related. The first and last are very separate entities; the second is probably related to the first but this cannot be said with complete assurance (see Blum, 1959).

SUNBURN

To most readers sunburn means an unpleasant blistering of the skin following exposure to sunlight. I use the term, however, to include a complex of related effects, ranging from a mild reddening of the skin, or *erythema*, to the severe blistering just mentioned. As a result of any degree of sunburn, melanin may increase in the epidermis — this we recognize as *suntan*. (For a more complete discussion, of sunburn, with extensive references see Blum, 1955a).

The erythema is the manifestation of dilation and consequent increased blood content of the minute vessels lying just beneath the epidermis. The photochemical reaction bringing about the dilation of the vessels has its locus in the epidermis, however, principally in the viable malpighian, where histological examination shows that cells may be injured or killed. The dilation of the vessels in the dermis is presumably due to substances which diffuse down from the injured epidermis. The corneum or outer horny layer of the epidermis protects against sunburn by absorbing a large proportion of the incident sunburning radiation before it reaches the malpighian — it is a very effective absorber.

While it seems safe for our purposes to consider the malpighian to be the locus of the principal changes underlying sunburn, the overlying corneum serving only a protective function, certain factors should be mentioned in this regard. Studies by Rottier and Mullink (1952) and Rottier (1953) indicate that photochemical changes brought about in the corneum may contribute to the erythema. But the eliciting wavelengths are, at least for the greater part, shorter than those found in sunlight, so this finding can have little or no concern in the present context. The sunburning radiation is absorbed in greatest part in the epidermis; but, at least in some white skins that have not been exposed for some time the longer wavelengths may penetrate to a small extent below, particularly in unexposed areas. The small fraction which reaches the minute vessels of the dermis may cause damage there, as shown by the inhibition of erythema (Blum and Terus, 1946); and it is possible that this may contribute to the blistering that occurs in some cases after severe exposure to sunlight.

The brownish color, or *suntan*, which develops some days after exposure of white skins to sunlight, involves the production of new melanin in the epidermis, although the earliest stage may represent migration of melanin that is already present, to a more superficial position. The formation of new melanin seems to be a response to injury — it also follows other kinds of insult to the epidermis. The color begins to fade after a time, but traces may persist for years. The fading is not all the result of removal or destruction of the melanin, but represents in part bleaching of the pigment by reduction, and the pigment may be subsequently darkened again by oxidation. It was shown just before the second World War by Henschke and Schultze (1939a, b), that the bleached pigment may be caused to darken by exposure to longer wavelengths than those that elicit its formation. These wavelengths — 0.3μ to 0.44μ — are much more plentiful in sunlight, and much less affected by the angle of the sun, than are those that produce the suntan. Darkening of preformed pigment may also be brought about by endocrine secretions, and probably by other influences mediated by the circulation. The pigment-darkening reaction seems to have no physiological significance in itself; but it is interesting to us, because it shows that the color of the skin cannot be taken as a reliable quantitative index of the amount of melanin present in the human epidermis. The degree of bleaching and darkening seems to vary widely in white skins.

It is common knowledge that the development of suntan is generally accompanied by a decreased sensitivity to sunburn, and it is perhaps natural to relate the two events — the eye tells us that the skin has darkened, and we may jump to the conclusion that it transmits less light of all wavelengths, including those we do not detect. About 1899, Niels Finsen performed a simple experiment which he supposed to prove this point. He painted areas of his arm with India ink before exposing it to sunlight. When he scaled the ink off later he found that the areas it had covered had not been sunburned. He reasoned that the melanin in the skin has the same protective effect as the India ink. Very little being known about sunburn at the time, he did not recognize that while India ink is opaque to ultraviolet light, he had no evidence that the same was true for melanin. Nevertheless Finsen's interpretation was accepted for 20 years without question, and still is by the majority of people.

About 1920, however, doubts began to arise as the result of observations by several investigators. It was noted that the immunity to sunburn disappears much more rapidly than the suntan — the immunity is usually gone in two months, whereas the tan may persist for years. And it was found that vitiliginous and albino skins, which do not form melanin, may develop a degree of immunity to ultraviolet light. An explanation was given in 1926 by Guillaume, who found that after exposure to ultraviolet light the epidermis, particularly the corneum, becomes thickened, and attributed the accompanying immunity to the enhanced absorption of the sunburning radiation in the latter layer. His findings were soon confirmed, and somewhat later it was shown by direct measurement that albino mouse epidermis increases its absorption of ultraviolet light after repeated exposures (Kirby-Smith *et al.*, 1942). As a result, it was generally accepted by those actively working in this field that the relative immunity to sunburn which follows exposure is due to a resultant thickening of the outer horny layer, although the acceptance of the role of melanin pigment in this regard persisted, generally, outside this small group. After all, there seemed no good reason to think that melanin should be a better absorber of ultraviolet light than the protein which makes up the greater part of the corneum.

But Negro skin is very refractory to sunburn, and if this could not be accounted for by high melanin content, some other explanation was needed. The epidermis of Negro skin had been reported to be thicker than that of white skins, and it seems to have been generally assumed by those working in this field that it was the thicker corneum which made the Negro skin less susceptible to sunburn — at least I accepted this explanation myself. A few years ago, however, Thomson (1955) made a comparative study and found that Negro corneum was indeed thicker than that of white skins, but also that the former was more opaque to the sunburning radiation per unit thickness. It seems reasonable to attribute the greater opacity to the higher melanin content, although this may not be fully established. The corneum is composed principally of protein which absorbs the sunburning radiation strongly; but its effectiveness as a protective light-filter is greatly enhanced by its flake-like structure, which scatters the light and thus increases the path-length through which the light rays must travel in the absorbing medium. The amount of melanin is much less than that of the protein, and it is unlikely that it is a much better absorber of the sunburning radiation; but because it is made up of small particles it is an effective scattering agent, and this may make it an important additional factor in the absorption of the sunburning radiation by the corneum. Thus, after all, the melanin may play a considerable protective role, as regards sunburn — but all we know definitely is that the horny layer of the epidermis of Negro skin is a more effective shield against the sunburning radiation than is the epidermis of white skins. Thus, while it is reasonable to assume that melanin plays a role in protection against sunburn — and this assumption will be made in the following discussion in this paper — it should be kept in mind that the point is not definitely proven.

But can immunity to sunburn be regarded as having survival value? Sunburn is essentially an acute effect, which while it may be briefly debilitating in severe cases involving a considerable area of the body, does not cause prolonged, systemic damage. It is seldom disfiguring, although it may cause deterioration of complexion after many years of exposure — this coming late in the lifespan is not likely to play a role in sexual selection. In many white societies suntan is looked upon today as a sign of health and beauty. As regards the female sex, fashion reversed itself in this regard about half a century ago, but the survival of the societies concerned does not seem to have been seriously affected thereby.

CANCER OF THE SKIN

Although it does not seem to be a matter of common knowledge, clinical, experimental, and geographical evidence converge to indict the sunburning portion of sunlight as a principal cause of cancer of human skin (see Blum, 1959). The cancers involved grow from the malpighian layer of the epidermis — many of them are not very malignant and mortality from this cause is relatively low. In white-skinned people these cancers are limited almost exclusively to the exposed parts, particularly the face. They are very rare in Negro skin, and when they occur show no preference for the exposed parts. There seems every reason to draw a parallel with the Negro's immunity to sunburn, attributing his low incidence to skin cancer likewise to the opacity of his corneum. Negroes do not show comparable immunity to other types of cancer, and indeed it is reported from the Kenya region of Africa that cancers of the skin occur not infrequently among natives in association with parasitic infection (Vindt, 1935).

Skin cancer does not, so far as we know, result from a single bout of sunburn, no matter how severe, but is a cumulative, "chronic" effect of exposures to sunlight repeated over a long period (Blum, 1959). Since these cancers are usually not lethal, and not very disfiguring except in late stages — as a rule they do not appear until late in life, well after mating — it would seem unlikely that cancer due to sunlight could have any great effect on racial survival in the sense of biological evolution.

Clear distinction should be made between these cancers and the very dangerous, though fortunately very rare, malignant melanomas which are cancers of a different type. The latter occur largely on parts of the body not exposed to sunlight.

ANTIRACHITIC ACTION

The same wavelengths that cause sunburn bring about an entirely different photochemical reaction — transformation of precursor substance into vitamin D. The site of the reaction can hardly be deeper than the epidermis, where these wavelengths are principally absorbed. It is difficult to estimate the effect of melanin on the efficiency of sunlight in producing Vitamin D — it might decrease formation by absorbing some of the effective radiation, or it is conceivable that by scattering in the corneum and consequent increase in path length, it might even enhance vitamin production in that layer.

Vitamin D is required for bone development and if it is lacking, the bone disease, rickets, results. Exposure to sunlight may prevent or cure this disease; but Man is not strictly dependent on sunlight in this regard, since vitamin D may also be introduced in the diet, and under most conditions of life the role of sunlight is probably not very great. Rickets is most frequent under crowded urban conditions where both diet and sunlight are limited. The disease most often affects children, and, since it is of crippling nature, its prevention could have survival value. But because of the complicating factor of diet, it would be difficult to estimate just how important sunlight might be as regards a given population living under natural conditions.

A TENTATIVE BALANCE SHEET

It is clear that the part played by melanin in the physiological responses of the human body to sunlight has aspects which require analysis in different ways, with regard not only to sunlight but to other environmental factors as well. Any classification of these aspects with regard to their advantages or disadvantages must be a very rough one. Still, it may be worth while to draw up a tentative balance sheet at this point in our discussion. In the one that follows, plus or minus ratings indicate estimated relative advantage of the high melanin content of negro skin as compared to the low melanin content of white skin.

Physiological effect	Negro skin	White skin
Solar heat load at high environmental temperature	−	+
Sunburn	+	−
Cancer of the skin	+	−
Prevention of rickets	±	±

Presented in this way the result seems equivocal, Negro skin having an advantage as regards sunburn and skin cancer, but a disadvantage as regards heat load at high ambient temperature. The advantage or disadvantage as regards antirachitic action is uncertain, but the latter seems the more probable. The balance sheet avoids the question of whether the advantages listed have significant survival value or not, and also how they might be related to the distribution of sunlight with latitude, that is, between the tropic zone and other zones. The latter question must now be taken up.

DISTRIBUTION OF SUNLIGHT
WITH LATITUDE AS REGARDS
PHYSIOLOGICAL RESPONSES OF MAN

On the whole, those who have assumed that Negroes inhabit the tropics because their skin pigment adapts them to the conditions of insolation in that zone, seem to have given little attention to the spectral character of sunlight and its distribution with latitude. It seems to have been generally assumed that since the tropics are hot there is more sunlight there, but the problem is not so simple as this. Reference to Figure 1A will show that total sunlight decreases less rapidly as the sun moves away from the zenith than does the sunburning portion. Obviously the solar heat load, being related to total sunlight, must vary differently with latitude than does the sunburning radiation.

Figure 2 gives a rough, general idea of the distribution of sunlight with latitude. Represented on the left of the map are distributions, with latitude, of the total energy of sunlight at noon under three con-

FIGURE 2. Map of the distribution of brown skin color (after Fleure, 1945). On the left, distribution of total sunlight with latitude. E, at equinox; S, at summer solstice; W, at winter solstice. On the right, distribution of sunburning radiation (wavelength shorter than 0.32μ) with latitude. E, at equinox; S, at summer solstice; W, at winter solstice. The curves on the right and left are based on values from Moon (1941). Note that the curves for summer and winter solstices are distorted by the Mercator projection. These curves, based on light incident upon a surface normal to the sun's rays, neglect scattering from the sky, which may be very important in the case of the sunburning radiation, and also neglect geometrical relationships of the human body profile with respect to the radiant environment. They are thus to be considered only as rough guides.

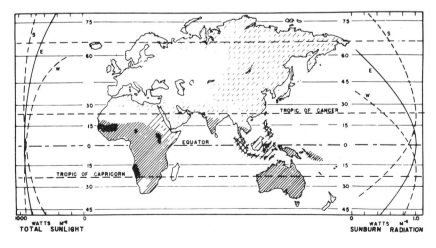

TOTAL SUNLIGHT

SUNBURN RADIATION

ditions: (W) with the sun at its northernmost excursion (summer solstice), when it is over the tropic of cancer (23° 44′ N); (S) with the sun at its southernmost excursion (winter solstice) when the sun is over the tropic of capricorn (23° 44′ S); and (E) with the sun over the equator (equinox). On the right of the figure are represented the distributions of the sunburning fraction of sunlight at the same respective positions of the sun. It is noted that the sunburning radiation is much more "concentrated" in terms of latitude than total sunlight; the amounts of energy are, of course, very different in the two cases.

It is clear from the diagram on the left, that at some times of the year a part of one temperate zone may receive more total sunlight than does a part of the tropic zone; indeed, the difference in this regard between the temperate and tropic zones is not so great as is commonly conceived. Even the Arctic and Antarctic zones receive a considerable amount of solar energy during parts of the year. So it is seen that the effect of the solar heat load in exacerbating collapse due to water loss should not be restricted to the tropics — at the time of the summer solstice, for example, other things being equal, it should be just as likely to occur at 47° N (about the latitude of Zürich or Quebec) as at the equator. The fact that the sun crosses the equator twice during the year, but reaches the tropic of cancer only once, should not be of importance in this regard, since "heat stroke" is an acute effect, that is, one that involves, at most, a few days' exposure to the sun. Much more important would be other aspects of the environment such as desert conditions, which are to be found in the temperate zones as well as in the tropics. As has been said, high melanin content of the skin should be a slight disadvantage under those conditions. But it could be of limited advantage in a cooler climate where heat gain might be desirable.

In a recent paper, Cowles (1959) stresses the advantage of black or brown pigment in reducing visibility, and suggests that this might have had survival value for Man, in the role either of predator or pursued, at some time in his evolution. Whatever the importance of this factor in natural selection, it would seem to be one which should be related more to local environmental situations than to a global distribution such as has been supposed as regards adaptation of Negro skin to life in the tropics. From the curves in Figure 2 it may be seen that the visible portion of sunlight, which is that part pertaining to Cowles' thesis, varies relatively little in its maximum intensity, from Tropic to Temperate zones, or even the Arctic, where summer sunlight is bright. On the whole it would seem that Cowles' argument should apply more to noctural vs. diurnal life, than to geographical distribution.

It is to be noted from the curves on the right of Figure 2 that the sunburning radiation varies more with latitude than does the total solar heat load. But nevertheless part of the temperate zones receive relatively high amounts at certain times of the year. At summer or winter solstice the chances of being sunburned should be about as great at 47° N or S, respectively, as at the equator, and with sufficient exposure sunburn may occur above the Arctic Circle. Of course, sunburn is an acute effect, and the situation should be somewhat different as regards the "chronic" effects, carcinogenesis and antirachitic action — because these depend on the total exposure to the sunburning radiation throughout the year, and the sun is near zenith in the tropics for a greater part of the year than it is in the temperate zones. But, nevertheless, parts of the temperate zones receive a relatively high annual incidence of the sunburning radiation.

In the United States the occurrence of skin cancer within the white population shows a north-south distribution which fits reasonably well with estimates of the distribution of the sunburning radiation, within the latitude range (32° to 41° N) (see Blum, 1959). But at most the incidence of these cancers is small, and, as has been said, probably could have little effect on racial survival. The Negro population has a very low incidence of skin cancer, but I think no one would venture to say that this in itself has played a significant role in the relative distribution of the Negro and White populations in our country. Fairly recent historical events have been obviously much more important in determining this distribution than has natural selection. Would it not seem reasonable to think that, correspondingly, at a much earlier time events not directly related to the environment played a dominant role in determining the distribution of the Negro and White races in the eastern hemisphere rather than biological adaptation to the climate of the particular areas they now inhabit?

As regards historical factors in the distribution of races, the Bushmen of Southern Africa offer a most interesting example. These people, at present restricted to the region of the Kalahari Desert, occupied a much greater area, including quite different terrain and climatic conditions, at the time of the entrance of Europeans into this region. Subsequently the Bushmen have been pushed gradually out of other areas and have taken refuge in the Kalahari. Here the remnants of the race live under very difficult conditions in an arid land with relatively sparse vegetation. They appear to have adapted themselves to a precarious existence under these conditions by learning to take advantage of what corners of the environment they may grasp, rather, so far as we know, than by any particular physiological adaptation. If we read the record right, they have lost at least one remarkable facet of their previous culture in doing this, the making of the rock paintings that have been attributed to them — not a surprising loss considering the complete preoccupation with survival which seems to be their present lot. (See Willcox, 1956; Van der Post, 1958; Thomas, 1959). A cultural change resulting from recent historical events imposing a new habitation area would thus seem to account for the Bushmen's present adjustment to a rigorous environment, rather than selection on a biological basis. May a similar situation not affect other distributions and cultures where the history is unknown, being farther in the past?

My information regarding the Bushmen has been greatly increased since this paper was first written, by conversations with Dr. B. Kaminer, who has studied these people at first hand in the Kalahari, and has taken color photographs of them. Dr. Kaminer pointed out to me by means of his photographs, the great amount of dirt and desert soil which these people, who have no opportunity to bathe, carry about on their skins. Even without physical measurements one can be quite sure, I think, that the amount of sunburning radiation that reaches the skin is greatly reduced, and consequently the importance of melanin as protection in this regard. Seeing these photographs one might conclude that the solar heat load should be determined more in terms of the reflectance of the soil from the local terrain, than in terms of that of the uncoated skin. The fact that the Bushmen tend to be brown rather than black would not seem of great importance. This observation seems still further to confuse the question of the adaptive value of melanin in "feral" Man or his ancestors, making its importance even more questionable.

Finally, we may ask whether the distribution of the dark-skinned races really fits very well with the distribution of sunlight. The comparison in Figure 2 does not seem to give very strong support. The map shown there is drawn after Fleure (1945), who has attempted to explain the distribution of skin color in part in terms of local climatic conditions, but his argument does not take into account the nature of the physiological factors concerned. Actually, the comparisons made in the present paper, regarding melanin pigment and physiological effects of sunlight, are based on what is known about White and Negro skins, since applicable data are only available regarding these; to what extent the brown-skinned peoples may fall into an intermediate position with regard to the physical and physiological factors that have been discussed we do not know.

A HISTORICAL NOTE

In 1871, Darwin wrote in his *Descent of Man* (p. 200 in the Appleton edition of 1913), as follows: "Dr. Sharpe remarks, that a tropical sun, which burns and blisters a white skin, does not injure a black one at all. . . . I have been assured by a medical man that some years ago during each summer, but not during the winter, his hands became marked with light brown patches, like, although larger than, freckles, and that these patches were never affected by sun-burning, while the white parts of his skin have on several occasions been much inflamed and blistered. . . . Whether the saving of the skin from being thus burned is of sufficient importance to account for a dark tint having been gradually acquired through natural selection, I am unable to judge."

The complete passage is of interest, but to conserve space I have quoted only those parts that seem particularly cogent here. It is to be noted that Darwin was properly cautious about his attribution of dark skin to natural selection. The evidence of association of relative immunity to sunburn with pigmentation we need not question, although, as is not infrequently the case, Darwin is using information at secondhand. But one may question the interpretations, while remembering how little was known at the time about the action of sunlight.

> The case of apparent immunity of pigmented patches on white skin to sunburn, is intriguing in the light of present knowledge. Was this, perhaps, a case of *vitiligo*?

Although Ritter had shown the existence of ultraviolet light in the sun's spectrum in 1801, only about the middle of the century was it realized that sunburn is caused by such radiation. This came about with an observation by the physicists Foucault and Despretz who were accidentally sunburned by the radiation from an electric arc with which they were experimenting; the matter was reported in a brief note by Charcot (1858). It had been thought before that time that sunburn resulted from heating the skin, and Darwin may still have been under this impression when he wrote. A more definitive demonstration that sunburn is due to ultraviolet light was reported by Widmark in 1889. Some of the more recent developments have already been noted.

Another early suggestion that skin color favors the residence of Negroes in the tropics is of interest. In 1887, Wedding presented, in a brief note before the Berliner Gesellschaft für Anthropologie und Urgeschichte, what appears to have been the first account of buckwheat poisoning in sheep, giving proof that sunlight is a precipitating factor. He showed that animals fed on the buckwheat plant developed lesions of the skin when subsequently exposed to sunlight, but that areas of the skin which he covered with tar did not display the lesions. We know today that this condition is brought about by a substance present in the buckwheat plant. When the plant is ingested, this substance gets into the blood stream and is carried to the skin, which it photosensitizes to wavelengths in the visible spectrum. Man seems never to eat enough buckwheat to become photosensitized in this way, and the basic photochemical mechanism is not related to sunburn (see Blum, 1941, 1950). Clearly, the phenomenon observed by Wedding has nothing to do with the normal responses of human skin to sunlight, but he was unaware of this — very little being known about such responses at that time, particularly with regard to spectral relationships. He suggested that the pigment in the Negro skin offered protection in the same way as did the tar he painted on his sheep, and that this was of advantage to the Negro in the tropics. He even went so far as to suggest that a ship be sent to the tropics with half the crew painted with walnut stain, for the purpose of studying the effects of tropical sunlight. His paper makes no mention of Darwin or natural selection.

I have often wondered how Wedding's paper came to be presented to an anthropological audience rather than to veterinary scientists. It described a discovery of first importance to the latter, but introduced only a misconception with regard to the study of Man.

GENERAL REMARKS

In examining the interrelations between certain physiological responses of Man and a particular facet of his environment — sunlight — we have found the situation more complex than it is generally thought to be. This particular environmental factor has more than one separate physiological effect on Man, and other environmental factors may play important roles in the overall result. The specific thesis examined — that high melanin content of the skin adapts to life in the tropics because it offers protection against sunlight — seems to have little to recommend it. The melanin might provide a degree of protection in some cases but could be detrimental in others. On the whole, one may doubt that the possession of melanin pigment makes very much difference one way or the other, and that it could serve as an important "handle" for natural selection seems most unlikely. And when we examine the distribution of sunlight, we find that the geographical distribution of skin color really does not correspond at all well with the suppositions of the thesis.

The particular point may not seem worth the laboring I have given it, and the removal of the notion from our thinking might not, in itself, affect very greatly our concepts of races and their origins. But certain doubts may be raised. We may be led to ask whether there are not other instances where survival value has been attributed to anatomical or physiological factors which it would be difficult to substantiate, or where pertinent aspects of the environment are not well understood. The case of adaptation of warm-blooded animals to cold climates, where Scholander (1955) has pointed out that the physiological and environmental factors concerned do not coincide with commonly accepted ecological and evolutionary ideas, seems another cogent example. Surely we may question the evidence in such cases without challenging the basic role of natural selection — I believe no one who has read my writings on evolution would accuse me of making such a challenge (e.g., Blum, 1955b, c).

What we really deal with here is the relationship between phenotype and environment, as I have said earlier, selection depending upon the closeness of fit between the two. Complete fitting is not to be expected in the complicated situations that prevail in nature. Rather, one may think of the overall agreement as the algebraic sum of many positive and negative values, representing advantageous and disadvantageous facets of the phenotype with respect to corresponding facets of the environment. If the sum of these values is positive, the phenotype, and consequently the genotype, should have selective advantage. The total balance sheet could contain many plus and minus values, large and small; the relationship of melanin to sunlight seems one of minor weight in the survival of human races. It might be extremely difficult to analyze the situation accurately, and one could go badly astray by underestimating the complexity of the factors concerned.

If a somewhat facetious illustration is permitted, I may point out that if we consider only the role of melanin pigment with regard to sunlight, Negro skin would seem to be highly adaptive to life on one of the snow-capped mountains near the equator. Here the sunburning radiation should be high, being enhanced by reflection from the snow field, and the protection afforded against it might be assigned a high positive value. The low reflectance of total sunlight from the skin could be also advantageous in this situation in maintaining body temperature by increasing the solar heat load. The importance of antirachitic action, whatever its sign, would seem to be minor compared to the general problem of maintaining adequate nutrition. The negative factor of concealment might also be slight because there would be so little wild game anyway. I am afraid that in spite of the positive values assigned to melanin, the overall fitting between phenotype and environment would have a rather high negative value in this case.

It seems so easy to read adaptive value into almost any aspect of an organism, particularly if our understanding of both physiology and environment is incomplete, as must so often be the case. If we yield to the temptation to find adaptive value in every racial or specific characteristic, do we not run the risk of reaching a position not unlike that of Dr. Pangloss — in spite of Candide's observations, and our own?

ABSTRACT

The widely accepted idea that melanin pigment in human skin protects against sunlight, and that this has bearing upon adaptation to life in the tropics and the distribution of races, is examined in terms of its physical and physiological aspects. Regarded in such terms the concept appears to have little merit. It is concluded that whereas the pigment may have a slight adaptive value as regards some aspects of the organism-environment relationship, it may be nonadaptive as regards others; and the respective values may depend upon various complicating factors of the environment. Moreover, the distribution of races according to skin color does not appear to conform well to what would be expected from the spectral distribution of sunlight.

REFERENCES AND NOTES

Included are a number of reviews where the reader will find an extensive literature cited, covering in more detail the rather wide range of material bearing on aspects of this general subject.

* And National Cancer Institute, National Institutes of Health, Department of Health, Education and Welfare, Bethesda, Maryland.

E. F. Adolph, *Physiology of Man in the Desert* (Interscience, New York, 1947).

H. Aron, Investigations of the action of tropical sun on man and animals, *Philippine J. Sci. (Med. Sect.)* **6**, 101–30 (1911).

R. E. Billingham and W. K. Silvers, The melanocytes of Mammals, *Quart. Rev. Biol.* **35**, 1–33 (1960).

H. F. Blum, *Photodynamic Action and Diseases Caused by Light* (Reinhold Publ. Corp., New York, 1941).

————, The physiological effects of sunlight on man, *Physiol. Revs.* **25**, 483–530 (1945a).

————, The solar heat load: Its relationship to total heat load and its relative importance in the design of clothing, *J. Clin. Invest.* **24**, 712–21 (1945b).

————, Radiation: Non-ionizing; photophysiology and photopathology, in *Medical Physics*, O. Glasser, Ed. (Yearbook Publishers, Chicago, 1950), II 753–66.

————, Sunburn, in *Radiation Biology*, A. Hollaender, Ed. (McGraw-Hill, New York, 1955a), II, chap. 13, 487–559.

————, *Time's Arrow and Evolution* (Princeton Univ. Press, Princeton, 2 ed., 1955b).

————, Perspectives in evolution, *Am. Scientist* **43**, 595–610 (1955c).

————, *Carcinogenesis by Ultraviolet Light: An Essay in Quantitative Biology* (Princeton Univ. Press, Princeton, 1959).

———— and W. S. Terus, Inhibition of the erythema of sun burn by large doses of ultraviolet radiation, *Am. J. Physiol.* **146**, 97–106 (1946).

Charcot, Erythème de la face et ophthalmie produits par l'action de lumière electrique, *Compt. Rend.* **5** (ser. 2), 63 (1858).

N. T. Clare, Photodynamic action and its pathological effects, in *Radiation Biology*, A. Hollaender, Ed. (McGraw-Hill, New York, 1955), III, chap. 15, 693–723.

C. S. Coon, S. M. Garn, J. B. Birdsell, *A Study of the Problems of Race Formation in Man* (Thomas, Springfield, 1950).

R. B. Cowles, Some ecological factors bearing on the origin and evolution of pigment in the human skin, *Am. Naturalist* **93**, 282–92 (1959).

H. J. Fleure, The distribution of types of skin color, *Geograph. Rev.* **25**, 580–95 (1945).

A. C. Guillaume, Le pigment épidermique, la pénétration des rayons u. v. et la mécanisme de protection de l'organisme vis-à-vis à ces radiations, *Bull. et mém. hôp. Paris* **40**, 1133–1135 (1926).

J. D. Hardy and C. Muschenheim, The radiation of heat from the human body. IV. The emission, reflection and transmission of infrared radiation by the human skin, *J. Clin. Invest.* **13**, 817–31 (1934).

———— and ————, Radiation of heat from the human body. V. The transmission of infrared radiation through the skin, *J. Clin. Invest.* **15**, 1–9 (1936).

———— and T. W. Oppel, Studies in temperature sensation. III. The sensitivity of the body to heat and the spatial summation of the end organ response, J. Clin. Invest. **16**, 533–40 (1937).

R. R. Heer, The absorption of human skin between 430 and 1,100 mμ for blackbody radiation at various color temperatures, *Science* **115**, 15–18 (1952).

V. Henschke and R. Schultze, Untersuchung zum Problem des Ultraviolett Dosimetrie. 3 Mitt. Über Pigmentierung durch langwelliges Ultraviolett. *Strahlentherapie* **64**, 14–42 (1939a).

————, Untersuchungen zum Problem der Ultraviolett Dosimetrie. 4 Mitt. Wirkung der sonnenstrahlen auf die Haut, *Strahlentherapie* **64**, 43–58 (1939b).

J. S. Kirby-Smith, H. F. Blum, H. G. Grady, Penetration of ultraviolet radiation into skin, as a factor in carcinogenesis, *J. Nat. Cancer. Inst.* 2, 403–12 (1942).

P. Moon, Proposed standard solar-radiation curves for engineering use, *J. Franklin Inst.* 230, 583–617 (1941).

T. F. Oppel and J. D. Hardy, Studies in temperature sensation. I. A comparison of the sensation produced by infrared and visible radiation, *J. Clin. Invest.* 16, 517–31 (1937a).

————, Studies in temperature sensation. II. The temperature changes responsible for the stimulation of the heat and organs, *J. Clin. Invest.* 16, 525–31 (1937b).

P. B. Rottier, The erythematous action of ultraviolet light on human skin. I. Some measurements of the spectral response with continuous and intermittent light, *J. Clin. Invest.* 32, 681–89 (1953).

———— and J. A. M. Mullink, Localization of erythemal processes caused by ultraviolet light in human skin, *Nature* 170, 574–75 (1952).

P. F. Scholander, Evolution of climatic adaptation in homeotherms, *Evolution* 9, 15–26 (1955).

————, Climatic rules, *Evolution* 10, 339–40 (1956).

E. M. Thomas, *The Harmless People* (Knopf, New York, 1959).

M. L. Thomson, The cause of the change in sweating rate after ultraviolet radiation, *J. Physiol.* 112, 31–41 (1951).

————, Relative efficiency of pigment and horny layer thickness in protecting the skin of Europeans and Africans against solar ultraviolet radiation, *J. Physiol.* 127, 236–46 (1955).

L. Van der Post, *The Lost World of the Kalahari* (William Morrow & Co., New York, 1958).

F. W. Vindt, Malignant disease in the natives of Kenya, *Lancet* 229, 628–30 (1935).

M. Wedding, *Zeitschrift für Ethnologie,* 19. Verhandlung der Berliner Gesellschaft für Anthropologie, Ethnologie, und Urgeschichte (1887), p. 67.

E. J. Widmark, Über den Einfluss des Lichtes auf die vorderen Medien des Auges. *Skand. Arch. Physiol.* 1, 264–330 (1899).

A. R. Willcox, *Rock Paintings of the Drakensberg* (Max Parrish, London, 1956).

B Mechanisms of natural selection

Dobzhansky, Th. 1947. Adaptive changes induced by natural selection in wild populations of *Drosophila. Evolution* 1, 1–16.

Lederberg, Joshua, and Esther M. Lederberg. 1952. Replica plating and indirect selection of bacterial mutants. *Jour. Bact.* 63, 399–406.

Kettlewell, H. B. D. 1956. Further selection experiments on industrial melanism in the *Lepidoptera. Heredity* 10, 287–301.

Allison, A. C. 1956. Population genetics of abnormal human haemoglobins. *Acta Genetica* 6, 430–34.

Loomis, W. Farnsworth. 1967. Skin-pigment regulation of vitamin-D biosynthesis in man. *Science* 157, 501–506.

Moody, Paul A. 1947. A simple model of "drift" in small populations. *Evolution* 1, 217–18.

Adaptive Changes Induced by Natural Selection in Wild Populations of Drosophila

Th. Dobzhansky

Columbia University

INTRODUCTION

The theory of the origin of adaptations through natural selection is more than a century old, if one takes as its inception the date of Darwin's first essay written in 1842. Nevertheless, no agreement as to the role played by natural selection in evolution has as yet been reached. Weismann called natural selection "all powerful," but, during the first quarter of the present century, the idea fell into disrepute because of a failure to comprehend the meaning of the mutation theory and Johannsen's experiments on pure lines. So wide a divergence of opinion has been possible because the theory of natural selection has rested either on deductions from very general propositions or on inference from indirect evidence. That adaptive evolution in nature is too slow a process to be observed within a human lifetime has been taken for granted almost universally. Furthermore, selection pressures which act upon non-pathological traits of wild species have been assumed to be small.

Recent observations have shown, however, that natural populations, even of higher organisms, sometimes undergo rapid adaptive changes. Some wild species react to seasonal alterations in their environment by cyclic modifications of their genetic structure. Knowing these

Reprinted from *Evolution* 1, 1–16 (1947), by permission of the author and publisher.

facts, direct observation and experimentation on natural selection has become possible. Controlled experiments can now take the place of speculation as to what natural selection is or is not able to accomplish. Furthermore, we need no longer be satisfied with mere verification of the existence of natural selection. The mechanics of natural selection in concrete cases can be studied. Hence, the genesis of adaptation, which is possibly the central problem of biology, now lies within the reach of the experimental method.

The first discovery of cyclic changes in the genetic composition of populations of wild species was made by Timofeeff-Ressovsky (1940). European as well as North American and Asiatic populations of the beetle *Adalia bipunctata* vary greatly in the elytral color pattern. Two color types, red and black, can easily be distinguished. They are known to differ by a single Mendelian gene. Near Berlin, where the species produces two and possibly three generations per year, the black type increases in relative frequency from about 37 percent to 59 percent from spring until autumn. During the winter the frequency of the black type is reduced and that of the red is increased. The beetle hibernates as an adult, the mortality among hibernating individuals being high. Only 4 percent of black individuals survive hibernation, while about 11 percent of the reds survive. The inference can be drawn that the black type is selected during the warm season.

The coloration of the Adalia beetle is a visible character easy to work with. In the corresponding Drosophila work, a character is used which is discernible only by microscopic examination of the larval salivary glands, namely the gene arrangement in the chromosomes. Variation of this character in species of Drosophila is due almost entirely to inversion of chromosome segments. Two or more such gene arrangements frequently occur in the same population. Since the carriers of different arrangements interbreed freely, some individuals have paired chromosomes with the same gene arrangements (inversion homozygotes) and others with unlike gene arrangements (inversion heterozygotes). Because the inversion homozygotes and heterozygotes are indistinguishable in external appearance, there was no reason to suppose that inversions are other than adaptively neutral characters. Not until Dobzhansky (1943, in *D. pseudoobscura*) and Dubinin and Tiniakov (1945, 1946, in *D. funebris*) found that populations which live in different habitats often differ in the relative frequencies of their gene arrangements, and that the composition of a single population may vary appreciably from season to season, was it realized that carriers of different gene arrangements may be favored or discriminated against by different environments.

The seasonal changes in the composition of the Adalia and Drosophila populations are adaptive responses of the living species to the succession of seasonal environments. It is important to note that such seasonal changes occur not only in organisms which, like the ones named above, produce several generations per year, but also in the longer lived ones. Gershenson (1945) has found changes of this sort in the hamster, *Cricetus cricetus*. Black and agouti individuals occur in Russian populations of this mammal, and the relative frequencies of these coat colors differ significantly in different seasons and in different places. The difference between the two color forms is due to a single gene.

Observations and experiments on natural selection in *Drosophila pseudoobscura* will be reviewed in the following pages. Previously published as well as unpublished data are discussed briefly; the latter will be presented in more details elsewhere.

LOCAL RACES

Fifteen different gene arrangements are known in the third chromosome of *Drosophila pseudoobscura*. None of them occur in the entire distribution area of the species. Hence, there is no "normal" or "wild-type" gene arrangement. On the other hand, the populations of most localities contain more than one, and up to seven, gene arrangements. Because of the free interbreeding of the carriers of different arrangements, many, frequently a majority, of wild individuals are inversion heterozygotes. The population of any locality can be described in terms of relative frequencies of different gene arrangements. The frequencies may differ in populations of different localities. Sometimes the differences are more or less proportional to the distances which separate the localities. Geographic gradients or "clines" are thus formed (Dobzhansky and Epling, 1944). An example of such clines is given in Figure 1.

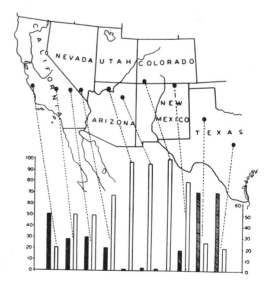

FIGURE 1. Frequencies (in percent) of Standard (black columns), Arrowhead (white columns), and Pikes Peak (hatched columns) chromosomes in populations of *Drosophila pseudoobscura* in certain localities in the western United States.

About 50 percent of third chromosomes in populations of south Coast Ranges of California have the so-called Standard gene arrangement, represented by black columns in Figure 1. But the frequency of Standard falls to between 20 and 30 percent in the Sierra Nevada and in the Death Valley regions which lie to the east of the Coast Ranges. Further east, in Arizona, the frequency falls to less than 5 percent, and still further east Standard chromosomes occur but rarely. The Arrowhead gene arrangement (white columns in Fig. 1) is very common in Arizona and New Mexico, so much so that populations of some localities seem to be homozygous for it. But its frequency decreases eastward as well as westward from Arizona, reaching about 20 percent in central Texas and in coastal California. The Pikes Peak gene arrangement (hatched columns in Fig. 1) is common in Texas, but rapidly decreases in frequency westward.

The transect across the southwestern United States shown in Figure 1 is roughly 1200 miles long. Differences in the frequencies of gene arrangements may be observed however between populations which live in localities only a dozen or so miles apart. For example, three localities on Mount San Jacinto, California, were sampled repeatedly between 1939 and 1946. The approximate distances between these localities are 10 to 15 miles. One Keen Camp, lies at an elevation of about 4500 feet in the ponderosa pine belt, the second, Piñon Flats, lies at 4000 feet in the much drier piñon forest, and the third, Andreas Canyon, lies at 800 feet on the desert's edge. The frequencies of gene arrangements in the populations of these localities are shown in Table 1. (Chromosomes with Standard gene arrangement are henceforth denoted as ST, Arrowhead as AR, and Chiricahua as CH.)

Table 1 shows that ST chromosomes are most frequent in the lowest locality, Andreas, and least frequent in the highest locality, Keen. CH chromosomes show the opposite relationship. No significant differences appear for AR chromosomes in the three localities (Dobzhansky, 1943). How common such altitudinal gradients are is an open question. Preliminary data suggest the existence of gradients among populations that occur at different elevations in the region of the Yosemite National Park, in the Sierra Nevada in California. Here, however, the ST and AR, and not CH chromosomes, vary in frequencies from locality to locality.

TABLE 1

Frequencies (in Percent) of Chromosomes with Different Gene Arrangements in Populations of Localities on Mount San Jacinto (California).

Locality	Gene arrangements				Numbers of chromosomes studied
	ST	AR	CH	Others	
Keen Camp	33.7	23.8	38.0	4.5	6634
Piñon Flats	40.7	25.1	29.1	5.1	4853
Andreas Canyon	57.6	24.0	15.3	3.0	3818

Thus, at Jacksonville, elevation about 800 feet, 40 to 45 percent of third chromosomes have ST and 20 to 25 percent have AR gene arrangement. At Lost Claim Campground, elevation about 3000 feet, the frequencies of both ST and AR are between 30 and 35 percent. At Mather, elevation 4600 feet, ST fluctuates between 20 and 40 percent and AR between 30 and 45 percent. Finally, at Aspen Valley, elevation about 6800 feet, ST falls to 20 and AR rises to almost 50 percent. The frequencies of CH chromosomes are between 15 and 20 percent in all the localities. The horizontal distance between the farthest localities, Jacksonville and Aspen Valley, is about 35 miles.

Altitudinal gradients in the frequencies of gene arrangements suggest that the differences between the inhabitants of different elevations on the same mountain range are adaptive and are produced by natural selection. This hypothesis is strengthened by the observations on seasonal changes and on experimental populations discussed in the following paragraphs.

SEASONAL CYCLES

The repeated samplings of the populations in the three localities on Mount San Jacinto (see above) have disclosed a very interesting fact, namely that the composition of a population may change quite significantly from month to month (Dobzhansky, 1943). Furthermore, these changes are regular and follow the annual cycle of seasons. In two of the three localities, namely at Piñon Flats and at Andreas Canyon, the changes are qualitatively similar. Figure 2 gives a summary of the data for Piñon Flats. In this figure, the observations for all six years of collecting are grouped by months. It can be seen that in spring (March) the population contains about 50 percent of ST chromosomes (shown in

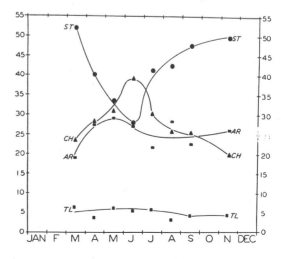

FIGURE 2. Changes in the frequencies of chromosomes with Standard (circles), Chiricahua (triangles), Arrowhead (horizontal rectangles), and Tree Line (squares) gene arrangements in the population of Piñon Flats, California. Ordinate—frequencies in percent; abscissa—months. Combined data for six years of observation.

Fig. 2 by circles), and slightly more than 20 percent CH chromosomes (shown by triangles). From March to June the frequency of ST declines to less than 30 percent and that of CH increases to just below 40 percent. During the summer, from June to September, the reverse change takes place, namely ST increases in frequency, and CH decreases, to about the same values which these gene arrangements had during the spring. The changes of the frequencies of AR chromosomes (rectangles in Fig. 2) are less regular than those of ST and CH, but on the whole AR seems to follow the same path as CH. No regular changes occur in the frequency of Tree Line chromosomes (squares in Fig. 2).

The changes at Andreas Canyon run parallel to those at Piñon Flats. From autumn till early spring the frequency of ST chromosomes keeps on a high level, and that of CH chromosomes on a low one. From March to June ST wanes and CH waxes in frequency. During the hot part of the summer very few *D. pseudoobscura* flies can be collected at Andreas Canyon. But when the population begins to build up in numbers in September, the ST chromosomes are found to have recovered their high frequency, while CH have dwindled to about the winter level. Curiously enough, no significant changes from month to month are detectable in the Keen Camp population. Because of the climate, the breeding season of the flies is clearly shorter at Keen Camp than at the other localities, but nevertheless fly samples have been collected at Keen Camp from April to September and even October. Such time intervals are amply sufficient to detect changes in the Piñon and Andreas populations, but no cyclic changes have been found at Keen Camp (Dobzhansky, 1943).

Interestingly enough, a different kind of change has taken place in the Keen Camp population during the period of observation, from 1939 to 1946. Namely, there seems to exist a noncyclic, or at any rate nonseasonal, trend toward decreasing frequencies of AR and CH and increasing ones of ST chromosomes. In 1939, only 28 percent of the third chromosomes found in the Keen locality had the ST gene arrangement; in 1942 the frequency rose to 36 percent, and in 1946 to 50 percent. The frequencies of AR and CH chromosomes in 1939 were 30 and 38 percent respectively. In 1946 only 15 percent of the chromosomes were AR and only about 28 percent CH. No such directional trends of change have appeared at Piñon Flats or at Andreas Canyon, although statistically significant differences in the composition of the populations from year to year have been recorded also in these localities (Dobzhansky, 1943, and a paper in press).

It will obviously be important to ascertain how general are the phenomena of cyclic seasonal and nonseasonal changes not only in different populations of *Drosophila pseudoobscura* but in other species as well. The fact that cyclic changes occur at Piñon Flats and at Andreas Canyon, but not at Keen Camp only some 15 miles away, makes generalizations at this time decidedly premature. Data are however available which show cyclic seasonal changes in the population of a locality in central Texas. Here the Arrowhead and Pikes Peak gene arrangements in the third chromosome of D. *pseudoobscura* are involved (Dobzhansky and Epling, 1944; cf. also Fig. 1). Unpublished data suggest that changes in the frequencies of ST, AR, and perhaps of CH chromosomes occur in populations of at least some of the localities in the Sierra Nevada.

NATURAL SELECTION AS A CAUSE OF THE SEASONAL CHANGES

The regular and cyclic nature of the changes observed in the populations of D. *pseudoobscura* on Mount San Jacinto can be most reasonably accounted for by natural selection as the prime causative factor. If during the spring the carriers of CH chromosomes leave more surviving progeny on the average than the carriers of ST chromosomes, then the frequency of CH will increase and that of ST will decrease. This is what happens from March to June (Fig. 2). The reversal of the change during the summer months points toward the hypothesis that, in the summer environments, the carriers of ST chromosomes survive or reproduce on the average more often than do the carriers of CH chromosomes. The absence of changes during the autumn and winter at Andreas Canyon suggests that flies of different chromosomal types are equivalent in reaction to the enviroments prevailing during these seasons.

But the great rapidity of the observed changes constitutes an apparently serious argument against accounting for them on the ground of natural selection. Indeed, at Piñon Flats the frequency of ST chromosomes falls from about 50 percent in March to 28 percent in June, and increases again to about 48 percent in September (Fig. 2). Even though Drosophila is a rapidly breeding insect, time intervals such as these can correspond to at most two to four generations. The selective forces that are necessary to bring about changes so swift as these must be very strong.

It should be remembered however that very little is known about the intensity of selective forces which operate in natural populations. The widespread opinion that these forces are generally weak, and their effects negligible except in terms of quasi-geological time is only an opinion and has no basis in factual data. To find in natural populations great selective pressures and the rapid changes produced by them may be unexpected but not inherently impossible. On the other hand, the occurrence of changes does not in itself prove that they are produced by natural selection. Such proof would be very difficult to adduce from observations of natural populations alone. The difficulty lies in the fact that, despite persistent effort, very little has been learned as yet about the food and shelter requirements of D. *pseudoobscura* in its natural habitats. Proof of selection by a method analogous to that employed by Timofeeff-Ressovsky in Adalia is still out of the question in Drosophila.

Nevertheless, the postulated high selective advantages and disadvantages of the carriers of different gene arrangements in different environments has made practicable a still more ambitious project: to demonstrate the occurrence of natural selection by means of laboratory experiments. For this purpose, a modification of the population cage devised for Drosophila by l'Héritier and Teissier is used. These cages are wooden boxes with glass or wire screen sides and a detachable glass top (Fig. 3). The bottom has 15 circular openings closed by corks which carry glass containers with culture medium. Wire loops hold the containers in place (Fig. 4). Several hundred flies are introduced into the cage at the beginning of the experiment. These flies are a mixture of individuals with different gene arrangements in desired proportions. Within a single generation, the population of the cage increases to the maximum compatible with the amount of food given. This is usually between two and four thousand flies. The numbers of eggs deposited in a population cage are tens to hundreds of times greater than the numbers of adult flies that hatch. The competition for survival is intense. (For a more detailed description of a population cage, see Wright and Dobzhansky, 1946.)

Once a month, or at other suitable intervals, samples of the eggs which have been deposited in the cages are taken, and the larvae which emerge from these eggs are grown in regular culture bottles. Salivary gland chromosomes of fully grown larvae are then examined.

It is known that many chromosomes in natural populations carry recessive lethals, semilethals, or viability modifiers. We are, however, interested not in the effects of individual chromosomes on the survival of the flies, but in the selective values of ST, AR, CH, and other chromosomes as classes. In other words, in our experiments it is desired to

FIGURE 3. A population cage.

FIGURE 4. A cork and a jar with culture medium used in population cages.

have flies which are genetically heterogeneous, regardless of whether they are inversion homozygotes or heterozygotes. Accordingly, the initial population of a cage is always made from a mixture of several strains of each of the inversion types to be studied. As a result flies homozygous for any given individual chromosome are relatively rare in such population cages.

SELECTIVE DIFFERENTIALS BETWEEN CHROMOSOMES FROM PIÑON FLATS

Twenty-nine experiments have been either completed or are now under way, employing populations the chromosomes of which were derived from ancestors collected at Piñon Flats. Some cages contained mixtures of ST and CH chromosomes, others of ST and AR, or of AR and CH, or of all three gene arrangements. Some were kept in incubators or constant temperature rooms at 25° C, others at $16\frac{1}{2}$° C, and still others at variable room temperatures between 20° and 26° C; some were exposed to alternation of day and night, others were kept in the dark. Two types of results have been obtained. First, at $16\frac{1}{2}$° C no significant changes in the frequencies of the gene arrangements have taken place. The relative frequencies present in the original population of the cage have been retained generation after generation. Second, at 25° C or at room temperatures, the relative proportions of the gene arrangements have changed with time until certain definitive equilibrium proportions have been attained.

Figure 5 shows an example of changes in the frequency of ST chromosomes observed in the population cage No. 35 at 25° C. On March 1, 1946, a population was introduced into this cage containing 10.7 percent ST and 89.3 percent CH chromosomes of Piñon Flats origin. In about a month, in early April, the frequency of ST has approximately doubled (21.7 percent), in early May nearly trebled (28.3 percent), and in early June nearly quadrupled (37.7 percent). By mid-November ST reached

FIGURE 5. Frequency of Standard chromosomes (in percent) in different months in the population cage No. 35.

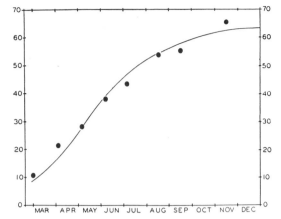

the frequency of 66.7 percent and by the end of December 71.0 percent. It can be seen, first, that the changes are greater when ST chromosomes are rare but relatively slight when they become frequent, and, second, that ST chromosomes never supplant entirely CH chromosomes. The final result of selection is a stable mixture of both ST and CH chromosomes.

Wright (in Wright and Dobzhansky, 1946) has analyzed mathematically the results of experiments like that illustrated in Figure 5. He has concluded that the simplest hypothesis to account for the data is that the highest adaptive value exists in ST/CH heterozygotes, and that both homozygous classes, ST/ST and CH/CH, are inferior to the heterozygotes. Furthermore, that the adaptive value of ST/ST homozygotes is higher than that of CH/CH homozygotes. The curve shown in Figure 5 is calculated on the assumption that the adaptive values of the ST/CH, ST/ST, and CH/CH classes of individuals are as 1.0 : 0.7 : 0.4, and that a fly generation had an average span of one month in population cage No. 35. The observed values fit the theoretical curve remarkably well.

Since the heterozygotes, ST/CH, are superior in adaptive values to both homozygotes, the final result of selection is not elimination of either CH or ST but establishment of a certain equilibrium at which both ST and CH gene arrangements occur in the population. Since ST/ST are superior to CH/CH homozygotes, the equilibrium frequency of ST is higher than that of CH. With the adaptive values indicated above, the population would be expected to reach equilibrium at about 67 percent ST and 33 percent CH. The results obtained in the experiment shown in Figure 5 agree with the expectation.

All the experiments in which mixtures of ST and CH chromosomes were kept at temperatures above 20° C have led to ST becoming more frequent than CH; whenever the experiments were continued long enough, equilibria were reached at values close to 70 percent ST and

30 percent CH. Under similar conditions, populations containing ST and AR have reached equlibria in which ST chromosomes are also more frequent than AR. The adaptive values of the three possible genotypes must therefore be ST/AR > ST/ST > AR/AR. Experiments with mixtures of AR and CH show that the hierarchy of adaptive values is AR/CH > AR/AR > CH/CH. Some experiments have been made in which population cages have contained mixtures of three gene arrangements, ST, AR, and CH. Equilibrium proportions are indicated at, roughly, 50–55 percent ST, 30–35 percent AR, and 10–15 percent CH.

The lack of perceptible changes in the population cages kept at $16\frac{1}{2}°$ C indicates that at that temperature the adaptive values of the inversion heterozygotes and homozygotes are more nearly similar than they are at higher temperatures. Such changes in the relative adaptive values of different genotypes at different temperatures have been observed experimentally (Dobzhansky and Spassky, 1944).

STAGE OF THE LIFE CYCLE AT WHICH SELECTION TAKES PLACE

The experiments summarized above demonstrate that, in some environments, the adaptive values of inversion heterozygotes and homozygotes are strikingly unlike. But these experiments tell us nothing of the stage of the life cycle at which the differential survival or reproduction take place. Natural selection may operate in a variety of ways. The chromosomal types may be characterized by differential mortality, or differential longevity, or fecundity, or differences in sexual activity, or combinations of two or more of these and other variables. The adaptive value of a chromosomal type is the net effect of interaction of all the variables.

Perhaps the simplest, though by no means the only possible, hypothesis would assume a differential mortality of the different chromosomal types among the crowded larvae in the population cages. Let the frequencies of the ST and CH gene arrangements in a population cage be q and $(1 - q)$ respectively. Provided that the flies mate at random with respect to gene arrangement, the proportions of heterozygotes and homozygotes among the eggs deposited in a population cage will be:

$$q^2 \text{ ST/ST} : 2q(1 - q) \text{ ST/CH} : (1 - q)^2 \text{ CH/CH}$$

If, however, the larvae which hatch from these eggs survive and reach the adult stage in a proportion 0.7 ST/ST : 1 ST/CH : 0.4 CH/CH, then the relative frequencies of the chromosomal types of the adult flies developed in a population cage will be:

$$0.7 \ q^2 \text{ ST/ST} : 2q(1 - q) \text{ ST/CH} : 0.4 \ (1 - q)^2 \text{ CH/CH}$$

The frequencies of the ST/ST, ST/CH, and CH/CH types have been determined in samples of larvae hatching from the eggs deposited in population cages but grown in regular culture bottles under approximately optimal conditions. The deviations from the $q^2 : 2q(1 - q) :$

$(1 - q)^2$ proportions are found to be relatively small in such samples. A sample of adult flies hatched in a population cage was now taken, and the chromosomal constitution of these flies was determined with the aid of a suitable method (Dobzhansky, 1947b). The numbers of ST/ST, ST/CH, and CH/CH flies which would be expected to occur in this sample if there were no differential mortality between the egg and the adult stage were calculated with the aid of the Hardy-Weinberg formula $q^2 : 2q(1 - q) : (1 - q)^2$. The observed and the expected values are as follows:

	ST/ST	ST/CH	CH/CH
Observed	57	169	29
Expected	78.5	126.0	50.5
Deviation	−21.5	+43.0	−21.5

Among the adult flies, the heterozygotes, ST/CH, are considerably more frequent, and the homozygotes less frequent, than expected on the basis of the Hardy-Weinberg formula. Since, as stated above, the Hardy-Weinberg proportions are approximately realized among the eggs deposited in the population cages, a differential elimination of ST/ST and CH/CH homozygotes at some time between the egg and the adult stage may be regarded established.

EXPERIMENTS ON CHROMOSOMES OF DIFFERENT GEOGRAPHIC ORIGIN

The above described experiments on the behavior of chromosomes with different gene arrangements in population cages have been made with flies the ancestors of which were collected at Piñon Flats, Mount San Jacinto. The ST, AR, and CH gene arrangements occur, however, in populations from most of the western United States, from British Columbia, and from Lower California. The question that naturally arises is whether or not the biological properties of these chromosomes are constant throughout the geographic area in which a given gene arrangement occurs (Mayr, 1945).

Population cage experiments are now in progress on mixtures of flies with different gene arrangements from Keen Camp and from Mather, California. These localities are respectively about 12 and 300 miles from Piñon Flats. The data so far obtained leave no doubt in that the adaptive properties of chromosomes with the same gene arrangement but of different geographic origin may be different. The relevant data will be published in more detail later; the following comparison will suffice as an illustration.

On March 2nd, 1946, population cage No. 36 was started with a mixture of about 12 percent ST and 88 percent AR chromosomes of Piñon Flats origin. In late November of the same year this population cage contained about 67 percent ST and 33 percent AR. It is obvious that when populations of ST and AR of Piñon Flats origin reach equilibrium,

FIGURE 6. Frequency of Standard chromosomes (in percent) in different months in the population cages Nos. 29 (white circles) and 32 (black circles).

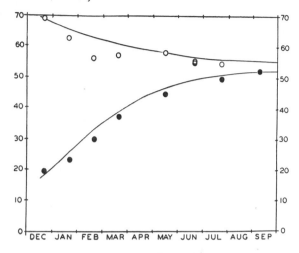

ST chromosomes are decidedly more common than AR. This is confirmed by the experiment No. 34, in which the initial population of a cage consisted on February 25th, 1946, of 85 percent ST and 15 percent AR. By late summer and autumn of the same year the frequency of AR in this cage fluctuated between 20 and 25 percent AR. But the results of experiments on ST and AR chromosomes of Mather origin are quite different. On December 22nd, 1945, population cage No. 29 was started with about 70 percent ST and 30 percent AR chromosomes from Mather. In late June and late July of 1946, when the experiment was terminated, the frequency of ST had fallen to 54–55 percent, and that of AR had risen to 45–46 percent. In a parallel experiment started simultaneously, the initial population of cage No. 32 contained 19 percent ST and 81 percent AR chromosomes of Mather origin. By late summer and autumn of 1946, the frequency of ST had risen in this cage to 50–54 percent, and the frequency of AR had fallen to 46–50 percent (Fig. 6). It seems safe to conclude that mixtures of ST and AR chromosomes of Mather origin reach equilibria at about 50–55 percent ST and 45–50 percent AR. This is significantly different from the behavior of ST and AR chromosomes of Piñon Flats origin. All the experiments described in this paragraph were carried out in a temperature-controlled room at 25° C.

Chromosomes with the same gene arrangement but of different geographic origin may, then, behave differently. This fact has a bearing on the problem of the genetic nature of the adaptive differences between chromosomes with different gene arrangements. The properties of a chromosome may, in general, depend on its gene contents, or on the gene arrangement itself (position effect), or on a combination of both factors. The different behavior of the ST and AR chromosomes of Piñon Flats and Mather origin proves that the gene contents of these chromosomes are different. We are evidently dealing with gene complexes evolved under the control of natural selection which confer upon their carriers ecological properties which adapt them to certain seasonal and local environments. Since inversions modify the gene arrangement and diminish the effective crossing over between the chromosomes involved, their biological function is binding together of the gene complexes of proven adaptive worth. In this sense, the effect of natural selection on the chromosomal inversions is indirect. For the purposes of this discussion, it must be borne in mind that the inversions may be simply structural characters marking chromosomes with different gene contents. Of course, the possibility still exists that the biological properties of chromosomes with different gene arrangement differ not only because of the dissimilarities of their gene contents but because of position effects as well.

HETEROSIS

In the experiments discussed above, the populations of the cages reached, or tended to reach, equilibria at which all the gene arrangements introduced into a cage at the beginning were preserved in certain proportions in the final population. Natural selection does not lead to the complete elimination of some and to fixation of other gene arrangements. The final outcome of the selective process is the establishment of those relative frequencies of the competing gene arrangements at which the average adaptive level of the population as a whole is the highest one attainable. This outcome of the selective process is explained by the fact that inversion heterozygotes, ST/CH, ST/AR, and AR/CH, possess adaptive values greater than the corresponding homozygotes ST/ST, CH/CH, and AR/AR. The populations at equilibrium contain the greatest possible proportions of the well adapted heterozygotes compatible with the lowest possible proportions of the relatively ill adapted homozygotes.

The superiority of the heterozygotes over the homozygotes is indicated in all but one experiment carried out at temperatures above 20° C. The single exceptional experiment, No. 31, was started on December 23, 1945. The initial population of the experimental cage contained 45 percent of ST chromosomes and 55 percent of chromosomes with the Tree Line gene arrangement, all the chromosomes descended from flies collected at Mather, California. Tree Line is a gene arrangement rather widespread geographically but relatively rare in most natural populations. In the population of Mather its frequency is approximately 10 percent of the total. The changes in population cage No. 31 were rapid. Within a single month, in late January of 1946, the frequency of Standard chromosomes had risen to 62 percent, while Tree Line fell to 38 percent. By mid-May of 1946 the corresponding frequencies were 82 and 18 percent, in late July 93 and 7 percent, and in mid-November 99 and 1 percent. It seems clear that no equilibrium is being reached in cage No. 31; instead, the Tree Line chromosomes were being eliminated and entirely supplanted by ST chromosomes. This is possible only because ST/ST homozygotes seem to have an adaptive value higher not only than Tree Line homozygotes but also than Standard/Tree Line heterozygotes.

The Tree Line gene arrangement seems to be deleterious to its carriers in homozygous as well as in heterozygous condition. The question naturally arises: why are Tree Line chromosomes retained in natural populations rather than eliminated by natural selection? A possible answer is provided by experiment No. 33, as yet uncompleted. The initial population of this cage, started on January 16th, 1946, consisted of 34 percent Arrowhead and 66 percent Tree Line chromosomes of Mather origin. Within a month, in mid-February, the proportions had changed to 58 and 42 percent respectively. The frequencies of AR chromosomes rose to 69 percent in mid-April, 75 percent in mid-July, and 80 percent in early November. It appears that, in this experiment, the Tree Line chromosomes are not eliminated entirely; instead, an equilibrium at about 80 percent AR and 20 percent Tree Line chromosomes is indicated.

Arrowhead/Tree Line heterozygotes are, under the conditions of this experiment, superior to both Arrowhead and Tree Line homozygotes. This explains not only the fact that the Tree Line gene arrangement is relatively rare but that it is nevertheless retained in natural populations. Tree Line chromosomes form adaptively valuable heterozygotes with AR but not with ST chromosomes present in the same populations. This assures the retention, but prevents excessive increase of the incidence, of the Tree Line gene arrangement in the species.

The classical theory of heterosis assumes that the restoration of vigor following intercrossing of inbred lines is due to the covering up of deleterious recessives by favorable dominants. The greater vigor observed in inversion heterozygotes as compared with homozygotes requires a different explanation. Inversion homozygotes found in natural populations of Drosophila are evidently no more "inbred" than are the heterozygotes in the same population. The lower adaptive value of homozygotes is, therefore, not due to manifestation of deleterious recessives normally covered up by their more favorable dominant alleles. The higher adaptive value of heterozygotes is, in this case, a product of the action of natural selection on the heterozygous genotypes, which are more widespread in natural populations than inversion homozygotes. In view of their greater frequency, the adaptive qualities of heterozygotes may be maintained by natural selection on a level higher than that in homozygotes.

ADAPTATION AND PLASTICITY

The conflict between adaptive fitness and genetic variability was pointed out by Haldane (1937), Dobzhansky (1937, 1938), and Mather (1943).

The mutation process furnishes the raw materials without which adaptive changes cannot be constructed, but the same process also unavoidably produces a multitude of poorly adapted variants. Restriction of the supply of heritable variability might permit a species to reach a higher level of immediate fitness, but it jeopardizes its adaptability to changing environments. When an adaptive change does occur it generally uses up a part of the available supply of variability and thus limits the possibilities of further change.

Observations and experiments on the gene arrangements in third chromosome of *Drosophila pseudoobscura* demonstrate that a remarkable adaptive mechanism exists in this species. The plasticity of the species is so great that it reacts by adaptive reconstructions of the genotype to environmental changes of even so ephemeral a nature as the succession of the year's seasons. There is no doubt that environmental changes in time and in space elicit adaptive responses of a more durable kind as well. And yet all the responses occur without expenditure of genetic variability stored in the populations. This great efficiency of the adaptive mechanism is made possible by the fact that the inversion heterozygotes are endowed with survival values greater than the inversion homozygotes.

We have seen that in the Piñon Flats population the frequencies of ST chromosomes increase and those of CH chromosomes decrease during the hot part of the summer (Fig. 2). In summer environments the adaptive values of the carriers of ST chromosomes are evidently higher than those of CH. Yet, during the spring months the carriers of CH seem to be superior to the carriers of ST chromosomes. An uncommonly hot or prolonged summer cannot eliminate all the CH chromosomes and thus endanger the welfare of the species during the ensuing spring. This is because the completion of the selective process in the summer environment would lead not to elimination of CH chromosomes but to establishment of a certain equilibrium of ST and CH gene arrangements. The genetic variability is, therefore, preserved intact and the species remains capable of immediate and rapid response to new environmental changes. This resembles the balanced polymorphism studied by Fisher (1930) and Ford (1940).

Adaptive mechanisms which permit very rapid reconstructions of the population genotype in accordance with the demands of the seasonal environment will probably be most important and widespread in species which inhabit the temperate and frigid climatic zones, as well as tropical territories in which great seasonal changes regularly occur. Inversion systems in which the heterozygotes possess adaptive values higher than the homozygotes are capable of responding very rapidly to alterations in the environment. The biological significance of heterozygosis for inversions is, however, not necessarily confined to seasonal changes. The high adaptive value of inversion heterozygotes may be desirable because it permits rapid adjustments to various microenvironments which are found in the same region and which are not connected with seasonal phenomena. Thus, inversions may be found also in tropical countries characterized by relatively invariant climates. Indeed, fragmentary data now available show that inversion heterozygotes occur very frequently in natural populations of some tropical species of Drosophila (Pavan, 1946, and unpublished data of the writer). Inversion heterozygosis may be now connected with seasonal changes also in some temperate zone species. Carson and Stalker (1947) found no seasonal changes in frequencies of inversions in *D. robusta* near St. Louis, and the present writer has ground to suppose that such changes are absent in populations of *D. persimilis* in the Sierra Nevada of California. The inversion mechanism may facilitate adaptation to different ecological niches within the same geographic environment. Here is a promising field for further studies.

SUMMARY

The gene arrangement in the third chromosome of *Drosophila pseudoobscura* is variable. Each gene arrangement occurs in populations of a definite geographic area. However, two or more gene arrangements may occur together in many populations. Inversion homozygotes and heterozygotes occur frequently in natural populations.

The relative frequencies of various gene arrangements in some populations undergo seasonal cyclic changes. These changes are produced by natural selection, and represent adaptive reconstructions of the population genotype, thus facilitating survival in different seasonal environments.

Some of the changes taking place in nature can be reproduced experimentally in "population cages" (Fig. 3). Populations containing desired proportions of chromosomes with different gene arrangements are introduced into the cages, samples of the eggs deposited by the flies in the cages are taken from time to time, and the incidence of the chromosomes of different types determined in these samples. Most experiments have been made with chromosomes derived from parents collected at Piñon Flats, Mount San Jacinto, California, and some from Mather, California.

The relative proportions of chromosomes with different gene arrangements remain constant in population cages kept at $16\frac{1}{2}°$ C. Changes are frequently observed in cages kept at temperatures above 20° C: the incidence of some gene arrangements increases and of others decreases. However, the final outcome of the selective process is rarely a complete replacement of one gene arrangement by another. Instead, an equilibrium is usually reached at which all gene arrangements present in the initial population of an experimental cage are retained, but often with frequencies very different from the initial ones. The establishment of equilibria in the populations indicates that individuals heterozygous for different gene arrangements (inversion heterozygotes) are characterized by the highest adaptive values, while homozygotes are relatively inferior in survival and reproduction. The correctness of this interpretation is demonstrated by means of observations on deviations from the Hardy-Weinberg proportions of heterozygotes and homozygotes among the adult flies developed in the population cages (see page 448).

The balanced polymorphism, resulting from the superiority of the heterozygotes over the corresponding homozygotes, permits the species to react adaptively to changes in its environment. The species is "buffered" against environmental change; at the same time, the adaptive responses do not consume or deplete the store of hereditary variability present in the species.

Received January 10, 1947

REFERENCES

H. L. Carson and H. D. Stalker, A seasonal study of gene arrangement frequencies and morphology in *Drosophila robusta, Genetics* **32**, 44 (1947).

Th. Dobzhansky, *Genetics and the Origin of Species* (Columbia Univ. Press, New York, 1937).

_____, The raw materials of evolution, *Sci. Monthly* **46**, 445–49 (1938).

_____, Genetics of natural populations. IX. Temporal changes in the composition of populations of *Drosophila pseudoobscura, Genetics* **28**, 162–86 (1943).

_____, Genetics of natural populations. XIV. A response of certain gene arrangements in the third chromosome of *Drosophila pseudoobscura* to natural selection, *Genetics* **32**, 142–60 (1947a).

_____, A non-seasonal change in the genetic constitution of a natural population of *Drosophila pseudoobscura, Heredity* **1**, 51–62 (1947b).

_____ and C. C. Epling, Contributions to the genetics, taxonomy, and ecology of *Drosophila pseudoobscura* and its relatives, *Carnegie Inst. Washington Publ.* **554**, 1–183 (1944).

_____ and B. Spassky, Genetics of natural populations. XI. Manifestation of genetic variants in *Drosophila pseudoobscura* in different environments, *Genetics* **29**, 270–90 (1944).

N. P. Dubinin and G. G. Tiniakov, Seasonal cycles and the concentration of inversions in populations of *Drosophila funebris, Amer. Natur.* **79**, 570–72 (1945).

_____, Structural chromosome variability in urban and rural populations of *Drosophila funebris, Amer. Natur.* **80**, 393–96 (1946a).

_____, Natural selection and chromosomal variability in populations of *Drosophila funebris, Jour. Heredity* **37**, 39–44 (1946b).

_____, Inversion gradients and natural selection in ecological races of *Drosophila funebris, Genetics* **31**, 537–45 (1946c).

R. A. Fisher, *The Genetical Theory of Natural Selection* (Clarendon Press, Oxford, 1930).

E. B. Ford, *Polymorphism and Taxonomy, Huxley's New Systematics* (Clarendon Press, Oxford, 1940).

S. Gershenson, Evolutionary studies on the distribution and dynamics of melanism in the hamster (*Cricetus cricetus* L.). II. Seasonal and annual changes in the frequency of black hamsters, *Genetics* **30**, 233–51.

J. B. S. Haldane, The effect of variation on fitness, *Amer. Natur.* **71**, 337–49 (1937).

K. Mather, Polygenic inheritance and natural selection, *Biol. Reviews* **18**, 32–64 (1943).

E. Mayr, Symposium on age of the distribution pattern of the gene arrangements in *Drosophila pseudoobscura*. Some evidence in favor of a recent date, *Lloydia* **8**, 70–83 (1945).

C. Pavan, Chromosomal variation in *Drosophila nebulosa*, *Genetics* **31**, 546–57 (1946).

N. W. Timofeeff-Ressovsky, Zur Analyse des Polymorphismus bei *Adalia bipunctata*, *Biol. Zblt.* **60**, 130–37 (1940).

S. Wright and Th. Dobzhansky, Genetics of natural populations. XII. Experimental reproduction of some of the changes caused by natural selection in certain populations of *Drosophila pseudoobscura*, *Genetics* **31**, 125–56 (1946).

Replica Plating and Indirect Selection of Bacterial Mutants

Joshua Lederberg
Esther M. Lederberg

*Department of Genetics**
University of Wisconsin

Elective enrichment is an indispensable technique in bacterial physiology and genetics (van Niel, 1949). Specific biotypes are most readily isolated by the establishment of cultural conditions that favor their growth or survival. It has been repeatedly questioned, however, whether a selective environment may not only select but also direct adaptive heritable changes. In accord with similar discussions in evolutionary biology (Huxley, 1942), we may denote the concepts of spontaneous mutation and natural selection in contrast to specific induction as "preadaptation" and "directed mutation," respectively. Many lines of evidence have been adduced in support of preadaptation in a variety of systems (Luria and Delbrück, 1943; Lea and Coulson, 1949; Burnet, 1929; Newcombe, 1949; Lewis, 1934; Kristensen, 1944; Novick and Szilard, 1950; Ryan and Schneider, 1949; Demerec, 1948; Welsch, 1950; also reviewed: Braun, 1947; Luria, 1947; Lederberg, 1948, 1949). This paper concerns an approach to this problem that makes use of a replica plating technique which facilitates the handling of large numbers of bacterial clones for classification on a variety of media.

METHODS

Replica plating. A frequent chore in bacteriological work is the transfer of isolates from one substrate to other selective or indicator agar media. In place of an in-

Reprinted from *Journal of Bacteriology* 63, 399–406 (1952), by permission of Joshua Lederberg and the American Society for Microbiology.

oculating needle, one might imagine a device consisting of many needle tips in fixed array, so that one operation would substitute for repeated transfers with a single needle. The requirements of this design are met by pile fabrics such as velvet or velveteen. The pile provides space in a vertical plane for moisture that might otherwise cause lateral smearing of any impression. (According to Dr. N. Visconti, in a private communication, dampened filter paper may be applicable to some replication problems considered by him independently of the present work.)

In our practice, twelve cm squares were cut from velveteen yardage, packed in large petri dishes, and sterilized in the autoclave. A square is placed, nap up, on a cylindrical wood or cork support of nine cm diameter and held firmly in place with a metal flange or hoop pushed over the fabric and around the rim of the support. The agar plate carrying the initial colonies is inverted onto the fabric with slight digital pressure to transfer the growth. The imprinted fabric then provides the pattern for transferring replica-inocula to subsequent plates impressed in the same way.

Replica plating is used to facilitate routine tests involving repetitive inoculations of many isolates on different media. Such tests are frequently required in genetic work, but the method should be applicable to other routine practice. Traits which lend themselves to classification by replica plating include antibiotic-sensitivity spectra, responses to bacteriophages (as in phage typing), fermentation characters, nutritional requirements, or any characteristic for which a selective or indicator agar medium can be devised. An application of replica plating to the detection of auxoheterotrophic mutants is illustrated in Figure 1, which also demonstrates the precision of the replicas. However, more faithful reproductions than those shown in the figure can be obtained with the use of dry, hard (2 or 2.5 percent) agar.

The type of initial growth to be replicated may be varied according to specific needs. It may consist of surface colonies, localized growths from stab or spot inocula, or, as in the latter part of this paper, confluent growth from dense inocula previously spread over the agar and incubated. Freshly seeded sites will yield replicas of restricted inoculum size. A single initial plate may be used to imprint more than one fabric if carryover from one replica plate to another vitiates serial transfer. A fabric square may be washed, sterilized, and used repeatedly.

Replica platings may be quantitatively variable and influenced by many physical factors in common with some conventional methods of repetitive inoculation. There is no practical limitation on the number of serial replicas available, except for the accumulation of moisture that may exude from the agar surfaces. The resolution depends on the texture of the agar, colonies, and fabric. Unless the initial colonies are very plump, the distortion in size and shape is minimal and usually less than illustrated in Figure 1. A crude estimate was made of the efficiency of transfer from initial plates spread with measured numbers of

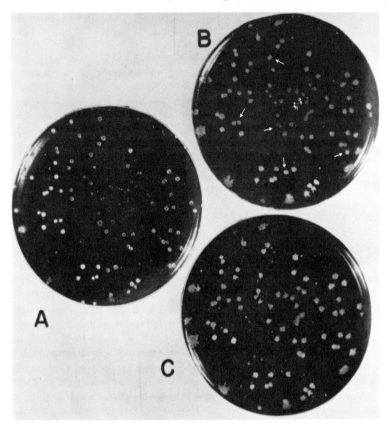

FIGURE 1. Replica plating for the isolation of auxotrophic colonies. *A*, Initial plate; *B*, Replica; both on complete agar medium. *C*, Second replica to minimal agar. The arrows designate the auxotrophic colonies which fail to grow on minimal medium. The resolution of these replicas is of fair to average quality.

Escherichia coli cells. Approximately 10 to 30 percent of the initial cells were transferred to the fabric, and an equal proportion again of these was found to be deposited on the replica plates.

RESULTS

Clonal occurrence of phage resistant mutants. Preadaptive mutation as the basis of bacterial resistance to phages has been supported by two types of evidence. Burnet (1929) succeeded in isolating phage resistant mutants of *Salmonella* by observing the colonial morphology of the R and S phases. The other evidence is biometric: Luria and Delbrück

(1943) working with *E. coli,* strain B and phage T-1, showed that the numbers of mutants selected from parallel broth cultures followed a clonal rather than a random sampling distribution. This was substantiated by more direct evidence of clonal occurrence of the mutants. Newcombe (1949) sprayed phage on films of growth on agar to assay them for their count of resistant mutants. The counts were greatly augmented by redistributing the growth at the time the phage was sprayed. The increase was believed to result from the (preadaptive) occurrence of the mutants in coherent clones. On the undisturbed plates, the assay would give the count of clones; the redistribution would give the total count of resistant cells.

The replica plating method allows a more direct demonstration of the clonal occurrence of the mutants: clones on an initial plate would be detected by the recurrence of resistant colonies at superimposable sites on serial replica-plates containing the phage. If the resistant cells did not exist already in clones on the initial plate, they should occur in only a random distribution in serial replicas from a confluent film of growth.

For this test, a culture (W-1), derived from *E. coli,* strain K-12, and the phage T-1 were used. The culture is fully sensitive to the phage T-1, as well as to streptomycin, and like most *E. coli* strains gives rise to resistant mutants at rates of approximately 10^{-7} and 10^{-10} per division, respectively.

The media used included "Difco penassay" broth in 5 or 10 ml volumes (referred to as "broth") and EMB lactose agar ("plain agar"). The replicas were made on EMB agar previously coated with ca 10^9 particles of T-1 per plate ("phage agar").

In a typical experiment, a dense broth culture was grown from a single colony on plain agar. One-tenth ml was spread on plain agar, and the plate was incubated 4 to 6 hours at 37°C. Serial replicas then were transferred, as described previously, to two or more phage agar plates which then were incubated overnight. The plates were marked either with a glass marking pencil or, for greater precision, by means of pins inserted into the velvet, which indented the agar. Figure 2 shows a typical result, except that a 0.01 ml inoculum was used to restrict the number of clones. In several experiments, at least half and often nearly all of the resistant mutants on the replica-plates recurred at congruent sites. The preoccurrence of the resistant cells in coherent families or clones within the confluent film on plain agar is inferred from this result.

Indirect selection of phage resistant mutants. The hypothesis of preadaptation would be further strengthened if adapted mutants could be isolated in pure culture without direct exposure of the bacteria to the selective agent. Replica plating has made this possible.

In the experiments of the previous section, the sites of preadapted mutants in the initial film of growth on plain agar are discernible from

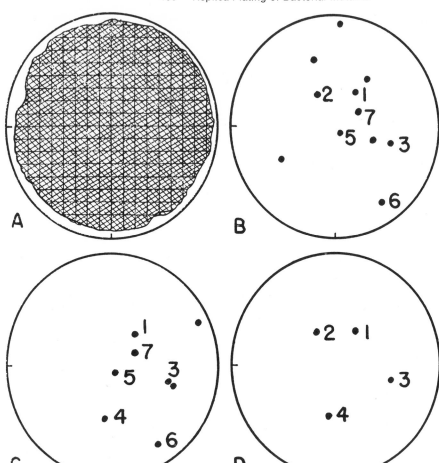

FIGURE 2. Clonal occurrence of mutants resistant to phage T-1. *A,* Initial or replica plate on plain agar with diffuse, confluent growth (semidiagrammatic). *B, C,* and *D,* Successive replicas from *A* to agar coated with phage, from tracing of a typical experiment. Superimposable colonies of resistant cells are numbered. These are concluded to be derived from small clones of resistant mutants already present at corresponding sites on the plain agar plate, *A.*

the replicas. If the initial inocula are made sufficiently dilute, there may be only one or a few clones on a single plate. If the congruent sites are chosen for the inoculum of a second broth tube, the mutants will be concentrated or enriched in about the same proportion as the cells per plate to the cells included in the inoculum. An enrichment of a hundred-fold was anticipated and confirmed for each stage and this sufficed for our experiments.

After incubation, the enriched broth is treated in the same way, except that a more diluted inoculum is spread on plain agar to give again but one or a few mutant clones per plate. After about four stages of indirect selection, the resistant clones appear as discrete colonies which can then be characterized, purified, and maintained by conventional methods.

The indirect selection for phage resistance was applied in two independent runs, both quite successful. The mutants showed the same indifference to the phage as did mutants previously isolated by direct selection. Their stability was verified by making ten serial loopful to broth transfers, for a total of about 100 bacterial generations in each series. The terminal cultures then were diluted and plated on plain agar. A total of 836 and 447 colonies tested, respectively, were all resistant to the phage as determined by replica platings; and by a few tests of cross-streaking colonies against the phage.

It should be reemphasized that the indirect selection line itself has not been exposed to the phage at any time. Its history consists of the transfer cycle: broth to plain agar to broth, with side transfers from agar to velvet discs used to imprint phage agar. Each broth was tested for any stray phage that might lead to fallacious conclusions with no indication of its presence. Replica plating thus provides a technique for isolating resistant or otherwise adapted mutants without altering the media in which the bacteria are grown.

Streptomycin resistance. In order to verify the general applicability of indirect selection, the procedure was also applied to streptomycin resistance. Instead of "phage agar," EMB agar containing 200 μg of streptomycin per ml ("sm agar") was used for the replica plates. The only deviation of these experiments from those with phage results from the extremely low rate of mutation to sm-resistance. In order to obtain any resistant mutants at all, the W-1 culture was transferred several times in large volumes of broth. Concentrated inocula, about 3×10^9 cells, were used on the initial plates. Only two or three resistants were seen in experiments with 20 or 30 initial plates. One mutant clone was found by recurrence on serial sm replicas, and its site on plain agar was used to initiate the selection. After six stages of enrichment, the sm-resistant was obtained in pure culture. Two hundred and thirty-nine colonies were tested after 100 additional generations of growth in broth, and all retained resistance to sm. The sequence of transfers was identical with that exercised in indirect selection for phage resistance. The transfer operation itself could not have been responsible for resistance, for the sm selections remained sensitive to the phage and vice versa.

The infrequency of sm-resistant mutants hinders the tests for clonal occurrence. The culture 58-278, derived from *E. coli,* strain K-12, has been found to exhibit a much higher rate for this mutation, about 10^{-7} per division (H. P. Treffers, personal communication). Replicas of films of this culture on plain agar to sm agar plates repeatedly gave patterns similar to those illustrated in Figure 1 for phage resistance. Indirect selection was also exerted successfully on this culture with results similar to those already described.

We conclude that resistance to streptomycin, as to phage, is a spontaneous mutation that occurs independently of the presence of the selective agent.

DISCUSSION

Indirect selection is experimentally but not logically dependent on the clonal occurrence of the mutants. The latter had been established inferentially by Luria and Delbrück (1943) and by Newcombe (1949). It shows that the adapted cells are not randomly distributed in space. The success of indirect selection provides a sound basis for this nonrandom clustering in hereditary transmission. In particular, neither the adaptive change nor its inheritance depends upon a specific environment, which is what we mean by spontaneous mutation or preadaptation.

This demonstration does not conflict with reversible adaptive responses to a specific environment which disappear after some generations of growth in an indifferent medium. Directed, but nonheritable, responses have been clearly demonstrated in adaptive enzyme formation (Monod, 1947) and may be involved in the resistance phenomena investigated by Eagle (1951). However, no unequivocal case of a mutation specifically directed by and adapting cells to a chemical agent has yet been defended, despite numerous attempts of varying clarity (e.g., Barer, 1951). The concept of the "genotype as the norm of reaction" is pertinent to this discussion. The status of a microorganism's reaction as realized at any time, i.e., its phenotype, will reflect its immediate history, but its competence to react is an intrinsic quality subject for the most part only to sporadic, indeterminate mutations.

Indirect selection and tests for clonal occurrence should be applicable to other adaptive systems, but some difficulties may be anticipated. With low mutation rates, sufficient numbers of cells must ·be used to allow a reasonable number of mutants to appear. Since the proportion of mutants should also increase in time (Novick and Szilard, 1950), the serial transfer of large volumes of cultures is also indicated. A very high mutation rate may also cause difficulties if preexisting clones are outnumbered by new mutations during the growth of the initial plates. This can be compensated for again by serial transfer in broth to pre accumulate mutants and by restricting the inoculum size and time of incubation of the initial plates. The presumably indifferent "plain medium" may prove to be adverse to the mutants. For example, it is not likely that sm-dependent mutants will be detected as clones in plain agar films. However, any applications of replica plating that fail to demonstrate the clonal occurrence of a mutant type may be controlled by suitably designed reconstruction experiments. These would involve the

463   *Lederberg, Lederberg*

addition of known numbers of directly selected mutants to the original cultures. If the intruded mutants are detected in clones, and new occurrences are not, this would support the conclusion that the latter is not of spontaneous origin.

Some adaptations may be less amenable to these approaches, depending on the availability of suitable selective media for the replica plates. An example may be the development of lactose-positive papillae in cultures of *E. coli "mutable"* on lactose-peptone agar. It would be necessary to devise a medium that would detect mutants in the replica inoculum without losing them in an avalanche of new mutations occurring on the indicator plate itself.

The indirect selection procedure is paralleled by improvement methods which depend upon the performance of the kinships of a plant or animal rather than its own phenotype, as for example in the selection of roosters for egg production breeding stock (Lush, 1945).

SUMMARY

A method, replica plating, was developed to permit the copying of a pattern of microbial growth from one initial agar plate to a series of others. The method uses velveteen or other fabrics to make the transfer without disturbing spatial relationships. It may be useful in the detection of biochemical mutants, classification of fermentation reactions, determination of antibiotic sensitivity spectra, and other routines requiring repetitive inoculation of several media.

Replica plates were used in an approach to the problem of the pre-existence of adaptive mutants prior to their selection by specific environments. Replicas to agar containing bacteriophage or streptomycin showed that mutants of *Escherichia coli* resistant to these agents existed in clones on the initial plates of indifferent agar medium. In addition, concentration or enrichment for such mutants was accomplished by taking inocula from bacterial films at sites demonstrated to contain mutants by replica plates. After several stages of enrichment, each type of resistant mutant was isolated in pure culture. The procedure at no time exposes the indirectly selected populations to the specific agent. These observations, therefore, are cited as confirmation of previous evidence for the participation of spontaneous mutation and populational selection in the heritable adaptation of bacteria to new environments.

Received for publication, August 31, 1951

REFERENCES AND NOTES

* No. 473. This work has been supported by grants from the Research Committee, Graduate School, University of Wisconsin, with funds supplied by the Wisconsin Alumni Research Foundation, and from the Division of Research Grants and Fellowships, National Microbiological Institute, National Institutes of Health, U. S. Public Health Service.

Gwenda R. Barer, The action of streptomycin on *Bacterium lactis aerogenes,* *J. Gen. Microbiol.* **5,** 1–17 (1951).

W. Braun, Bacterial dissociation, *Bact. Revs.* **11,** 75–114 (1947).

F. M. Burnet, "Smooth-rough" variation in bacteria and its relation to bacteriophage, *J. Path. Bact.* **32,** 15–42 (1929).

M. Demerec, Origin of bacterial resistance to antibiotics, *J. Bact.* **56,** 63–74 (1948).

H. Eagle, The development of increased bacterial resistance to antibiotics as an adaptive process, *Bact. Proc.* **1951,** 56 (1951).

J. Huxley, *Evolution, the Modern Synthesis* (Harper, New York, 1942).

M. Kristensen, Recherches sur la fermentation mutative des Bactéries, *Acta Path. Microbiol. Scand.* **21,** 214–38 (1944).

D. Lea and C. A. Coulson, The distribution of the numbers of mutants in bacterial populations, *J. Genetics* **49,** 264–85 (1949).

J. Lederberg, Problems in microbial genetics, *Heredity* **2,** 145–98 (1948).

———, Bacterial variation, *Ann. Rev. Microbiol.* **3,** 1–22 (1949).

I. M. Lewis, Bacterial variation with special reference to behavior of some mutable strains of colon bacteria in synthetic media, *J. Bact.* **28,** 619–38 (1934).

S. E. Luria, Recent advances in bacterial genetics, *Bact. Revs.* **11,** 1–40 (1947).

——— and M. Delbrück, Mutations of bacteria from virus sensitivity to virus resistance, *Genetics* **28,** 491–511 (1943).

J. L. Lush, *Animal Breeding Plans* (Iowa State College Press, Ames, 1945).

J. Monod, The phenomenon of enzymatic adaptation, *Growth* **11,** 223–89 (1947).

H. B. Newcombe, Origin of bacterial variants, *Nature* **164,** 150 (1949).

A. Novick and L. Szilard, Experiments with the chemostat on spontaneous mutations of bacteria, *Proc. Nat. Acad. Sci. U.S.* **36,** 708–19 (1950).

F. J. Ryan and Lillian K. Schneider, Mutations during the growth of biochemical mutants of *Escherichia coli, Genetics* **34,** 72–91 (1949).

C. B. van Niel, The "Delft School" and the rise of general microbiology, *Bact. Revs.* **13,** 161–74 (1949).

M. Welsch, Recherches sur l'origine de la résistance microbiènne à la streptomycine, *Bull. Acad. Roy. Med. Belg.* **15,** 454–71 (1950).

Further Selection Experiments on Industrial Melanism in the *Lepidoptera*

H. B. D. Kettlewell

Genetic Laboratories, Department of Zoology, University of Oxford

1. PREVIOUS EXPERIMENTS

In a previous paper (Kettlewell, 1955), I recorded the results of extensive mark-release-recapture experiments undertaken in 1953 on the Peppered Moth, *Biston betularia* Linn. and its two melanic forms, *carbonaria* Jordan and *insularia* Th-Mieg (Plate 2, Fig. 6). These experiments were carried out in a circumscribed area of woodland, the Christopher Cadbury Bird Reserve, situated about six miles from the industrial and heavily polluted area of Birmingham. The results then obtained may be summarised as follows:

(*a*) When released onto available trunks and boughs, their normal resting places, over 97 percent of *carbonaria* (the black form) appeared to the human eye to be inconspicuous. Conversely, nearly 89 percent of the light form of the Peppered Moth were adjudged conspicuous (Plate 1, Fig. 2).

(*b*) Direct observation on the released insects showed that by late afternoon 54 percent of the light form had disappeared but only 37 percent of the *carbonaria*. Furthermore, we witnessed both Robins (*Erithacus rubecula* L.) and Hedge Sparrows (*Prunella modularis* L.) take the moths from off the trees, and they did this selectively and, on the majority of occasions, in an order of conspicuousness as previously scored by us.

(*c*) Recapture figures, reflecting a dif-

Reprinted from *Heredity* **10**, 287–301 (1956), by permission of the publisher.

PLATE 1.

FIGURE 1. *Typical betularia* (left) and its melanic *carbonaria* (right) at rest on lichened tree trunk, Deanend Wood, Dorset.

FIGURE 2. *Typical betularia* and its melanic *carbonaria* at rest on lichen-free tree trunk near Birmingham.

FIGURE 3. Song Thrush, *Turdus ericetorum* L., examining tree trunks from the ground with a *carbonaria* in its beak.

PLATE 2.

FIGURE 1. Nuthatch, *Sitta europaea* L., in the act of taking *typical betularia* from lichened tree trunk, Deanend Wood, Dorset. This species took 40 *carbonaria* to 11 *typical* while under observation.

FIGURE 2. Spotted Flycatcher, *Muscicapa striata* L., about to take *carbonaria* from oak trunk, Deanend Wood, Dorset. This species was seen to take 81 *carbonaria* to 9 *typical*.

FIGURE 3. Robin, *Erithacus rubecula* L., with *carbonaria* in its beak taken from lichened tree trunk, Deanend Wood, Dorset. There were 3 *typicals* on this trunk at the moment of this photograph being taken. This species took 12 *carbonaria* to 2 *typical* whilst being watched.

FIGURE 4. Yellowhammer, *Emberiza citrinella* L., searching tree trunk. Deanend Wood, Dorset. A pair took altogether 20 *carbonaria* and on no occasion whilst under observation did they discover the *typical* form which, on every occasion, was offered in equal numbers to the black.

FIGURE 5. Male Redstart, *Phoenicurus phoenicurus* L., with *typical betularia* in its beak in a wood near Birmingham. This species took 43 *typical* to 15 *carbonaria* whilst under observation.

FIGURE 6. *Typical Biston betularia* L., its melanic *carbonaria* Jordan, and *f. insularia* Th-Mieg, another melanic.

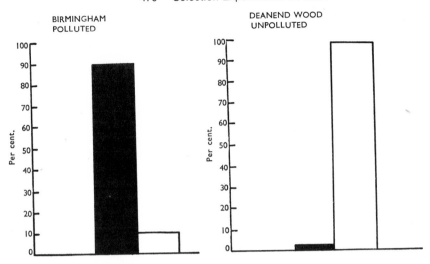

FIGURE 1. Local population frequencies.

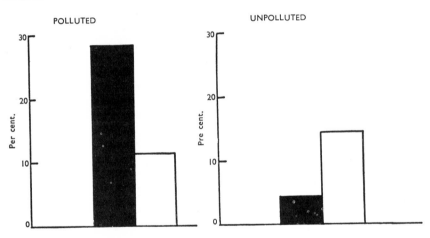

FIGURE 1a. Recapture frequencies.

ferential mortality rate, showed that more than twice as many *carbonaria* survived as *typical* (27.5 to 13 percent) (Fig. 1*a*).

These experiments showed that birds act as selective agents and that the melanic forms of *betularia* are at a cryptic advantage in an industrial area such as Birmingham. It was essential to repeat these observations during a subsequent season and to extend them by carrying out comparable mark-release-recapture experiments in unpolluted countryside. This paper provides details of such work, which was undertaken in 1955.

2. A REPEAT OF THE
SELECTION EXPERIMENTS
IN THE BIRMINGHAM DISTRICT

Immediately following successful mark-release-recapture experiments in the summer of 1955 in an unpolluted wood in Dorset (recorded later in this paper) we moved camp to the Christopher Cadbury Bird Reserve near Birmingham, which I had chosen in 1953 as being likely to offer the optimum conditions for my requirements. I had three objects in view in this undertaking. Firstly to repeat a small mark-release experiment similar to that of 1953. Secondly, to give Dr. Tinbergen an opportunity of filming the experiments so as to make a visual record of them in the same way that he had done previously in Dorset, and thirdly to check the local phenotype frequencies, after having released 137 male and 34 female *typical betularia* in 1953.

(a) *Mark-release-recapture results.* Altogether a total of 227 *betularia* were released over two periods, 154 *carbonaria,* 64 *typical* (and 9

TABLE 1

Release Experiments for *B. betularia* (Males Only). Rubery, Near Birmingham, 1955.

Date	Releases			Total	Catches			Total	Recaptures			Total
	C	T	I		C	T	I		C	T	I	
8.7	54	23	(5)	82	62	7	5	74	. . .	. . .	. . .	. . .
9.7	. . .	. . .	. . .	. . .	73	11	1	85	33	11	0	44
10.7	100	41	(4)	145	51	5	2	58	3	2	0	5
11.7	. . .	. . .	. . .	. . .	50	7	2	59	46	2	(2)	50
12.7	. . .	. . .	. . .	. . .	89	7	5	101	0	1	0	1
13.7	. . .	. . .	. . .	. . .	25	4	0	29	. . .	. . .	. . .	. . .
14.7	. . .	. . .	. . .	. . .	53	2	1	56	. . .	. . .	. . .	. . .
15.7	. . .	. . .	. . .	. . .	20	2	2	24	. . .	. . .	. . .	. . .
16.7	. . .	. . .	. . .	. . .	13	2	0	15	. . .	. . .	. . .	. . .
17.7	. . .	. . .	. . .	. . .	20	2	0	22	. . .	. . .	. . .	. . .
18.7	. . .	. . .	. . .	. . .	15	2	2	19	. . .	. . .	. . .	. . .
19.7	. . .	. . .	. . .	. . .	5	1	0	6	. . .	. . .	. . .	. . .
20.7	. . .	. . .	. . .	. . .	10	1	0	11	. . .	. . .	. . .	. . .
Totals	154	64	(9)	227	486	53	20	559	82	16	2	100

	1955			Total	1953			Total
	C	T	I		C	T	I	
Wild Birmingham population percent phenotype (Fig. 2)	86.94	9.48	3.58	559	85.03	10.14	4.83	621
Percent return of releases = recaptures	53.25	25.0	(22.2)	100	27.5	13.0	17.4	149

The letters C, T, and I stand for carbonaria, typical *and* insularia *respectively throughout this paper.*

insularia), see Table 1. Of these, I recaptured a total of 100, 82 being *carbonaria*, 16 *typical* (and 2 *insularia*), see Tables 1 and 1A. This represents a return of 52.25 percent of the *carbonaria* release and 25 percent of the *typical* (*insularia* 22.2). Once again we recaptured twice as many of the black form as of the light, but this differed from the 1953 releases which were spread over 11 days, when we recaught 27.5 percent of *carbonaria* and 13 percent of *typical*. Whether the present increased return rate was due to the greater efficiency of our recapture methods, or to decreased predation, diminished migration or a small natural population, I am unable to say. But it is important to note that the *relative* return figures were of the same order as in my previous series of experiments.

(b) Dr. Tinbergen succeeded in filming Redstarts (*Phœnicurus phœnicurus* L.) taking and eating our releases (Plate 2, Fig. 5), and I am able to give in Table 2 his records of the predation which took place on two days whilst he kept observation from a hide. In each case the two forms were released in equality and subsequently replenished at intervals *after all of one form had been taken*. In this way, he recorded that 43 of the pale *typical* form were eaten to 15 of the black form *carbonaria* and, on the majority of occasions, two or more *typicals* were eaten before a *carbonaria* was discovered. Once again we were able to show that the presence of a conspicuous light coloured *typical* immediately put the better hidden *carbonaria* at a disadvantage which they would not otherwise have incurred if they had been released on their own.

(c) A total of 559 wild *betularia* were caught over a period of 13 nights, *carbonaria* 486, *typical* 53 and *insularia* 20, giving the percentages respectively of 86.94, 9.48 and 3.58 (see Table 1). This compares with 621 *betularia* taken over 11 nights in 1953 with *carbonaria* 85.03 percent, *typical* 10.14 percent and *insularia* 4.83 percent. Furthermore, Table 3 demonstrates that for the 6 nights on which light and

TABLE 1A

Birmingham Recaptures, 1953 (See Appendix).

Date	Observed			Total	Expected		
	C	T	I		C	T	I
25.6	5	1	2	8	2.50	3.00	2.50
26.6	0	0	0	0	0.0	0.0	0.0
27.6	0	1	2	3	1.68	0.56	0.76
28.6	9	4	2	15	8.81	5.00	1.19
29.6	0	0	0	0	0.0	0.0	0.0
30.6	17	2	1	20	13.89	5.10	1.57
1.7	41	6	0	47	37.11	8.66	1.24
2.7	30	2	1	33	24.92	7.07	1.01
3.7	26	2	0	28	22.94	5.06	0.0
4.7	12	0	0	12	10.18	1.52	0.30
Totals	140	18	8	166	121.46	35.97	8.57

assembling traps were both in operation the total catch (= wild population + releases) showed a similar proportion of each phenotype as coming to both methods of collecting. It again compares with the high degree of consistency with my 1953 figures, see Table 3A.

This small repeat experiment fully corroborated the findings of the previous one, namely that the pale *typical* form, as found in unpolluted countryside, is at a cryptic disadvantage in an industrial area. The fact that birds eliminate these selectively, thereby affecting the evolution of the Peppered Moth, was again recorded.

TABLE 2

Observation on Predation of *B. betularia,* by Redstarts for 2 Days Only (by Dr. N. Tinbergen from His Hide), Birmingham, 1955.

	Typical	*Carbonaria*	*Total*
19.7 A.M.	12	3	15
20.7 A.M.	14	3	17
P.M.	17	9	26
Total	43	15	58

N.B. *Replenished to equality as soon as all three of either phenotype had been taken.*

TABLE 3

Comparative Methods of Collecting at M.V. Light and Assembling Traps for 6 Nights Only. Birmingham, 1955.

	8th July			*9th July*			*10th July*			*11th July*			*12th July*			*13th July*			*Totals*		
Phenotypes	C	T	I	C	T	I	C	T	I	C	T	I	C	T	I	C	T	I	C	T	I
M.V. light traps	32	6	2	9	5	0	23	4	2	19	1	0	72	7	4	12	2	0	167	25	8
Assembling traps	30	1	3	97	17	1	31	3	0	77	8	4	17	1	1	3	0	2	255	30	10

TABLE 3A

Comparison of the Proportion (Percent) of Phenotypes Which Came to M.V. Light and to Assembling.

Year	Birmingham 1953 *(for 10 nights)*				Birmingham 1955 *(for 6 nights)*			
Phenotypes	C	T	I	Total	C	T	I	Total
M.V. *light—*								
Totals	263	47	24	433	167	25	8	200
Percentage	83.60	10.85	5.55	100	86.44	10.17	3.39	100
Assembling—								
Totals	281	34	13	328	255	30	10	295
Percentage	85.68	10.36	3.96	100	83.5	12.5	4	100

3. SELECTION EXPERIMENTS IN
UNPOLLUTED COUNTRYSIDE

It can be presumed that melanic mutations take place at intervals throughout the range of *Biston betularia*. To test their selective advantages or disadvantages by mark-release-recapture experiments, it would be advantageous, therefore, to choose a location where the melanic *carbonaria* was only maintained by recurrent mutation. A wood having such specifications and, at the same time, suitable in other requirements such as offering isolation and free access by rides was not easy to find. Moreover, amenities for housing the very large number of pupæ necessary to ensure specimens for release had to be available on the site. A large number of woods in Devon and Cornwall, where only the *typical* light coloured form of *Biston betularia* occurs, were investigated, but were found to be unsuitable for one reason or another. Eventually a peninsula of extremely heavily lichened woodland was found in Deanend Wood, Dorset (Fig. 2), and in 1954 I was able to visit it for a single night with a view to collecting a random sample of *betularia*. Twenty specimens were taken assembling to virgin females, of which 19 were *typical* and 1 *insularia*. There were no *carbonaria*. Furthermore, leaf washings from locally collected samples showed a small degree of pollution only. Accordingly, in 1955, in mid-June, I set up camp in these woods. Suitable sheds were found to house the three thousand *betularia* pupæ. An electric generator with mercury vapour traps was installed in the centre ride and the periphery of the wood was lined with cages destined to contain virgin females, so that at night the whole release area would be subject to a concentration of female assembling scent and this, no doubt, succeeded in holding a proportion of our male releases within the area of woodland.

The experiments were designed so that each aspect of the work could be compared with the previous Birmingham results, and the methods employed came under the following headings:

(1) Scoring values as gauged by human standards.

(2) Direct observation as to what happened to the individuals so scored.

(3) Recapture figures which provided data over longer periods.

On every occasion, recapture results were assessed on male Peppered Moths only, because of the impossibility of recapturing females. However, these were used as releases for continuous observation from hides where, at the same time as a film record which was made, the order of predation of each insect was noted.

(i) SCORING VALUES FOR CRYPSIS

The technique of scoring previously used was to assess, in the first place at a distance of two yards, whether a released moth was (*a*) conspicuous, or (*b*) inconspicuous. Subsequently, three categories were

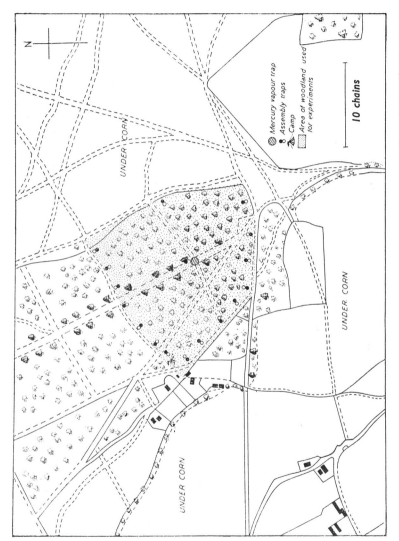

FIGURE 2. Deanend Wood, Dorset.

allowed for each, so that the score for (*a*) would be either −1, −2, or −3, and for (*b*) +1, +2, or +3, depending on the distance at which the insect faded into its background. As pointed out in the previous paper, this method of scoring worked satisfactorily in the Birmingham experiments. It came as a surprise then to find that, of 120 *typicals* released in Deanend Wood during the first few days, all were classed as inconspicuous, with 85 percent scoring +3. Conversely, all 75 *carbonaria* scored by us appeared conspicuous and 80 percent of these scored −3. In view of the random sample of the release points selected, it appeared unnecessary to continue the arduous procedure of scoring the cryptic value of each individual release, and it was accepted that in these woods, to the human eye, the majority of the light *typical* form were extremely well hidden, and the *carbonaria* were nearly always conspicuous (Plate 1, Fig. 1).

(ii) DIRECT OBSERVATION

(a) *A record of the number of individuals present or absent by late afternoon.* Early on in the experiments an apparent deficiency of the light *typical* form was recorded when the afternoon check on releases took place. There were also many *carbonaria* missing. In the present work, in regard to the other melanic *insularia,* the numbers used, though quoted, were so small that they have no significance. It became increasingly obvious that one was passing over the *typical* form on the lichened tree trunks, and they are practically impossible to see. To test this, I did a check immediately following the morning's release, in an area where my continual presence prevented predation. All the *carbonaria* were present, but over 30 percent of the *typicals* were unaccounted for. The cryptic efficiency of the *typical* on a lichened background is, in fact, greater than that of *carbonaria* on the blackened Birmingham tree trunks. For this reason, this type of recording was discontinued.

(b) *Observation from hides.* In the course of filming, Dr. Niko Tinbergen, who had to spend the greater part of each day in a hide, recorded the order in which predation occurred. These figures are added to my own observations. It must be emphasised that these records were of concentrations of female *betularia* necessary for photography, but that they played no part in my release-recapture figures. On each occasion, an equal number of black and white forms were used at the commencement, but it was found impracticable to replace each phenotype after it had been taken. Their numbers were replenished after the last of one phenotype had been eaten, thus preventing simple statistical analysis. By doing this, it will be appreciated that the bias was, thereafter, in favour of that phenotype which had been eliminated previously, and it was found that on the majority of occasions the more conspicuous of the two forms were all taken before any of the others. This behaviour was common to five species of birds to a greater or lesser degree, as will

TABLE 4

Direct Observation on Predation by Five Species
of Birds. Deanend Wood, Dorset, 1955.

	Observer	*Carbonaria*	*Typical*	
Spotted Flycatcher	N. T.	46	8	
(*Muscicapa striata* L.)	H. B. D. K.	35	1	
Nuthatch	N. T.	22	8	
(*Sitta Europaea* L.)	H. B. D. K.	9	0 (first day)	
	H. B. D. K.	9	3 (second day)	
Yellow Hammer	N. T.	8	0	
(*Emberiza citrinella* L.)	H. B. D. K.	12	0	
Robin	N. T.	12	2	
(*Erithacus rubecula* L.)				
Thrush	N. T.	11	4	
Turdus ericetocum L.				
Total predation observed (for days when records were kept)	. . .	164	26	Total 190

Note. *On all occasions these observations commenced with equal numbers of both phenotypes. We replaced them when all of one phenotype had been taken.*

be seen from the figures in Table 4 (Plate 1, Fig. 3, and Plate 2, Figs. 1, 2, 3 and 4).

(iii) RECAPTURE RESULTS

Releases were undertaken on fourteen occasions in all, making a total of 969 individuals, 473 being *carbonaria* and 496 *typical*. I recaptured 30 *carbonaria* and 62 *typical*. For all types of release we got back 12.5 percent of the *typical* form, but only 6.3 percent of the *carbonaria*. For various reasons about to be discussed, the releases on three days should be excluded from this total as they are unduly biased in one way or another. This gives a figure of 799 releases for the 11 correct days: 406 being *carbonaria* and 393 *typical*. I got back 19 *carbonaria* and 54 *typical,* being 4.68 and 13.74 percent respectively (see Tables 5 and 5A).

4. DISCUSSION AND RELEASE PROBLEMS

Various types of release techniques were undertaken with the object of finding the best way of subjecting as many individuals as possible, under natural conditions, to maximum predation for the longest time. I propose, therefore, to discuss these in some detail, and to give reasons for excluding three sets of figures from the table due to the unsatisfactory nature of the releases.

TABLE 5

Release Experiment Figures for *B. betularia*
(Males Only). Deanend, Dorset, 1955.

Date (1953)	Releases C	T	I	Total	Catches C	T	I	Total	Recaptures C	T	I	Total
(13.6)	(37)	(38)	(9)	(84)	...	...	...	...	...	...	...	...
14.6	8	17	2	27	4	17	2	23	(4)	(1)	(1)	(6)
(15.6)	(8)	(25)	(1)	(34)	2	27	5	34	2	9	(3)	14
(16.6)	(22)	(40)	(0)	(62)	1	34	2	37	(0)	(0)	(0)	(0)
17.6	...	...	...	...	7	58	3	68	(7)	(7)	(0)	(14)
18.6	42	65	(3)	110	0	30	1	31	0	1	0	1
19.6	39	72	0	111	2	26	1	29	2	6	0	8
20.6	24	57	0	81	1	44	2	47	1	3	0	4
21.6	42	29	0	71	1	13	2	16	1	4	0	5
22.6	...	...	...	...	5	13	1	19	5	4	0	9
23.6	...	...	...	...	... No releases ...			...	... No captures ...			...
24.6	...	...	...	...	... No releases ...			...	... No captures ...			...
25.6	82	43	0	125	1	11	0	12	0	0	0	0
26.6	...	...	...	...	3	8	1	12	2	2	0	4
27.6	51	28	0	79	0	8	0	8	0	0	0	0
28.6	22	22	0	44	1	20	0	21	1	5	0	6
29.6	17	18	0	35	0	14	0	14	0	5	0	5
30.6	24	11	0	35	4	11	1	16	3	6	0	9
1.7	...	...	...	...	2	9	0	11	2	2	0	4
2.7	...	...	...	...	0	7	0	7	0	0	0	0
3.7	...	...	...	...	...	...	...	...	...	...	...	...
4.7	55	31	0	86	...	...	...	...	...	...	...	...
5.7	...	...	...	...	0	9	0	9	0	7	0	7
Totals	473	496	15	984	34	359	21	414	30	62	4	96

	C	T	I	Total
Wild Deanend population	(4)	297	17	318
Percent phenotype (Fig. 2)	(Possible escapes)	94.60	5.4	
Release after 1 day of self-determination	2	4	(1)	
Percent phenotype	...	...	...	
Percent return of releases	6.34	12.50	(26.67)	

I used 84 *betularia* in the first experiment (13/6/55). These were released on only twenty trees, the reason for this small number of release points being that I had been unable to locate and prepare the other trees in the area. The result was that I produced a high concentration of moths on comparatively few tree trunks (an average of 4 per tree), nor were the two forms on every occasion released in equality per tree. The late afternoon check showed that in nearly every case the moths were either all present or all absent per tree. Subsequently, by direct observation, Dr. Tinbergen and I found that a concentration of releases increased the predation risk for all present, even though the birds took the more conspicuous ones first. It will be noted that on this occasion

TABLE 5A

Deanend Recaptures, 1955.

Date	Observed			Total	Expected		
	C	T	I		C	T	I
(13.6)	(6)	(3)	(3)	(12)	(5.29)	(5.43)	(1.29)
14.6	1	7	2	10	2.96	6.30	0.74
(15.6)	(0)	(1)	(0)	(1)	(0.24)	(0.74)	(0.03)
(16.6)	(8)	(8)	(0)	(16)	(5.68)	(10.32)	(0)
17.6	. . .	. . .	. . .	. . .	. . .	. . .	. . .
18.6	2	8	0	10	3.81	5.91	0.27
19.6	1	2	0	3	1.05	1.95	0
20.6	2	4	0	6	1.78	4.22	0
21.6	4	4	0	8	4.73	3.27	0
22.6	. . .	. . .	. . .	. . .	. . .	. . .	. . .
23.6	. . .	. . .	. . .	. . .	. . .	. . .	. . .
24.6	. . .	. . .	. . .	. . .	. . .	. . .	. . .
25.6	2	2	0	4	2.62	1.38	0
26.6	. . .	. . .	. . .	. . .	. . .	. . .	. . .
27.6	1	5	0	6	3.87	2.13	0
28.6	0	7	0	7	3.50	3.50	0
29.6	3	8	0	11	5.34	5.66	0
30.6	2	1	0	3	2.06	0.94	0
4.7	0	7	0	7	4.47	2.52	0
Totals	32	67	5	104	47.40	54.27	2.33

we recaptured 4 *carbonaria* and 1 *typical* (expected — near equality). It is possible that, apart from a faulty release technique, a further point may have played a part in the production of these figures. The birds in this wood were unlikely to have had any previous experience of the Black Peppered Moths, and it is conceivable therefore that at first some of them did not recognise them as an article of diet. Dr. Tinbergen did, in fact, record a similar incident in one of the Birmingham 1955 experiments. A Wren (*Troglodytes troglodytes* Linn.) flew onto a tree trunk on which was released a very conspicuous *typical* (Birmingham frequency 10 percent) and after scrutinising it closely it flew away without attacking it. It is, however, possible that the noise of the ciné camera disturbed it at this point.

The next release (14/6/65), which was considered satisfactory, was conducted with a greatly lowered concentration. Twenty-seven *betularia* were, in fact, put onto 23 trees.

The release on the 15th was designed to test whether the presence of a *carbonaria* on the same tree trunk as a *typical* lowered the latter's expectation of survival. Apart from the 8 male *carbonaria* released, females had, on this occasion, to be used also (because of a temporary lack of *carbonaria* males), so that each of the male *typicals* had a black moth on the same tree trunk. Two trees, however, were used as controls, and on these two *typicals* were released on each, with no accompanying melanics. The late afternoon examination (6 P.M.) gave the surprising result that no *betularia* of any form were to be found on any of the release trees, with the exception that one of the control trees (without a *carbonaria* being present) had two *typicals* on it. The following night, out of 37 *betularia* caught at light and assembling traps, none were from the releases of the 15th. The next night, however, I recaught one *typical* (out of 68) from this release. This would seem to provide additional evidence to the statement I made in my original paper (p. 336), "From this it would appear that, when a conspicuous insect had been found, it at once put other insects in the immediate vicinity at a disadvantage because of the bird's active searchings." For these reasons I feel that the release conducted on the 15th should not be included.

The following day (16/6/55) a release was undertaken between 5 and 6 P.M., long after the maximum predation time of birds. The object was to test whether, having excluded predation, the design of experiment favoured unduly one phenotype more than another. Twenty-two *carbonaria* and 40 *typical* were released. Of these, 7 *carbonaria* and 6 *typical* were retrapped the same night (expected — 4.61 to 8.39). It will be noted that this represents the return of nearly a quarter of our releases on the 16th. I am unable to account for the increased proportion of *carbonaria* recaptures over *typical*, which occurred this night, but in view of the absence of predation it suggests that the recapture arrangements did not unduly favour the return of the *typicals* more than the *carbonaria*. We have, however, already shown that in the Birmingham experiments there was no difference in the proportion of the three phenotypes which were collected, firstly, at mercury vapour light traps and, secondly, at assembling traps containing females of all three phenotypes (proportions of *carbonaria*, light and assembling, 85 percent to 86 percent, and *typical* 10.8 to 10.4 percent). Furthermore, we are able to report similar findings in this present set of experiments (see Table 6). In view of these facts, and that this release was not designed to reflect the degree of selective predation, and that little in fact could have taken place, it is better to extract the results, along with those of the other two previously mentioned, from those which are about to be considered.

It can be seen from this that the act of predation is no simple response

TABLE 6

Comparative Methods of Collecting at M.V. Light and Assembling Traps. Deanend, 1955.

Phenotypes	Carbonaria	Typical	Insularia	Total	
M.V. light—					
Totals	14	166	12	192	
Percentage	7.29	86.77	5.94	100	
Assembling—					414
Totals	20	193	9	222	
Percentage	9.01	86.94	4.05	100	

to a single stimulus. It involves, apart from insect cryptic efficiency, such other considerations as insect density, bird conditioning, and searching intensity per trunk, stimulated by an immediate previous experience of finding a conspicuous insect. All other releases were in fact conducted in a uniform manner (with the exception of one other satisfactory method used). In these, on every occasion, there was one phenotype released per tree, and the experiment was conducted over a larger area of woodland. Furthermore, as in the Birmingham experiments, other species of moths which were inhabiting the wood were released within the area at the same time, to minimise the effect of conditioning. This, of course, involves a great deal of extra work, but it is necessary. One further point was noted, that the same trees must not be used as release points on each day, as the birds became conditioned to them.

The "other method" of release referred to was used successfully on 18th June. This took place just before sunrise, between 4 and 4.30 A.M. Forty-two *carbonaria*, 65 *typical* (and 3 *insularia*) were allowed to fly out of their separate boxes which had been previously warmed on the engine of my car. The majority flew and took up positions on the boughs and trunks of nearby trees. I, therefore, used many release points within the area. This method was not repeated because it is necessary to get each insect airborne over a very short period of time, which was difficult due to the coldness of the morning, so that by the time the last few flew, birds were active and, in fact, a Spotted Flycatcher (*Muscicapa striata* L.) chased and caught two *typical betularia*. A too early release, on the other hand, would involve a number of the moths coming to the various traps in action from the previous night. With the exception of the two *typicals* taken by birds, it appeared that this release was satisfactory. One *carbonaria* and 6 *typical* were subsequently recovered.

We have produced evidence that, in undertaking any release experiments involving the use of cryptic insects which normally pass the day concealed on their appropriate backgrounds, due regard must be taken of such factors which affect predation as density, proximity of an individual which has been scored conspicuous, bird conditioning for recognition of a particular species, or for the place of release. To avoid all these complications, individual releases, undertaken over a large area containing many trees, are essential.

5. CONCLUSIONS

We are now in a position to review firstly, two separate series of release experiments conducted in an industrial district: secondly, to compare figures obtained from these with the data from a similar release undertaken in an unpolluted and heavily lichened wood in Dorset.

In regard to the Birmingham experiments: in the second of the two series which were carried out, scoring for crypsis was not repeated as it was unnecessary, neither the trees nor the phenotypes having altered since 1953. Direct observation on bird predation in each case showed that the *typical* light form was eaten more frequently than *carbonaria,* and the deficiency of this light form in our recapture figures can be attributed in each case to selective elimination by birds, as such other considerations as sampling errors, a different life span or migration rate for each phenotype, can be ruled out of the repeat experiment for the same reasons as given in 1953.

On comparing the Birmingham figures for crypsis with those of Deanend Wood, Dorset, we found a complete reversal. Over 97 percent of the *carbonaria* in the former location were scored inconspicuous, whereas 89 percent of the *typicals* were adjudged conspicuous. In Deanend Wood, of the *carbonaria,* all were scored conspicuous, whilst of the *typicals* all were inconspicuous. Furthermore, of these, 85 percent were given the highest mark for cryptic efficiency.

Consequently the observed bird predation on both occasions in Birmingham showed elimination in favour of *carbonaria.* In 1953, a total of 18 *betularia* were kept under continuous observation, half being *carbonaria* and half *typical.* All the nine *typicals* were observed to be eaten by Robins and Hedge Sparrows, but only 3 *carbonaria*; the remaining 6 were never discovered and, in fact, survived the day up to 7 P.M. In the recent work, Dr. Tinbergen recorded that a pair of Redstarts and their young took 43 *typicals* to 15 *carbonaria* during experimental releases in which both black and light forms were used in equality (Table 2).

On the other hand, in Deanend Wood, Dorset, the reverse was observed: 5 species of birds took 190 *betularia* whilst being watched (Table 4). Of these, 164 were *carbonaria* and 26 *typical.* It must be accepted, therefore, that the *carbonaria* has an approximate 6:1 advantage in Birmingham, and the reverse was true for Deanend. In regard to the recaptures, on each occasion in Birmingham I got back twice as many *carbonaria* as *typicals,* but in Deanend I recaptured three times as many *typical* as the melanic (Text Fig. 1*a*). Furthermore, if the collecting techniques employed were comparable in each case, it would appear that the predation intensity was greater at Deanend. Fewer individuals of each phenotype survived. This is also reflected in the nightly recapture totals (assuming, once again, that our collecting efficiency was comparable). In the 1953 large-scale Birmingham experiments, the average return within 24 hours was 19 *betularia* per 100 releases. For Deanend, it was 9 per 100. It is, however, the selective predation and not the total predation with which we are concerned in these present investigations.

6. SUMMARY OF ALL THREE EXPERIMENTS

1. The Peppered Moth, *Biston betularia*, is one of about seventy species of moth which are at present in the process of changing their

populations from light to dark individuals. The common Industrial Melanic = form *carbonaria* is black, and another = form *insularia,* which is not an allelomorph, varies from light to heavily speckled specimens (Plate 2, Fig. 6).

2. This paper records two complementary series of experiments, involving the release of nearly 2000 marked moths, to test the relative camouflage or cryptic advantages of the normal light-coloured *betularia* and its melanic form *carbonaria*. This was carried out in the first place near the industrial area of Birmingham where the *carbonaria* form represents about 87 percent of the population. Secondly, a similar experiment was undertaken in a heavily lichened and pollution-free wood in rural Dorset, where *carbonaria* does not normally occur or, if it does, at a very low frequency. (The other melanic, *insularia,* though mentioned, was used in too small numbers to have significance.)

3. The first series was a repeat of similar work I carried out in 1953, and fully corroborates the conclusions previously published (Kettlewell, 1955).

4. On each occasion, the more conspicuous of the two forms was deficient in numbers amongst the recaptures; *typical betularia* in Birmingham and *carbonaria* at Deanend Wood, Dorset.

5. (i) Scoring for conspicuousness as recognised by Man, and (ii) direct observation of the released insects showed that birds were responsible for their elimination, both in polluted and unpolluted countryside, and this took place selectively in each case, and in an order which varied according to the camouflage efficiency of each phenotype in relation to its background.

6. In unpolluted and heavily lichened countryside melanic forms are maintained only by recurrent mutation, and are rapidly eliminated because of their conspicuousness.

7. In industrial areas this limitation no longer exists; in fact it is the pale-coloured *typical* which is now eliminated. This applies also to areas far to the east of them, because of the prevailing westerly wind, where large areas of England subject to pollution "fall-out" are deficient in lichens.

8. Predation alone is responsible for the fact that in the Birmingham district I got back only 50 percent of the *typicals* that were expected from the proportions of the two forms released. In contrast, at Deanend, it was the *carbonaria* form which was deficient. In fact I recaptured only 67 percent of the number expected.

9. The difference in cryptic coloration alone could be responsible for the rapid spread of the Industrial Melanics. There are also, however, other character and behaviour differences between them and their *typical* forms. These are at present the subject of investigation.

Received March 22, 1956

REFERENCES AND NOTES

Acknowledgments. I wish to thank the Nuffield Foundation, who have enabled me to undertake this work, also Dr. N. Tinbergen for his observations and records whilst filming the experiments. I am grateful to Dr. E. B. Ford, F.R.S., for his advice and to Dr. P. M. Sheppard for his constructive criticism.

H. B. D. Kettlewell, *Heredity* 9, 323–42 (1955).

APPENDIX

Table 1A (p. 472) reflects a different method of analysing the 1953 recaptures, to that shown in the previous paper. The original recapture figures (Kettlewell, 1955, Table 5) record the number of marked individuals which returned each night. The present table takes into account the number of days each individual has been in the wild. Thus a recaptured insect showing three marks is entered under each of the three releasing days separately.

Population Genetics of Abnormal Human Haemoglobins

A. C. Allison

Cell Metabolism Research Unit,
Department of Biochemistry,
University of Oxford

Ten genetically controlled abnormal haemoglobin types have now been characterized (haemoglobins S, C, D, E, G, H, I, J, K and M). Their properties have recently been summarized by Zuelzer, Neel and Robinson (1956). The genes for haemoglobins G, H, I, J, K and M seem to be rather uncommon in most populations, so that they can properly be regarded as mutants which are kept at a low frequency by the operation of selection against them; this occurs when any two abnormal haemoglobin genes come together in the same individual and thereby produce an anaemia.

On the other hand, the genes for haemoglobins S, C and E, and the thalassaemia gene, have attained high frequencies in many human populations despite the fact that selection operates against homozygotes and against those who carry two different abnormal haemoglobin genes. These characters are undoubtedly polymorphic. The case of haemoglobin D, which seems to be present in about 2 percent of Sikhs and to produce a homozygote with polycythaemia as the only detectable abnormality (Bird and Lehmann, 1956) is marginal, but probably represents a true polymorphism.

An adequate explanation for the polymorphism of the sickle-cell character in East Africa is available. Electrophoretic analyses performed in 729 African infants show the proportion of sickle-cell

Reprinted from *Acta Genetica* 6, 430–34 (Karger, Basel/New York, 1956), by permission of the author and S. Karger A.G.

homozygotes expected from the Hardy-Weinberg law, which confirms that there is no significant selection against sickle-cell homozygotes *in utero*. Similar analyses carried out on 6840 adult Africans show that on both the East and West sides of the continent the proportion of sickle-cell homozygotes surviving to adult life is less than 20 percent of the average survival of all genotypes (Allison, 1956b). This order of survival is confirmed by clinical studies. The sickle-cell heterozygote seems to have a considerable advantage — up to 25 percent — over other genotypes. The advantage can be attributed mainly to resistance against *falciparum* malaria, although other factors (e.g., resistance to hookworm infestation — Raper, 1956) may play a subsidiary part. It can now be taken as established that children who are heterozygous for the sickle-cell gene have lower malaria parasite counts than other children. Since the mortality from *falciparum* malaria is known to be related to the height of the parasite count (Field, 1949), it seems reasonable to conclude that the mortality from malaria will be lower in sickle-cell heterozygotes than in other genotypes. And there is direct evidence that the heterozygotes rarely, if ever, develop potentially fatal complications of malaria, such as cerebral malaria and blackwater fever (Raper, *loc. cit.*). The advantage of the heterozygote appears also in their significantly higher incidence in adult than in infant African populations (Allison, 1956b). The distribution of the sickle-cell gene is also in accordance with this hypothesis: in Africa and elsewhere high frequencies are attained only in malarious regions. Thus, the equilibrium of the sickle-cell gene and its normal allelomorph in East Africa seems to be stable, with the sickle-cell heterozygote at an advantage and the homozygote sub-lethal.

In West Africa the position is complicated by the presence of a third allelomorph, the haemoglobin C gene. A year ago, when the position was reviewed by Allison (1956a), the only information available was that the haemoglobin C gene was present at a frequency of about 5 percent in the Southern Gold Coast and had not been found in East Africa. Since it was known that persons who inherit the sickle-cell gene from one parent and the haemoglobin C gene from the other sometimes develop a condition very like sickle-cell disease (see, e.g., Smith and Conley, 1954), Allison postulated that the sickle-cell and haemoglobin C genes must tend to be mutually exclusive in human populations. Extensive data published since then (Edington and Lehmann, 1956; Allison, 1956b) have provided a fair overall picture of the distribution of the sickle-cell and haemoglobin C genes in West Africa and have confirmed Allison's postulate. The frequency of the haemoglobin C gene rises to 13.5 percent in the Dagomba tribe of the Northern Territories of the Gold Coast; in this tribe the frequency of the sickle-cell gene is only 2 percent. On all sides of this main focus the populations tested have shown a cline of descending frequencies of the haemoglobin C gene and increasing frequencies of the sickle-cell gene. The negative correlation between the frequencies of the two abnormal genes appears in Figure 1.

FIGURE 1.

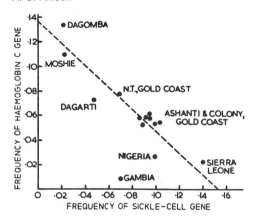

Allison (1956b) has also made a preliminary calculation of the fitnesses of the various genotypes on the basis of electrophoretic tests of haemoglobin specimens in 1042 adult Africans from the Gold Coast. The reduced viability of sickle-cell and haemoglobin C homozygotes and the sickle-cell : haemoglobin C heterozygote is reflected in the relatively low frequency of persons with these genotypes in the adult population. Equating viability between birth and reproductive age with fitness, the following estimates of fitness were obtained (symbols of Allison, 1955):

$$Hb^A/Hb^S = 1.138 \qquad Hb^C/Hb^C = 0.550$$
$$Hb^A/Hb^C = 1.103 \qquad Hb^S/Hb^C = 0.407$$
$$Hb^A/Hb^A = 0.976 \qquad Hb^S/Hb^S = 0.192$$

All homozygotes are at a disadvantage, the normal less than the abnormal; the Hb^S/Hb^C heterozygote is also at a disadvantage, but the other heterozygotes are favoured.

The conditions required for genetic equilibrium of three allelomorphs have been analysed by Owen (1953) and by Penrose, Smith and Sprott (1956). The latter have shown that with the fitness values quoted above the equilibrium is stable but only by quite a small margin. It is uncertain whether Hb^S and Hb^C would, in fact, return to the same proportion if there were a chance variation. By slightly altering the fitness values, a semi-stable equilibrium is obtained, in which, if the frequencies are disturbed from the equilibrium values within a definable subspace, they will remain at their new values. If they are moved outside the subspace, they will be restored by selection to some point within the subspace, not necessarily the original point.

In this instance the equations determining the subspace lead to a single equation $162a_2 + 127a_3 = 24$, where a_2 is the frequency of Hb^S and a_3 is the frequency of Hb^C. It is therefore interesting to see whether the values of Hb^S and Hb^C observed in different West African populations fit this equation. The data so far published are given in Table 1.

TABLE 1

Population	Number tested	Hb^s	Hb^c	$162a_2 + 127a_3$	Observer
Dagomba, N. Gold Coast	71	0.021	0.134	20.42	1
Moshie, N. Gold Coast	115	0.022	0.105	16.95	1
Dagarti, N. Gold Coast	97	0.047	0.072	16.76	1
Miscellaneous, N. Gold Coast	275	0.069	0.078	21.09	2
Zabrama, Togoland	63	0.103	0.048	22.79	2
Ashanti, Gold Coast	102	0.108	0.044	23.09	2
Ga, S. Gold Coast	174	0.098	0.043	21.34	2
Fanti, S. Gold Coast	156	0.103	0.052	23.29	2
Ewe, S. Gold Coast	167	0.112	0.045	23.85	2
Twi, S. Gold Coast	104	0.101	0.048	22.46	2
Miscellaneous, S. Gold Coast	283	0.096	0.049	21.74	1
Miscellaneous, Nigeria	247	0.109	0.027	21.18	2
Miscellaneous, Sierra Leone	218	0.140	0.023	25.60	2
Miscellaneous, Gambia	1442	0.070	0.009	12.48	2

Observers: (1) Edington and Lehmann (1956); (2) Allison (1956b).

In view of the relatively small number of individuals on which the gene frequency and fitness estimates are based, the values of $162a_2 + 127a_3$ are in fair agreement with expectation in all populations except the Gambians. Most of the observed values are somewhat below 24, which suggests that the estimates of fitness may not be quite correct. The Gambia seems to be a marginal region with a very heterogeneous population in which the frequencies of the abnormal haemoglobin genes may not yet have been stabilized by selection (Allison, 1956b). On the whole, these results suggest that the other West African populations tested have lived long enough in relatively uniform environments to show frequencies of the abnormal haemoglobin genes close to those predicted for a semi-stable equilibrium from the estimated fitnesses of the several genotypes.

With such a system, there is only a small probability that the haemoglobin C gene could have attained the high frequencies now observed if it had arisen by mutation in a population already having a high frequency of the sickle-cell gene. The most likely inference is that the haemoglobin C gene has been favoured in some population in or near the Northern Gold Coast having a low frequency of the sickle-cell gene. The haemoglobin C gene diffused out of this area into populations with higher frequencies of the sickle-cell gene, and through selection the frequencies of the two abnormal genes have been brought to various points close to the subspace for a semi-stable equilibrium as defined above.

The population genetics of haemoglobin E and thalassaemia in South-East Asia and the Mediterranean countries have not been worked out, but it seems likely that the situation will turn out to be quite similar to that obtaining in the case of the sickle-cell and haemoglobin C genes in Africa.

REFERENCES

A. C. Allison, *Science* 122, 640 (1955).

———, *Cold Spring Harbor Symp. Quant. Biol.* 20, 239 (1956a).

———, *Ann. Hum. Genet.* 21, 71 (1956b).

G. W. G. Bird and H. Lehmann, *Man* 56, 1 (1956).

G. M. Edington and H. Lehmann, *Man* 56, 34 (1956).

J. W. Field, trans. *R. Soc. Trop. Med. Hyg.* 43, 33 (1949).

A. R. G. Owen, *Heredity* 7, 151 (1953).

L. S. Penrose, S. M. Smith, D. A. Sprott, *Ann. Hum. Genet.* 21, 90 (1956).

A. B. Raper, *Brit. Med. J.* 1, 965 (1956).

W. W. Zuelzer, J. V. Neel, A. R. Robinson, *Progr. Haemat.* 1, 91 (1956).

DISCUSSION

J. V. Neel (Ann Arbor, Michigan): Dr. Lehmann and Dr. Allison have presented in a beautifully clear fashion certain aspects of the problems associated with the abnormal hemoglobins. It is a comment on the swift progress of the field of human genetics that until 8 years ago we did not even recognize the existence of abnormal hemoglobins.

First of all I should like to endorse Dr. Lehmann's plea for an elastic terminology. My collaborators and I have evidence that gene responsible for hemoglobin C_1 is not an allele of the gene responsible for hemoglobin S. The Thalassæmia locus seems separate from both of these, while there are theoretical reasons for postulating that the production of hemoglobin F depends upon activity at still another locus. This is going to be a situation of some genetic complexity, where the need for an adjustable and descriptive terminology is great.

Secondly I would mention the recent finding of my collaborators and myself that hemoglobin J otherwise known on the basis of a single family, occurs in approximately 1% of Liberians. It is tempting to speculate from the known distributions of hemoglobins J, C and S that here are three successive stages in the process whereby a "new" human gene becomes established and disseminated.

Finally, with respect to the "malaria hypothesis," as I pointed out last year in the Galton lecture, the hypothesis demands a higher death rate from malaria than many malariologists would accept. If the malaria hypothesis becomes firmly established, and results in a reappraisal of malaria deaths, here is a new example of the uses of the genetic approach. I would hope that in accepting the malaria hypothesis we not abandon the search for other factors of importance in maintaining this polymorphism, since here we have a situation which will be widely quoted, and the need to be critical is great.

Skin-Pigment Regulation of Vitamin-D Biosynthesis in Man

VARIATION IN SOLAR
ULTRAVIOLET AT DIFFERENT
LATITUDES MAY HAVE CAUSED
RACIAL DIFFERENTIATION IN MAN

W. Farnsworth Loomis*

Department of Biochemistry,
Brandeis University

Vitamin D mediates the absorption of calcium from the intestine and the deposition of inorganic minerals in growing bone; this "sunshine vitamin" is produced in the skin, where solar rays from the far-ultraviolet region of the spectrum (wavelength, 290 to 320 millimicrons) convert the provitamin 7-dehydrocholesterol into natural vitamin D (1) (Fig. 1).

Unlike other vitamins, this essential calcification factor is not present in significant amounts in the normal diet; it occurs in the liver oils of bony fishes and, in very small amounts, in a few foodstuffs in the summer (see Table 1). Almost none is present in foodstuffs in winter.

Chemical elucidation of the nature of vitamin D has made it possible to eradicate rickets from the modern world through artificial fortification of milk and other foods with this essential factor. Before this century, however, mankind resembled the living plant in being dependent on sunshine for his health and well-being, a regulated amount of vitamin D synthesis being essential if he were to avoid the twin dangers of rickets on the one hand and an excess of vitamin D on the other.

Unlike the water-soluble vitamins, too

Reprinted from *Science* 157, 501–506 (August 4, 1967), by permission of the author and *Science*. Copyright 1967 by the American Association for the Advancement of Science.

490

much vitamin D causes disease just as too little does, for the calcification process must be regulated and controlled much as metabolism is regulated by the thyroid hormone. The term *vitamin D* is, in fact, almost a misnomer, for this factor resembles the hormones more closely than it resembles the dietary vitamins in that it is not normally ingested but is synthesized in the body by one organ — the skin — and then distributed by the blood stream for action elsewhere in the body. As in the case of hormones, moreover, the rate of synthesis of vitamin D must be regulated within definite limits if both failure of calcification and pathological calcifications are to be avoided.

Synthesis of too little vitamin D results in the bowlegs, knock-knees, and twisted spines (scoliosis) associated with rickets in infants whose bones are growing rapidly. Similar defects in ossification appear in older children and women deprived of this vitamin; puberty, pregnancy, and lactation predispose the individual toward osteomalacia, which is essentially adult rickets. In osteomalacia the bones become soft and pliable, a condition which often leads to pelvic deformities that create serious hazards during childbirth. Such deformities were common, for example, among the women of India who followed the custom of purdah, which demands that they live secluded within doors and away from the calcifying power of the sun's rays (2). Cod-liver oil or other source of vitamin D is a specific for rickets and osteomalacia, the usual recommended daily dosage being 10 micrograms or 400 international units (1 I.U. = 0.025 microgram of vitamin D).

Ingestion of vitamin D in amounts above about 100,000 I.U. (2.5 milligrams) per day produces the condition known as hypervitaminosis D, in which the blood levels of both calcium and phosphorus are markedly elevated and multiple calcifications of the soft tissues of the body appear. Ultimate death usually follows renal disease secondary to the appearance of kidney stones (3). Although this condition has been described only in patients given overdoses of vitamin D by mouth, similarly toxic results would probably follow the natural synthesis of equal doses of vitamin D by unpigmented skin exposed to excessive solar radiation. The body appears to have no power to regulate the amount of vitamin D absorbed from food and no power to selectively destroy toxic doses once they have been absorbed. These facts suggest that the physiological means of regulating the concentration of vitamin D in the body is through control of the rate of photochemical synthesis of vitamin D in the skin.

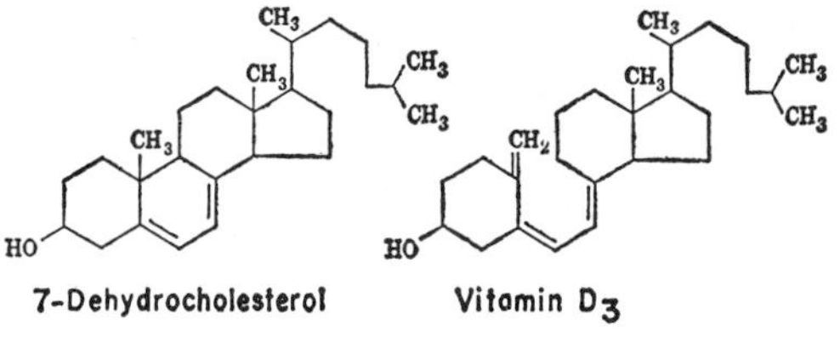

FIGURE 1. Chemical structures of 7-dehydrocholesterol and vitamin D_3.

7-Dehydrocholesterol   Vitamin D_3

TABLE 1

Vitamin-D Content of Two Fish-liver Oils and of the Only Foodstuffs Known to Contain Vitamin D. [From K. H. Coward, *The Biological Standardization of the Vitamins* (Wood, Baltimore, 1938), p. 223.]

Fish-liver oil or foodstuff	Vitamin-D content (I.U./gram)
Halibut-liver oil	2000–4000
Cod-liver oil	60–300
Milk	0.1
Butter	0.0–4.0
Cream	0.5
Egg yolk	1.5–5.0
Calf liver	0.0
Olive oil	0.0

It is the thesis of this article that the rate of vitamin-D synthesis in the stratum granulosum of the skin is regulated by the twin processes of pigmentation and keratinization of the overlying stratum corneum, which allow only regulated amounts of solar ultraviolet radiation to penetrate the outer layer of skin and reach the region where vitamin D is synthesized. According to this view, different types of skin — white (depigmented and dekeratinized), yellow (mainly keratinized), and black (mainly pigmented) — are adaptations of the stratum corneum which maximize ultraviolet penetration in northern latitudes and minimize it in southern latitudes, so that the rate of vitamin-D synthesis is maintained within physiological limits (0.01 to 2.5 milligrams of vitamin D per day) throughout man's worldwide habitat.

Figure 2 provides evidence in support of this view, for it is apparent that there is a marked correlation between skin pigmentation and equatorial latitudes. In addition, the reversible summer pigmentation and keratinization activated by ultraviolet radiation and known as suntan represents a means of maintaining physiologically, constant rates of vitamin-D synthesis despite the great seasonal variation in solar ultraviolet radiation in the northern latitudes.

ULTRAVIOLET TRANSMISSION
AND VITAMIN-D SYNTHESIS

In 1958 Beckemeier (4) reported that 1 square centimeter of white human skin synthesized up to 18 I.U. of vitamin D in 3 hours. Using this figure, we calculate that an antirachitic preventive dose of 400 I.U. per day can be synthesized by daily exposure of an area of skin approximately equal to that of the nearly transparent pink cheeks of European infants (about 20 square centimeters). Perhaps this explains

FIGURE 2. Distribution of human skin color before 1492. [Adapted from Brace and Montague, *Man's Evolution* (Macmillan, New York, 1965), p. 272.]

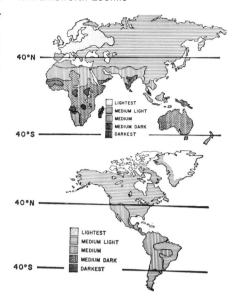

why mothers in northern climates customarily put their infants out-of-doors for "some fresh air and sunshine" even in the middle of winter.

From this high rate of synthesis by only a small area of thin unpigmented skin, one can calculate the daily amount of vitamin D that would be synthesized at the equator by the skin of adults who exposed almost all their 1½ square meters (22,500 square centimeters) of body surface during the whole of a tropical day. Such a calculation shows that the skin of such individuals would synthesize up to 800,000 I.U. of vitamin D in a 6-hour period if the stratum corneum contained no pigment capable of filtering out the intense solar ultraviolet radiation.

Direct evidence that pigmented skin is an effective ultraviolet filter was provided by Macht, Anderson, and Bell (5), who used a spectrographic method to show that excised specimens of whole skin from Negroes prevented the transmission of ultraviolet radiation of wavelengths below 436 millimicrons, while excised specimens of white skin allowed radiation from both the 405- and the 365-millimicron bands of the mercury spectrum to pass through.

These early studies with whole skin were refined by Thomson (6), who used isolated stratum corneum obtained by blistering the skin with cantharides. He found that the average percentage of solar radiation of 300- to 400-millimicron wavelength transmitted by the stratum corneum of 22 Europeans was 64 percent, while the average for 29 Africans was only 18 percent. There was no overlapping of values for the two groups (Fig. 3), but there was considerable variation within each group, the values for the Europeans varying from 53 to as high as 72

FIGURE 3. Variation of transmission of solar ultraviolet light (3000 to 4000 angstroms) through the stratum corneum, plotted against thickness of this layer. ⊙, Europeans; ×, Africans. The numbers in parentheses after initials are percentages for reflectance of blue light on the forearm. [From M. L. Thomson (6).]

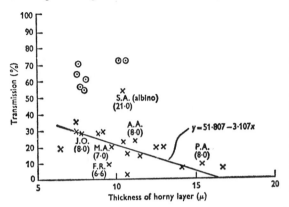

percent and those for the Africans (who were mainly Ibos but also included men from most of the Nigerian tribes) varying from 36 to as low as 3 percent.

In his careful studies, Thomson measured skin thickness as well as pigmentation and found that the former was a minor variable. Studies on the degree of blackness of the various African specimens were made by skin-reflectance measurements. These showed that the darker the skin is, the lower is the percentage of ultraviolet radiation transmitted. One specimen from an albino African showed transmission of 53 percent — a value within the range for the European group. Thomson concluded from these studies that skin pigmentation was mainly responsible for protecting the African from excessive solar ultraviolet radiation, the thickness of the horny layer in Africans playing only a minor role. Thomson did not mention the fact that skin pigmentation and thickening of the horny layer in Africans would protect against excessive vitamin-D synthesis as well as sunburn.

Thomson's results indicate that African stratum corneum filters out solar ultraviolet radiation equivalent to between 50 and 95 percent of that which reaches the vitamin-D-synthesizing region of the skin of Europeans. This explains "the fact, agreed to by all, that of all races the Negro is most susceptible to rickets" (7). It is clear from Thomson's figures that exposure of the face of Negro infants to winter sunlight in Scandinavia would result in synthesis of too little vitamin D to meet the infant's body requirements.

It was Hess who first proved that sunlight could cure rickets (8). Seeking experimental proof of a relationship between skin pigmentation and rickets, he took six white and six black rats and placed them on a rachitogenic diet containing low amounts of phosphorus. Exposing both groups to a critical amount of ultraviolet light, he found that all the white rats remained healthy while all the black rats developed rickets. He concluded (9), "It is manifest that the protective rays were rendered inert by the integumentary pigment."

To return now to Thomson's results and consider their bearing on hypervitaminosis, they explain why deeply pigmented Africans living near the equator and exposing almost all their body surface to the ultraviolet of the tropical sun do not suffer from kidney stones and other evidences of hypervitaminosis. Under conditions where untanned Europeans would synthesize up to 800,000 I.U. per day, deeply pigmented Africans would synthesize 5 to 10 percent as much; thus their daily production would fall within the acceptable range.

In this connection it is significant that Reinertson and Wheatley (*10*) found that the 7-dehydrocholesterol content of human skin does not vary significantly between Negroes and Whites. Skin from the back, abdomen, and thigh of adults of both races averaged 3.8 percent (standard deviation, 0.8 percent), the lowest result in their series being obtained in a specimen of the epidermis of the sole, an area that receives no radiation at all, while the highest result among adults was from a Negro. The highest content of all was found in a specimen from a 2-week-old infant that showed 8.8 percent of the provitamin, a fact that correlates well with the especially high need for vitamin D during the first 2 years of life.

In their paper and ensuing discussion, the above workers emphasize that 7-dehydrocholesterol is found almost entirely beneath the stratum corneum, thus establishing the fact that in man it is not present in the secretions of the sebaceous glands as it is in birds and some northern fur-covered animals which, respectively, obtain their vitamin D by preening or by licking their fur after the provitamin has been converted into the vitamin on the surface of the body. It would appear that vitamin D is made in man solely by the irradiation of the provitamin in the layers underneath the stratum corneum, a mechanism that would allow efficient regulation of the biosynthesis of this essential factor by varying the degree of ultraviolet penetration through differing amounts of pigmentation in the overlying stratum corneum.

ORIGIN OF WHITE SKIN

Having originated in the tropics where too much sunlight rather than too little was the danger, the first hominids had no difficulty in obtaining sufficient amounts of vitamin D until they extended their range north of the Mediterranean Sea and latitude 40°N (Fig. 2), where the winter sun is less than 20 degrees above the horizon (*11*) and most of the needed ultraviolet is removed from the sun's rays by the powerful filtering action of the atmosphere through which the slanting rays have to pass. Before the present century, for example, there was a very high incidence of rickets among infants in London and Glasgow, because in these latitudes the midday sun is less than 35 degrees from the horizon for 5 and 6 months, respectively, of the year; in Jamaica and other southern localities, on the other hand, the sun's midday altitude is never less than 50 degrees and rickets is almost unknown (*2*). The farther north one goes, the more severe becomes this effect of latitude on the availability of winter ultraviolet radiation, an effect compounded by cloudy winter skies.

Having evolved in the tropics, early hominids were probably deeply pigmented and covered with fur, as are most other tropical primates. The first adaptation one might expect therefore to lowered availability of ultraviolet light as they moved north of the Mediterranean would be a reduction of fur, for Cruikshank and Kodicek have shown (12) that shaved rats synthesize four times more vitamin D than normal rats do.

As early hominids moved farther and farther north, their more deeply pigmented infants must have been especially likely to develop the grossly bent legs and twisted spines characteristic of rickets, deformities which would cripple their ability to hunt game when they were adults. In this connection, Carleton Coon has written (13), "Up to the present century, if black skinned people were incorporated into any population living either north or south of the fortieth degree of latitude, their descendants would eventually have been selected for skin color on the basis of this vitamin factor alone." Howells agrees (14): "This variety of outer color has all the earmarks of an adaptation, of a trait responding to the force of sunlight by natural selection." The skin, he continues "admits limited amounts of ultraviolet, which is needed to form vitamin D, but presumably diminishes or diffuses dangerous doses by a screen of pigment granules."

Even in 1934 Murray clearly recognized the implications of these facts (15): "As primordial man proceeded northwards into less sunlit regions, a disease, rickets, accomplished the extinction of the darker, more pigmented elements of the population as parents and preserved the whiter, less pigmented to reproduce their kind and by progressive selection through prehistoric times, developed and established the white race in far northern Europe as it appears in historic times; its most extreme blond types inhabiting the interior of the northern-most Scandinavian peninsula."

FIGURE 4. Distribution of early stone tools throughout the tropics of the Old World and in Europe as far north as 50°N. [From Brace and Montague, *Man's Evolution* (Macmillan, New York, 1965), p. 231.]

It is a curious fact that Murray's thesis is almost unknown to the general public, including physiologists, biochemists, and physicians, and that it is not generally accepted by anthropologists, with the exception of Coon and Howells, quoted above, even though it fits the facts of Figure 2. Both in Europe and China, skin pigmentation becomes lighter as one goes north, and it is lighter in young children; in almost all races the skin is lighter in the newborn infant (16) and gradually darkens as the individual matures, a change that parallels the declining need for vitamin D.

WHEN DID EUROPEAN HOMINIDS BEGIN TO TURN WHITE?

On the basis of the conclusion that white skin is an adaptation to northern latitudes because of the lowered availability of winter ultraviolet radiation, it appears probable that the early hominids inhabiting western Europe had lost much of their body hair and skin pigmentation even half a million years ago. Anthropological evidence indicates that early hominids such as the Heidelberg, Swanscomb, Steinheim, Fontechevade, and Neanderthal men lived north of the Mediterranean Sea — particularly during warm interglacial periods (17). It is important to recognize that the effect of latitude on the availability of ultraviolet light in winter is not related to climate but operates steadily and at all times, through glacial and interglacial periods alike.

Hand axes and other early stone tools have been found throughout the tropics of the Old World and also in Europe as far north as the 50th degree of latitude (Fig. 4). The presence of such stone tools as far north as England and France shows that some early hominids must already have adapted to the lowered level of ultraviolet radiation and consequent danger of rickets by partial loss of body hair and skin pigmentation, for without such adaptation they would have probably been unable to survive this far north.

England is at the same latitude as the Aleutian Islands, and no stone tools such as those found in southern England and France have ever been found in other areas at this latitude — for example, Mongolia and Manchuria. The unique combination of temperate climate and low levels of winter ultraviolet radiation in England and France is due to the powerful warming effect of the Gulf Stream on this particular northern area, which is unique in the world in this respect, for the Japan current in the Pacific is not as powerful as the Gulf Stream and warms only the Aleutian Islands, where no hominids existed until very recently.

Occupation of northern Europe and even Scandinavia up to the Arctic Circle seems to have taken place during the Upper Paleolithic, when presumably partially depigmented men already adapted to latitude 50°N lost nearly all their ability to synthesize melanin and so produced the blond-haired, blue-eyed, fair-skinned peoples who inhabit the interior of the northernmost part of the Scandinavian peninsula.

It has been held that the abundant appearance of stone scrapers in the Upper Paleolithic indicates that this far-northern extension of man's habitat followed his use of animal skins for clothing, a change that would select powerfully for infants with nearly transparent skin on their cheeks, who were thus still able to synthesize a minimum antirachitic dose of vitamin D even when fully clothed during the Scandinavian winter. Certainly the pink-to-red cheeks of northern European children are uniquely transparent; their color is due to the high visibility of the blood that circulates in the sub-epidermal region.

The one exception to the correlation between latitude and skin color in the Old World is the Eskimo; his skin is medium dark and yet he remains completely free of rickets (18) during the long dark arctic winters. Murray noted long ago that the Eskimo's diet of fish oil and meat contains several times the minimum preventive dose of vitamin D, concluding (15), "Because of his diet of antirachitic fats, it has been unnecessary for the Eskimo to evolve a white skin in the sunless frigid zone. He has not needed to have his skin bleached by centuries of evolution to admit more antirachitic sunlight. He probably has the same pigmented skin with which he arrived in the far north ages ago." Similar considerations would apply in the case of any coastal peoples of Europe and Asia, who would have been able to expand northward without depigmentation as long as they obtained sufficient vitamin D from a diet of fish; only when they ventured into the interior would antirachitic selection for blond types, as in Scandinavia, presumably have taken place.

YELLOW, BROWN, AND BLACK ADAPTATION

Human skin has two adaptive mechanisms for resisting the penetration of solar ultraviolet: melanin-granule production in the Malpighian layer and keratohyaline-granule production in the stratum granulosum. Melanin granules are black, whereas the keratohyaline granules produce keratin (from which nails, claws, horns, and hoofs are formed), which has a yellowish tinge. Particles of both types migrate toward the horny external layer, where they impart a black (melanin), yellow (keratin), or brown (melanin and keratin) tinge to the skin.

Thomson has shown (6) that, in Negroes, melanization of the stratum corneum plays the major role in filtering out excessive ultraviolet radiation, keratinization of the horny layer playing only a minor part. Mongoloids on the other hand have yellowish skin, since their stratum corneum is packed with disks of keratin (13) that allow them to live within 20 degrees of the equator even though their skin contains only small amounts of melanin (Fig. 2). On the equator itself, however, even Mongoloid-derived peoples acquire pigmentation — for example, the previously medium-light-skinned Mongoloids who entered the Americas over the Bering Straits at latitude 66°N as recently as 20,000 to 10,000 years ago (Fig. 2).

Even white-skinned peoples have to protect themselves against excessive doses of solar ultraviolet radiation in summer, for, as Blum has pointed out (19), on 21 June the solar ultraviolet is as intense in Newfoundland as it is at the equator, since at that time the two regions are at the same distance from the Tropic of Cancer (at 23°27'N). (At the equator, the solar ultraviolet is never less than on this date, while in Newfoundland it is never more.) In other words, adaptation to the variable intensities of solar ultraviolet in the north requires not only winter depigmentation but also the evolution of a reversible mechanism of summer repigmentation to keep the rate of vitamin-D synthesis constant throughout the year. It is significant that both the keratinization and melanization components of suntan are initiated by the same wavelengths which synthesize vitamin D, for it would be difficult to design a more perfect defense against excessive doses of vitamin D than this reversible response to ultraviolet light of these particular wavelengths — a pigmentation response that is further protected by the painful alarm bell of sunburn, which guarantees extreme caution against overexposure to solar ultraviolet in untanned individuals suddenly encountering a tropical sun.

Defenses against production of too much vitamin D therefore range from (i) reversible suntanning, as in Europeans, through (ii) constitutive keratinization, as in the Mongoloids of Asia and the Americas, to (iii) constitutive melanization, as in African and other truly equatorial peoples. The physiological superiority of melanization as a means of protection against ultraviolet was demonstrated by the ability, historically documented, of imported Nigerian slaves to outwork the recently adapted American Indians in the sun-drenched cane fields· and plantations of the Caribbean and related tropical areas.

Additional evidence for the view that melanization of the stratum corneum is primarily a defense against the over-synthesis of vitamin D from solar ultraviolet is provided by the fact that the palms and soles of Negroes are as white as those of Europeans; *only* the palms and soles possess a thickly keratinized stratum lucidum (Fig. 5) under the external stratum corneum, which renders melanization of the latter unnecessary. The same reasoning explains the failure of the palms and soles of whites to sunburn during the summer.

Coon has written (13), "We cannot yet demonstrate why natural selection favors the prevalence of very dark skins among otherwise unrelated populations living in the wet tropics, but the answer may not be far away." Since overdoses of vitamin D administered orally are known to result in prompt and serious consequences, such as calcifications in the aorta and other soft tissues of the body, kidney stones, secondary renal disease, and death, it would appear that oversynthesis of vitamin D is sufficiently detrimental in young and old to favor the gradual selection for deeply pigmented skin near the equator, as seen, for example, in the repigmentation that has taken place among the equatorial American Indians during the last 10,000 years (Fig. 2).

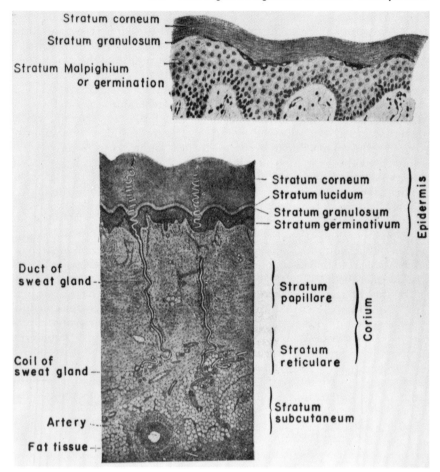

FIGURE 5. Vertical section from (top) the shoulder and (bottom) the sole of the foot of a Caucasian adult. [From J. L. Bremer, *A Textbook of Histology* (Blakiston, Philadelphia, 1936).]

SECONDARY RESULTS OF
PIGMENTATION AND DEPIGMENTATION

It is known that black skin absorbs more heat than white skin; the studies of Weiner and his associates (20) show that black Yoruba skin reflects only 24 percent of incident light whereas untanned European skin reflects as much as 64 percent. Of themselves, these facts would lead one to expect that reflective white skin would be found near the equator while heat-absorbing black skin would be found in cold northern climate.

Since the exact opposite is true around the world, it seems clear that man has adapted his epidermis in response to varying levels of ultraviolet radiation despite the price he has had to pay in being badly adapted from the standpoint of heat absorbance and reflectance of visible and near-infrared wavelengths. Similar considerations naturally apply to summer pigmentation due to suntan; ultraviolet regulation rather than heat regulation explains why Caucasians are white in the winter but pigmented in the summer.

In addition to being badly adapted for maximum heat absorbance, white-skinned northern peoples are known to be particularly susceptible to skin cancer (21) and such skin diseases as psoriasis and acne. Therefore, only some powerful other advantage, such as relative freedom from rickets, would explain the worldwide correlation between high latitudes and white skin, for without some such factor it would seem that black or yellow skin would be the superior integument.

From this and other evidence, such as the fact that lion cubs and the young of other tropical animals develop rickets in northern zoos unless given cod-liver oil (2), it appears probable that depigmentation occurred north of latitude 40°N (a line marked by the Mediterranean Sea, the Great Wall of China, and the Mason-Dixon line) as an adaptation that allowed an increased penetration of winter ultraviolet radiation and consequent freedom from rickets. Certainly no other essential function of solar ultraviolet is known for man besides the synthesis of vitamin D.

SUMMARY

The known correlation between the color of human skin and latitude (Fig. 2) is explainable in terms of two opposing positive adaptations to solar ultraviolet radiation, weak in northern latitudes in winter yet powerful the year around near the equator. In northern latitudes there is selection for white skins that allow maximum photoactivation of 7-dehydrocholesterol into vitamin D at low intensities of ultraviolet radiation. In southern latitudes, on the other hand, there is selection for black skins able to prevent up to 95 percent of the incident ultraviolet from reaching the deeper layers of the skin where vitamin D is synthesized. Selection against the twin dangers of rickets on the one hand and toxic doses of vitamin D on the other would thus explain the worldwide correlation observed between skin pigmentation and nearness to the equator.

Since intermediate degrees of pigmentation occur at intermediate latitudes, as well as seasonal fluctuation in pigmentation (through reversible suntanning), it appears that different skin colors in man are adaptations of the stratum corneum which regulate the transmission of solar ultraviolet to the underlying stratum granulosum, so that vitamin-D photosynthesis is maintained within physiological limits throughout the year at all latitudes.

REFERENCES AND NOTES

* The author is Rosenfield Professor of Biochemistry in the Graduate Department of Biochemistry, Brandeis University, Waltham, Massachusetts.

1. A. White, P. Handler, S. L. Smith, *Principles of Biochemistry* (McGraw-Hill, New York, 3 ed., 1964), p. 981.

2. C. H. Best and N. B. Taylor, *The Physiological Basis of Medical Practice* (Williams and Wilkins, Baltimore, 3 ed., 1943), pp. 1102, 1105.

3. F. Bicknell and F. Prescott, *The Vitamins in Medicine* (Grune and Stratton, New York, 3 ed., 1953), p. 578.

4. H. Beckemeier, *Acta Biol. Med. Ger.* 1, 756 (1958); _____ and G. Pfennigsdorf, *J. Physiol. Chem.* 214, 120 (1959).

5. D. I. Macht, W. T. Anderson, F. K. Bell, *J. Amer. Med. Assoc.* 90, 161 (1928); W. T. Anderson and D. I. Macht, *Amer. J. Physiol.* 86, 320 (1928).

6. M. L. Thomson, *J. Physiol. London* 127, 236 (1955).

7. A. F. Hess and L. J. Unger, *J. Amer. Med. Assoc.* 69, 1583 (1917).

8. _____, *ibid.* 78, 1177 (1922).

9. A. F. Hess, *ibid.*, p. 1177.

10. R. P. Reinertson and V. R. Wheatley, *J. Invest. Dermatol.* 32, 49 (1959).

11. F. Daniels, Jr., in *Handbook of Physiology*, D. B. Dill, E. F. Adolph, C. G. Wilber, Eds. (American Physiological Society, Washington, D.C., 1964), pp. 969–88.

12. E. M. Cruikshank and E. Kodicek, *Proc. Nutr. Soc. Engl. Scot.* 14, viii (1955).

13. C. Coon, *The Living Races of Man* (Knopf, New York, 1965), pp. 232, 234.

14. W. W. Howells, *Mankind in the Making* (Doubleday, New York, 1959), p. 270.

15. F. G. Murray, *Amer. Anthropol.* 36, 438 (1934).

16. E. A. Hooton, *Up from the Ape* (Macmillan, New York, 1946), p. 466.

17. It is possible that the most northern or "classic" Neanderthal died out some 35,000 years ago in western Europe because of rickets which became severe when the arctic weather of the last glaciation made it necessary for him to dress his infants warmly in animal skins during the winter months, a change that would drastically reduce the area of their skin exposed to solar ultraviolet.

18. W. A. Thomas, *J. Amer. Med. Assoc.* 88, 1559 (1927).

19. H. F. Blum, *Quart. Rev. Biol.* 36, 50 (1961).

20. J. S. Weiner, G. A. Harrison, R. Singer, R. Harris, W. Jopp, *Human Biol.* 36, 294 (1964).

21. H. F. Blum, in *Radiation Biology*, A. Hollaender, Ed. (McGraw-Hill, New York, 1955), II, 487, 509, 529.

22. The work discussed here was partially supported by grant E-443 of the American Cancer Society to Brandeis University, Waltham, Massachusetts. This article is Graduate Department of Biochemistry Publication No. 505.

A Simple Model of "Drift" in Small Populations

Paul A. Moody

University of Vermont

Dubinin and Romaschoff (1932) described a model to illustrate scattering of variability. It consisted (Dobzhansky, 1941: 162–63) of a bowl containing 100 numbered marbles. In each "generation" 25 marbles were withdrawn at random and discarded; in addition, 25 marbles were withdrawn and each was replaced by two marbles bearing the same number as the one withdrawn. In this way the number of marbles remained constant but there was a progressive decline in variability. In from 108 to 465 generations "homozygosis" of the population was attained, i.e., all the marbles bore the same number.

The model described below has the advantage that it simulates actual conditions in bisexual reproduction more closely than does the one mentioned above, and that it avoids the artificial regularity introduced by doubling the frequency of 25 percent of the alleles in each generation. While this doubling can be demonstrated to occur *on the average*, it can scarcely be presumed to occur without exception in every generation when the population is small.

The equipment for the model consists of wooden beads of two colors. The only requirement is that the beads be of uniform size and that the beads of the two colors not be distinguishable by the sense of touch. I use red beads to represent "A" genes, blue beads to represent "a" genes.* Beads are tied together in pairs to represent zygotes: two red beads

Reprinted from *Evolution* 1, 217–18 (1947), by permission of the author and publisher.

to represent the zygote AA, one red bead and one blue bead to represent the zygote Aa, two blue beads to represent the zygote aa. The number of "zygotes" so prepared depends upon the size of the population to be established; there must be a sufficient reserve supply of each "zygote" so that the entire population can, if necessary, be composed of but one genotype (all AA, or all Aa, or all aa). A bowl containing single red and blue beads in equal numbers completes the equipment.

The initial "population" can be of any constitution desired. I began with a small population conforming to Hardy's ratio (Dobzhansky, 1941: 156 ff.): three pairs of red beads, six pairs consisting of one red and one blue bead, three pairs of blue beads. The genotypic constitution represented was, accordingly, 3AA : 6Aa : 3aa. These pairs of beads were placed together in a small box, thoroughly mixed, and then withdrawn at random, two pairs at a time. In this way "matings" were arranged by chance. A record of the pairings was made. The matings actually obtained in a first trial of this process were as follows: Aa × aa; AA × Aa; AA × aa; AA × Aa; Aa × Aa; Aa × aa.

With the matings arranged by chance, the next step consists of determining the offspring from each mating, also by chance. I chose to assume that the population was stationary in size — that each pair of parents merely replaced itself, producing two offspring which survived to reproduce. Obviously, other assumptions can be applied in the use of the model. If both parents are homozygous the two offspring must both be of one genotype, thus they can be recorded immediately. The bowl containing single red and blue beads in equal numbers is used to determine the genotypes of offspring if either parent is heterozygous. If the parents are Aa × Aa, two beads are withdrawn simultaneously and at random; obviously both beads may be red (AA), one may be red, one blue (Aa), or both may be blue (aa). The beads are immediately replaced in the bowl and the contents of the latter are mixed before the next drawing. The drawing is made twice for each mating, to produce the two "offspring." If the genotypes of the parents are AA × Aa, only one bead is withdrawn at random, since the only variable is the contribution of the Aa parent, the "gamete" from the AA parent being of necessity A. This drawing is made twice for each mating. A comparable situation prevails when the parents are Aa × aa. In the first trial, the offspring actually obtained from the matings listed at the end of the preceding paragraph were assorted as follows: 1AA, 10Aa, 1aa.

The offspring so obtained form the parents of the next generation; pairs of beads to represent them are placed in the small box mentioned above. In the case of the first trial mentioned, one pair of red beads, ten pairs consisting of one red bead and one blue bead, and one pair of blue beads were placed in the box, mixed thoroughly, and then withdrawn two pairs at a time as before. The matings having been arranged by chance in this manner, the offspring from the matings were determined by chance, using the bowl containing red and blue beads in equal numbers, as described in the preceding paragraph. In the trial mentioned, the offspring in this generation proved to consist of 1AA, 6Aa, 5aa. These formed the parents of the succeeding generation. Pairs of beads representing them were placed in the small box, withdrawn two at a time as before, the offspring from these matings were determined, and so on, generation after generation.

In the series referred to, "drift" accomplished fixation of one genotype in the 134th generation. The offspring produced in that generation were all of the genotype AA, the gene "a" having been irrevocably lost from the population. Twice before, at the 46th and the 67th generations, only one of the 24 genes in the offspring was "a" (11AA, 1Aa, 0aa). But each time there was a "rally" on the part of the "a" genes and their number increased in subsequent generations. Thus the model gives evidence of the tenacity with which the laws of chance *tend* toward maintenance of the equilibrium expressed by Hardy's ratio, even when populations are very small. This tendency may be overcome with relative rapidity at any time, however. For example, at the end of the 115th generation the population consisted of 2AA, 7Aa, 3aa, a slightly less auspicious composition for the fixation of "A" than the parents of the first generation had afforded. Yet 19 generations later the gene "a" was completely eliminated.

Table 1 summarizes the genotypic structure of these final twenty

TABLE 1

Genotypic Structure of the Final Twenty Generations of a Sample Series Which Culminated in the Loss of One Allele from the Population.

Generation No.	Distribution of genotypes		
	AA	Aa	aa
115	2	7	3
116	5	4	3
117	5	3	4
118	4	6	2
119	5	5	2
120	4	7	1
121	4	7	1
122	3	8	1
123	3	9	0
124	6	5	1
125	7	5	0
126	9	2	1
127	8	4	0
128	9	2	1
129	9	3	0
130	9	3	0
131	10	2	0
132	10	2	0
133	11	1	0
134	12	0	0

generations and gives graphic illustration of the manner in which "drift," once inaugurated, can continue to fixation of one gene.

The simple model described above simulates reduction of variability in small populations through operation of the laws of chance (1) upon matings and (2) upon subsequent production of zygotes. It mimics an actual bisexual population closely enough so that relatively inexperienced students appreciate its applicability with ease. It affords visual evidence that chance acting in small populations can effect the changes predicted by theory.

REFERENCES AND NOTES

* Beads obtained from Ward's Natural Science Establishment, Rochester, New York.

Th. Dobzhansky, *Genetics and the Origin of Species* (Columbia Univ. Press, New York, 2 ed., 1941).

N. P. Dubinin and D. D. Romaschoff, Die genetische Struktur der Art und ihre Evolution, *Biol. Zhur.* 1, 52–95 (1932).

C Population control

Christian, John J., and David E. Davis. 1956. The relationship between adrenal weight and population status of urban Norway rats. *Jour. Mammal.* **37**, 475–86.

Clough, Garrett C. 1965. Lemmings and population problems. *Amer. Sci.* **53**, 199–212.

Pincus, Gregory, Celso R. Garcia, John Rock, Manuel Paniagua, Adaline Pendleton, Felix Laraque, Rene Nicolas, Raymond Borno, and Vergniaud Pean. 1959. Effectiveness of an oral contraceptive. *Science* **130**, 81–83.

The Relationship Between Adrenal Weight and Population Status of Urban Norway Rats

John J. Christian
David E. Davis

It has been proposed that changes in the size of animal populations exert density-dependent effects on the physiology of individuals in these populations (Christian, 1950). Theoretically, the magnitude of the physiological alterations would increase with increases in population size until there is a cessation of population growth followed by a decline or, in extreme cases, a population crash. Emphasis was placed on the adaptive reactions of the pituitary-adrenocortical and reproductive systems to density-dependent stimuli which were presumably socio-psychological in nature. Therefore these stimuli would be effective throughout the history of a population, changing only in magnitude with changes in population size. Environmental hardships, such as food shortages and disease, of necessity would be imposed on and additive to this basic response to density.

A direct relationship between adrenal weight and population density was demonstrated in the laboratory with albino and wild house mice in populations of fixed size (Christian, 1955a, b). A similar relationship was demonstrated in freely growing populations of wild house mice maintained in the laboratory (Christian, 1956). Increases in adrenal weight resulted primarily from cortical hypertrophy. Subsequently it was shown that the adrenal weights of wild Norway rats

Reprinted by permission of the American Society of Mammalogists from *The Journal of Mammalogy* **37**, 475–86 (1956).

decreased following an artificial reduction of population (Christian and Davis, 1955). Finally, the subordinate rats of a group, as determined by losing fights, exhibit increased adrenocortical activity with eventual cortical hypertrophy (Barnett, 1955). The latter work suggests a socio-psychological mechanism by which population density might be related to adrenal activity in rats.

None of these experiments has demonstrated a corresponding relationship between population density and adrenal weight in natural populations. The present experiments were designed to examine natural populations for such a relationship.

The opinions or assertions contained herein are the private ones of the writers and are not to be construed as official or reflecting the views of the Navy Department or the naval service at large.

METHODS AND PROCEDURE

The rats (*Rattus norvegicus*) in 21 blocks of Baltimore City were used. Each city block is effectively an island and its rats form a discrete population unit, since immigration and emigration of rats is negligible or absent (Davis, 1953). The rats obtain their food from the abundant and relatively constant supply of garbage available in the back yards. Harborage is found in and around houses, fences, trash piles, and old buildings, and its availability remains fairly constant unless a housing rehabilitation program is in progress. These city blocks provide numerous discrete populations of rats ideal for the study of population

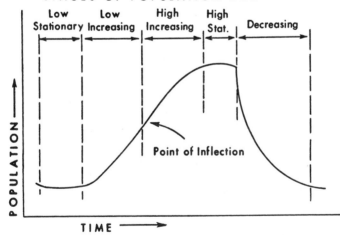

FIGURE 1. Hypothetical growth curve divided into stages of population development as described in the text. Each population of rats was placed in one of the five population stages at the time of collecting each sample.

phenomena under natural conditions. The quantitation of environmental factors is still a major problem, however, which has been discussed in detail by Davis (1953) along with the effects of environmental variation on rat populations. Food and harborage were believed to be adequate in all of the blocks used in the present experiment.

Each block population selected for study had a long history of repeated censuses by the method of Emlen, Stokes, and Davis (1949). This method cannot reliably detect population changes of less than 10 percent. This degree of insensitivity is unimportant in the present experiment, since relatively large changes in population usually were used, and for the most part these were produced artificially or stimulated by trapping. The histories of the rat populations in these blocks were used to estimate maximum values for the populations as well as to assign a stage of growth for each population, whenever a sample was taken, by estimating in which portion of a hypothetical growth curve the population lay immediately prior to trapping. The growth curve used (Fig. 1) was composed of a sigmoid positive increasing portion succeeded by a high stationary phase of indefinite length and finally a decreasing phase, and broadly conformed to the general growth form of populations (Allee, Emerson, Park, Park, and Schmidt, 1949). Experience has shown that such a general curve is sufficiently close to the observed facts so that its various stages may be applied to rat populations, even though it is not precisely defined at present. The curve was divided somewhat arbitrarily into the following stages: low stationary, low increasing, high increasing, high stationary, and decreasing as shown in Figure 1. One of us (D. E. D.) assigned every population to one of these stages each time it was sampled. The same author also made all of the censuses for this study.

Bimonthly censuses were made of each population for at least a year prior to the start of the present program in March, 1952. The following procedure was followed between March, 1952, and February, 1953. The population was estimated and a week later approximately 50 percent of the rats were trapped, and another census was made about two weeks later. The rat populations were initially selected so that they were high increasing, high stationary, or decreasing, and were large enough for adequate sampling. Six weeks later another census was made and another sample trapped, providing samples in the low stationary and low increasing categories. Another sample was trapped at varying intervals of time later, depending on the history of the particular population. The dates of trapping, population stages, and other pertinent data are given in Table 1. The assigned population stages can be considered only reasonably close approximations because of the limitations of quantitating the various factors of the environment and of the population itself for natural populations.

Subsequent to February, 1953, samples were taken and stages assigned without necessarily repeating the procedure following the initial trapping for the earlier populations. Block populations were programmed for further study which in some instances had to be abandoned because of the inability to obtain samples of adequate size. These blocks are self-evident in Table 1.

The weight in decigrams, length from the tip of the nose to the base of the tail in centimeters, and reproductive status were determined for each rat in the laboratory. The carcass was placed in 10 percent neutral formalin. At a later date the weights of the paired adrenal glands, paired thyroid glands, pituitary gland, and thymus were obtained on torsion balances to the nearest 0.1 milligram for all but the pituitary, which was weighed to the nearest 0.01 milligram. Representative sections of these glands and of the various visceral organs of rats from the first group of populations studied were taken for microscopic study. They were prepared by routine paraffin imbedding and stained with hematoxylin and eosin. Four rats with obvious pathological conditions that might affect the adrenal weight were discarded from further consideration. Three rats had adrenal medullary tumors and one had a renal abscess. Microscopic study was abandoned after February, 1953. Leptospirosis, Salmonellosis, and infestations of *Capillaria* are exceedingly common in the rats of Baltimore City. Studies by Davis (1951) indicate that the prevalence of Salmonellosis and Leptospirosis is the same for increasing, stationary, and decreasing populations; so that these diseases would not affect the present study. The same holds true for Capillariasis in rats weighing more than 199 grams. The vast majority of rats in this study were above this weight, and none was used that weighed less than 100 grams. The collection of thyroid, thymus, and pituitary weights was abandoned at the same time as the microscopic studies.

TABLE 1

Dates of Collection, Preceding Estimates of Population Size, and the Sizes of the Sample Trapped of Male and Female Norway Rats from Baltimore City Blocks Together with the Mean Adrenal Values (See Text) for Each Sex, Grouped According to Population Stage.

Block number	Date trapped	Pre-trap popn. est.	No. of females, >100 gm in sample	Adrenal wt. as mean % of ref. values	No. of males, >100 gm in sample	Adrenal wt. as mean % of ref. values
			Low Stationary Populations			
070421	May 52	45	7	94.81	3	130.07
070513	Oct. 52	48	7	103.29	8	97.45
140158	May 52	10	0	—	2	105.85
140220	May 52	48	12	89.92	7	118.57
140222	May 52	45	14	100.01	9	105.05
140226	June 52	47	10	89.25	5	124.84
140344	June 52	20	2	91.55	6	114.88

Low Increasing Populations

070421	Dec. 52	85	4	96.90	8	90.69
070426	Nov. 52	120	15	95.07	23	79.69
080750	May 52	15	4	92.48	2	84.15
140111	Nov. 52	43	12	79.67	7	84.93
140118	May 52	47	3	69.03	2	80.00
140132	Feb. 53	75	4	76.20	7	92.09
140138	July 52	59	15	98.63	14	102.31
140201	May 52	63	10	110.52	14	101.35
140222	Dec. 52	75	19	95.61	13	93.58
140222	Feb. 53	76	8	96.51	9	102.11
140226	Oct. 52	66	5	100.72	4	92.68
140332	Feb. 53	44	3	101.37	2	92.95

High Increasing Populations

070410	May 52	46	5	102.64	0	—
070410	Dec. 52	88	9	105.82	11	93.51
070421	Mar. 52	90	13	103.64	17	101.69
070506	Oct. 52	43	5	81.80	3	97.63
140111	Dec. 53	150	6	92.23	0	—
140118	Mar. 52	77	9	96.32	7	99.13
140118	Mar. 53	100	22	101.52	19	102.37
140158	Nov. 52	34	11	107.96	2	79.85
140201	Jan. 53	88	13	122.94	20	99.09
140201	Dec. 53	135	0	—	6	104.42
140220	Jan. 53	90	15	100.32	16	110.89
140222	Dec. 52	90	0	—	5	93.82
140344	Jan. 53	35	5	91.88	0	—
140134	Dec. 53	140	6	94.78	0	—

High Stationary Populations

070411	Mar. 52	35	8	93.79	2	119.65
070505	Mar. 52	49	6	110.15	7	88.70
070513	Feb. 53	63	16	124.89	8	79.21
110403	Dec. 53	80	0	—	6	137.40
140132	Oct. 52	45	10	79.36	3	114.63
140138	Nov. 51	75	17	86.39	11	111.74
140220	Mar. 52	81	15	107.06	12	118.66
140222	Apr. 52	75	13	110.01	13	98.28
140226	Apr. 52	67	4	107.50	11	115.25

Decreasing Populations

070410	Mar. 52	153	25	117.65	38	102.98
080750	Mar. 52	30	8	102.19	4	94.88
140158	Mar. 52	35	17	112.54	3	112.33
140201	Mar. 52	92	20	119.28	14	102.18
140322	Apr. 52	81	18	109.01	12	114.68
140322	June 52	58	12	97.17	5	108.16
140344	Apr. 52	58	13	114.95	14	130.69

The rats varied from 100 to more than 600 grams; hence it was necessary to find a relationship between adrenal weight and body size which would permit the use of rats of every size in any sample, as the number of rats in most samples would not permit further subdivision into weight classes. Several transformations of the data were tried and the best straight line relationship was found to be the logarithm of the adrenal weight on the body length exclusive of the tail. A regression of the logarithm of the adrenal weight on length was determined for each sex, using over 1000 urban and rural rats from a variety of population densities, to obtain a standard line for reference. With few exceptions the rats in the present study comprised the urban rats used in determining these regressions. The equations for the regressions and their graphical representations are given elsewhere (Christian and Davis, 1955). There was no detectable difference between the urban and rural rats in the relationship of the logarithm of adrenal weight to length for either sex. A reference adrenal weight was determined for each body length for each sex from the regressions, and the adrenal weight of each rat in the study was converted to a percentage of the reference value for the appropriate length and sex. A mean value was determined from the individual percentages for each sex in every sample trapped (Table 1).

The unit of measurement used throughout this study is the mean value of the particular organ for the rats trapped in each block. Analyses of variance (Snedecor, 1946) were used throughout this study for evaluating the data unless otherwise specially noted.

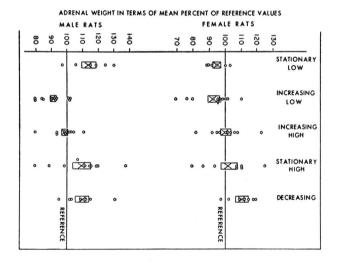

FIGURE 2. The mean adrenal value for each sex for each sample (shown as a circle) of Norway rats plotted on the population stage. The mean adrenal value for each population stage is also shown (as an X) with its standard error.

RESULTS

Adrenal glands. The adrenal values, given as the means of the individual percentages of reference weights for each sex and sample, are grouped according to the stage of population growth (Table 1) together with the sample sizes for each sex and the estimated number of rats in the population immediately prior to trapping. The mean adrenal values for each sample are shown plotted against the appropriate assigned stage of population growth (Fig. 2). The mean value for each sex and stage and its standard error are also shown.

There was a significantly greater variation in the mean adrenal values between stages than within stages of population growth for each sex (Females: $P < 0.02$; males: $P < 0.001$), indicating that changes in adrenal weight (relative to body length) are associated with the stages of population development. It is apparent that the adrenal glands of male and female rats responded alike to all stages of population except the low stationary (Table 2, Fig. 2). There was a progressive increase in the mean adrenal value from both sexes starting with the low increasing populations, progressing through the high increasing and high stationary stages, and ending with an overall 18 percent increase in adrenal value in the decreasing populations. The mean change in adrenal weight value was approximately 6 percent per stage of population (Fig. 2).

The adrenal glands differed markedly with respect to sex in their response to low stationary population status. The adrenal values of the female rats from these populations were essentially the same as those from low increasing populations and were therefore close to the lowest weights observed. On the other hand, the highest mean adrenal weight

TABLE 2

Mean Relative Weights of the Adrenal, Thymus, Thyroid and Pituitary Glands for Each Stage of Population for Norway Rats from Baltimore City Blocks.

Stage of population	Sex	Number of samples	Paired adrenal wt. as mean % of ref. values ± std. error	Mean thymus wt., mg/100 gm ± std. error	Mean pituitary wt., mg/100 gm ± std. error	Mean paired thyroid wt., mg/100 gm ± std. error
Low stationary	F	6	94.97 ± 2.35	117.0 ± 40.3	4.48 ± 0.25	12.30 ± 0.72
	M	7	113.82 ± 4.41	71.7 ± 12.4	4.29 ± 0.88	11.44 ± 1.39
Low increasing	F	12	92.73 ± 3.43	85.0 ± 9.2	3.91 ± 0.30	12.40 ± 0.48
	M	12	91.38 ± 2.31	59.2 ± 8.8	2.79 ± 0.02	11.79 ± 0.72
High increasing	F	12	100.15 ± 2.94	80.6 ± 12.1	4.11 ± 0.62	11.68 ± 0.65
	M	10	98.24 ± 2.62	76.8 ± 14.6	2.77 ± 0.07	12.06 ± 0.44
High stationary	F	8	102.39 ± 5.23	73.1 ± 11.5	4.48 ± 0.49	12.79 ± 0.80
	M	9	109.28 ± 5.40	70.9 ± 13.4	3.91 ± 0.56	11.94 ± 0.76
Decreasing	F	7	110.40 ± 3.90	58.0 ± 16.7	4.38 ± 0.54	12.47 ± 0.77
	M	7	109.41 ± 4.35	53.7 ± 9.9	3.50 ± 0.49	12.40 ± 1.12

TABLE 3

The Mean Adrenal Value of Both Sexes for Each
Population Stage and Month of Capture. Months
Represented by Only One Population Stage and
All Low Stationary Populations Have Been
Excluded.

	Low increasing	High increasing	High stationary	Decreasing
October	92.8	89.7	97.0	—
November	84.8	93.9	99.6	—
December	94.2	97.4	137.4*	—
February	91.7	—	102.1	—
March	—	100.8	106.3	108.0
April	—	—	107.8	117.3

Represents a single value.

value of the male rats was for the low stationary stage, exceeding the
mean adrenal value for the decreasing stage, although not significantly.
It is quite apparent that there is a fundamental difference with respect
to sex in the stimuli to the adrenal cortices in low stationary populations
of urban rats.

The population stages have been arranged, in Table 3, in such an order
that, according to the hypothesis proposed in this paper, the mean
adrenal weights would be expected to increase from left to right. It
will be observed that this is the case with only one exception. Moreover,
since the various rows of the table confine the results to very small
time intervals, the effect noted within any single row is independent of
seasonal change. Thus if there is any seasonal effect it does not affect
the trends noted within the rows of this table. Low stationary populations were omitted because of the marked difference between male and
female adrenal weights. Months represented by a single population
stage were likewise omitted.

Thymus gland. There was a suggestive decrease in the weights of
the thymus glands of female rats from low stationary through decreasing population stages (Table 2, Fig. 3). The variation in thymus weight
with population stage was not significant, nor was the difference between the extremes of the means. There was no suggestion of a pattern
of weight change with population stage in the thymus glands of male
rats. The thymus weights of the two sexes did not differ significantly.

Pituitary gland. The mean pituitary weight relative to body weight
(milligrams/100 grams) with its standard error is given for each population stage for each sex (Table 2). The relative pituitary weights were
consistently greater in the female than in the male rats ($P < 0.01$)
(Table 2, Fig. 3). The relative pituitary weights of the female rats showed
no significant variation with population stage. The variation with population stage in the relative weights of the male pituitary glands appeared

FIGURE 3. The mean weights and their standard errors in milligrams per 100 grams of body weight of the thymus, thyroid, and pituitary glands of Norway rats plotted for each population stage for each sex.

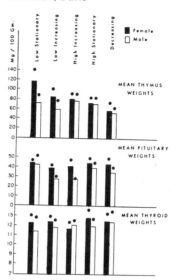

to parallel roughly the changes in adrenal weight (Fig. 3), but these changes were without significance. However, regressions of male mean adrenal values on relative pituitary weight and vice versa had slopes significantly different than zero (P < 0.001) suggesting positive relationship between the weights of the adrenal and pituitary glands of the male rats.

Thyroid gland. There was no detectable relationship between thyroid gland weight and population stage (Table 2). The weights of the thyroid glands from male and female rats were not significantly different.

DISCUSSION

Intraspecific competition has been assigned a major role in regulating and limiting population growth (Allee, Emerson, Park, Park, and Schmidt, 1949). It has been shown that such competition between animals of the same species becomes more pronounced as populations increase and is manifested by decreased reproduction, growth, and survival (Davis, 1949; Calhoun, 1950). It is generally assumed that food, harborage, or other environmental necessities impose the limits on population growth and that intraspecific competition is to a large extent the medium through which these factors operate. It was suggested, however, that population growth might be limited purely by social competition in spite of an abundance of all of the usual environmental necessities (Christian, 1950). Presumably such sociopsychological pressures, as indeed they would have to be, would act as density-dependent stimuli to the pituitary-adrenocortical axis producing a progressive enlargement of the adrenal cortex and reduction in reproduction as the population increased. A point finally would be reached when a failure of reproduction would result in a failure of population growth. The animals in such a population presumably would be extremely susceptible to any additional insult. A decline in population might be expected to result from an additional burden which was beyond the ability of the animal to cope with it.

In order to verify such an hypothesis it was necessary to show that there is a density-dependent adrenocortical response independent of supplies of food, water, and harborage. Experiments in the laboratory with fixed and freely growing populations of white and wild house mice established the existence of such a mechanism, using the weights of the adrenal glands and reproductive organs as indicators (Christian, 1955a, b, 1956). The amount of adrenocortical tissue was shown to be positively related to the level of population. The present experiments are an extension of experiments with laboratory populations designed to establish whether adrenal weight (as a measure of cortical mass) was related to population status under natural conditions.

There was a positive relationship between the weights of the adrenal glands adjusted for body length and stages of population growth for urban Norway rats. There was a progressive increase in adrenal weight in both sexes as population status progressed from low increasing, through high increasing and high stationary, to decreasing. The adrenal glands in decreasing populations were 18 percent heavier than in low increasing populations. These changes in adrenal weight occurred over and above any possible seasonal variation, although a seasonal effect could not be ruled definitely in or out. So far these data fit our hypothesis and coincide with the results of experiments in the laboratory, as increases in adrenal weight occurred with stages of population growth in spite of an excess of the usual environmental necessities. The marked difference between the sexes in their adrenocortical responses to low stationary populations is difficult to interpret. One would expect a decrease in adrenal weight following a decrease in population and the release of density-dependent social pressures resulting in very low adrenal weights in low stationary populations. Apparently this is true for female rats, but not for males. The reason for male rats attaining their greatest adrenal weight in low stationary populations is not known. It may be that there is considerable strife among the males in these populations, perhaps resulting from reestablishing their social orders following a decrease in population. If so, it is hard to explain why the adrenal weights of male rats decreased following an artificial 50 percent reduction in population size (Christian and Davis, 1955). However, the changes in adrenal weight in these experiments were on the whole predictable from the assumption that density-dependent sociopsychological factors operate as stimuli to the pituitary-adrenocortical system. Evidence that such social factors exist in rats has been presented by Barnett (1955) and Calhoun (1950). Frank (1953), in discussing his studies on experimental crashes in *Microtus* populations, has suggested that such a mechanism is operative, but that a final additional insult is necessary to initiate a precipitous crash with the syndrome of hypo-glycemic shock when a population attains a peak level.

The alterations in adrenal weight in the present experiments were attributed to changes in adrenocortical mass. The adrenal medulla of rats does not contribute to changes in adrenal weight (Rogers and Richter, 1948), consequently changes in weight must result entirely from changes in cortical mass. Furthermore, adrenal weight was shown to be directly related to cortical mass and in turn to population size in mice (Christian, 1955b, 1956).

The apparent decrease in the weights of the thymus glands of female rats with increasing population density (and adrenal weight), although not significant, is suggestive of the thymico-lymphatic involution usu-ally associated with increased adrenocortical function (Selye, 1950). A direct relationship between the weights of the pituitary and adrenal glands was seen in the male, but not in the female rats. This difference cannot at present be explained.

Throughout these experiments there was a considerable degree of variability which may have obscured the significance of changes in the weights of some of the organs. Unfortunately such variability is un-avoidable with the presently available unprecise techniques for working with wild populations and their environment. The greatest error occurs in the stationary populations where estimation of the population status is least critical. Rapidly increasing or decreasing populations are usually clearly defined, but slowly changing populations may be erroneously classified as stationary, as their changes may be too small to be detected by the methods used. However, such errors in classification would do no more than place the population in one category higher or lower than its correct one. It is assumed that any such errors which may have been made are randomly distributed and have little effect on the final results.

The variability in adrenal weight throughout the experiment (Table 1) prompted further thought on the population mechanics of these rats. The population of rats in each block is composed of discrete colonies that tend to merge as the population increases, whereas they remain quite discrete at low levels of population. It may be that each colony acts as a discrete population in its effect on the adrenal cortex; for example, one colony may be a dense population while another in the same block may be just the opposite. Grouping such diverse colonies into a single value for each block would tend to increase the variability in the results. This problem needs to be examined further, as a prelimi-nary analysis suggests that each colony indeed acts as a discrete popula-tion unit. Any colony effect in the present experiments has been over-ridden by the use of a large number of populations and population samples.

SUMMARY AND CONCLUSIONS

There was a significant relationship between the weights of the adrenal glands relative to body length and population status in 49 samples of Norway rats from 21 blocks in Baltimore City. The adrenal glands of both sexes increased regularly in weight as the population status progressed along a hypothetical growth curve in successive stages from low increasing, through high increasing and high stationary, to decreasing stages. The adrenal glands in decreasing populations were approximately 18 percent heavier than in populations that were in the low increasing stage. Male and female rats reacted differently to populations in the low stationary category. The adrenals of male rats were heaviest in these populations, while those of the female rats were essentially the same weight as in low increasing populations. The changes in adrenal weight with population status were on the whole consistent with the concept that there is a density-dependent sociopsychological stimulus to the pituitary-adrenocortical system that may be a major factor in the regulation of population growth. The changes in adrenal weight could not be attributed to seasonal variation.

There was a significant positive relationship in male rats between the relative weights of the pituitary and adrenal glands which was not observed in the female rats. A decline in the weight of the thymus gland of female rats with increasing population density and adrenal weight was suggestive but not significant. No relationship was found between population status and the pituitary glands of male rats or the thyroid glands from either sex.

It is concluded that there is a density-dependent stimulus to the pituitary-adrenocortical system of wild Norway rats that operates independently of season or supplies of the usual environmental necessities.

Received January 16, 1956

REFERENCES AND NOTES

Naval Medical Research Institute, National Naval Medical Center, Bethesda, Maryland; and The Division of Vertebrate Ecology, The Johns Hopkins School of Hygiene and Public Health, Baltimore, Maryland.

W. C. Allee, A. E. Emerson, O. Park, T. Park, K. P. Schmidt, *Principles of Animal Ecology* (W. B. Saunders Co., Philadelphia, 1949).

S. A. Barnett, Competition among wild rats, *Nature* 175, 126 (1955).

J. B. Calhoun, The study of wild animals under controlled conditions, *Ann. N.Y. Acad. Sci.* 51, Art. 7, 1113–1122 (1950).

J. J. Christian, The adreno-pituitary system and population cycles in mammals, *Jour. Mamm.* 31, 247–59 (1950).

———, Effect of population size on the weights of the reproductive organs of white mice, *Amer. Jour. Physiol.* 181, 477–80 (1955a).

———, Effect of population size on the adrenal glands and reproductive organs of male mice in populations of fixed size, *Amer. Jour. Physiol.* 182, 292–300 (1955b).

————, Adrenal and reproductive responses to population size in mice from freely growing populations, *Ecology* 37, 258–73 (1956).

———— and D. E. Davis, The reduction of adrenal weight in rodents by reducing population size, trans. *N. Amer. Wildl. Conf.* 20, 177–89 (1955).

D. E. Davis, The role of intraspecific competition in game management, trans. *N. Amer. Wildl. Conf.* 14, 225–31 (1949).

————, The relation between the level of population and the prevalence of Leptospira, Salmonella, and Capillaria in Norway rats, *Ecology* 32, 465–68 (1951).

————, The characteristics of rat populations, *Quart. Rev. Biol.* 28, 373–401 (1953).

J. T. Emlen, A. W. Stokes, D. E. Davis, Methods for estimating populations of brown rats in urban habitats, *Ecology,* 30, 430–42 (1949).

F. Frank, Untersuchungen über den Zusammenbruch von Feldmausplagen (*Microtus arvalis* Pallas), *Zool. Jahrb. (Systematik)* 82, 95–136 (1953).

P. V. Rogers and C. P. Richter, Anatomical comparison between the adrenal glands of wild Norway, wild alexandrine, and domestic Norway rats, *Endocrinology* 42, 46–55 (1948).

H. Selye, *Stress* (Acta, Inc., Montreal, 1950).

G. W. Snedecor, *Statistical Methods* (Iowa State College Press, Ames, 1946).

Lemmings and Population Problems

Garrett C. Clough

The best scientific problems are never completely solved because they always lead to new questions. A good scientist seldom contemplates any accomplished piece of work without seeing new unsolved problems, scarcely suspected before, rising from it. A good example is the subject of lemmings, the legendary rodents which march into the sea — or at least so folklore proclaims. In recent years, the lemming question has been removed from the realm of myth, and biologists have collected much new information to clarify and redefine the problem. But study has uncovered new mysteries, and this particular biological phenomenon now appears even more complex and provocative than before.

The periodic wanderings of masses of Norwegian lemmings (*Lemmus lemmus*) in the mountain regions of Scandinavia stimulated many imaginative and superstitious explanations in former centuries. Some of these tales persist today. While I was in Norway in 1963 and 1964, some people questioned me about the suicidal urge which is supposed to cause the lemmings to fling themselves into the sea, or inquired if I had seen any angry lemmings burst apart with excess rage. Though serious scientists have long since dismissed such legends, the fanciful myths have been replaced in the scientific literature by a set of equally imaginative hypotheses. These have been built by critical biologists upon firm observations and experimental results, but they remain

Reprinted from *American Scientist* **53**, 199–212 (1965), by permission of the author and publisher.

FIGURE 1. An early stage in a lemming fight. The approach of the one on the left is being repelled with a defensive threat posture and squeaks of the animal on the right. Most of the encounters between wild lemmings never proceeded beyond this stage.

temporary ideas suggesting what new studies should be made in order to learn more. Much of what we have learned, in addition, may have bearing on the problems created by human population increase and rapid technological development of our environment.

Two facets of the lemming's life are of tremendous interest and importance. The first is that their population numbers change so drastically from time to time. The second is that, occasionally, great numbers of lemmings move considerable distances from their original homes. These two aspects of lemming biology may not be so closely related as was once thought.

The Norwegian lemming is one species of a rodent subfamily (*Microtinae*) whose 70 or so species are very common throughout the north-temperate and arctic zones. Various mice, voles, and lemmings are included here, all with the same general appearance of compact body, short neck, and small ears and tail. Most of these small rodents exhibit marked fluctuations in their numbers over periods of 3 to 4 years. Sometimes, as in an outbreak in Oregon and Washington in 1959–60, some of these animals will become so abundant that they cause much damage to man's crops. Five species of this group are called lemmings — three in the New World, including Greenland, and two in the Old World. Lemmings are arctic residents.

A PEAK LEMMING YEAR

My wife and I were fortunate to begin our study in the middle of a peak lemming year. We arrived in the Dovre mountains of south-central Norway in June, 1963. Our home for the next two summers and periodic week-long trips throughout the winter was a small cabin just below the timber line. The first summer, lemmings were everywhere — under our cabin, in the fields next to us, along the stream from which we took our water. The colorful little animals ran from our path wherever we walked, whether through the upper forest zone of low birch trees, on the wet bogs, or over the high open tundra. Lemmings were the most obvious animals of the landscape. For the previous ten years, lemmings had been virtually absent from this area. Biologists had captured a few by extensive trapping in 1960, but most residents hadn't noticed any at all in the past decade. Then skiers first saw some animals above the snow during the 1963 Easter holidays. For a few weeks at the end of April and beginning of May, during the time of snow melt, wandering lemmings were seen by local residents in the birch tree belt. By the time we arrived on June 8, the animals had apparently settled down. I found them plentiful from the sub-alpine birch belt and above the tree line in

FIGURE 2. The author observes lemmings on their home grounds in the upper birch woods in south-central Norway. In Scandinavia, the trees growing at the highest altitudes are birch, not spruce as in the United States.

the low-alpine dwarf shrub belt to the mid-alpine grass-heath belt. The large adults which had survived over the winter were all sexually mature with the females either bearing young or suckling new-born. The small size of the juveniles indicated that these probably had been born after the spring wandering period. Four species of voles of the genera *Microtus* and *Clethrionomys* were abundant also.

A lemming year is accompanied by remarkable changes in the numbers of many other animals, too. These small rodents feed upon plant material exclusively — in the case of the lemming, on moss, sedge and grass. They occupy the basic animal position in the food chain which converts vegetable matter into animal flesh. The snowshoe hare, certain small birds, the willow grouse and the ptarmigan share this position with them. Predatory animals depend upon these herbivores for their food supply.

This summer, the lemmings and voles provided an extra-abundant source of food for the various arctic predators. There were ten successful nests of short-eared owls on the high marsh close to my study area. A Norwegian ornithologist told me that no owl nests had been found there in the last eight years. Rough-legged hawks and marsh hawks were more numerous than usual, and the nests I visited had many lemming and vole carcasses in them. The rarer snowy owls nested in the higher mountains to the south, where lemmings were also abundant. Foxes and weasels were plentiful and could sometimes be seen hunting in the daytime. The attention of these predators was so largely concentrated on the rodents that the grouse and ptarmigan were left relatively free to raise large broods to maturity in the summer, and in the fall the hunters had an exceptional season.

For many years the cyclic nature of the lemming populations has been known (1). Most records of northern fur trapping show a fluctuating number of pelts. In Norway, the weasel and fox returns follow the lemming years closely. The Hudson's Bay Company fur records from Canada show regular fluctuations in lynx, fox, and weasel pelts. Population changes in bird predators are also noticeable. In the northern United States, winter invasions of snowy owls from Canada follow the decline of the lemmings and other small rodent populations farther north.

POPULATION THEORIES

The attempted explanations of small mammal cycles may be put into three groups. The first approach looks for the cause of cycles in the environment. If some environmental factor, either physical or biological, could be found which varied in its expression at the same rate as the animal numbers, then a strong case for a causal relationship could be established. Such factors as temperature and rainfall, sunspots, lunar cycles, predator populations and disease organisms were examined. Although some of these may influence the rodent numbers, none of them has been shown to be consistently connected to the cycles. This type of theory has been dismissed as the sole explanation by practically every-one who has looked into the question.

A second group of theories developed the idea of an interaction be-tween the rodent population and some aspect of its biological environ-ment. The rodent numbers and the other side of the balance were supposed to have an oscillating relationship. In these theories, the small mammals were considered to be one part of a dynamic predator-prey, parasite-host, or plant-herbivore interaction. We can imagine a simplified example of the latter case. Suppose the rodents are so nu-merous that they eat up all of their food supply. Most of them will die from starvation after the plants have been destroyed. In the following years, the grasses recover to full growth and the rodents can begin to increase again with the renewal of food. In a few years, the high powers of rodent procreation tip the balance all over again. A number of biolo-gists have evidence which seems to fit such theories (2, 3, 4).

The third and most recent approach to the problem places the cause within the population itself. These are the theories of self-regulation or self-limitation which propose that the forces which promote increase are strongest when the population is lowest and weakest when the popu-lation is highest. This is the familiar concept of feedback, applied to an ever-changing population.

A self-regulation theory was first suggested as an explanation of animal cycles by J. J. Christian in the United States in 1950 and has since stimulated much work. Three things determine the numbers of animals of a single species at one place: the birth rate, the death rate, and the movements of individuals to and from the place. This group of theories argues that the birth and death rates are dependent in some way upon the numbers of animals present. Social stresses — such as the amount of fighting, interference with maternal behavior, or general antagonistic contacts between individuals — may increase as the popu-lation density increases. There has been ample evidence in laboratory rodents that such social stress acts detrimentally on various internal organs of the individuals (5). The adrenal glands of animals experi-mentally exposed to crowded conditions or to trained aggressor animals (6) usually enlarge in the same way that they do when an animal is exposed to most physical or chemical hardships. According to these theories, the adrenal change makes the animal more susceptible to additional stresses and strains of life. As the body's master gland, the pituitary, is called upon to support additional adrenal hormone produc-tion, it reduces its own output of the hormones which serve in turn to develop the reproductive organs and hormones. Thus, fewer young may be conceived; and those that are born may not be so healthy or the mother may fail to care for them properly. This may be the key to the declining birth rates and mounting death rates which often culminate in a precipitate drop in the population. These ideas have much support (7), but are not yet proven.

There is a balance among the endocrine glands within one individual just as there is among the individual members within a species population and among the various species of plants and animals within a complex natural community. These three systems of increasing size — a single animal, a species population, and a community of plants and animals — are similar, in that each system is composed of many parts so organized that a change in one part results in a compensatory change in other parts.

Today, support and criticism for both the self-regulatory theories and the plant-herbivore balance theory can be found. Much of the evidence for the self-regulation comes from laboratory experiments on semidomestic animals. It is much more difficult to conduct critical experiments or to gather sufficient material on wild populations. Some of the data concerning endocrine glands and resistance to stress of wild animals do not agree with the theory. For example, the weights of adrenal glands of Canadian lemmings from peak populations are no different (8), or lower than (9) those of lemmings captured at periods of low population. In earlier work I have done (10), there was no difference in the resistance to stress or in adrenal weight between freeliving voles in very dense populations and those from sparse conditions, after allowing for the variability due to season and reproductive condition. The foremost Scandinavian student of lemmings, Dr. Olavi Kalela of the University of Helsinki, emphasizes the plant-herbivore balance.

FIGURE 3. These young rough-legged hawks have been supplied with more lemmings than they can consume.

There are now some hints that the plant food of lemmings may exhibit fluctuations in nutritive quality which in turn influence birth and death rates of the lemmings (11). If these ideas are true, then the entire cycle problem is moved down one level and includes a problem of plant cycles. The men who have spent many summers studying lemmings in Alaska also place considerable emphasis on the plant-lemming interaction, for there the lemmings sometimes devour their entire food supply (2).

MEANING TO HUMANS

Whatever the underlying mechanisms are, the cyclic changes of lemming numbers have been attained after a long evolutionary history since the Pleistocene glaciers or even earlier. As might be expected, the ideas devised to explain animal cycles — especially the finding that life in crowded conditions can have profound physiological effects — are now being used to discuss human population problems. But, in my view, there are too many basic differences to justify much of this speculation. For one thing, historically, human populations have shown only a steadily increasing growth over thousands of years — or no significant change in the case of some isolated peoples. There has never been the regular, short-term rise and fall seen in the rodent populations. For another difference, although it is probably true that humans crowded into urban centers are plagued by certain mental and physical diseases of civilization, their birth rates are not greatly inhibited (if at all) nor their mortality rates increased. In fact, the birth rates are comparatively high among the people who live with the poorest conditions of nutrition, housing and, perhaps, even emotional and mental hardships. Finally, I can see no evidence of an evolutionary adaptation for overall limitation of human numbers, either by self-regulation or by a balance with the environment. By cultural and technological revolution, humans have so rapidly outgrown their original niche in the balanced system of nature that we no longer know *where* we belong in the ecosystem of the earth.

Great as the differences are between man and lemmings, we can learn some things about human populations by studying lemmings. Certain physiological comparisons are valid, for we and the lemmings are mammals who share many of the same biochemicals and internal functions. We are learning a great deal about how animal numbers are regulated in nature, about the mammal's physiological reaction to stress, about the delicate functions of the integrated hormone system, about the organization and function of natural communities, and about the evolutionary adaptations to various environments. In addition, when we learn to know intimately the lives and histories of wild creatures which we use as inspirations in our stories and mythologies, we often can look upon ourselves and our fellow men with a greater perception, appreciation, and tolerance. Biologists also study lemmings to satisfy deep personal curiosity about important unsolved phenomena of nature, partly because the animals are such delightful, pretty creatures to watch, and partly out of a desire to travel into the peaceful, adventurous arctic tundras and beautiful lonely mountains of the north.

MASS WANDERINGS

What makes the lemming famous to the general public is the animal's spectacular mass emigrations. Sensational accounts of great hordes of lemmings moving down from the mountains — some of the stories date back to the sixteenth century — are based on actual events, though the movements are by no means so overwhelming as they are sometimes painted. Finnish ecologists, working in the northernmost tip of their country, have learned that lemmings actually make two trips annually, usually short journeys made from the winter habitat to the summer home (12). These relatively short trips occur during April and May and then again in late summer and fall before the snow comes. In the summer, lemmings prefer wet peat lands where the grass and moss grow best. In the winter, when these places are frozen, they prefer drier areas where a dense snow cover protects them and their food supply. Often the movements occur vertically up and down the mountain slopes. These biennial treks between summer and winter homes take place regardless of population density, and may be a special phenomenon which evolved in the Norwegian lemmings to make best use of the

FIGURE 4. A view from timberline in the Dovre Mountains. In late summer lemmings wandered down the slopes onto the fields and marshlands.

topography, vegetation types, and the climate of the European arctic regions. The species of lemmings inhabiting Canada, Alaska, and Greenland seldom move from their homes in this manner. The topography there is flatter and the vegetation much more monotonous than in Norway. Since the cyclic fluctuations of lemming numbers are not a special characteristic, but one shared to some degree by all the small mammals from the temperate zone northwards, it appears that the underlying explanations for these two events are fundamentally different.

But all is not clear, by any means. Sometimes lemmings do behave in a way which seems completely maladaptive or neurotic. The peak population which I watched all through the summer began to move downward from the alpine shrub and lichen zones rather suddenly in mid-July. During the short night and early morning hours, I could see individual animals proceeding at a steady pace down along a hiking trail. While I sat at a convenient observation point where a road crossed a small river, as many as forty lemmings per hour passed by. These animals were not heading toward a good wintering ground. In fact, by September and October, when the first snows came, many of them had settled in the large, low-lying marsh and in a hayfield devoid of green grass. None of them survived the winter here. Other wandering lemmings began to appear at the nearest town and surrounding pine forests twelve miles away down the valley.

SOCIAL ANTAGONISM

The great antagonism and aggressiveness in these lemmings probably plays an important role in such irrational wanderings of a portion of the peak population. It was easy to learn something about the detailed daily activities of some lemmings because, unlike many small mammals, they were readily seen in the daytime. Perhaps their broken black and light coloring serves as disruptive camouflage and makes them willing to expose themselves in the open. By marking lemmings with paint and by clipping away bits of fur, I could identify individuals on sight as I sat quietly in the birch woods.

Lemmings must be the most antisocial and antagonistic of all rodents. Every single time I saw two lemmings meet face to face, there was some sign of agonism (attack, defense, or escape behavior). At the mildest level, this agonistic behavior took the form of a slight squeak with the assumption of a threatening upright posture by one animal, and a corresponding low submissive stance by the other. They might then separate or might proceed into the second stage which involved mutual pushing of the forefeet in a boxing bout. In the wild, animals either parted peacefully at this stage or one animal turned and fled with the other in pursuit. Loud squeaks usually accompanied the boxing and chase. These encounters were very frequent during the summer. Newly-weaned litters were continually being added to the already crowded active ranks. At times, I saw five or six individuals sitting or eating at the same moment within fifteen feet of me. During observation periods on five days in mid-July, I heard an average of 5.6 squeaks per hour but this had declined to 1.8 squeaks per hour during five days at the end of August. The first period represents the start and the second period represents five to six weeks after the start of the wandering movements.

The large mature females were always the winners in the conflicts I witnessed in the birch woods. They chased away everyone, from males larger than themselves to young recently emerged from the nest. Perhaps these dominant, aggressive matrons triggered the social stress within the population. In any case, it seems reasonable to assume that all this social uproar accounted for the wanderings of part of the population. Only middle-sized lemmings were seen wandering at first. The very young and the older breeding segment of the population stayed behind at the good homesites where food was still available. At the beginning of the wandering period, two-thirds of the animals were males. Almost all of these males and most of the females were sexually mature, but the females were not pregnant. By the end of August, the sex ratio among the wanderers was equal and a few smaller, sexually immature animals were included. Once on the move, lemmings were antisocial to an extreme. They moved completely alone. Whenever two wanderers met by chance, there was squeaking and rapid avoidance. On a few occasions, I placed a lemming in a small cage of wire netting on the emigration path. Lemmings who came moving downhill did not change their pace or direction even if they walked within a foot of the caged animal. The aggression displayed among those who settled in the open hayfields was very great. Here they could not avoid each other and we could see and hear them outside our cabin, running, chasing, and squeaking at each other.

The agonistic encounters among the birch wood residents or between two wandering lemmings never reached the stage of biting and rolling together in a fight as it invariably did between captive lemmings confined to a limited space. I did not find any wild lemmings with scars and wounds. The difference between behavior of free-living and confined animals deserves greater emphasis in evaluating evidence on population problems. Whenever I placed two wandering lemmings together in a small cage, they fought savagely until one of them died, always within 24 hours. They met face to face and exchanged bites directed at the mouth and chin, their sharp incisors easily tearing through the skin. Even in large floor pens (four by eight feet), with plenty of food and shelter, six or eight lemmings would fight so much that all but two or three would be dead in less than a week. At the time of death, they were severely wounded and emaciated. In captivity, voles are much more tolerant than lemmings. I could keep ten bank voles together in a small cage. After a few hours of shoving and squeaking they would quiet down and the next day would all be huddled together in a nest in one corner. Ten meadow voles, placed in a floor pen of 15 square feet, will fight and wound each other slightly but all will survive if adequate food and cover is provided (*13*).

Generally, the social structure of a population of mice and voles is based upon a spacing-out of the individuals in suitable habitat. Each individual has a limited range of movement — about a quarter of an acre, depending upon season, sex and type of habitat. Mature females tend to defend their own territory and to prevent other females from encroaching on it. Males have large home ranges which usually overlap those of a few females. When the numbers of our common wood mouse increase, some individuals seek space in less favorable places nearby, or the home ranges and territories may be compressed (*14*). Sometimes, the territorial defense of field voles may relax enough to allow two females to live amicably together, or the offspring of one mother to remain in her range even after she has another litter (*15*). This does not seem to happen among the Scandinavian lemmings.

OPEN QUESTIONS

It is still unclear, if behavioral differences exist between individuals in low and high density populations, how great and how significant they

FIGURE 5. Three-week-old lemmings are well able to care for themselves. Their eyes open at 12 or 13 days of age and weaning is over during the third week. More than twelve young can be born at once but the usual litter size is 5 to 8.

are. Perhaps the social stress among the adults is reflected in the new-born. Prenatal influences have been demonstrated in white mice and rats in the laboratory (*16, 17*). Young white mice, born to mothers who had been subjected to crowding or obnoxious stimuli, were different in some behavioral responses from those born to uncrowded and undis-turbed mothers. The experimental young were less active and slower to explore unfamiliar areas than the control animals. However, dif-ferent results were found in a comparable study with laboratory rats (*18*). If it were true that prenatal influences were acting on wild lem-mings born in peak years, these animals may be less able to adjust to the crowded conditions than their parents were.

It has also been suggested that behavioral changes through the gen-erations might be related to genetic changes (*19*). That genes may affect agonistic behavior and other behavioral characteristics of mam-mals is known (*20*). The pattern of response to social encounters may also be partly the result of learning by the young after they leave the nest and meet dominant adults. Frequent experience of conflicts may reduce their tolerance towards other lemmings. Aggressiveness, like all other complex forms of behavior, is formed by close interaction between inherited (non-learned) and acquired (learned) factors (*21*). This whole discussion must be highly speculative since the experimental evidence on these questions is meager.

Only a portion of the lemmings in my study area undertook the wan-

FIGURE 6. The Dovre study area in March when the lemming population crash was nearly complete on all habitats.

dering which led them into unsuitable habitats. A certain portion may have maintained their regular habits with the seasonal change of habitat. After the winter snow cover had arrived in late October and all wandering had ceased, I found lemmings living in all habitats; good and bad, from the lower pine forest, on the marsh and hayfields, in the birch woods, and above in the low and mid-alpine belts. But my traplines already were showing decreased populations. The population decline had started.

When I returned to the mountains on the first of March, I did not find a single lemming. In one week's time I saw only a few rodent tracks in the snow. This astounding disappearance of the lemmings was verified in the spring. Although we spent the entire months of May and June in a thorough and complete search, we found only five bank voles where the year before, lemmings and voles had overrun the ground. Traces of lemming work under the snow and a few decaying carcasses were present in all habitats but the overwinter die-off had been virtually complete.

There had been nothing severe in the winter weather to cause this population crash. Only sixty miles to the northeast, in the valley on the other side of the Dovre mountains, lemmings were still plentiful. There, the lemmings had successfully survived the winter in pine forests, birch woods, and even on close-cut hay fields. During the month of May, 1964, they wandered along the roads and in the woods.

I do not know the cause of the mass mortality of the lemmings. Lemmings and other microtine rodents do not always decline from a population peak so rapidly or always during the winter. The decline may occur slowly over a two-year period and, if a short crash does occur, it may be at any season of the year (22). Much must be learned before the mysteries of the lemmings are solved. Whether the social stress in high density populations is a strain on the endocrine system, as it is in some animals, is still a question. Studies on the quality of wild rodents' food supplies are just starting. Lemming problems should be followed on all biological levels, from the organs and hormones within the individual to the complete community of soil, climate, plants, and related animals. Work in biochemistry, endocrinology, genetics, physiology, nutrition, ecology, and animal behavior will contribute to future studies of these problems.

The lemmings, as a species, are remarkably successful residents of the harsh arctic regions despite, or rather because of, the fact that their population explosions are so extravagant with individual lives. Without these periodic irruptions of individuals, the species might have met, long ago, either of two fates leading to extinction. With a lower capacity for reproduction, the species might not have survived the especially severe climatic hardships which occasionally occur. A greater reproductive capacity, coupled with better ability to tolerate social stress and crowding, might have led to total destruction of their food supply.

As things are, the hordes of lemmings present during peak years never irreversibly damage their resources. Most of the individuals are lost, but some are always left to reestablish the populations. Behind the drastic periodic changes in lemming numbers measured in terms of years and decades, there exists the fundamental stability of the arctic community from times before the appearance of modern man.

One important thing the non-biologist can learn from all this work is an appreciation of ecological complexity, of the interdependence of every living creature. Even the self-regulation theory of animal cycles does not, by any means, imply that a population of animals is independent. I have already noted that lemming events have tremendous repercussions for many animals about them. The life of a single animal or plant, including the human, is understandable and definable in terms of a group of individuals occupying a certain place in a dynamic, living community. Knowledge and understanding of this fact seem very hard to get across to people all over the world, whether in the highly educated countries or in the semiliterate ones. And yet it is just this sort of appreciation which is needed to guide so many of our own activities. Man is one part of the whole system of nature. We have become such a powerful species that our activities have powerful effects, often resulting in great compensatory changes or even destruction in the ecosystems that we touch.

REFERENCES AND NOTES

Acknowledgements. For assistance in Norway, I thank Dr. Yngvar Hagen, Director of the Norwegian State Game Research Institute and Professor Arne Semb Johansson, University of Oslo.

I wish to acknowledge the guidance of Dr. John T. Emlen, Jr., in the early planning of this study, The National Institute of Mental Health, U.S. Public Health Service for a research grant to conduct the work, and The N.Y. State Cooperative Wildlife Research Unit at Cornell University for facilities during the preparation of the manuscript. Above all, I thank Elena Jahn Clough, my wife, for her help in all phases of the project.

1. C. H. Elton, *Voles, Mice and Lemmings* (Clarendon Press, Oxford, 1942), 496 pp.
2. F. Pitelka, Some aspects of population structure in the short term cycle of the brown lemming in northern Alaska, *Cold Spring Harbor Symp. Quant. Biol.* **22**, 237–52 (1957).
3. D. Q. Thompson, The role of food and cover in population fluctuations of the brown lemming at Point Barrow, Alaska, trans. *N. Amer. Wildl. Conf.* **20**, 166–76 (1955).
4. D. Lack, Cyclic mortality, *J. Wildl. Mgmt.* **18**, 25–37 (1954).
5. J. J. Christian, Endocrine adaptive mechanisms and the physiologic regulation of population growth, in *Physiological Mammalogy,* Mayer and Van Gelder, Eds. (Academic Press, New York, 1963), pp. 189–353.
6. F. H. Bronson and B. E. Eleftheriou, Chronic physiological effects of fighting in mice, *Gen. and Comp. Endocr.* **4**, 9–14 (1964).

7. J. J. Christian and D. E. Davis, Endocrines, behavior, and population, *Science* **146**, 1550–1560 (1964).

8. C. Krebs, Lemming cycle at Baker Lake, Canada during 1959–62, *Science,* **140**, 674–76 (1963).

9. D. Q. Thompson, Ecology of the lemmings, unpubl. report to Arctic Inst. N. Amer. (1954), 64 pp.

10. G. C. Clough, Viability of wild voles, *Ecology* **46** (1), 119–34 (1965).

11. O. Kalela, On the fluctuations in the numbers of arctic and boreal small rodents as a problem of production biology, *Ann. Acad. Scient. Fenn.,* A IV **66**, 1–38 (1962).

12. _____, Seasonal change of habitat in the Norwegian lemming (*Lemmus lemmus*), *Ann. Acad. Scient. Fenn,* A IV **55**, 1–72 (1961).

13. J. Warnock, The effects of crowding on the survival of meadow voles (*Microtus pennsylvanicus*) deprived of food and water, Ph. D. thesis, Univ. of Wisconsin (1963).

14. L. F. Stickel, *Peromyscus* ranges at high and low densities, *J. Mammal.* **41**, 433–41 (1960).

15. F. Frank, The causality of Microtine cycles in Germany, *J. Wildl. Mgmt.* **21**, 113–21 (1957).

16. W. R. Thompson, Influence of prenatal maternal anxiety on emotionality in young rats, *Science* **125**, 698–99 (1957).

17. K. Keeley, Prenatal influence on behavior of offspring of crowded mice, *Science* **135**, 44–45 (1962).

18. C. H. Hockman, Prenatal maternal stress in the rat, *J. Comp. Physiol. and Psych.* **54**, 679–84 (1961).

19. D. Chitty, Population processes in the vole and their relevance to general theory, *Can. J. Zool.* **38**, 99–113 (1960).

20. E. Caspari, Genetic basis of behavior, in *Behavior and Evolution,* A. Roe and G. G. Simpson, Eds. (Yale Univ. Press, New Haven, 1958), pp. 103–27.

21. W. C. Dilger, Behavior and genetics, in *Roots of Behavior,* E. L. Bliss, Ed. (Harper, New York, 1962), pp. 35–47.

22. G. C. Clough, Viability of wild voles under various conditions of population density, season and reproductive activity, Ph.D. thesis, Univ. of Wisconsin (1962).

Effectiveness of an Oral Contraceptive

EFFECTS OF A PROGESTIN-ESTROGEN COMBINATION UPON FERTILITY, MENSTRUAL PHENOMENA, AND HEALTH

Gregory Pincus
Celso R. Garcia
John Rock
Manuel Paniagua
Adaline Pendleton
Felix Laraque
Rene Nicolas
Raymond Borno
Vergniaud Pean*

In previous papers we described the effectiveness of certain 19-nor steroids, when orally administered, as inhibitors of ovulation in animals (1) and man (2). Subsequent studies demonstrated that the combination of a small amount of estrogen with these progestins permitted the regular, repeated induction of artificial menstrual cycles in women taking the medication from the 5th to the 25th day of the cycle (3, 4). This property of maintaining normal menstrual cyclicity along with repression of ovulation led to the experimental testing of a norethynodrel-estrogen combination as an oral contraceptive, and reports of the first 18 months of a study made in San Juan, Puerto Rico, have been made (4, 5). After our initial experience in San Juan, two projects were initiated in Humacao, Puerto Rico, and one in Port-au-Prince, Haiti. We have recently collected and analyzed the data (to November 1958) from these four projects (6) and present here the outstanding findings derived from these data; 830 subjects took the medication for a total of 8133 menstrual cycles, or 635 woman-years.

The same regimen of tablet-taking was followed in all projects — namely, one tablet a day (10 mg of norethynodrel plus 0.15 mg of ethinyl estradiol 3-methyl ether) from the fifth through the 24th day of the menstrual cycle. Regular

Reprinted from *Science* 130, 81–83 (July 10, 1959), by permission of Celso R. Garcia and *Science*.

visits were made to each subject, and a record was kept of the length of each cycle, the nature of the menstrual flow, the occurrence of "side reactions," the frequency of coitus, the number of days of tablet-taking that were missed, and any other noteworthy phenomena. In addition, physical examinations of representative samples of each group were made from time to time, and in October 1958, data were obtained for over one-third of the women in each project from pelvic examinations, two liver-function tests (thymol turbidity and cephalin flocculation), endometrial biopsies, and vaginal smears.

Sixteen certain and one probable pregnancy occurred in women taking the medication; this represented a rate of 2.7 pregnancies per 100 woman-years and a 96-percent reduction in the premedication rate of 61.2 pregnancies per 100 woman-years. In Table 1 we present the distribution of these pregnancies according to the number of days of tablet-taking that were missed in the cycle in which conception occurred. It is clear that if the regimen is followed faithfully, practically 100-percent contraception occurs; it is also clear that the rate of conception is proportional to the number of tablets missed. Analysis of the data indicates no habituation to the medication — that is, pregnancies occurred at about the same rate in long-term users as in short-term users.

Among the menstrual-cycle phenomena recorded we observe the following: (i) a mean cycle length of 28.6 days with a normal frequency distribution; (ii) the occurrence of flow during the course of medication (breakthrough bleeding) in 2 percent of the cycles; (iii) a temporary amenorrhea in 0.8 percent of the cycles, with regular withdrawal bleeding in 99.2 percent; (iv) a reported increase of menstrual flow in 6 percent of the cycles, no change in 46 percent, and a decrease in 48 percent; (v) no significant change during medication cycles in the reported incidence of pain associated with menstruation.

SIDE REACTIONS

"Side reactions," such as nausea, headache, dizziness, vomiting, gastralgia, and malaise, were reported in 10.9 percent of the 4988 cycles in San Juan, in 6.3 percent of the 1410 cycles in the first Humacao project, in 18.3 percent of the 658 cycles of the second Humacao project, and in 7.3 percent of the 1077 cycles of the Port-au-Prince project. In each instance the largest percentage of these reactions was reported in the first cycle of medication and declined to low levels thereafter. The similarity of reactions to those common in early pregnancy and their subsequent subsidence is noteworthy. Similarly, the frequency of breakthrough bleeding was highest in the first medication cycle.

These data suggest an accommodation to the medication, probably involving uterine response to the level of the stimulation established by the drug. However, interesting results were found in a double-blind study of placebo versus true medication effect in which women continuing to use conventional contraceptives were given either a placebo or

TABLE 1

Pregnancies According to Number of Tablets Missed.

Number of tablets missed	Number pregnant	Rate per 100 woman-years
0	1?	0.2
1–5	5	7.7
6–19	11	43.3

the true drug. In 41 cycles of 15 women taking the placebo, breakthrough bleeding occurred in 4.9 percent, suggesting that medication was not responsible, and reactions were reported in 17.1 percent of the cycles, suggesting a psychogenic factor; in 30 cycles of 13 women given the true medication, a higher incidence of breakthrough bleeding (16.7 percent) and of reported reactions (23.3 percent) occurred, but these values are not significantly higher on a statistical basis. Furthermore, in 48 cycles of 15 women (separated by a great distance from the others) who were given the medication with no admonition as to possible reactions or menstrual irregularity, the frequency of breakthrough bleeding was 2.1 percent and that of reactions, 6.3 percent.

On being questioned at the October examinations, approximately 55 percent of the subjects reported weight increases occurring during medication, 25 percent reported no change, and 20 percent reported weight decreases. Similar questioning concerning general health disclosed that 39 percent felt an increase, 10 percent a decrease, and the balance no change, in well-being. Concerning libido, 20 percent reported an increase, 22 percent a decrease, and the balance no change. However, the data on frequency of coitus disclose that increasing frequency was reported by approximately 50 percent, decreasing frequency by 40 percent, and no change by 10 percent.

The data on over 200 pelvic examinations disclose: (i) a restoration of involuted *postpartum uteri* to normal size but not to hypertrophy even after 30 or more cycles of medication; (ii) an inconsistent change in the degree of cervical erosion; (iii) no pathological changes in the adnexae or vagina. No pathological breast changes were seen, and all vaginal smears were negative by Papanicolaou stain. Among the 148 liver-function tests, one was positive with respect to liver-tissue damage, a frequency consistent with the occurrence of this condition in the general population of these areas.

EFFICACY

In San Juan 86 women who withdrew from the project after 1 to 20 cycles of medication were observed further, and the occurrences of pregnancy were noted. The data, presented in Table 2, indicate no impairment of fertility in those not regularly using other means of

TABLE 2

Data for Individuals Who Withdrew from the San Juan Project.

No. of cycles prior to withdrawal	No. of individuals	No.	Other contraceptives not used regularly*		No.	Other contraceptives used regularly†	
			Percent pregnant	Exposure (months)		Percent pregnant	Exposure (months)
1– 5	55	30	87	6.2	25	16	55
6–10	16	10	80	5.0	6	17	39
11–15	7	6	67	11.0	1	0	
16–20	8	8	88	4.2			
Totals	86	54	83	6.1	32	15	52

* The mean conception rate is 193 per 100 exposure years.

† The mean conception rate is 27 per 100 exposure years.

contraception, and no tendency toward impairment in long-term as compared with short-term users. The mean conception rate of 193 per 100 woman-years of exposure is not significantly different from the pre-medication rate of 244 per 100 woman-years for the San Juan subjects prior to medication. The oral contraceptive would appear to be ten times as effective as the other contraceptives used.

For certain subjects who had been taking the standard dose of the drug, the dosage was halved in 224 cycles and quartered in 46. Relevant data presented in Table 3 indicate no significant difference between the efficacy of norethynodrel at the 10- and 5-mg levels, but indicate a tendency toward shorter cycles and an accompanying increased frequency of premature bleeding at the 2.5-mg level. Since we have previously shown (3) that adequate endometrial sustainment requires a level of the ethinyl estradiol methyl ether at least double that (0.037 mg) present in the quartered dose, the possibility of controlling breakthrough bleeding by means of higher estrogen dosage is being tested. It should be noted that no conceptions occurred at these lower dosage levels.

TABLE 3

Effects of Lowering Dosages on Menstrual-Cycle Phenomena.

Dose per day (mg)	No. of cycles	Mean length (days)	Subjects		
			With reactions (%)	With breakthrough (%)	With amenorrhea (%)
2.5	46	26.2 ± 0.51	8.7 ± 4.1	15.2 ± 5.3	2.2 ± 2.2
5.0	224	27.3 ± 0.20	12.5 ± 2.2	2.7 ± 1.1	2.2 ± 1.1
10.0	4718	27.9	10.9	2.0	2.2

TABLE 4

Reasons for Withdrawal.

Reason	San Juan		Humacao-R		Humacao-P		Haiti	
	No.	%	No.	%	No.	%	No.	%
Reactions	64	28.2	5	41.8	10	32.3	3	7.3
Not interested	36	15.9	1	8.3	0	0.0	17	41.5
Pregnant	12	5.3	1?	8.3	1	3.2	3	7.3
Unrelated illness	16	7.0	0	0.0	0	0.0	2	4.9
Husband opposed	5	2.2	0	0.0	0	0.0	1	2.4
Moved	34	15.0	3	25.0	6	19.3	9	22.0
Sterilized ♂ or ♀	29	12.8	1	8.3	6	19.3	0	0.0
Separated	20	8.8	0	0.0	6	19.3	2	4.9
Miscellaneous	11	4.8	1	8.3	2	6.5	4	9.7
Total withdrawing	227		12		31		41	
Total No. of subjects	438		117		126		149	
Percent withdrawing	51.8		10.3		24.6		27.5	

ACCEPTABILITY

The acceptability of this method of contraception may be examined by listing the reasons given for withdrawal from each project. These are presented in Table 4. In three projects, 28.2 to 41.8 percent of those withdrawing did so because of reactions; in the fourth project, lack of interest was the prime cause of withdrawal. Between them, these two reasons account for 32 to 50 percent of the withdrawals. Since the reactions are in large measure psychogenic, means for dealing with them may be devised. We have, in fact, shown that an antacid, or even a placebo, pill will relieve up to 90 percent of these reactions (4, 5). The lack of interest is due chiefly to lack of motivation among an economically low-level group. The actual rate of withdrawal was highest for the first year of operation of the San Juan project, in which 50 percent of the subjects who started had withdrawn by the end of the year. In contrast, in the Humacao-R project, 11 percent of those who started had withdrawn by the end of the year. We believe these high withdrawal rates for the San Juan project to be due to the following factors: (i) the availability of sterilization for contraception as well as the availability of other means economically practical; (ii) frequency of moving, chiefly to the continental United States; (iii) improvement in economic situation, which makes larger families less undesirable; and (iv) difficulties attendant upon initiating and testing this new method of contraception. Actually, among those starting the second year of medication, the withdrawal rate fell to 30 percent, and in Humacao-R, to less than 1 percent. In the latter project is a stable group of very poor women who are highly motivated, and in this project, begun a year after the one in San Juan, the supervisor had full knowledge of the difficulties encountered during the first year in San Juan. It is perhaps significant that in Haiti, where the population is also quite poor but where it is less stable, the first year's rate of withdrawal for all causes was 34 percent.

QUESTIONS AND ANSWERS

For the period studied, the foregoing data appear to us to answer the following questions, in the manner indicated: (i) Is the method contraceptively effective? yes; (ii) does it cause any significant abnormalities of the menstrual cycle? no; (iii) does it adversely affect the reproductive tract and adnexae? no; (iv) does it have physiologically adverse effects generally? no; (v) does it affect the sex life of the subjects adversely? no; (vi) does it impair fertility upon cessation? no; (vii) may a low dosage level of the drug be used? yes; (viii) is the method acceptable? yes, but to an extent which varies with motivation, economic situation, and other factors (7).

REFERENCES AND NOTES

* The authors are affiliated with the Worcester Foundation for Experimental Biology, Shrewsbury, Mass.; the Reproductive Study Center, Brookline, Mass.; the Family Planning Association of Puerto Rico, Rio Piedras; the Ryder Memorial Hospital, Humacao, Puerto Rico; and the *ad hoc* Research Group, Port-au-Prince, Haiti.

1. G. Pincus, M. C. Chang, E. S. E. Hafez, M. X. Zarrow, A. Merrill, *Science* **124**, 890 (1956).
2. J. Rock, G. Pincus, C. R. Garcia, *ibid.* **124**, 891 (1956).
3. G. Pincus, J. Rock, C. R. Garcia, *Ann. N.Y. Acad. Sci.* **71**, 677 (1958); G. Pincus, *Proceedings Symposium on 19-Nor Progestational Steroids* (Searle Research Laboratories, Chicago, Ill., 1957), p. 105.
4. G. Pincus, J. Rock, C. R. Garcia, E. Rice-Wray, M. Paniagua, I. Rodriguez, *Am. J. Obstet. Gynecol.* **75**, 1333 (1958).
5. G. Pincus, *Postgrad. Med.* **24**, 654 (1958).
6. _____, J. Rock, C. R. Garcia, "Proceedings 6th International Conference on Planned Parenthood" (New Delhi, in press).
7. This study was aided by research grants from G. D. Searle and Co. and from the Planned Parenthood Federation of America.

Epilogue

Lerner, I. Michael. 1959. The concept of natural selection: A centennial view. *Proc. Amer. Phil. Soc.* **103**, 173–82.

The Concept of
Natural Selection:
A Centennial View*

I. Michael Lerner†

*University of California,
Berkeley*

Several years ago, Sir Isaiah Berlin in writing an essay on Tolstoy's philosophy of history took his text from a fragment of the Greek poet Archilochus, which said: "The fox knows many things, but the hedgehog knows one big thing." Berlin's imaginative interpretation of this line was that writers, thinkers, or perhaps all of humanity can be divided into the two classes of foxes and hedgehogs. The ideas of the foxes are centrifugal, diffuse; they range over a variety of levels not integrated by a single theme; they lack a unifying focal point. In the realm of thought and creation the foxes follow many ends which may be unrelated and which do not form a cohesive system. The hedgehogs, on the other hand, are characterized by centripetal thinking directed towards a unitary inner vision. They are single-minded in their intellectual pursuits and, no matter how versatile they may be in their endeavors, the hedgehogs point to and are guided by the one big thing. Aristotle, Shakespeare, Balzac were foxes. Plato, Dante, Dostoyevsky were hedgehogs. Had Berlin considered biologists, he might well have placed Pasteur among the foxes. Darwin would most certainly have stood supreme as a hedgehog.

The one big thing towards which Darwin's thoughts and writings were directed was, perhaps, not so much Evolution

Reprinted from *Proceedings of the American Philosophical Society* 103, No. 2, 173–82 (1959), by permission of the author and the American Philosophical Society.

as the principle of Natural Selection. This was the concept that allowed the formulation of an acceptable theory of secular change in organic nature. Evolution had been discussed for more than two millennia before Darwin and Wallace. The idea, however, lacked conviction because, in the face of so much evidence for it, no generally comprehensible way in which evolution could have occurred was apparent to its proponents. Even the notion of natural selection was not exactly brand new in 1858. As an explanation of the presence of adaptations within species it had been considered by one or another natural philosopher from classical antiquity onwards. But as a mechanism for the origin of species, natural selection was apparently advanced only in the nineteenth century. The South Carolina-born Dr. Wells mentioned it as if he took it for granted in "An account of a white female, part of whose skin resembles that of a Negro" some forty years before Darwin and Wallace. Patrick Matthew apparently alluded even more casually to natural selection a few years later in an appendix to a volume on *Naval Timber and Arboriculture*. Yet the revelation that a single principle can embrace the evolutionary changes in all systematic categories, that the same basic process is operative at all levels of life wherever self-replicating units exist, came from Darwin and Wallace.

Their one big thing, natural selection, set at rest the doctrine of special creation. In combination with our knowledge of Mendelian inheritance acquired since Darwin's day, it rendered obsolete such alternative theories of evolution as were based on extra-mechanical agencies, or on direct adaptation of organisms to their immediate environment (that is, on inheritance of acquired characters), and exposed them as sins against Occam's razor. Natural selection furnished the binding principle for a general or unified theory of historical change in the living world. It made evolution not only understandable and acceptable, but beyond that, caused it to become of commanding significance in man's thinking about himself.

OBJECTIONS TO NATURAL SELECTION

This is not to say that the doctrine of natural selection was generally accorded, immediately upon its appearance, the status of dogma. In fact, over the last hundred years the thesis of natural selection has been doubted, questioned, derided, ridiculed, and on several occasions buried with considerable pride, pomp, and circumstance. Nevertheless, over the passage of years the concept has weathered its criticisms and survived its funerals, gathering strength after each successive interment. No serious student of biology today questions the actuality of organic evolution. Neither is there any disagreement as to the reality of natural selection, although its importance relative to other phenomena responsible for descent with modification may be in dispute. Even those considered to be militant foes of the view that natural selection is of primary significance in all phases of the evolutionary process, acknowledge, as for example did the late Richard Goldschmidt, that "every biologist agrees that selection and isolation are the basic working methods of evolution." The objection that Goldschmidt took towards what he used to call hyper-selectionists was not addressed to their belief in selection but rather to their ideas as to what was being selected. Thus arguments may still flourish as to whether selection operates with respect to minor or major mutational steps, how exclusive an agent it is under one or another circumstance, in what particular way it interacts with other processes in determining a given evolutionary change, whether it has been completely suspended in man under the recent developments in combatting sterility, disease, and old age, and with respect to many other issues. But there is no longer any doubt that natural selection is more than a theoretical possibility — it is unquestionably a logically imperative necessity in any accounting for evolution.

Generally speaking, there have been six kinds of criticisms raised against natural selection. The gravamen of the first kind was against evolution itself rather than natural selection as such. This issue is of no significance today. Secondly, teleologically minded biologists objected to the apparent purposelessness of natural selection. Condemnation on these grounds has little validity in the climate of present-day science, though I shall have occasion to return to this point in another connection. Thirdly, Darwin's own hypothesis regarding the basis of hereditary transmission created difficulties for the concept of natural selection. They were, however, dispelled when Mendelism entered the scene. Fourthly, Mendelian inheritance itself was misguidedly used to buttress the opposition to natural selection. Population geneticists have effectively demolished criticisms of this type; moreover they have demonstrated how particulate inheritance following Mendelian principles greatly augments the probable role of natural selection in evolution. Fifthly, objections have been raised, undoubtedly justifiably, against the intemperate support of natural selection by its earlier proponents, who attributed to the process consequences which we now know are ascribable to mating system, isolation, chance, and interactions of these factors with each other and with selection. And lastly, the most common and continually recurring opposition to natural selection is based on a misunderstanding of what is meant by the term. In spite of the fact that in recent years Fisher, Wright, Haldane, Muller, Dobzhansky, Ford, Simpson, Mayr, Stebbins, and countless others have repeatedly expounded the concept of natural selection, it still seems to remain an uncrossable *pons asinorum* for many refractory naturalists. It is difficult to know what, if anything more, should be done about this class of objections.

None of these categories of dissent from the idea of natural selection is a matter of serious concern at the present. Proof of the participation of natural selection in some situations is, of course, not tantamount to proof of its sufficiency to account for all evolutionary change. But no serious student of the subject insists on this extreme view. It is enough to say that the notion of natural selection as a major component of the evolutionary process has not only been theoretically established and empirically observed in the wild and in the laboratory, but it no longer falls entirely within the qualitative realm of science: natural selection can now be quantitatively treated and in many instances has been actually measured.

Thanks to post-Mendelian studies on the bases of hereditary transmission, and particularly to the developments in both theoretical and experimental population genetics in the last thirty years, our understanding of the operation of selection in nature has been vastly increased. Because of that, a prodigious embarrassment of riches on which to base a general discussion faces any reviewer of the subject. I shall therefore confine myself to a few aspects of the issue at large, trusting that other contributions to this program will cover at least some of the territory I neglect. In particular, I propose to pass over the speciation or splitting level of evolution, since it involves interaction with isolation, which is to be considered here by others infinitely more versed than I in this question. I should also note that, in considering post-Darwinian advances in the field of natural selection, I prefer omitting all mention of individual contributions to the risk of finding myself sire to an invidious, or even a merely provocative, list of names.

THE DEFINITION OF
NATURAL SELECTION

It may be appropriate at this point to define natural selection. Darwin himself did so in a number of ways. Thus (quoting from the sixth edition of *The Origin of Species*), he says:

As many more individuals of each species are born than can possibly survive; and as, consequently, there is a frequently recurring struggle for existence, it follows that any being, if it vary however slightly in any manner profitable to itself, under the complex and sometimes varying conditions of life, will have a better chance of surviving, and thus be *naturally selected*. From the strong principle of inheritance, any selected variety will tend to propagate its new and modified form.

Elsewhere we read:

This preservation of favourable individual differences and variations, and the destruction of those which are injurious, I have called Natural Selection, or the Survival of the Fittest.

Some exegesis of the operative words in these passages is called for. In particular, three questions may be asked. Is Darwin's term *selection* synonymous with *choice*? Is *survival* to be taken in the precise meaning of the word or is it used figuratively, including the ability to reproduce? What does the term *fittest,* which Darwin adopted from Herbert Spencer, signify in the context of the rest of the definition?

Regarding the first question, Darwin says;

> In the literal sense of the word, no doubt, natural selection is a false term, but who ever objected to chemists speaking of the elective affinities of the various elements? — and yet acid cannot strictly be said to elect the base with which it in preference combines. It has been said that I speak of natural selection as an active power of Deity; but who objects to an author speaking of the attraction of gravity as ruling the movements of the planets? Everyone knows what is meant and is implied by such metaphorical expressions; and they are almost necessary for brevity. So again it is difficult to avoid personifying the word Nature; but I mean by Nature, only the aggregate action and product of many natural laws, and by laws the sequence of events as ascertained by us.

It seems clear that, despite the fact that Darwin in his argument leaned very heavily on analogies between the results of purposeful and directed artificial selection of plants and animals by man with what is observed in the wild, he did not see in selection a process in which deliberative judgment or choice on the part of any agency plays a part.

With respect to the second question, the meaning of survival, the vast majority of writers on evolution take Darwin's usage of this word literally. They assume that Darwin meant that discrimination between what he considered the fit and the unfit was entirely by death and did not involve the broader and more relevant differences in ability to produce living offspring. Darwin, however, was not as naive as he is often represented. In discussing struggle for existence, he says: "I should premise that I use this term in a large and metaphorical sense including dependence of one being on another, and including (which is more important) not only the life of the individual, but success in leaving progeny." Thus, although Darwin may have erroneously accepted the view that survival is necessarily the major component of natural selection, he understood that the crux of the selection process lies not merely in the ability of an individual to survive longer than others, but in its greater capacity for production of living offspring; that is to say, not only in survival of individuals within a generation, but of groups over a period of generations.

This fact enables us to answer the third question, that regarding the interpretation which must be given the word *fittest,* or rather, the term *fitness.* The expressiveness of Spencer's superlative seduced Darwin into accepting "survival of the fittest" as being equivalent to "natural selection." As a result, many early evolutionists and a fair proportion of those naturalists of today whom the literature of population genetics has bypassed attached anthropomorphic value judgments to selection. Yet neither strength of character nor moral goodness, neither extreme size nor high intelligence, nor even long life *per se* causes an individual to produce more offspring, that is to say, make it fit in Darwin's sense. Indeed, often organisms which are totally undistinguished by any physical standards, organisms exhibiting average dimensions for various properties, in fine, individuals which are mediocre for any traits obvious to the human eye, are the ones that are most successful in propagating themselves. They are therefore the *fittest*. If there is one thing upon which the most factious partisans of various currents of evolutionary thought agree, it is that fitness of an individual, in the context of the natural selection principle, can mean only the extent to which the organism is represented by descendants in succeeding generations. Fitness can be discussed in absolute terms or expressed relatively to the average of a group. Immediate or more remote generations of descent may be chosen as a point of reference. Enumeration of offspring or some other way of assessing the "amount" of progeny left may be resorted to. But in all instances, fitness must refer to the ability of an organism to leave surviving offspring.

A habitual fallacy, shared by both the opponents and the supporters of evolution by natural selection, is the idea that any part of evolution may be explained by saying that the fittest individuals have the most offspring. When fitness is considered with reference to evolutionary phenomena, such statement is logically circular and begs the question. If capacity of reproduction is the criterion of fitness, the only connecting proposition between reproduction and fitness which avoids tautology is that individuals having most offspring are the fittest ones. This is neither an assumption, nor a hypothesis to be proven, but merely a definition.

Darwin's description of natural selection can now be paraphrased to say (1) that in nature individuals differ among themselves, (2) that their differences are in part determined by heredity, and (3) that, therefore, whenever these differences are correlated with fitness, that is, success in leaving offspring, the properties of the more fit individuals will be represented in succeeding generations to an increasing extent. Thus, changes in the make-up of successive generations are determined in a measure by the inequalities between the reproductive rates of individuals differing in hereditary endowment, that is to say, by different *genotypes*. More concisely, natural selection then is the *differential reproduction of genotypes*. The carriers of various genetic constitutions have *phenotypes* (to wit, somatic properties whether or not they happen to be apparent to the human observer) which differ in their capacity to produce surviving progeny in their particular environment. The genotypic composition of the next generation is then modified, and changes in phenotypes are produced to the degree to which phenotypes are genetically determined.

ADVANCES SINCE DARWIN

Darwin and Wallace arrived at their conclusions about the role of natural selection in evolution by deduction. Assuming the validity of their basic premises, natural selection can be inferred as a consequence independently of actual experience. *The Origin of Species* was essentially an attempt at *a posteriori* justification of Darwin's thesis based on the mustering of a great volume of descriptive evidence in its support. Since 1859 the premises underlying Darwin's chain of reasoning have been subjected to test many times. Thus, differential reproduction of individuals could often be ascertained by counting and statistical analysis of only a moderate degree of sophistication. Similarly, the dependence of such differential reproduction at least in part on hereditary differences was demonstrated both by verifiable inference from observation in nature and by laboratory experiment. But our achievements since Darwin are not limited merely to a further accumulation of examples (including those in ultramicroscopic organisms not even dreamt of in Darwin's philosophy) or to the development of less equivocal proofs of evolution than Darwin had at his disposal. Much more can be said about post-Darwinian advances in the study of natural selection. A sampling of illustrations chosen from different areas of evolutionary knowledge charted in recent decades bespeaks this fact.

The first of these may be provided by the insight that has been acquired into the basis of hereditary transmission. It is this knowledge that furnished the necessary link between selection and evolution. Darwin made somewhat vague references in *The Origin of Species* to the operation of the "strong principle of inheritance." He was fully aware of the deficiencies in his knowledge of the mechanism of heredity. They led him to formulate a speculative and somewhat improbable, even in the light of a century ago, hypothesis of blending inheritance. This principle in turn forced Darwin to espouse the postulate that acquired characters were transmissable, because otherwise continued variability in natural populations could not be accounted for. It was not until Mendelian theory was developed that such pathetically artless conjectures as, for instance, the direct hereditary effects of use and disuse of organs and parts of the body, became superfluous. Three aspects of Mendelism were especially important in this connection: (1) the particulate basis of the units of inheritance to which we may refer as *genes*, (2) the distinction between phenotype and genotype, and (3) the statistical nature of the phenomena of heredity. It was also in large part Mendelian inheritance that resolved the problem of persistent variation and, more generally, led to the possibility of quantifying evolutionary processes.

Symbolic representation of evolution, taking into account all but unique events, has now been arrived at. It is based on the description of the evolutionary process in terms of changes in the frequencies of alternative genes (or chromosomes) in a population. Indeed, the expression "survival of the fittest" can be applied with much more justice to the behavior of genes over many generations than to that of individual organisms within one. From the quantitative approach an understanding of the components of selection-induced alterations in fitness (those due not only to changes in gene frequencies, but also to modifications of the environment and of the mating system, as well as to gene interaction) has been gained. Methods for estimating the extent to which a population can be transformed by selection have been devised. Quantitative bases for systems of correlated response (i.e., effects on traits which themselves are not being subjected to selection pressure) characterizing changes under selection have been established. The utility of these developments for breeding practice is obvious. But equally important are the possibilities they have opened for a quantitative approach to selection in terms of observations of living beings in nature or of the paleontological record.

Another sphere of study which has contributed to an increased comprehension of a natural selection is that dealing with the materials on which selection operates. The notion that individuals differ in hereditary endowment presupposes that a mechanism by which such differences can arise exists. Selection experiments, followed by the discovery of artificial means of producing mutations in the hereditary material, and the many elaborate investigations on the nature of mutational changes and effects, made it clear that hereditary variants on the gene level do not arise as a consequence of selection. Variability for selection to act upon must therefore be supplied by mutation (or subsequent to mutation, by hybridization). It is not entirely correct to say, as has often been done, that the mutation process is a completely haphazard one. The structures that mutated genes can assume are not random. For instance, not all possible combinations of the elements of which genes are made possess the power of self-duplication, without which genes would not exist. But the non-randomness of mutations does not mean that selection determines the direction of phenotypic effect which gene mutations have.

More recent studies, including those on the physical chemistry of hereditary material, may be expected to clarify eventually many related points which are still obscure. For example, the question of how random the genes subjected to selection are with respect to their spatial relations within organized units of higher order, such as chromosomes, needs additional elucidation which breeding experiments with any of the higher organisms are incapable of supplying efficiently. Similarly, the relation between the amount of actual structural change involved in a gene mutation and the degree of phenotypic effect the change may lead to in the developing or adult organism still remains to be explored. The relative importance in different circumstances of the hierarchy of selection materials — genes, chromosomes, genomes, total genotypes, populations — is another aspect of evolution on which more light may be expected to be forthcoming.

On another level, the relationships between natural selection and adaptation has been illuminated by the semantic analysis of the term fitness. The early evolutionists chose their examples of adaptive traits, presumed to have originated by selection, on the basis of entirely anthropomorphic interpretations as to what constitutes an advantage to a plant or animal. We now know that adaptive traits are those contributing to increased fitness in any way whatever, rather than only those with spectacular manifestations on the ingenuous level of Kipling's *Just So Stories*. The important effects of natural selection are more subtle than the provision of tigers with stripes or leopards with spots for alleged purposes of camouflage. Physiological and biochemical properties very often are more likely to be of significance in determining an individual's fitness than are conspicuous morphological differences which sometimes may be by-products rather than criteria of selection. Moreover, fitness is determined by a combination of a great many somatic features, or rather by the phenotype as a whole. It follows from this: (1) that the selective value of any one character may vary, depending on the particular totality of traits in which it is found, (2) that the selection pressure applied to any single trait (which, of course, is an abstraction by an investigator from the total phenotype) is bound to be very small, and (3) that, considered with respect to single genes, the process of natural selection is usually very slow. These deductions accord well with the evidence on the rate and complexity of evolutionary change in nature which tended to puzzle the early Darwinians.

They also lead to the idea that the most adapted kind of individual is not one conforming to some phenotypic norm, but rather one whose development and reproductive life history is adjustable to varying environmental conditions in such a manner as to preserve high fitness. The most successful population is similarly one that can meet the challenge of environmental changes between generations. In other words, homeostatic devices stabilizing the individual's own reproductive performance have a high selective value, while a heterogeneous genetic make-up, even behind a uniform phenotypic facade within a single generation, may be an advantage to a population. These considerations, backed by ever-accumulating experimental and descriptive evidence, suggest the importance in evolutionary thought of such concepts as buffered and balanced genotypes, integrated gene pools, and coadaptation, which no doubt will be discussed on this occasion by others.

I would, nevertheless, like to call attention to these general ideas, without entering into the exposition of their full meaning, in alluding to some other aspects of natural selection. For one thing, they are of significance in the process in which natural selection, by utilizing interactions between components of genotypes, endows whole populations with properties transcending those attributable to their individual members. For another, these concepts are relevant to the currently controversial issue regarding the autonomy of single genes in the selection process.

Reducing the argument to its simplest terms, there is, on the one hand, the belief that the selective values of genes are reasonably independent of the genotypic combinations in which they occur. That is to say, genes which are found to be highly deleterious to fitness when forming part of one genotype are, in this view, considered extremely unlikely to be advantageous in another genotype. Ranged on the opposing side is the opinion that, since selection is primarily concerned with genotypes, the effects of individual genes in a given genetic context are not necessarily predictable from their behavior in another genetic background, be it only different with respect to a single member of a gene pair. Needless to say, the proponents of neither view claim that their interpretation entirely excludes the contrary one. Rather, the argument relates to the comparative importance of the two kinds of genes (those with predictable and those with unpredictable behavior) in evolution and in breeding practice. The same question can also be raised, with some poignancy, with reference to the human species, since, for example, estimates of the extent of genetic damage produced by ionizing radiation differ on the alternative hypotheses of gene action.

These broad issues also bear upon the relative importance of the different types of selection which we have learned to distinguish since Darwin's day. Thus *directional* selection produces transformation of a population along the time axis, while *disruptive* selection may result in the splitting of a group into subgroups. These two kinds of selection are progressive, in the limited sense of leading to new forms of life. *Stabilizing* selection is conservative. It operates by rejection of variants and maintains the population at an equilibrium. Of the several forms of pressure antagonistic to the preservation of fitness which selection must counterbalance, those of mutation and segregation are of greatest import. Elimination of deleterious mutants by selection is a process that has been long recognized. The significance of selection against non-optimal genotypes which arise in every generation as a result of segregation of chromosomes in the process of germ-cell formation, however, has been appreciated only recently. Studies from many fields, for example, those on wild and cage populations of *Drosophila*, on artificial irradiation, on the use of hybrid vigor in breeding economic plants and animals, on cytogenetics of grasshoppers, on aberrant forms appearing under intense inbreeding, and many others, argue for at least as great an evolutionary importance of selection against segregation as of that against mutation. Mutations are needed to provide a basis for further evolution. But the ones not useful at any given time in the phylogeny of a population are eliminated or kept from increasing in frequency by selection. Without selection against segregation, genetic variability already present could be lost. William Blake's affirmation that "to be an error and to be cast out is a part of God's design" seems to be an apt description of selection against both mutation and segregation, though invoking Blake in this connection leaves me open to the charge of citing the Scriptures to my own purpose.

Another evolutionary precept which has been recognized since Darwin (in fact, in contradiction to Darwin) is that selection, far from being blind, operating entirely by chance, and begetting successful kinds of organisms only as a result of improbable accidents, may be correctly described as a *creative* process. This term can, of course, be used in a variety of senses. In reference to natural selection its meaning is well illustrated by quoting what Michelangelo conceived the process of creation to be. The opening lines of one of his best known sonnets says in a somewhat free translation:

> The best of artists has that thought alone
> Which is contained within the marble shell;
> The sculptor's hand can only break the spell
> To free the figures slumbering in the stone.

In the same way, natural selection does not originate its own building blocks in the form of mutations of genes. But from them it does create complexes; it solves in a diversity of ways the great variety of problems that successful individuals and populations face; it builds step by step, even if by trial and error, entities of infinite complexity, ingenuity, and be one inclined to say so, beauty. Granted that it needs appropriate raw materials, that it may not necessarily be able to make a silk purse out of a sow's ear; yet, interacting with other evolutionary mechanisms, it has created the human species out of stuff which in its primordial stage may have looked no more promising.

MISCELLANEOUS IMPLICATIONS

The epithet creative is often interpreted to mean *effectively* causing, in the Aristotelean sense. Indeed, taking mutant genes and higher order components of genotypes as the *material* cause of evolutionary change, application of the adjective creative to natural selection is undoubtedly sanctioned by our present knowledge of the process. Nonetheless, the term raises some fundamental questions regarding causalities in evolution and may even provoke charges of teleology, long a dirty word in science. I do not mean, of course, that any mystical doctrines of ends involving inner perfecting principles or entelechy can be imputed to modern evolutionists. Neither design by supernatural agencies, nor an *élan vital*, from a comprehensive laboratory analysis of which we are supposedly forever barred, nor yet any guiding plan of morphological and physiological perfection, needs detain us in this discussion. Indeed, Bergson and other militant teleologists of yesteryear would find little comfort in the distinct possibility that, if there is an Aristotelean final cause of evolution which directed all preceding events in the animate world, it may turn out to be the Götterdammerung initiated by man's mastery of subatomic forces. Be that as it may, there is no necessity to assume that increased adaptation of organisms under natural selection represents the purposive end of the evolutionary process. Adaptation and adaptability simply provide means toward increased fitness; they should be viewed not as causes but as consequences of natural selection.

At the same time it must be realized that natural selection depends, in addition to variation (production of materials for selection to work on) and heredity (perpetuation of successful variants), on still a third factor, namely, the *potentiality* to produce young in excess of parental numbers. Only in the presence of this factor can inequalities of rate of reproduction between individuals exist in a group not heading for extinction. When the inequalities systematically relate to genotypic differences between individuals, natural selection is said to take place. In other words, while capacity for propagation beyond that needed to maintain constant population size does not ensure that natural selection will occur, it is a necessary condition for natural selection in any group which is to survive.

Darwin, who was, of course, mechanistically minded, spoke somewhat obscurely of the laws of Growth and Reproduction underlying selection. Samuel Butler came out directly with the vitalistic tenet that there exists a "universal innate desire on the part of every organism to live beyond its income." We may instead talk of an empirically discovered biological analogy to the first law of motion, namely that living matter if left alone will tend to increase itself indefinitely. Whatever the formulation, natural selection must always operate to maintain or to increase the frequency of genotypes which have the highest relative fitness. This process as a rule cannot lead to a decrease in absolute fitness except under special circumstances involving changes in the direction of selection or in mating system. The exceptions do not invalidate the proposition that natural selection *defined* as inequality of reproductive ability, that is to say, of fitness, also *causes* fitness to increase. Thus we are either attributing immanency to natural selection, or at the least, after having eliminated one tautology by our definition of fitness, we have come upon another. Logical dilemmas of this sort are, of course, not unique to the issues involved in natural selection or, indeed, to biology in general. I am sure that any competent philosopher could easily solve seeming paradoxes of this kind. The difficulty is that no two schools of philosophy seem to agree on the correct solution. It was for good reason that Bertrand Russell once said that causality is one of the two great scandals (induction being the other) in the philosophy of science. I have mentioned the problem here merely to indicate that, with all of the knowledge now acquired on the process of selection in nature, its logical status in evolution is still uncertain and undoubtedly controversial.

It was very likely misplaced confidence in their comprehension of natural selection or, perhaps, confusion between evolution as a law and natural selection as its instrumentality, that has led numerous social scientists and political philosophers of various hues and persuasions to project the notion of natural selection from biological to cultural systems. Such terms as progressive adaptation, struggle for existence, survival of the fittest, proved to be equally irresistible to materialists and idealists, to mechanists and teleologists, to prophets of *laissez-faire* capitalism and to heralds of the proletarian revolution. Yet, as has already been noted, the only value connotation that natural selection in its proper interpretation has refers to reproductive ability. Furthermore, it operates in a self-perpetuating system of particulate units, the relative proportions of which in a population change as a consequence of selection. Is there really an exact or even a moderate analogy of this principle in social evolution?

If so, it does not seem to have been established by any of the varieties of self-styled social Darwinists, especially when social institutions are dealt with. It is, indeed, possible that intergroup selection occurs between religious or cultural segments of the human species whenever they differ in birth rates. But the often-asserted inevitability of communist domination of the world, for example, is not rooted in unequal reproductive rates. Again, ethically dubious business practices allegedly sanctioned by the purported natural law of dog-eat-dog seem remote from the biological phenomenon from which they are supposed to derive support. Perhaps, the source of confusion does lie in the value constructs of "steady advance," "struggle for survival" and so forth, which have become attached to natural selection by its early enthusiasts. Darwin himself, taking the cue from Wallace, Galton, and Spencer, has unfortunately contributed to these mists of error, especially in *The Descent of Man,* though even in that book he confined himself, broadly speaking, to biological and not to social aspects of "natural selection as affecting civilized nations."

That organic evolution is based on natural selection can be considered to be demonstrated. Whether cultural evolution, in which generations communicate with each other by means different from information coded within replicates of the units of hereditary transmission, also is, remains to be seen. Needless to say, Mendelism is not a prerequisite to natural selection. Cytoplasmic transmission of particles, whatever its role in evolution is, can, no doubt, be shown to be subject to the same process. But self-propagation is essential to natural selection, whereas systematic historical changes in the extra-biological aspects of the world surrounding us could have happened without natural selection in the biological sense of the term.

A possible exception to this dictum may be found in the events leading to the origin of life. If autocatalytic processes of reproduction can be said to have occurred before protoplasm made its appearance on earth, chemical evolution culminating in living matter could have depended, as has been suggested by some, on natural selection. On the other hand, if the view is taken that self-reproduction is the exclusive property of living matter, natural selection cannot have antedated life.

One more point with reference to common misinterpretations of the basis of natural selection may be considered. It has often been said that the development of modern medicine and other technological advances combined with certain humanitarian and religious notions has led to the suspension of natural selection in man. As evidence, exercise of therapeutic measures against various congenital diseases is cited and examples are given from an increasing list of defects which used to be, but no longer are, disabling. It is assumed that carriers of genotypes predisposing to such conditions were in the past at a selective disadvantage, while currently their reproductive ability is not under any handicap. Hence, it is argued, natural selection is being interfered with by euthenic measures. More often than not, a dire warning that the human race is thereby slowly committing suicide is added.

It is entirely true that many genotypes which rendered their possessors unfit in earlier days do so no more. Natural selection now, therefore, is not based on the same components of fitness or results in the same directional changes as before. But this is by no means the same thing as saying that natural selection is not operative. What has happened is that the environment, the adjudicator of which genotypes are fit, has been altered. The therapy that has become available is a feature of the new environment. The determinants of fitness may have become changed, but inequalities in reproduction were not thereby eliminated. An analogy is provided by one of the classical cases of empirically observed natural selection in a lower form of life.

In certain species of moths dark and light colored forms occur. The dark kind is generally hardier and hence would have been expected to be more fit. However, its melanic pigmentation makes it more conspicuous to predators. Therefore, in early observations at certain localities the light forms were generally found to be more numerous than the dark ones. Since the Industrial Revolution, however, increasing amounts of soot and similar waste products began to spread around the countryside. This provided increased protection to the melanic forms in manufacturing districts. As a result, their higher reproductive capacity now gave them an advantage over the light forms so that in many industrial areas the latter now approach extinction. Natural selection here has reversed its direction. A gene that was deleterious in its net effects in the earlier environment has now become advantageous. The basis of fitness has been changed, but natural selection still went on. This kind of change has undoubtedly occurred many times in the past history of man, for instance, when fire-making tools were invented, thereby affording protection to some genotypes which were formerly disadvantageous.

Susceptibility to many diseases may then not contribute any more to differences in fitness of man. It is not impossible that resistance became in some instances an encumbrance. More likely, however, major importance in determining fitness was assumed by genes in control of other phenotypic traits. For instance, the genetically determined aspects of the ability to provide young with food obtained by strength may have now lost their positive selective value. On the other hand, genes for philoprogenitiveness in a world in which conception is under man's volitional control may have become of correspondingly greater import in the selective process.

Exactly how disgenic in terms of human values today's natural selection may be is difficult to tell. Selection which might have the most serious potential consequences to mankind could be that operating through the medium of differential reproductive rates of groups with differing intelligence. However, there are reasons to believe that this process may be of the stabilizing kind, maintaining constant genotypic frequencies rather than shifting them in a direction commonly agreed to be an undesirable one.

Generally speaking, selection in man is probably not as stringent as it was in the past, though this is by no means certain. The immense increase in the average number of surviving offspring which occurred in the last century does not of itself constitute conclusive evidence for lowered selection intensity. In any case, the actual reproductive rate in man is, of course, still greatly below its biological maximum, which means that there is still considerable opportunity for selection to occur. Evidence that inequalities in fitness currently observable are independent of genotypic constitutions would doubtlessly be difficult to obtain. Even so, it would seem that only when man has achieved such complete mastery over his environment that all possible human genotypes will be equally likely to produce the average number of surviving progeny, can we be sure that natural selection has ceased in our species.

IN CONCLUSION

I have ranged somewhat widely, even if not deeply, over the subject assigned to me. Before closing I would like to make it clear that population genetics, the discipline which has contributed most to our present understanding of natural selection, is only entering the stage of adolescence. Its attainment of maturity depends on a synthesis with its sibling doctrines of physiological, biochemical, and other branches of genetics, which should bring into fuller clarity our picture of evolution, and should fill the numerous gaps in our knowledge of the organic world. Evolution is the most fundamental biological law yet discovered. Natural selection is the basic mechanism implementing it. The principle of descent with modification, creatively, albeit opportunistically, husbanded by natural selection, is as firmly established as any concept in biology. But what we have learned so far about natural selection is obviously only the beginning. What remains to be learned is immeasurably more. Truth, said Bacon, is the daughter of Time, and one hundred years is not a long period in the history of mankind. Furthermore, giant-slayers abound in the scientific woods through which we have to travel to our goal of understanding ourselves and the living universe. It is then not inconceivable that the role now assigned to natural selection some day may have to be reevaluated. However, if more adequate explanations are found for the phenomena in the animate world which we currently view as being consequent to natural selection, the ensuing revolution in our thought will have to be as great as that produced by Darwin and Wallace a century ago.

NOTES

* Commemoration of the Centennial of the Publication of *The Origin of Species* by Charles Darwin, Annual Meeting of the American Philosophical Society, April, 1959.

† Professor of Genetics at the University.

Glossary

This set of definitions does not pretend to be exhaustive. A number of terms in the papers are difficult to define in this limited space, and in most cases they are peripheral to a reasonable understanding of the papers.

Acinar Lumen
: Region of pancreas gland with acinar cells containing zymogen granules.

Acrosome Filament
: The acrosome is the bag-like structure at the tip of the head of animal sperm. It contains enzymes which digest egg membranes during fertilization. In some animals a membranous filament from the acrosome reaches the egg cytoplasm and permits the passage of the sperm into the egg.

Actinomycin D
: An antibiotic which specifically inhibits the synthesis of messenger RNA.

Adventive Embryos
: Embryos developing from cells other than the fertilized egg. Some such embryos originate from cells of the nucellus and are called nucellar embryos.

Agouti
: A mammalian coat color resulting from the brown and yellow bands on each hair.

Aldehyde
: Organic compounds with the carbonyl group (C=O) at one end of their carbon chain.

Aleurone Layer
: The outer layer of the endosperm of certain seeds which is characterized by granules of storage protein (aleurone granules).

Aliquot
: One of an equal number which comprise the whole.

Allelomorph
: Allele; one of several forms of a gene. Alleles occupy the same position on homologous chromosomes.

Amorphous
: Without definite shape.

Ampholytes
: Compounds having the properties of both acids and bases.

561

α-Amylase   The amylases are a group of enzymes which split starch into simple sugars.

Anaerobic Organisms   Organisms not requiring oxygen to live.

Anaphase   The stage of mitosis when chromosomes have separated and are moving to opposite poles of the spindle.

Anastomoses   Connections.

Androgenetic Haploids   Organisms with a single pair of chromosomes contributed by the male parent.

Å (Angstrom)   A unit of measurement. One angstrom = 0.01 micron (μ). A micron is 0.001 of a millimeter (mm). There are 25 mm to the inch.

Angiosperms   The flowering plants. Plants with seeds inclosed in an ovary.

Anion   A negatively charged ion. An ion is an electrically charged atom or atoms. Cations are positively charged ions. Their names are derived from the charge of the electrode to which they are attracted. Anode: positive electrode; cathode: negative electrode.

Anthocyanin   A class of red, purple, and blue plant pigments found in cell vacuoles, and responsible for these colors in flowers, fruits, stems, etc.

Aplanospore   A single celled spore of algae, which is non-motile but is liberated from the parent cell.

Apomictically   Reproduction from seeds which developed without fertilization.

Ascorbate   Vitamin C.

Autolysis   The self-destruction of cells.

Autoradiography   A technique used for the localization of radioisotopes in tissues and in cells. The living material is subjected to the radioisotope, then killed, sectioned, and placed on a glass slide. A photographic emulsion sensitive to the radiation from the isotope is placed over the slide. The location of the isotope can be detected by the grains in the overlying emulsion.

Autotrophes   Organisms, such as green plants, able to manufacture their own food from inorganic matter.

Auxins	A class of plant growth hormones characterized by their activity in the oat coleoptile curvature assay.
Auxoheterotrophic	A micro-organism requiring nutritive factors in addition to those required by the wild strain from which it was derived.
Bacteriophages	Viruses which infect bacteria.
Biosynthesis	Synthesis of organic compounds within living cells.
Biotin	One of the "B Vitamins."
Birefringence	The property of oriented particles and molecules which results in the double refraction of a beam of incident light. Objects exhibiting birefringence will glow when observed through the polarizing microscope.
Biuret	A color test for determining the amount of protein in a sample.
Blastomeres	Cells of the blastula. The blastula is that stage in the development of the amphibian embryo characterized by a hollow ball of cells. This stage ends with the onset of gastrulation signaled by the formation of the blastopore.
Blastoporal Lip	The dorsal lip is a region above the blastopore. The blastopore is a hole formed during gastrulation as a result of an inflow of cells from the surface of the embryo. It is the opening of the primitive gut and marks the position of the future anus.
Buffer	A substance which inhibits changes in pH.
Calines	Hypothesized plant hormones specifically responsible for the growth of different plant organs. They have not been isolated and characterized.
Cambium	Lateral meristems in plants, responsible for secondary growth.
Cantharides	Poisons from a particular group of beetles.
Carpospores	Spores formed from filaments derived from the zygote of red algae.
Caseinolytic	The breakdown of casein. This protein is a major component of milk.
Catalase	An enzyme which splits hydrogen peroxide (H_2O_2) into water and oxygen.

Catalyzed	A catalyst is a compound which speeds up chemical reactions without itself being utilized in the reaction. Enzymes function as catalysts in living systems.
Cathepsins	Intracellular enzymes which destroy protein.
Centriolar Complex	The neck of the sperm consists of two centrioles and the base of the flagella.
Chert	A type of rock composed of hydrated silica and various impurities.
Chloramphenicol	An antibiotic frequently used in experimental work to specifically inhibit protein synthesis.
Chlorophyll	The green pigments in plants which absorb the visible light utilized in photosynthesis. Chlorophyll belongs to a class of compounds called porphyrins which are also found in hemoglobin and cytochrome.
Chloroplasts	Bodies in plant cells bounded by a double membrane which contain chlorophyll. In leaves of higher plants they are often disc-shaped and usually $5-10\mu$ in diameter. The interior of the chloroplast consists of a complex membrane system containing chlorophyll, surrounded by an aqueous protein matrix called the stroma. Carbohydrates are synthesized in the stroma.
Chondrogenic Cells	Embryonic cartilage cells.
Chorda-Mesoderm	The region of the gastrula's mesoderm layer which will form the notochord.
Chromatophores	Pigment-containing cells.
Chromomeric	Chromomeres are the dark-banded regions of chromosomes. They are particularly noticeable in giant salivary chromosomes.
Chromosomes	Structures within the nuclei of eukaryotic organisms, composed of nucleic acids and protein. They are the sites of the Mendelian genes.
Cleistogamous	Closed flowers in which self-pollination occurs.
Clone	A population derived from one individual as a result of asexual reproduction. All members of the population are genetically identical or very similar to the original parent.

Coleoptile	An embryonic structure of certain monocotyledenous plants which forms a sheath around the first leaf during germination.
Collagen	Fibrous protein which is a major constituent of connective tissue.
Congeners	Belonging to the same group.
Coprolites	Fossilized dung.
Cotyledons	Storage organs of the plant embryo. They frequently have a leaf-like structure and function on seedlings.
Crypsis	Concealment by coloration.
Cysteine	A sulphur-containing amino acid frequently used as a reducing agent.
Cytochromes	Compounds composed of proteins and iron-containing porphyrins. The cytochromes are located in mitochondria and chloroplasts where they are intimately involved in energy-yielding electron transport systems.
Cytokinesis	Cell division.
Diagenetic	Relating to the reconstructive process by which changes are produced in sedimentary rocks during or immediately after their deposition and which is caused by such forces as the weight of overlying strata or hot waters.
Dialysis	A technique for separating small molecules from large molecules such as protein. The mixture is put in a bag made of a membrane permeable only to the small molecules. The bag is placed in water and the small molecules diffuse into the water leaving the large molecules inside the bag.
Dicotyledons	One of the subclasses of flowering plants. The embryos have two cotyledons.
Dimorphism	Two shapes or forms.
Divalent cations	Positively charged ions (see def. for *ion*) with a bonding capacity or valence of 2.
Ectoderm	The outer layer of the gastrula. It will develop into nerve tissue and the outer layer of the skin.
Electron Microscope	A microscope in which an electron beam passes through the specimen and is focused upon a fluorescent screen. A beam

of electrons has a much shorter wavelength than visible light and much smaller objects can be resolved in the electron microscope than in microscopes employing the longer wavelengths of visible light.

Electrophoresis   A technique for separating compounds by subjecting charged particles in a liquid to an electric field. The particles will migrate to the respective electrodes depending upon their charge.

Elytral   Refers to the elytrum, the modified forewing of beetles which serves as a protective cover for the hindwing.

Endergonic   Energy requiring; in this case, the synthesis could only be driven by an energy source like ATP.

Endometrium   Mucous membrane lining the uterus.

Endosperm   In flowering plants it is the triploid storage tissue in the seed.

Epon   A type of plastic used for embedding tissue so that extremely thin sections of the tissue can be cut and viewed in the electron microscope.

Erg   A unit of work defined as a force of one dyne acting through a distance of one centimeter. A dyne is a unit of force producing an acceleration of one centimeter per second for each second the force acts on a mass of one gram. The erg is a common measurement of light energy.

Exovate   As used in the text, the cytoplasm that leaked outside of the cell.

Flavoproteins   Proteins combined with derivatives of the yellow pigment riboflavin. They are enzymes acting as hydrogen carriers in the terminal part of cell respiration.

Free Radical   Molecules with odd or unpaired electrons. They are unstable intermediates in certain reactions.

Gastrulation   The event in embryo development when movement of cells from outside to inside the embryo results in the formation of the basic germ layers.

Geologic Time Table   The time scale of the earth's past consists of a series of major and minor divisions.

The fossil record is the basis for this time table and each division is characterized by the abundance of particular organisms in rocks of known age. The divisions are relative rather than absolute, so the time allocated to each division differs from one authority to the next.

Era	Period	Epoch	Millions of years from beginning of period (approx.)
Cenozoic	Quaternary	Recent	.025
		Pleistocene	1
		Pliocene	10
		Miocene	25
	Tertiary	Oligocene	40
		Eocene	60
		Paleocene	75
Mesozoic	Cretaceous		130
	Jurassic		165
	Triassic		200
Paleozoic	Permian		280
	Upper Carboniferous		320
	Lower Carboniferous		345
	Devonian		405
	Silurian		425
	Ordovician		500
	Cambrian		600
Precambrian	Proterozoic Archeozoic		3000+

Genotype : Genetic constitution of the organism. The specific set of genes present in each cell.

Geotropism : The response of plant parts to gravity.

Glucose : A six carbon sugar ($C_6H_2O_6$) widely distributed in plants and animals. It is also called dextrose. The basic units of starch and cellulose are glucose.

Gramineous Plants : The grasses.

Haemoglobin : Hemoglobin; the iron-containing pigmented protein of blood cells which carries oxygen.

Helix	A spiral moving around a cone or cylinder. A coiled spring and the thread of a screw are examples of a helix.
Hematoxylin	A dye used to stain cells. Nuclei are particularly well stained with this dye.
Heterosis	Hybrid vigor. Organisms resulting from crosses between two inbred lines often display superior growth and reproductive ability.
Heterotrophes	Organisms, such as animals, unable to manufacture their own food from inorganic matter.
Homozygotes	Individuals with the same alleles for a particular type of character on homologous chromosomes.
Hydrolysates	Breakdown products of protein produced by splitting the protein with water. In the text, hydrolysis was induced by acid treatment.
Hypertrophy	Enlargement of an organ as a result of cell enlargement.
Hypoglycemic	Glucose deficiency in the blood.
Indoleacetic Acid	A naturally occurring plant growth hormone.
Intermediate Metabolism	The steps in the oxidation degradation of food materials in living cells.
Isotopic	As used here, it refers to different forms (chick and mouse) of a common cell type (chondrogenic).
Karyotype	The typical characteristics of the complement of chromosomes in the somatic cells of a particular species.
Ketone	Organic compounds with the carbonyl group ($C{=}O$) at a location other than the end of the carbon chain.
Kinin	A member of a class of plant growth regulators which are very active in inducing cell division. They are currently termed cytokinins.
Lamina	The blade or broad, flattened portion of a leaf.
Lyophilized	The process of dehydrating frozen material.

Lysozomes	Single membrane-bound cell organelles containing digestive enzymes.
Malpighian Tubules	Tubular excretory glands in insects.
Meniscus	Curved upper surface of a column of liquid.
Meristems	Regions of active cell division. Apical meristems of a plant stem occur at the tip and produce all the cells forming the primary tissues of the stem. Lateral meristems, such as the vascular and cork cambium, produce the secondary tissue.
Mesenchyme	Embryonic connective tissue derived from the mesoderm.
Mesocotyl	That portion of the axis of certain monocotyledenous plants between the base of the coleoptile and the primary root.
Micron (μ)	One thousand microns = one millimeter (mm). Ten millimeters = one centimeter (cm). There are 2.5 cm per inch.
Microphotometry	A technique for determining the light absorption characteristics of parts of cells and organelles.
Mitochondria	Double membrane-bound bodies of variable shapes about 0.2μ long found in all cells which utilize atmospheric oxygen in their respiration. It is within this organelle that much of this aerobic respiration takes place. See paper by Green and Hatefi.
Mitotic Spindle	The fibers visible during mitosis and meiosis which are attached to the chromosomes and which appear to arise from loci at opposite ends of the cell.
M (Molar)	One gram molecular weight of a compound in enough water to make one liter.
Monoecious	The occurrence of both female and male sex organs on one plant.
Morphogenesis	The development of form.
Morulloid	A mass of cells shaped like a mulberry.
Myoblasts	Embryonic muscle cells.
Myogenic Cells	Embryonic muscle cells.
Ninhydrin	A compound producing a blue color in contact with amino acids.

Nucleoside Phosphate	Compounds composed of a purine or pyrimidine base, a five carbon sugar, and phosphoric acid. The phosphoric acid is attached to the sugar.
Obligate Anaerobic Photo-autotroph	An independent photosynthesizing organism which can only live in an anaerobic environment.
Obligate Heterotrophes	Organisms which can only exist if supplied with an external food source. Some plant-animals like *Euglena* can live either as autotrophes or as heterotrophes.
Óg	A mutant gene of the silk moth, *Bombyx mori*.
Ontogeny	Development throughout the life-span of an individual.
Organelle	An organized structure in the cytoplasm of a cell with a specific function, e.g., a chloroplast or mitochondrian.
Organic Soup	A term used to describe the warm shallow seas rich in organic compounds where life is thought to have arisen.
Orthogonal	At right angles. The layers of fibrils tend to be at right angles to each other.
Paper Chromatography	The separation of mixtures of organic compounds on filter paper dipped in solvents. The compounds separate because of their different solubility in the solvent and their differential absorption to filter paper.
Parenchyma	Thin walled and relatively unspecialized cells of plants.
Peptides	Compounds composed of two or more amino acids. See *peptide linkage*.
Peptide Linkage	The type of bond formed between amino acids. The amino group (NH_2) of one amino acid joins with the carboxyl group (COOH) of another amino acid. Water is produced when this bond (—NH—CO—) is formed.
pH	A unit of measurement of the concentration of hydrogen (H^+) or hydroxyl (OH^-) ions in solution. An excess of hydrogen ions provides an acid solution with a pH below 7. An excess of hydroxyl ions

provides an alkaline or basic solution with a pH above 7. A neutral solution has a pH of 7.

Phagocytosis   The ingestion of solid material by cells as a result of the invagination and pinching off of the cell membrane to form an internal vesicle containing the particle.

Philoprogenitiveness   The loving and caring for one's offspring.

Phloem   The tissue of the plant vascular system composed of sieve-cells, sieve tubes, and associated parenchyma and fibers. The transport of most organic compounds occurs in the phloem.

Phosphorylation   The addition of phosphate.

Photolysis   Chemical decomposition induced by light.

Photosynthesis   A process by which an organism converts light energy to chemical energy. This energy is subsequently used to synthesize carbon compounds with carbon from atmospheric carbon dioxide.

Pinocytosis   Ingestion of a portion of the surrounding fluid by a cell. The cell membrane invaginates and pinches off thus forming a vesicle containing the fluid.

Plastids   A class of double membrane-bound organelles in plant cells. They frequently contain pigments. The green chloroplasts give that color to leaves, and chromoplasts give the orange color to carrots, oranges, and tomatoes.

Polycythaemia   An increase in red blood cells.

Polymer   An organic molecule consisting of a long chain of similar units. The polymer has different properties than the subunits.

Polymerization   The process of linking together molecules to form a long chain or polymer.

Polymorphism   Morphological variations within the same population.

Polysaccharide   A long chain carbohydrate often composed of simple sugars. Starch and cellulose are examples.

Porphyrin   A class of organic compounds with a complex ring structure which are of great importance in biological systems. Chlorophyll, hemoglobin, and cytochrome contain porphyrins.

Precambrian	The geologic era preceding the Paleozoic. It ended approximately 600 million years ago. The characteristic fossils of this era are algae, bacteria, and fungi.
Proline	An amino acid which is incorporated into collagen protein.
Proteases	Enzymes which break down protein.
Proteolytic	Protein-destroying.
Pupa	An immobile and non-feeding stage in the life cycle of many insects between the larva and adult stages.
Purines	A class of nitrogenous bases with a double ring structure. They are major components of nucleic acids.
Pyrimidines	A class of nitrogenous bases with a single ring structure. They are major components of nucleic acids.
QO_2	Oxygen uptake in microliters per milligram dry weight per hour.
Radioautographs	Method of localizing radioactive compounds on a paper chromatogram. X-ray film is placed over the chromatogram and kept in the dark for one or two weeks. The developed film shows dark spots corresponding to radioactive regions on the paper. The specific compounds can then be removed from the paper and identified.
Reticulate Spheroidal Bodies	Round structures with a network-like surface.
Sarcomeres	The repeating units in transverse sections of muscle fibrils consisting of a pair of alternating light and dark bands.
Scion	That portion of a plant which is removed and grafted onto another plant.
Septate Filaments	Filaments possessing cross walls.
Sickle-Cell	A condition of red blood cells when they are sickle-shaped. This condition is caused by an abnormal hemoglobin and results in anemia.
Somites	Segmented blocks of mesoderm adjacent to either side of the notochord.

Specific Activity of Radio-active Isotopes	Disintegrations per second per gram of compound.
Spectrophotometer	An instrument used to measure the absorption of particular wavelengths of light by a particular material.
Spores	Cells with hard resistant walls which persist in unfavorable environments. In plants, the products of meiosis are usually called spores.
Steroids	A class of lipids with a basic structure of four rings of carbon atoms. They exert many physiological effects. Vitamin D and the sex hormones are examples of steroids.
Stoichiometric	Stoichiometry is the part of chemistry concerned with determinations of the proportions in which elements combine and with weight relations in reactions.
Symbiotic Relationship	The close association of two different organisms. Mutual benefit frequently results from this association.
Sympatric	Occupation of the same territory by different populations or species.
Tachytelic	Evolving at a rapid rate.
Tactoid	Oriented particles sometimes formed by proteins in solution.
Telophase	The last stage of mitosis when the daughter nuclei have reformed.
Template	A pattern for copying a specific form.
Tetrasporic	Tetraspores are spores of certain red algae which are the products of meiosis which germinate to form the gametophyte generation.
Thalassaemia	A condition characterized by abnormal smallness and increased resistance of the red cells.
Thermal Polymerization	The formation of a polymer by means of heat.
Thyroxin	An amino acid containing iodine. It is a hormone produced by the thyroid gland.
Totipotency	As used in the text, all the potential for development into a complete organism.
Tracheoles	Terminal portions of the tubular air-conducting system of insects. The tracheoles ramify throughout the tissue.

Trypsin	An enzyme which breaks down protein.
Villafranchian	Lower portion of the Pleistocene Epoch. It preceded the first major glaciation period of the ice age and lasted about 0.5 million years. It saw the origin of modern mammalian genera and is named after a fossil site in Italy.
Vycor Tubes	Reaction vessels made of a special glass allowing the transmission of ultraviolet light.
Zygote	Product of the fusion of two sex cells or gametes.
Zymogen Granules	Intracellular bodies in the excretory cells of the pancreas which contain proteolytic enzymes.